Field Guide
to the
WILD FLOWERS
of Britain and Northern Europe

LAROUSSE

Field Guide to the WILD FLOWERS *of Britain and Northern Europe*

Written by
DAVID SUTTON

Illustrated by
PETER CHESTERTON, JOHN DAVIS
& COLIN EMBERSON

LAROUSSE

Larousse plc
Elsley House, 24–30 Great Titchfield Street,
London W1P 7AD

This edition published by Larousse plc 1996

10 9 8 7 6 5 4 3 2 1

First published by Kingfisher 1988

A CIP record for this book is available from
the British Library

ISBN 0 7523 0041 5

Phototypeset by Southern Positives and
Negatives (SPAN), Lingfield, Surrey
Colour separations by Newsele Litho, Milan
Printed in Portugal

CONTENTS

INTRODUCTION

This Field Guide is designed to be taken with you when you take a walk in the countryside or through parts of towns where plants are left to grow wild. Wherever possible, take the book to the plant and not *vice versa*. It is illegal to dig up wild plants in several countries, and the picking of wild flowers by 'flower lovers' has led to the virtual extinction of many attractive species.

In an illustrated Field Guide to plants, it is not possible to include all species for the area: a standard set of European floras and illustrations would take up one or two library shelves and would be far too costly and heavy to take into the countryside. A selection must be made. The main categories for exclusion are non-flowering plants, such as conifers, ferns and mosses; trees and shrubs, with the exception of plants such as Heathers and Roses which are usually thought of as 'flowers'; and grass-like plants including sedges and rushes – for all of these are identified using more technical detail and require specialist treatment. Preference has been given to the common and widespread plants. Many of the foreign species that have become naturalized are included; they are now often more common than the native plants.

The final selection of more than 800 species gives a reasonable coverage of at least the common plants of the British Isles, Ireland, northern France, Belgium, Luxembourg, Holland, West Germany and Denmark, and includes many plants of Norway and Sweden. Some plants have been included because they are highly distinctive and well known, despite their rarity (for example, Lady's-slipper: page 275).

Equipment

Finding and identifying wild flowers is an immensely satisfying hobby requiring a minimum of expense. A hand-lens with a magnification of about ten times is a useful purchase for examining the structure of flowers. It is possible to buy one with a small scale attached for making accurate measurements. A notebook is useful for recording details of the plant, particularly the colouring, number, relative size and extent of fusion of the petals; the arrangement and division of the leaves; and the sort of fruit, including any method by which it opens.

You may wish to record your 'find' with a photograph. A single-lens reflex camera is the most useful sort of camera for general photography of flowers. In order to see any detail of small flowers it is necessary to buy some sort of close-up lens, preferably giving about 1:1 reproduction. When taking a picture, bear in mind that the flower is usually much brighter than its background. It may be necessary to under-expose the film by one or even two f.-stops to avoid losing detail in the petals. Using electronic flash can make it easier to obtain good depth of focus, sharpness and reliable exposures, but gives a less 'natural' result. Try and identify your plant in the field wherever possible, because identification from photographs can prove difficult.

HOW TO USE THIS BOOK

If you find a plant and have no idea of what it is, use the key starting on page 13 – which should limit your search to a specific group of pages. If you have a rough idea of the identity, turn to the relevant part of the book (using the colour codes explained on page 16) and you will find similar species grouped on adjacent pages. Match the species against the illustrations, but always check through the description for confirmation. The description of the plant is mostly summarized in a facts panel, which contains the same elements for every species. This layout departs from the practice in most Field Guides and floras, where the descriptions are often very brief and inconsistent.

The arrangement of species on a page is for a main species (of which several different elements are illustrated) and up to four further similar species. For the similar species, only the parts of the plant used for identification are shown, rather than a whole plant or flowering shoot. These similar species are often as common as the first.

This colour shows which group of plants each species belongs to. Use it to help you find the different groups as you flick through the book. The colour code is explained on p. 16.

A text summarizes the overall look of the plant, drawing attention to its most important distinguishing features, and adds points of interest regarding its biology, history or significance to humankind.

A facts panel provides a detailed summary of the type and size of the plant; where and when to look for it; the form of the stems, leaves and underground parts, flower-heads and flowers, fruits and seeds.

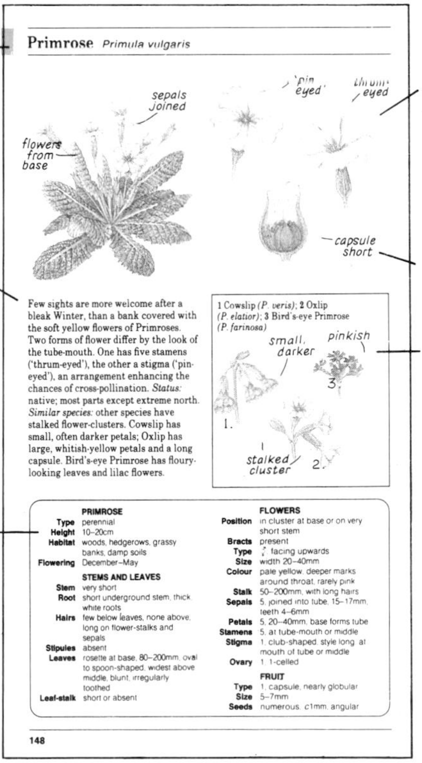
Primrose *Primula vulgaris*

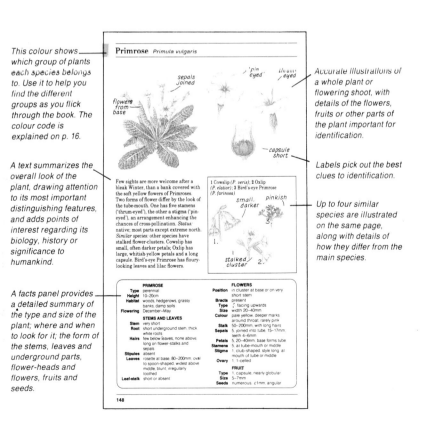

Few sights are more welcome after a bleak Winter, than a bank covered with the soft yellow flowers of Primroses. Two forms of flower differ by the look of the tube-mouth. One has five stamens ('thrum-eyed'), the other a stigma ('pin-eyed'), an arrangement enhancing the chances of cross-pollination. *Status:* native; most parts except extreme north. *Similar species:* other species have stalked flower-clusters. Cowslip has small, often darker petals; Oxlip has large, whitish-yellow petals and a long capsule. Bird's-eye Primrose has floury-looking leaves and lilac flowers.

1 Cowslip *(P. veris)*; 2 Oxlip *(P. elatior)*; 3 Bird's-eye Primrose *(P. farinosa)*

	PRIMROSE
Type	perennial
Height	10–20cm
Habitat	woods, hedgerows, grassy banks, damp soils
Flowering	December–May
	STEMS AND LEAVES
Stem	very short
Root	short underground stem, thick white roots
Hairs	few below leaves, none above, long on flower-stalks and sepals
Stipules	absent
Leaves	rosette at base, 80–200mm, oval to spoon-shaped, widest above middle, blunt, irregularly toothed
Leaf-stalk	short or absent
	FLOWERS
Position	in cluster at base or on very short stem
Bracts	present
Type	⚥, facing upwards
Size	width 20–40mm
Colour	pale yellow, deeper marks around throat, rarely pink
Stalk	50–200mm, with long hairs
Sepals	5, joined into tube, 15–17mm, teeth 4–6mm
Petals	5, 20–40mm, base forms tube
Stamens	5, at tube-mouth or middle
Stigma	1, club-shaped, style long, at mouth of tube or middle
Ovary	1, 1-celled
	FRUIT
Type	1, capsule, nearly globular
Size	5–7mm
Seeds	numerous, *c*1mm, angular

148

Accurate illustrations of a whole plant or flowering shoot, with details of the flowers, fruits or other parts of the plant important for identification.

Labels pick out the best clues to identification.

Up to four similar species are illustrated on the same page, along with details of how they differ from the main species.

Introduction

THE HISTORY OF WILD FLOWERS

In order to understand why wild flowers grow where they do today, it is necessary to have a basic understanding of the events that have shaped the flora of the region. Before about 15,000 years ago, much of the northern part of Europe was covered by a continuous sheet of ice, for the world was still in the grip of the last glaciation. Then the ice began to retreat, and bare ground left behind became available for colonization. Although plants are generally perceived as static, lacking the faculty of movement common to animals, seeds of plants travel great distances by varied means. So populations of plants spread into the new territory just as surely as the animals that migrated with them. When the ice first started to retreat, such colossal volumes of water were still frozen solid that the sea-level was about 30 metres lower than it is today. What are now France, Britain and Ireland were connected by land, so that the earliest colonist plants had no difficulty spreading through the area.

Quick-growing herbaceous plants were the first to flower and set seed in the new surroundings, but trees and bushes with wind-dispersed seeds soon arrived. Slow-growing, heavy-seeded trees were among the last to arrive. As the sea-level rose to its present level, land connections between many parts of the area were severed, making further immigration of species much more difficult. Gradually, the herbs and bushes gave way to a succession of trees and most of northern Europe disappeared under almost continuous forest. The main exceptions were mountain-tops, cliffs, screes, coastlines and rivers.

Then about 5,000 years ago, a dramatic change took place. People arrived on the scene and started cutting and burning trees. The upland forest was easier to fell than in the rich valleys, so was first to be turned over to crops and pasture for livestock. As successive waves of human colonists came up from the south, they brought their own crops and with them the weeds of crops. Recent history of the vegetation is dominated by humans. Large numbers of foreign species have been introduced from all over the world, deliberately as garden plants and crops, or inadvertently with crop seed and imported products such as sheep's fleeces. It becomes more and more difficult to find any natural vegetation – and great care must be taken to protect what little remains.

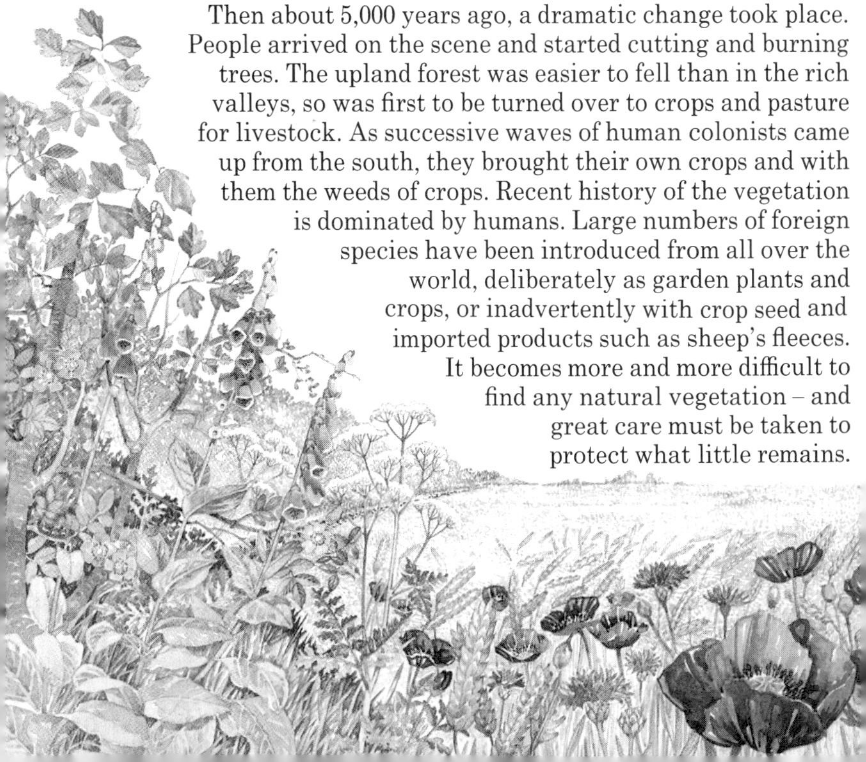

WHERE TO FIND WILD FLOWERS

Where a plant will grow is determined by a combination of temperature, exposure to sun and wind, rainfall, type of soil (especially the presence of certain minerals and drainage), plus the influence of surrounding plants. Plants such as Field Eryngo, restricted to the south of the area covered by the book, are often more common towards the Mediterranean region. Mountain plants of the south, such as Mountain Avens, are often found at much lower altitudes in the extreme north.

Soils formed over chalk or limestone rocks are alkaline and lime-rich. Plants tolerating such soils, including many Orchids, are usually not found elsewhere. Similar alkaline or base-rich soils are formed above certain other rocks and on coastal dunes containing large amounts of sea-shells. Heathers and Bilberry require a soil that is lime-free. They are found on the acid soils which occur above sand, forms of granite or sandstone, and peaty soils of bogs and moorland. Plants which survive on the salty soils around the coasts often will not grow elsewhere. On the grassy parts of salt-marshes, Sea Aster is found, whereas Sea-purslane clings to the edges of channels and Glasswort is found on the mud. Grassy ledges of sea-cliffs are home to Rock Samphire and Sea Campion, whereas Sea Bindweed is found on sand-dunes.

The level of water in the soil is determined by rainfall, the ability of the soil to retain moisture, and the local water-table. Some plants, such as the Large-flowered Butterwort, are found only in high rainfall areas to the south-west of the area. Plants of damp meadows in river-valleys include the Fritillary. Other plants needing wetter soils are found in marshes and bogs or by streams, rivers and lakes. True aquatic plants need to grow in the water and usually have submerged or floating leaves. Conversely, some plants prefer to grow on free-draining soils, such as those formed in crevices among rocks or scree and shingle. Some plants require the ground to be completely cleared before seeds will germinate: these are the plants of cornfields or other cultivated ground, and include Common Poppy and Cornflower. Plants such as Field Scabious thrive in competition with grasses and other herbaceous plants in sunny meadows. Relatively few wild flowers can grow in the deep shade of mature woodland; most woodland flowers are found in clearings and on the lighter margins. Those that do grow on the woodland floor, such as Bluebell, complete most of their growth and flowering before the trees fully open their leaves.

Introduction

HOW TO IDENTIFY WILD FLOWERS

Identifying wild flowers becomes easier with experience. Half the battle is knowing what to look for. The main distinguishing features are summarized below and some of the terms are explained.

Type
Plants which grow from seed, flower and fruit all within a year are called annuals. Biennials start into leafy growth in one year but flower the next. Perennials flower and fruit over successive years. Aquatic plants live floating or submerged in water. Parasitic wild flowers obtain nourishment from other plants; saprophytes from decaying leaves.

Stems
Stems may be upright, angled upwards or low-growing and can have distinct lines, angles, or wing-like sides. Some plants climb by twining stems, leaf-stalks or tendrils. Heights are expressed in centimetres to make them comparable. The tiny Rootless Duckweed is less than one tenth of a centimetre tall but climbers like Traveller's-joy have stems several thousand times taller, becoming thick and woody, and reaching the tops of trees.

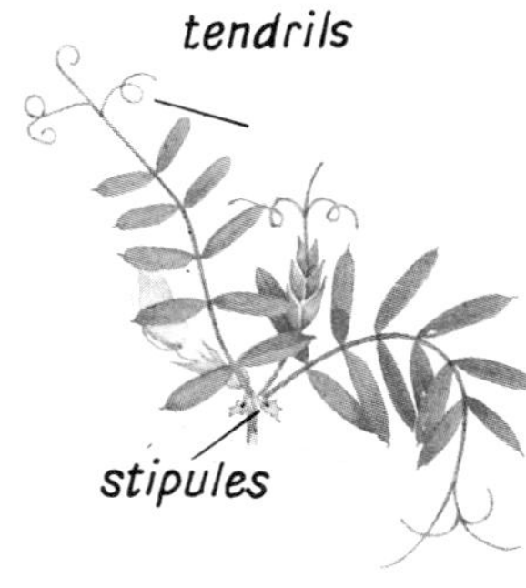

Roots
Included under this heading are all below-ground parts. Most annuals have finely divided, fibrous roots. A long, tapered tap-root is found in many biennials; perennials often die back to a woody stock. Some plants have creeping, rooting underground stems. A bulb is a short stem with fleshy leaf-bases; the corm of Cyclamen is a swollen, upright underground stem; tubers of Hemlock Water-dropwort are swollen parts of the roots. Parasitic plants have roots that invade the tissues of other plants.

Leaves, stipules and hairs
Note the arrangement, whether paired or otherwise on the stem or all at the base (often as a rosette); the shape of the blade (expanded part), whether it is divided into leaflets, and whether the edge is unbroken, toothed, spiny or lobed. Plants which grow both in water and on land often have two sorts of leaf. Leaves often have a stalk at the base, and beneath this there may be a pair of stipules. Those of Large Bird's-foot-trefoil resemble an extra pair of leaflets. The presence of hairs, and size, shape, density or position can help identify a species. They may be gland-tipped and sticky or make the plant look woolly.

Flowers
Although size and colour are usually the most obvious features of flowers, there are many other useful characteristics for identification. It is important to understand the structure of a flower.

Sepals
Number, shape and size of sepals may vary between species but most are green and rather leaf-like. Note whether the sepals differ in size or are joined at the base. In Dandelion, the sepals of the individual flowers form a ring of bristles and become the 'parachute' of the fruits.

Petals
The number of petals is important, and whether they are equal or unequal. Look to see whether the petals are joined together towards the base. There is not always an obvious tube-like part, but if petals are joined then they usually fall together as in the Forget-me-nots.

Perianth
If the petals and sepals are not readily distinguished, then the term perianth applies to both. The parts of the perianth can be green and sepal-like, as in Sea-purslane, or petal-like, as in Fritillary.

Type
The male (♂) parts of a flower are the stamens, whereas the female (♀) parts are the stigma, usually with a stalk-like part (style) attaching it to the ovary. Most flowers have both male and female parts and are termed hermaphrodite (⚥). Male and female parts can be on separate types of flower – both on the same plant, as in Sea-purslane, or on different plants, as in Common Nettle.

Stamens
The number of stamens, and whether they are hidden by the base of the petals or protruding, can help distinguish plants. In flowers of the Daisy family and Bellflowers, the stamens join to form a tube with the pollen-bearing parts (anthers) opening inwards.

Stigmas and ovary
A flower can have a single ovary or multiple ovaries, as in the Buttercups. An ovary can have a single stigma or many. Inside, there may be a single cavity containing the developing seeds, or the ovary can be few- or many-celled through division by internal walls. An ovary may be above the base of the petals or beneath, as in Willowherbs and Orchids.

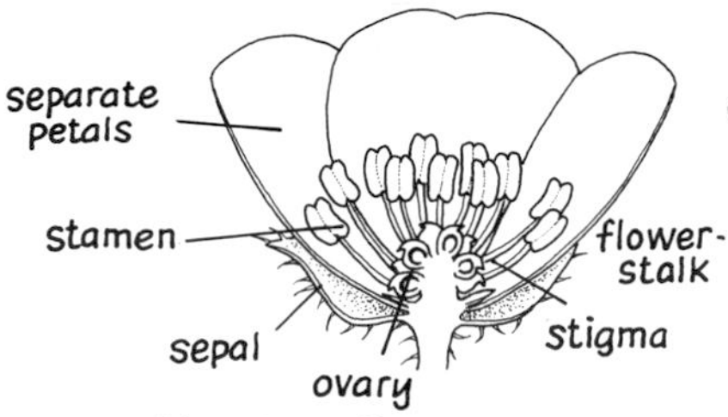

Meadow Buttercup
Ranunculus acris

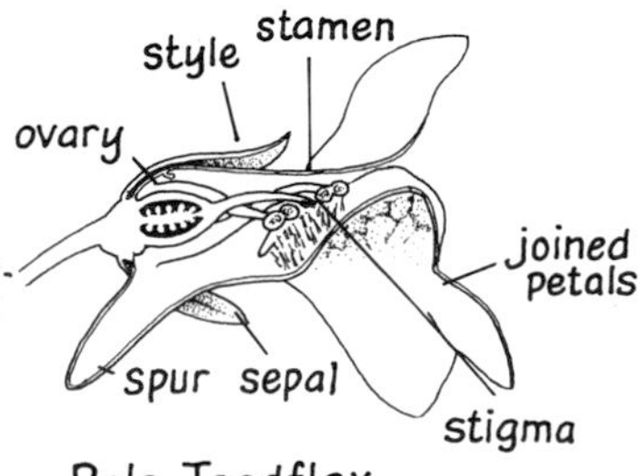

Pale Toadflax
Linaria repens

Introduction

Flower-stalk

This can vary from being upright to turning downwards so that the flower is nodding or pendulous. The stalk may be much longer than the flower, or shorter, or sometimes absent.

Flower-head

Flowers can arise singly from the base of a leaf or tip of a stem, but often are clustered to form a flower-head. This may be elongated, unbranched and spike-like, or branched in some way. A branched, umbrella-shaped head, with flowers mostly at the same level, is typical of the Carrot family. The flowers may be so tightly clustered that the whole flower-head appears as a single flower, as in the Daisies. The tiny flowers in the head are called florets. Those florets in the centre are often smaller and of a different shape from the outer, strap-shaped florets. Surrounding the florets is the ring of green structures called bracts and the whole flower-head has a stem resembling a flower-stalk.

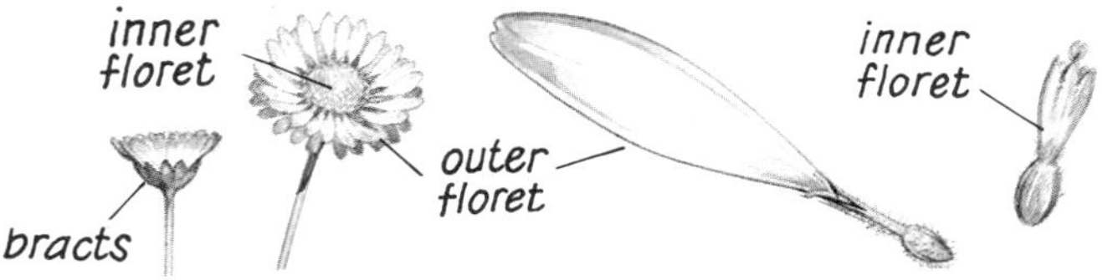

Bracts

These occur mostly at the base of a flower-stalk or the base of a flower-head. They are mostly like small leaves but can be papery or scale-like. Bracts are often larger towards the base of a flower-head and become indistinguishable from normal leaves. Slender bracts of the Bluebell are coloured like the flowers.

Fruits and seeds

Important things to note about fruits are the number of them produced by a single flower, whether they are fleshy or dry, and whether they open to release the seeds. A typical fleshy sort of fruit is the berry of a Bilberry. Wild Strawberry appears to have a berry-like fruit but this is the swollen base of the flower, the actual fruits being the pips on the surface. By far the majority of fruits have outer layers which become dry as the fruit ripens. The fruit of the Poppy (a capsule) opens by a ring of pores around the top. Pods are elongated fruits that split open, and are found in relatives of the Peas. Plants related to the Cabbages have pod-like fruits. Dry fruits that do not open are usually nut-like, containing a single seed. Number, size, shape, surface features and colour of seeds can all be useful in recognition.

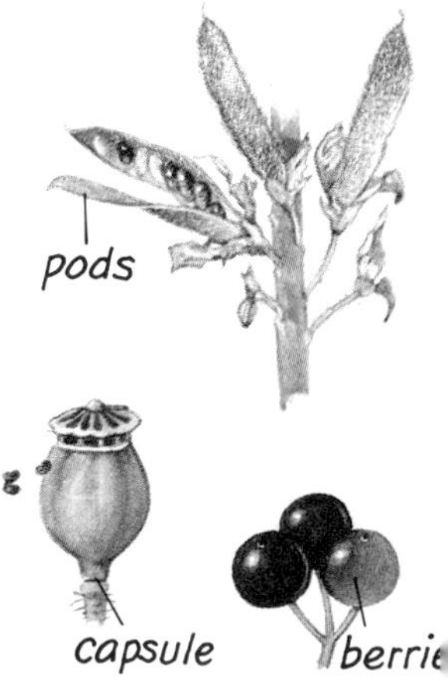

KEY TO SPECIES

This key provides an illustrated guide to groups of species and their page numbers. At each stage, read the first numbered statement and see if it describes your plant. If not, then the second statement with the same number includes all other plants left at that stage of the key. Move on to the next statement below and repeat the process. Some of the distinctive groups of wild flowers fall within the first few categories but many wild flowers need closer examination.

1 **water plants; leaves mostly floating or submerged**
Amphibious Bistort 22; Water-lilies 40; Crowfoots 41; Water-cresses 57; Water-milfoils 128; Fool's Water-cress, Water-dropworts 137–138; Water-violet 152; Water-starwort 165; Bladderworts 202; Shoreweed 203; Arrowhead 248; Frogbit 249; Pondweeds 251; Duckweeds 265.

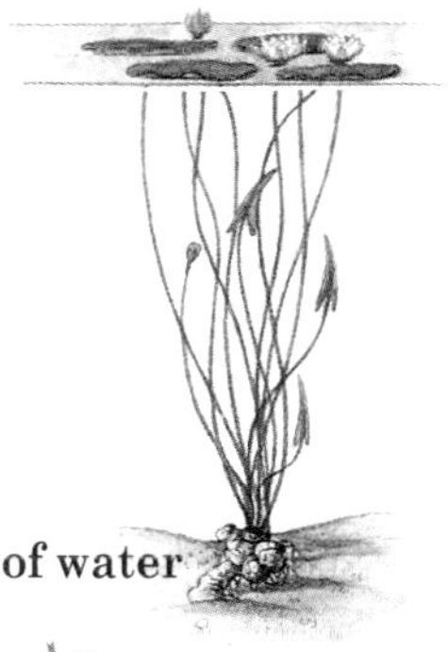

1 **not water plants or all leaves normally out of water**
2 **leaves and stems without green pigment**
Dodder 164; Broomrapes 200; Bird's-nest Orchid 274. (*cf.* Colt's-foot 230; Meadow Saffron 254.)

2 **leaves and stems with green pigment**
3 **flowers green or brown, usually without distinct petals**
4 **climbing plants**
Hop 20; Black-bindweed 23; Traveller's-joy 49; Bryonies 122; Ivy 129.

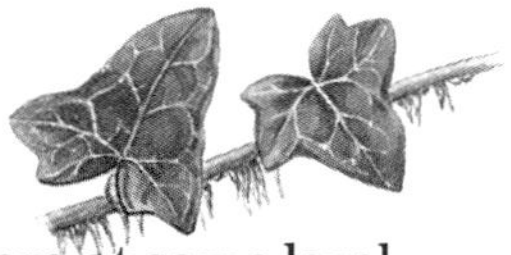

4 **not climbing plants**
5 **leaves on stems, in pairs or clusters at same level**
Mistletoe 19; Nettles 21; Sea-purslane 27; Glassworts 28; Pearlworts 34; Golden-saxifrages 77; Mercuries 112; Wood Sage 174; Figworts 187; Branched Plantain 205; Moschatel 207; Herb-Paris 258; Twayblades 272.

5 leaves all at base of plant or scattered around stem
Asarabacca 18; Pellitory-of-the-wall, Docks, Goosefoots 21–28; Hellebores 46; Meadow-rues 51; Swine-cress 63; Golden-saxifrages 77; Burnets 85; Lady's-mantle 90; Spurges 113; Carrots 130, 134–135; Plantains 203–205; Cudweeds 220; Mugwort 225; Lords-and-Ladies 264; Orchids 267, 273.

3 flowers with distinct petals, not green or brown
6 flowers in compact, rounded heads
Clovers 99–101; Sea-holly 131; Thrift 154; Teasels 210–211; Sheep's-bit 214; Daisies, Dandelions, Thistles 215–247.

6 flowers not in compact, rounded heads
7 flowers in broad, flat-topped or umbrella-shaped clusters
Stonecrops 74–75; Meadowsweet 79; Carrots 130–144; Hemp-agrimony, Yarrow, Tansy 216, 224, 228.

7 flowers not in broad, flat-topped clusters
8 petals of different sizes
9 petals separate from the base
Larkspurs 50; Fumitories 55; Mignonettes 72; Peas 91–105; Milkworts 114; Balsams 115; Violets 118–119; Butcher's-broom 259; Snowdrop 261; Irises 263; Orchids 266–275.

9 petals joined above base
Vervain 172; Mints 173–183; Figworts, Broomrapes, Butterworts 186–201; Honeysuckles 206; Teasels 210–211.

8 petals all the same size
10 petals fewer than 4 or more than 5
Birthwort 18; Buttercups 44, 47–49; Black Bryony 122; Loosestrifes 123; Enchanter's-nightshades 125; Chickweed Wintergreen 153; Arrowhead 248; Flowering-rush 250; Lilies, Daffodils 252–262; Lords-and-Ladies 264.

10 4–5 petals
11 petals separate from the base
12 4 petals
Pearlworts 34; Traveller's-joy 49; Meadow-rues 51; Poppies 52–54; Cabbages 56–71; Tormentil 88; Allseed 107.

12 5 petals
13 leaves on stems, in pairs or clusters at same level
Pinks, Purslanes 29–39; Fairy Flax 107; Crane's-bills 108–111; St John's-worts 116–117; Rock-roses 121.

13 leaves all at base of plant or scattered around stem
Bistorts 22–23; Buttercups 41–51; Stonecrops, Saxifrages, Sundews 73–77; Grass-of-Parnassus 78; Roses 79–90; Wood-sorrels 106; Flaxes 107; Mallows 120.

11 petals joined above base
14 4 petals
Willowherbs 124–127; Heathers 146–147; Bedstraws 158–160.

14 5 petals
15 leaves on stems, in pairs or clusters at same level
Pimpernels 150–151; Gentians 155–156; Periwinkles 157; Valerians 208–209.

15 leaves all at base of plant or scattered around stem
White Bryony 122; Wintergreens 145; Bilberry 147; Primroses 148–149; Bogbean 152; Brookweed 153; Thrift 154; Jacob's-ladder 161; Bindweeds 162–164; Forget-me-nots 166–171; Nightshades 184–185; Mullein 186; Bellflowers 212–214.

Introduction

PLANT NAMES

Common names vary greatly and some species have over a hundred local names in a single country. As a simplification, English-language names have been standardized to the list published by the Botanical Society of the British Isles (Dony, Jury and Perring, 1986). Plants lacking a common name are usually recently naturalized, or grow only in certain countries covered by the book.

Scientific names are more stable and international in usage. Most are consistent with the standard European flora (Tutin *et al.* (Editors), 1964–1980) but some are updated using more recent British floras. Each scientific name is made up of a genus (plural: genera) name, with an initial capital letter, and a species name starting with a small letter. A third, subspecies (abbreviated subsp.) name is used to distinguish geographical variation within a species. A multiplication symbol (×) between the first two names indicates a hybrid between two species.

Order of plants

The plants in this book are arranged more or less in systematic order, those genera with similar construction of flowers and fruit being placed together in families and given a single name in the list below. Each group of families is given a colour reference marker. Use this coloured square at the corner of the pages to help you find the different groups of plants as you flick through the book.

- *Asarabacca and Mistletoe*
- *Docks, Goosefoots, Hop and Nettles*
- *Pinks and Purslanes*
- *Buttercups and Water-lilies*
- *Cabbages, Poppies, Fumitories and Mignonettes*
- *Stonecrops, Saxifrages and Sundews*
- *Roses and Grass-of-Parnassus*
- *Peas*
- *Crane's-bills, Spurges, Wood-sorrels and Flaxes*
- *St John's-worts, Milkworts and Balsams*
- *Violets, Mallows, Rock-roses and Cucumbers*
- *Willowherbs, Loosestrifes and Water-milfoils*
- *Carrots and Ivy*
- *Primroses, Heathers, Wintergreens and Thrift*
- *Bedstraws, Gentians and Periwinkles*
- *Bindweeds, Jacob's-ladder and Water-starworts*
- *Mints and Forget-me-nots*
- *Figworts, Nightshades, Butterworts and Broomrapes*
- *Plantains*
- *Valerians, Teasels, Honeysuckles and Moschatel*
- *Daisies and Bellflowers*
- *Arrowhead, Frogbit and Flowering-rush*
- *Lilies, Daffodils and Irises*
- *Orchids, Lords-and-Ladies and Duckweeds*

WILD FLOWERS

OF·BRITAIN·&·NORTHERN·EUROPE

Asarabacca *Asarum europaeum*

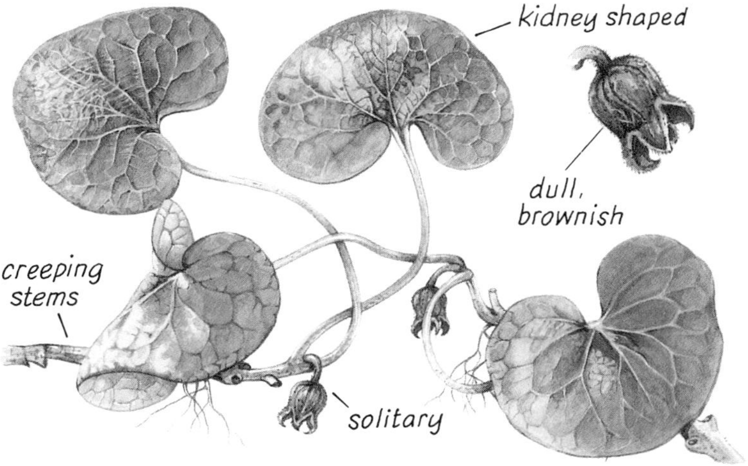

The lustrous, kidney-shaped leaves of this species are more noticeable than the curious 3-lobed flowers which are held close to the ground. Both the native Asarabacca and exotic relatives are popular as garden plants for their cyclamen-like foliage. Asarabacca was once used for respiratory ailments and complaints of the liver; it is used no longer because of harmful side effects. *Status:* native or escaped from cultivation; widespread but rare in Britain, absent from Ireland. *Similar species:* Birthwort has more upright stems and clusters of tubular, yellow flowers.

Birthwort *(Aristolochia clematitis)*

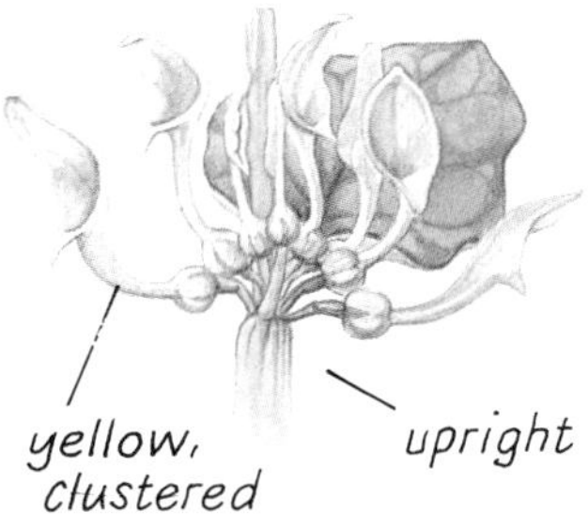

	ASARABACCA
Type	perennial
Height	low-growing
Habitat	woods
Flowering	May–August
	STEMS AND LEAVES
Stem	5–10cm long, creeping, rooting
Root	branched, creeping stock
Hairs	short hairs on stems and flowers
Stipules	absent
Leaves	on alternate sides of stem, 25–100mm, kidney-shaped, glossy dark green, tip rounded, edge smooth, base heart-shaped
Leaf-stalk	longer than blade

	FLOWERS
Position	single, from tip of stem
Bracts	absent
Type	⚥ inconspicuous
Size	11–15mm
Colour	dull purplish brown
Stalk	longer than flower
Perianth	3, triangular, equal, pointed, joined at base into short tube
Stamens	12
Stigmas	usually 6
Ovary	1, usually 6-celled
	FRUIT
Type	capsule, opening irregularly, globular, the perianth attached
Size	7–9mm
Seeds	numerous, 2–3mm, flattened

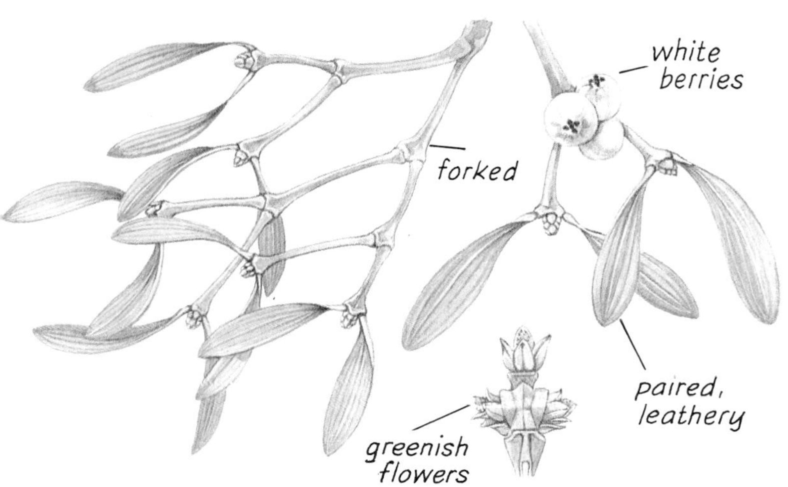

Bright, yellowish-green foliage springing from the branch of an otherwise bare tree in winter distinguishes the Mistletoe from a distance. Its special roots invade the tissues of the host tree and take nourishment, although the plant makes some of its own food using sunlight. Mistletoe grows on a large range of deciduous trees; it is especially common on Apple, although uncommon on Oak and found only rarely on conifers. Birds eating the berries wipe off sticky seeds from their beaks on to a branch, where the seeds grow into new plants. Mistletoe is familiar through the Christmas tradition of kissing under a sprig of the plant – magical properties have been attributed to the plant throughout the ages. In particular, the plants that grew on Oak featured much in ancient ceremonies of the Druids. Mistletoe has been used medicinally to treat heart disease and many different nervous disorders. *Status:* native; most of area except for some northern parts and Ireland. (There are no similar species.)

	MISTLETOE
Type	perennial
Height	20–100cm
Habitat	parasite mainly on deciduous trees
Flowering	February–April
	STEMS AND LEAVES
Stem	woody at base, repeatedly forking, green
Root	specially modified to invade wood of tree
Hairs	absent
Stipules	absent
Leaves	paired on opposite sides of stem, 50–80mm, narrow, sometimes curved, leathery, tip blunt, edge unbroken, base narrowed
Leaf-stalk	short
	FLOWERS
Position	3–5 clustered at tip of stem, on ♂ or ♀ plants
Bracts	joined to flower-stalks
Type 1	♂ without sepals
Type 2	♀ with 4 sepals, 2–4mm
Size	4–6mm
Colour	greenish yellow
Stalk	short
Perianth	4, sepal-like, broadest at base, blunt
Stamens	4, joined to petals
Stigma	1
Ovary	1, 1-celled
	FRUIT
Type	1, berry, white, mostly globe-shaped
Size	6–10mm
Seeds	1, sticky

Hop *Humulus lupulus*

A rather coarse, tough vine climbing by tendril-like tips to the twining stems. The backward-pointing, stiff hairs provide extra anchorage but can give a painful scratch. Cultivated plants are trained up strings supported by tall poles in fields. Tough fibres from the stems have been used in the manufacture of cloth and a form of paper has also been made from the stems. Tips of young shoots are edible and can be used fresh in salads or cooked like Asparagus, the latter method being favoured by the Romans. Hops produce the characteristic bitter taste of beer, a use extending at least back to the Middle Ages, and belong to the same family as the drug plant that yields marijuana. Extracts from the female flowers have a mild sedative action and have been used for insomnia and nervous ailments. *Status:* native or often naturalized; common, most of area. (There are no similar species.)

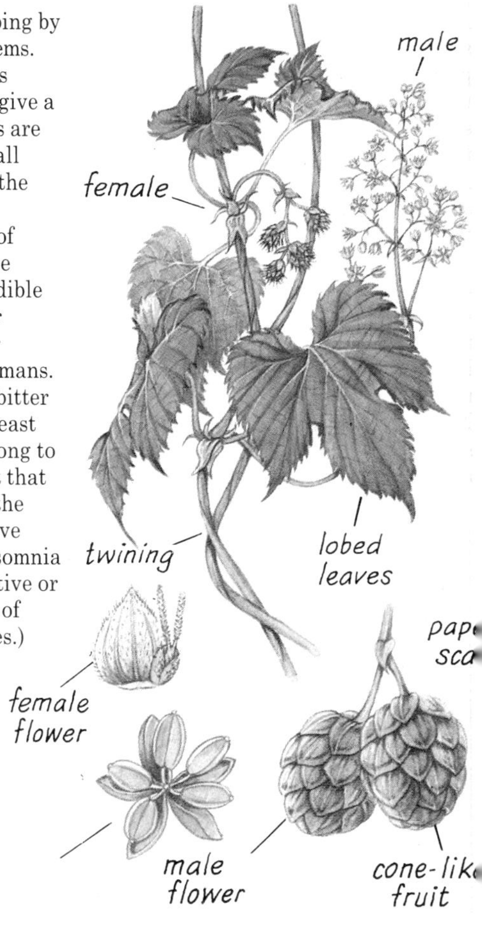

	HOP
Type	perennial
Height	300–600cm
Habitat	hedges and bushes
Flowering	July–August
	STEMS AND LEAVES
Stem	climbing, twisting clockwise
Root	fibrous
Hairs	stiff, backward-pointing
Stipules	present
Leaves	paired on opposite sides of stem, mostly 100–150mm, 3–5 lobed, pointed, edge toothed, base heart-shaped
Leaf-stalk	about equal to blade
	FLOWERS
Position	numerous, in pendulous clusters, ♂ and ♀ flowers on different plants
Bracts	♀ up to 10mm, oval, becoming papery
Type 1	♂ in loose, branched cluster
Type 2	♀ in cone-like head, 15–20mm, yellowish green
Size	*c*5mm
Colour	green
Stalk	present only in ♂
Perianth	♂ 5-parted, ♀ undivided
Stamens	♂ with 5
Stigmas	♀ with 2
Ovary	1, 1-celled
	FRUIT
Type	cone of papery scales enclosing nut-like fruits
Size	cone 30–50mm
Seeds	not released

A species notorious on account of stinging hairs which cover most of the plant. Brushed lightly, the brittle tip of the stiff hair breaks off depositing a small drop of formic acid which causes the stinging sensation. Young shoots, rich in Vitamin C, can be eaten: the stinging action is destroyed by cooking. Some populations of the Common Nettle do not sting, but the reputation of the species ensures that those are rarely detected. Nettles provide the main food plant for many familiar butterflies. *Status:* native; common in most of area. *Similar species:* Small Nettle is an annual favouring lighter soils. Pellitory-of-the-wall has red stems and leaves with softer, stingless hairs.

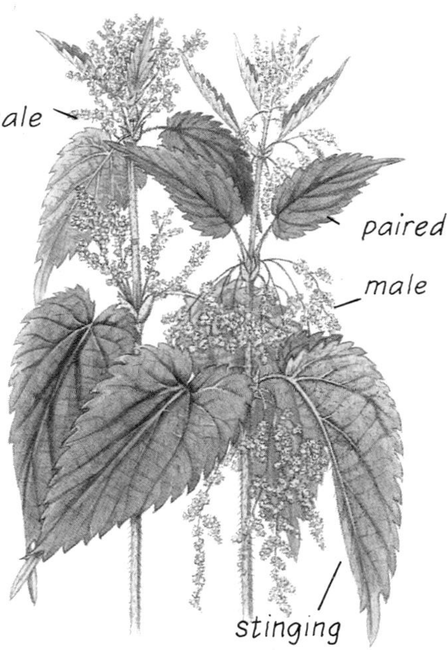

1 Small Nettle *(U. urens)*; **2** Pellitory-of-the-wall *(Parietaria judaica)*

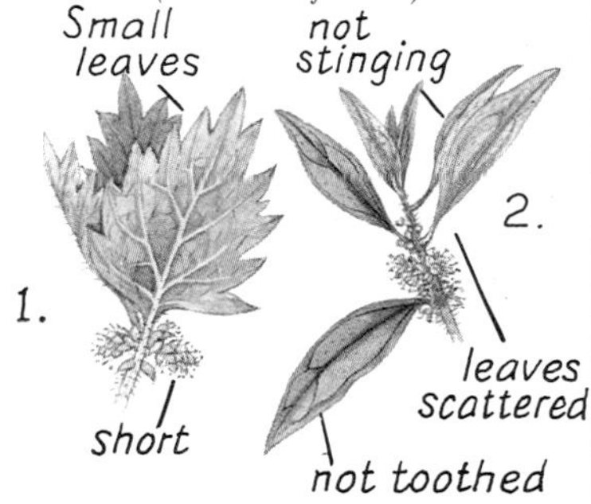

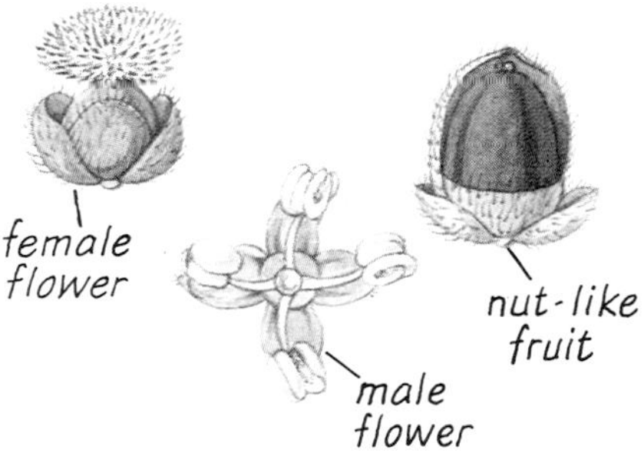

	COMMON NETTLE
Type	perennial
Height	30–150cm
Habitat	hedgerows, woods, waste places; mainly rich soils
Flowering	June–August
	STEMS AND LEAVES
Stem	creeping or upright
Root	tough, yellow, fibrous
Hairs	stiff, mostly stinging
Stipules	present
Leaves	paired on opposite sides of stem, 40–80mm, oval, tip pointed, edge sharply toothed, base heart-shaped
Leaf-stalk	shorter than blade
	FLOWERS
Position	numerous, in branched, spike-like clusters from leaf-base, ♂ and ♀ flowers on different plants
Bracts	absent
Type 1	♂ with equal perianth-lobes
Type 2	♀ with unequal perianth-lobes, *c*1mm
Size	1.5–2mm
Colour	yellowish green
Stalk	absent
Perianth	4-parted
Stamens	4, springing open when ripe
Stigma	1, feathery
Ovary	1, 1-celled
	FRUIT
Type	single, nut-like, oval, enclosed by withered flower
Size	1–1.5mm
Seeds	not released

Amphibious Bistort *Polygonum amphibium*

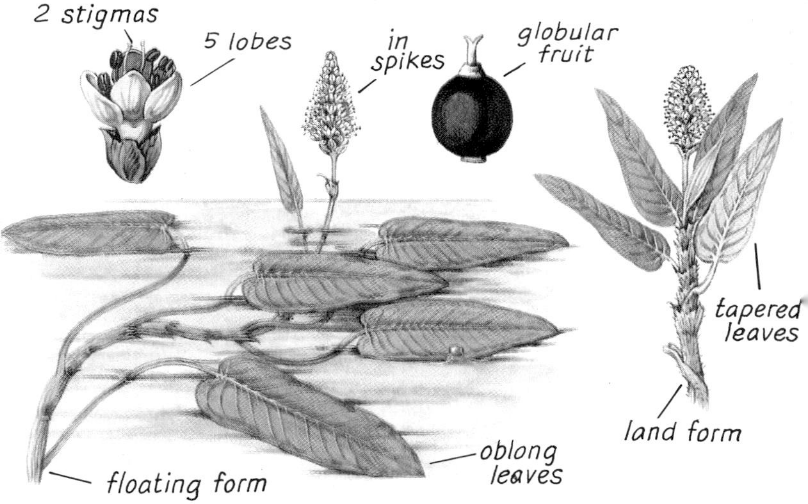

An attractive plant with spikes of pink or red flowers, usually rising from the surface of a lake. There is a land form with more upright stems and tapered, hairy leaves. The common name refers to this amphibious nature, but 'bistort', meaning 'twice twisted', refers to the convoluted roots of Common Bistort. *Status:* native, in suitable places through most of region. *Similar species:* Common Bistort has slender, upright stems, smaller upper leaves and three stigmas. The nearly hairless Redshank and hairy Pale Persicaria are two weed species with smaller flowers.

1 Common Bistort *(P. bistorta)*;
2 Redshank *(P. persicaria)*;
3 Pale Persicaria *(P. lapathifolium)*

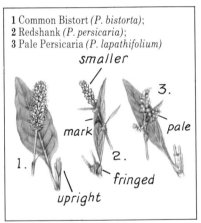

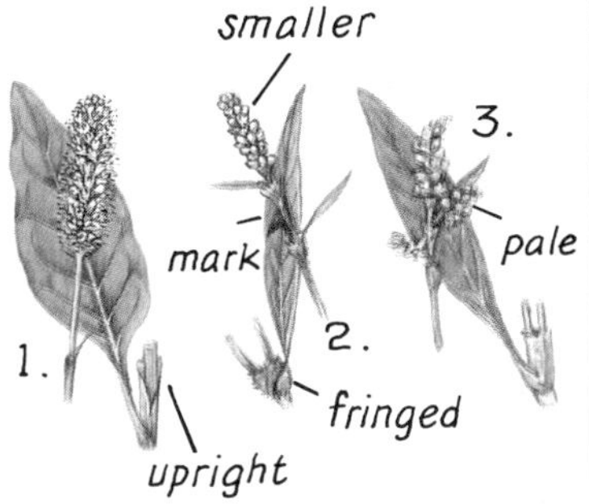

	AMPHIBIOUS BISTORT
Type	perennial
Height	floating form 30–75cm long; land form to 50cm
Habitat	lakes, canals, slow-moving rivers or by water
Flowering	July–September
	STEMS AND LEAVES
Stem	floating, rooting, sometimes upright
Root	creeping rhizome
Hairs	hairless or with short hairs
Stipules	joined forming tube
Leaves	spirally arranged on stem
Leaves 1	floating form 50–150mm, oblong, blunt, edge unbroken, base square or heart-shaped
Leaf-stalk	20–60mm
Leaves 2	land form pointed, base broader, rounded
Leaf-stalk	mostly short
	FLOWERS
Position	numerous, in blunt spike at tip of stem
Bracts	scale-like
Type	⚥
Size	5–7mm
Colour	pink or red
Stalk	shorter than flower
Perianth	5-lobed, 3–5mm, lobes petal-like, equal
Stamens	5
Stigmas	2
Ovary	1, 1-celled
	FRUIT
Type	single, nut-like, enclosed by dried flower, globular, brown
Size	2–3mm
Seeds	not separate

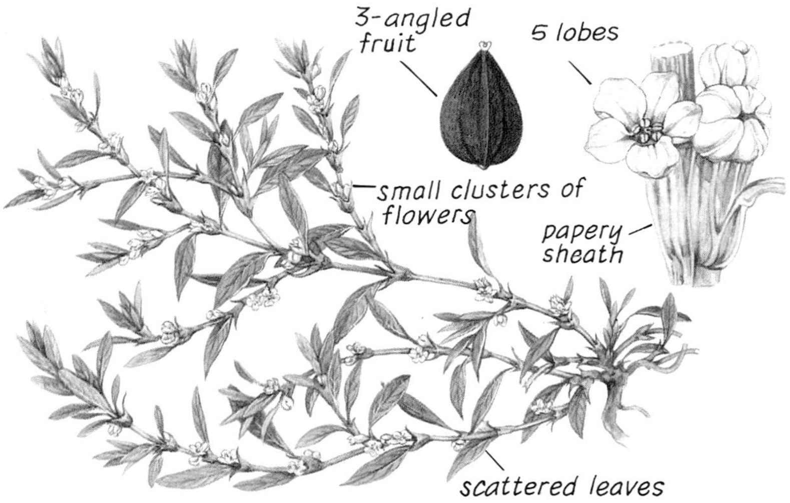

Although very common, Knotgrass is often overlooked because of its rather insignificant flowers. The common name refers to the swelling where the leaf joins the stem in many species of Knotgrass. *Status:* native; common through most of region. *Similar species:* Water-pepper, from damp places, has longer flower-heads, brown stipules. Black-bindweed is a climbing plant of cultivated and waste ground. Much larger at up to 2m tall, Japanese Knotweed was introduced to gardens but is now widely naturalized.

1 Water-pepper *(P. hydropiper)*; **2** Black-bindweed *(Fallopia convolvulus)*; **3** Japanese Knotweed *(Reynoutria japonica)*

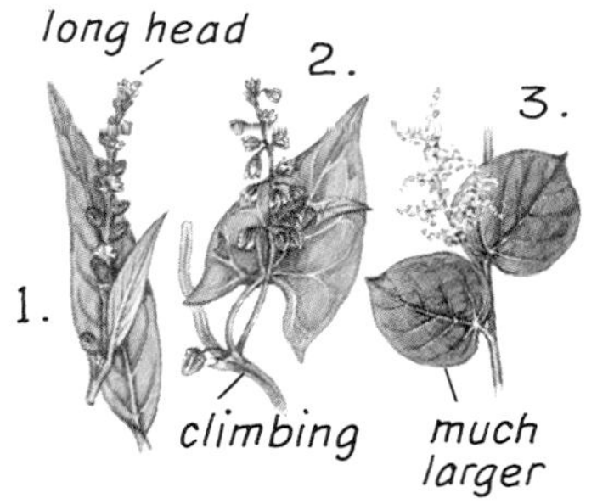

KNOTGRASS

Type	annual
Height	5–100cm
Habitat	cultivated land, waste places, often near sea
Flowering	July–October

STEMS AND LEAVES

Stem	upright or low-growing
Root	fibrous
Hairs	absent
Stipules	silvery, joined forming tube round stem
Leaves	spirally arranged around stem, 20–50mm, spear-shaped, tip pointed, edge unbroken, base narrowing into stalk
Leaf-stalk	about equal to stipules

FLOWERS

Position	single or in loose clusters of 2–6 from base of leaf
Bracts	insignificant
Type	⚥
Size	3–4.5mm
Colour	greenish with pink or white edges
Stalk	absent
Perianth	5-lobed, 2–3mm, joined at base into short tube
Stamens	5–8
Stigmas	2
Ovary	1, 1-celled

FRUIT

Type	1, nut-like, 3-angled, enclosed by dried flower
Size	2.5–3.5mm
Seeds	not separate

Sheep's Sorrel *Rumex acetosella*

Perhaps the most distinctive feature of this plant is the foliage, which acquires a brilliant crimson hue late in the season and on poor soils. Pollen is carried by the wind from the male plants to the feathery stigmas of the female plants. *Status:* native; common, most of area. *Similar species:* Common Sorrel has leaves with backward-pointing lobes, the upper clasping the stem. Formerly prized as a vegetable, the acid-tasting leaves were used much as lemons are today. Mountain Sorrel has kidney-shaped leaves mostly arising near the root.

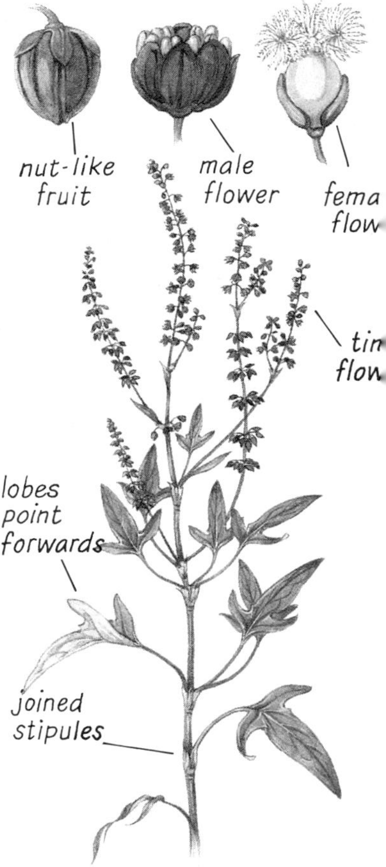

1 Common Sorrel *(R. acetosa)*;
2 Mountain Sorrel *(Oxyria digyna)*

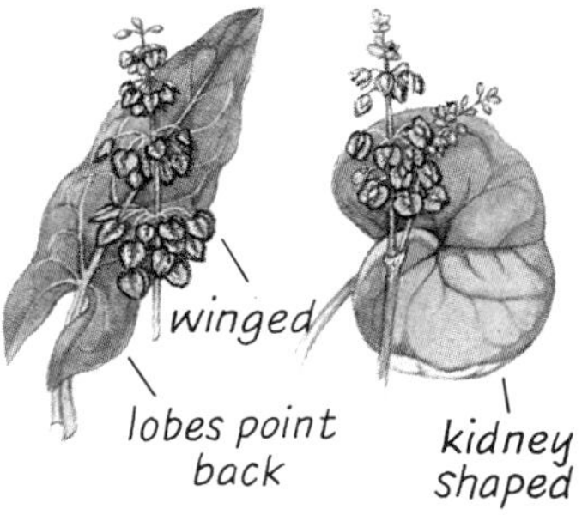

	SHEEP'S SORREL
Type	perennial
Height	up to 30cm
Habitat	heaths, grassland, waste ground; acid soils
Flowering	May–August
	STEMS AND LEAVES
Stem	upright or turning upright
Root	creeping, budding to make new stems
Hairs	absent
Stipules	joined forming tube
Leaves	on alternate sides of stem, up to 40mm, narrowly oval, often red-tinged, pointed, base usually with 2 forward-curving lobes
Leaf-stalk	longer than blade or absent above

	FLOWERS
Position	numerous, in branched clusters, ♂ and ♀ flowers on different plants
Bracts	absent
Type 1	♂ with stamens
Type 2	♀ 1.5–2mm, with ovary
Size	*c*2mm
Colour	green, becoming crimson
Stalk	nearly equal to flower
Perianth	6-lobed, 3 small, 3 larger
Stamens	6
Stigmas	3, feathery
Ovary	1, 1-celled
	FRUIT
Type	single, nut-like, 3-angled, enclosed by withered flower
Size	1.3–1.5mm
Seeds	not released

A large-leaved plant, familiar to gardeners as a difficult weed to pull and to children as an antidote for the nettle's sting. The lobes of the perianth change in shape in fruit and differ between species, forming wings, inflated bladders or wart-like bumps. *Status:* native; generally common although rarer in north. *Similar species:* three Docks lack the long teeth on the perianth-lobes. Curled Dock has broad, rounded lobes; Clustered Dock has lobes only half as large; and the aquatic Water Dock has triangular lobes with an elongated outgrowth.

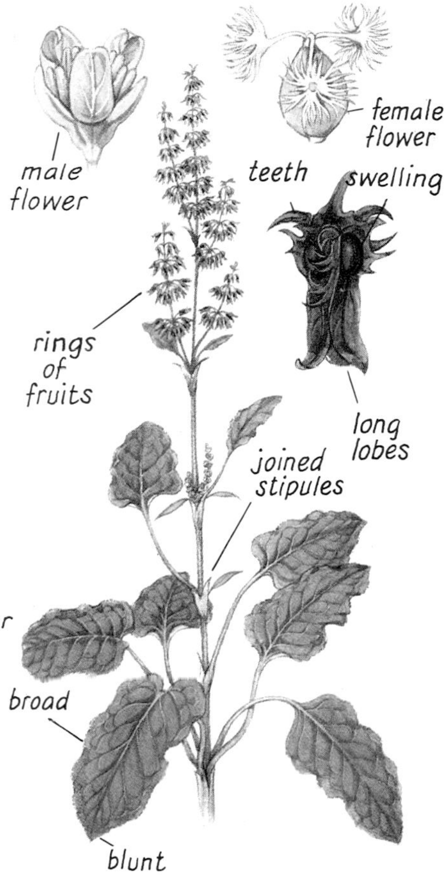

1 Curled Dock *(R. crispus)*;
2 Clustered Dock *(R. conglomeratus)*;
3 Water Dock *(R. hydrolapathum)*

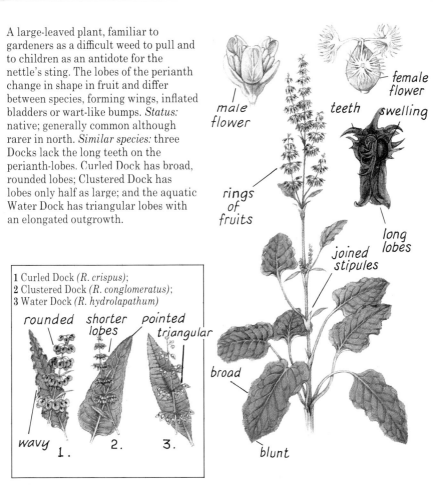

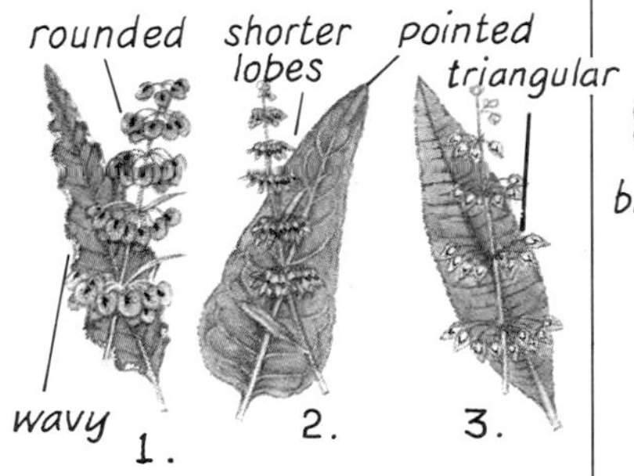

BROAD-LEAVED DOCK

- **Type** perennial
- **Height** 60–120cm
- **Habitat** field margins, hedgerows, cultivated, waste ground
- **Flowering** June–October

STEMS AND LEAVES

- **Stem** upright, branched
- **Root** stout tap-root
- **Hairs** underside of leaves slightly hairy
- **Stipules** joined forming tube
- **Leaves** on alternate sides of stem, to 250mm, oblong or upper tapered, blunt, edge fine-toothed, base square or heart-shaped
- **Leaf-stalk** longer than blade on lower leaves, shorter above

FLOWERS

- **Position** numerous, in rings
- **Bracts** absent
- **Type** mostly ⚥
- **Size** *c*3mm
- **Colour** green and white, turning crimson
- **Stalk** usually longer than flower
- **Perianth** 6-lobed, 1–2mm, the 3 large inner triangular with long teeth and corky outgrowth
- **Stamens** 6
- **Stigmas** 3, feathery
- **Ovary** 1, 1-celled

FRUIT

- **Type** 1, nut-like, surrounded by flower
- **Size** 5–6mm
- **Seeds** not released

Fat-hen *Chenopodium album*

Perhaps the most common of a group of similar weed species with rather fleshy stems, Fat-hen is often striped with white or pink, and has angular leaves. It has been used as a vegetable and grain since the Stone Age, although largely abandoned in recent times. *Status:* native; common throughout area. *Similar species:* Good-King-Henry is perennial with triangular leaves, often lobed at the base. Orache species have separate male and female flowers, the latter enclosed by two bracts. Spear-leaved Orache has leaves squarer-based than Common Orache.

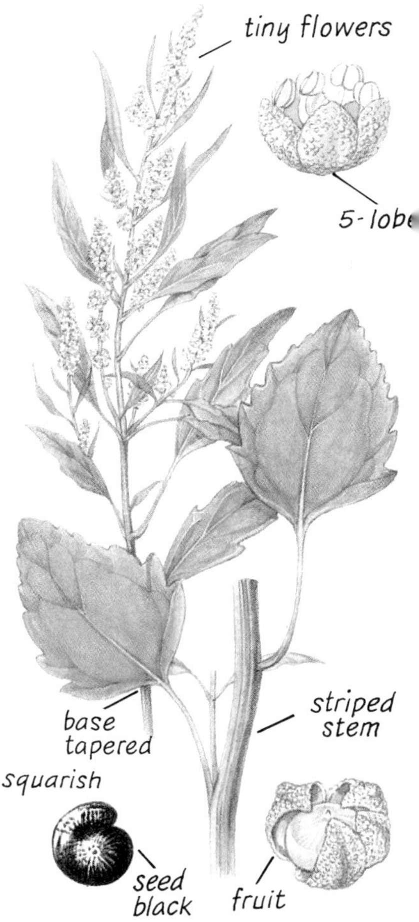

1 Good-King-Henry *(C. bonus-henricus)*; **2** Common Orache *(Atriplex patula)*; **3** Spear-leaved Orache *(A. prostrata)*

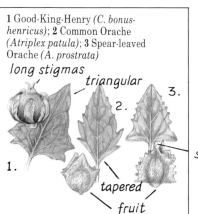

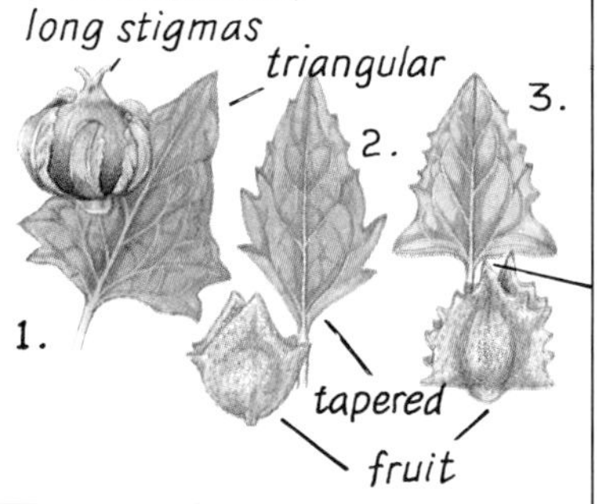

	FAT-HEN
Type	annual
Height	10–150cm
Habitat	cultivated and waste ground; mostly rich soils
Flowering	July–October
	STEMS AND LEAVES
Stem	upright, often striped with pink, slightly ridged
Root	fibrous
Hairs	small, swollen, giving a floury look
Stipules	absent
Leaves	spirally arranged, 12–82mm, diamond- to spear-shaped, tip pointed, edge unbroken or shallowly toothed, base wedge-shaped
Leaf-stalk	shorter than blade

	FLOWERS
Position	numerous, in small clusters grouped in spikes
Bracts	present
Type	⚥
Size	*c*1.5mm
Colour	pale green
Stalk	more or less stalkless
Perianth	5-lobed, each *c*1mm, oval, sepal-like
Stamens	5
Stigmas	2 on forked style
Ovary	1, 1-celled
	FRUIT
Type	1, not opening, forming thin layer, enclosed by withered flower
Size	1.3–2mm
Seeds	1, 1.25–1.85mm, black, faintly grooved

Found in salt-marshes, forming shrubby mounds with silvery leaves and tight clusters of tiny flowers, Sea-purslane tolerates flooding but prefers upper parts of the marsh, fringing the edges of channels. *Status:* native; coasts, except for parts of north. *Similar species:* glossy-leaved Sea Beet, its fruits loosely clustered together, is the same species as cultivated Beetroot and Sugar Beet. Frosted Orache, from sandy shores, has diamond-shaped, toothed leaves and thick bracts, while Grass-leaved or Shore Orache has narrow, scarcely toothed leaves and thin bracts.

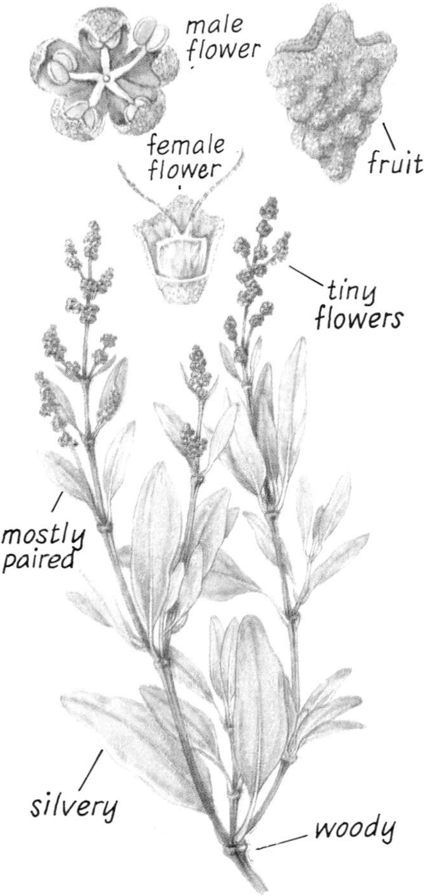

1 Sea Beet *(Beta vulgaris* subsp. *maritima)*; **2** Grass-leaved Orache *(Atriplex littoralis)*; **3** Frosted Orache *(A. laciniata)*

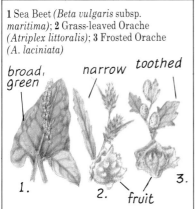

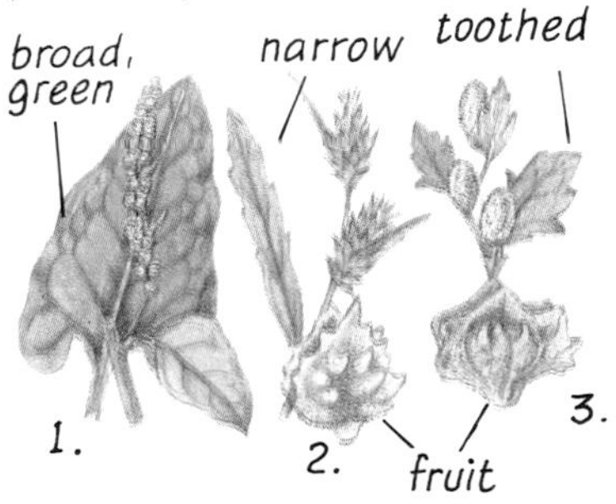

	SEA-PURSLANE
Type	perennial
Height	45–150cm
Habitat	salt-marshes, usually on top edges of gulleys
Flowering	July–September
	STEMS AND LEAVES
Stem	woody below, turning upwards, often rooting
Root	short, creeping rhizome
Hairs	swollen, floury-looking
Stipules	absent
Leaves	paired on opposite sides of stem or alternate above, 10–40mm, elliptical, slightly fleshy, blunt, edge unbroken
Leaf-stalk	3–10mm
	FLOWERS
Position	numerous, spikes at stem-tip or leaf-base, ♂ and ♀ flowers on same plant
Bracts	2 3-lobed, bract-like parts cover ♀ flower
Type 1	♂ with perianth
Size	*c*2mm
Colour	mostly brownish yellow
Stalk	absent
Perianth	5-lobed
Stamens	5
Type 2	♀ without perianth, *c*1.5mm
Stigmas	2
Ovary	1, 1-celled
	FRUIT
Type	1, not opening, thin, hidden by 3-lobed bracts
Size	3–5mm
Seeds	1, *c*3mm, not released

Glasswort *Salicornia europaea*

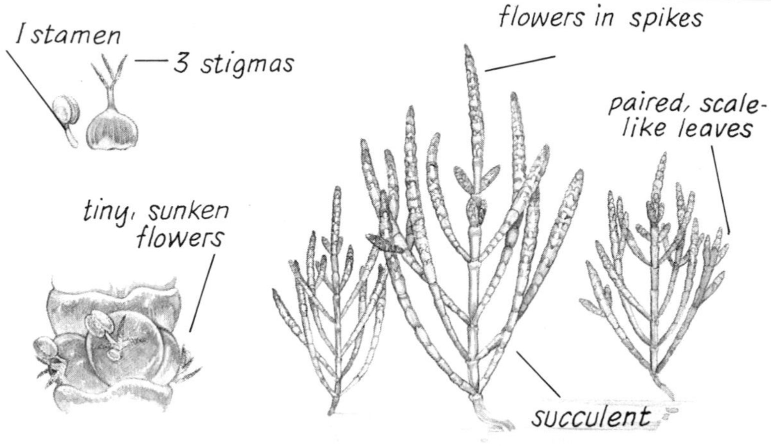

A seemingly leafless succulent plant, at times so plentiful that acres of salt-marsh are covered by nothing else. The anomaly of an apparent desert-plant immersed in water is explained by the sea-water's salinity, which draws water from the plant. *Status:* native; common around coasts except for parts of north. *Similar species:* Perennial Glasswort has woody, rooting stems and flowers with two stamens. Related salt-marsh plants with more normal leaves include Annual Sea-blite with bluntish leaves, and Prickly Saltwort with spine-tipped leaves.

1 Perennial Glasswort *(Arthrocnemum perenne)*; **2** Annual Sea-blite *(Suaeda maritima)*; **3** Prickly Saltwort *(Salsola kali)*

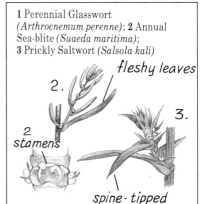

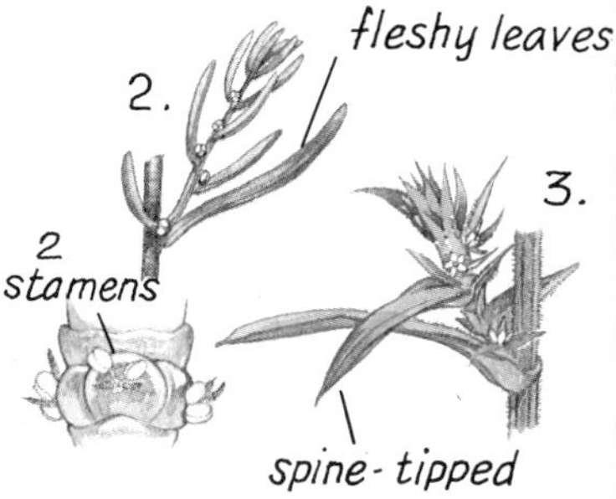

	GLASSWORT
Type	annual
Height	10–40cm
Habitat	salt-marshes; sandy mud
Flowering	August
	STEMS AND LEAVES
Stem	upright, often yellowish green, translucent
Root	fibrous
Hairs	absent
Stipules	absent
Leaves	paired on opposite sides of stem, joined except for tips into tube forming stem-segments, succulent, tip blunt, edge unbroken
Leaf-stalk	absent

	FLOWERS
Position	clusters of 3 on stem-segments towards stem-tip, forming tapered spike
Bracts	present
Type	⚥, partly sunken into stem-segment
Size	*c*2.5mm
Colour	green
Stalk	absent
Perianth	indistinctly 3-lobed, roundish, succulent
Stamen	1, shortly stalked, scarcely projecting
Stigmas	3
Ovary	1, 1-celled
	FRUIT
Type	single, papery-walled
Size	*c*2mm
Seeds	1.2–1.8mm, covered with hairs

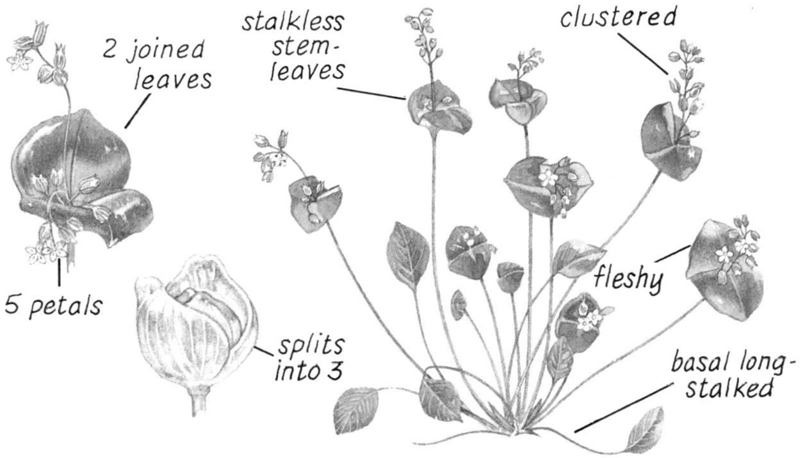

Rather a succulent-looking plant with a pair of rounded leaves joined near the top of the stem, forming a green, cup-like foil for the white flowers. *Status:* introduced from western North America; scattered in south and west of area. *Similar species:* Pink Purslane differs in the larger, pink flowers and the stem leaves are not joined by their bases. Although related, Blinks looks quite different, with branched, rooting stems, narrow leaves and tiny flowers. It is usually found in water or on damp, seasonally flooded ground.

1 Pink Purslane *(M. sibirica)*; 2 Blinks *(M. fontana)*

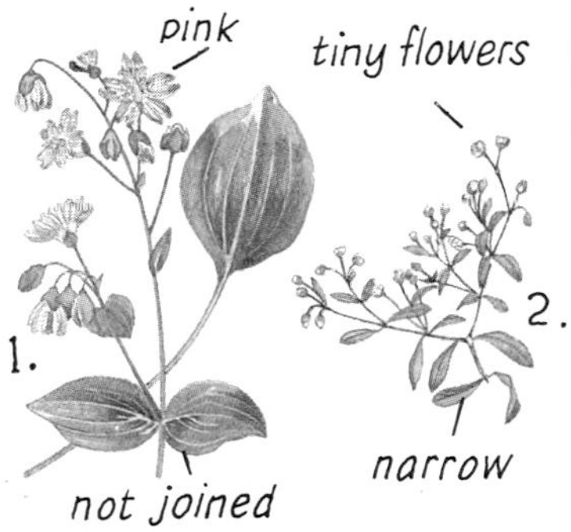

	SPRINGBEAUTY
Type	annual
Height	10–30cm
Habitat	cultivated and waste ground; mainly sandy soils
Flowering	May–July
	STEMS AND LEAVES
Stem	more or less upright
Root	fibrous
Hairs	absent
Stipules	absent
Leaves	at base or paired on opposite sides of stem
Leaves 1	basal 10–25mm, elliptical to diamond-shaped, pointed to bluntish, edge unbroken
Leaf-stalk	longer than blade
Leaves 2	2 stem-leaves joined, more or less blunt
Leaf-stalk	absent
	FLOWERS
Position	few, in unbranched cluster
Bracts	absent
Type	⚥
Size	5–8mm
Colour	white
Stalk	twice as long as sepals
Sepals	2, 1.5–3mm, oval
Petals	5, 2–3mm, all similar, sometimes notched at tip
Stamens	5, joined to petals
Stigmas	3
Ovary	1, 1-celled
	FRUIT
Type	single capsule, splitting into 3 parts, nearly globular
Size	*c*2.5mm
Seeds	1–3, *c*2mm, black, glossy

Greater Stitchwort *Stellaria holostea*

The thread-like lower part of Stitchwort's stem looks impossibly thin and supports the plant only with the aid of its neighbours. Mixed with powdered acorns, the plant was used to treat a stitch or similar pains in the side. *Status:* native, common throughout area. *Similar species:* three other Stitchworts have whitish, papery bracts. Marsh Stitchwort has flowers 12–18mm across and bluish leaves; Lesser Stitchwort has flowers 5–12mm long and green leaves; Bog Stitchwort has smaller flowers, with petals shorter than the sepals.

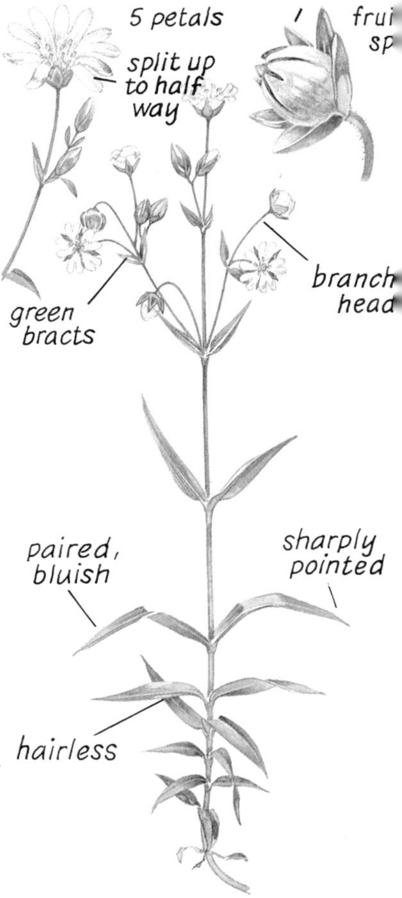

1 Lesser Stitchwort *(S. graminea)*;
2 Marsh Stitchwort *(S. palustris)*;
3 Bog Stitchwort *(S. alsine)*

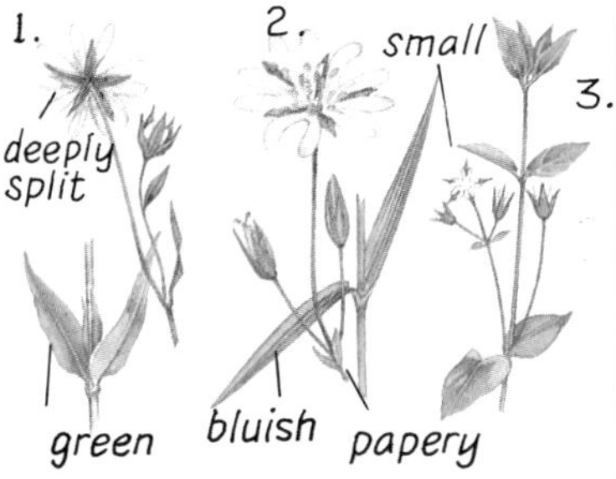

	GREATER STITCHWORT
Type	perennial
Height	15–60cm
Habitat	woods or hedgerows
Flowering	April–June
	STEMS AND LEAVES
Stem	turning upwards, slender at base, sharply 4-angled
Root	slender, creeping stock
Hairs	hairless or hairy above
Stipules	absent
Leaves	paired on opposite sides of stem, 40–80mm, narrowly spear-shaped, bluish, finely pointed, edge rough, base rather broad
Leaf-stalk	absent

	FLOWERS
Position	few, in loose heads
Bracts	leaf-like
Type	⚥
Size	20–30mm
Colour	white
Stalk	longer than flower
Sepals	5, 6–9mm, spear-shaped, with narrow, papery edge
Petals	5, 8–12mm, equal, split to about half-way
Stamens	10
Stigmas	3
Ovary	1, 1-celled
	FRUIT
Type	globular capsule, splitting into 6
Size	6–8mm
Seeds	numerous, 1.5–2mm, kidney-shaped, reddish-brown, rough with tiny outgrowths

This ubiquitous weed flowers at almost any time of the year, as weather permits, with insignificant petals shorter than the sepals. The stems are rather fleshy but weak, so that the Chickweed flops over the ground or other plants. Poultry and cage birds are fond of the seed. *Status:* native; very common throughout area. *Similar species:* two related species differ in having stalked leaves and ten stamens. Greater Chickweed has petals little longer than the sepals; and Wood Stitchwort has petals about twice as long as the sepals. Water Chickweed has large petals and five stigmas.

1 Greater Chickweed *(S. neglecta)*; 2 Wood Stitchwort *(S. nemorum)*; 3 Water Chickweed *(Myosoton aquaticum)*

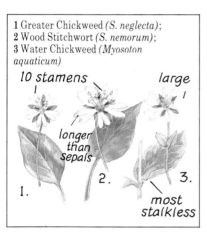

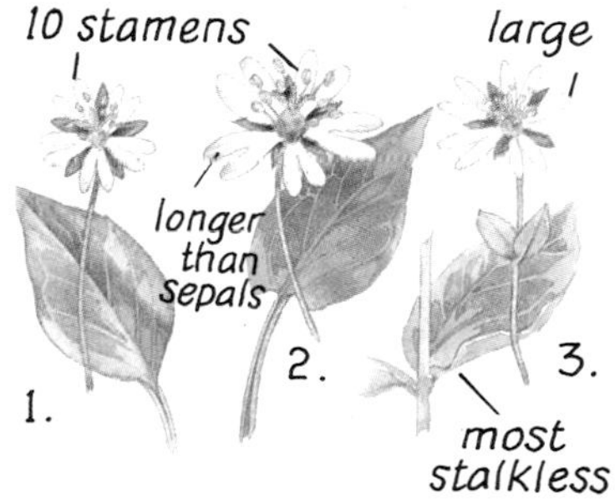

	COMMON CHICKWEED
Type	annual
Height	5–40cm
Habitat	cultivated and waste ground; mostly rich soils
Flowering	January–December
	STEMS AND LEAVES
Stem	much-branched, low-growing, turning upwards
Root	slender tap-root
Hairs	2 lines along stem, sepals stickily hairy
Stipules	absent
Leaves	paired on opposite sides of stem, 3–25mm, oval or elliptical, pointed, edge unbroken
Leaf-stalk	stalked or upper stalkless

	FLOWERS
Position	many, loose head at stem-tip
Bracts	present
Type	⚥
Size	6–10mm
Colour	white
Stalk	lengthening in fruit
Sepals	5, narrow papery edge
Petals	5, mostly shorter than sepals, deeply 2-lobed
Stamens	usually 5, rarely up to 8
Stigmas	3
Ovary	1, 1-celled
	FRUIT
Type	single capsule, narrowly egg-shaped, splits into 6
Size	5–6mm
Seeds	many, 0.9–1.3mm, kidney-shaped, rough

Common Mouse-ear *Cerastium fontanum* subsp. *glabrescen*

Trailing through short grass or over open ground, the softly hairy shoots of the Common Mouse-ear often cover extensive areas bearing small clusters of starry, white flowers. *Status:* native; widespread throughout area. *Similar species:* Field Mouse-ear has larger petals, about twice as long as the sepals. Two annuals with petals no longer than the sepals are distinguished by the fruit-stalk. Sticky Mouse-ear is short-stalked, so there are tight clusters of fruits; and Little Mouse-ear has longer stalks and loose heads in fruit.

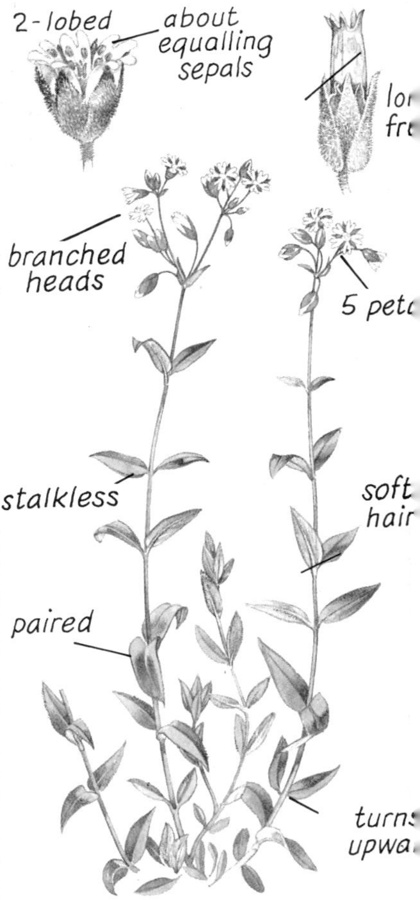

1 Sticky Mouse-ear *(C. glomeratum)*; **2** Little Mouse-ear *(C. semidecandrum)*; **3** Field Mouse-ear *(C. arvense)*

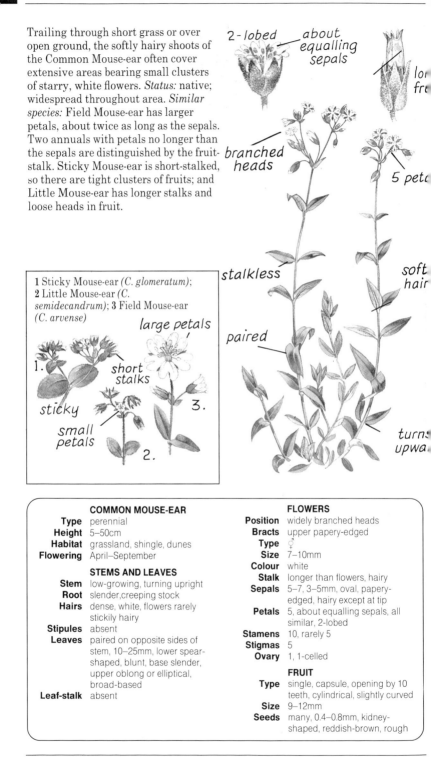

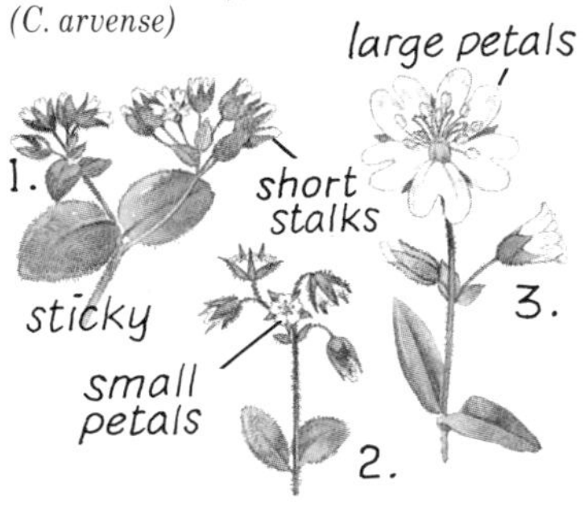

	COMMON MOUSE-EAR
Type	perennial
Height	5–50cm
Habitat	grassland, shingle, dunes
Flowering	April–September
	STEMS AND LEAVES
Stem	low-growing, turning upright
Root	slender,creeping stock
Hairs	dense, white, flowers rarely stickily hairy
Stipules	absent
Leaves	paired on opposite sides of stem, 10–25mm, lower spear-shaped, blunt, base slender, upper oblong or elliptical, broad-based
Leaf-stalk	absent

	FLOWERS
Position	widely branched heads
Bracts	upper papery-edged
Type	⚥
Size	7–10mm
Colour	white
Stalk	longer than flowers, hairy
Sepals	5–7, 3–5mm, oval, papery-edged, hairy except at tip
Petals	5, about equalling sepals, all similar, 2-lobed
Stamens	10, rarely 5
Stigmas	5
Ovary	1, 1-celled
	FRUIT
Type	single, capsule, opening by 10 teeth, cylindrical, slightly curved
Size	9–12mm
Seeds	many, 0.4–0.8mm, kidney-shaped, reddish-brown, rough

Arenaria serpyllifolia Thyme-leaved Sandwort

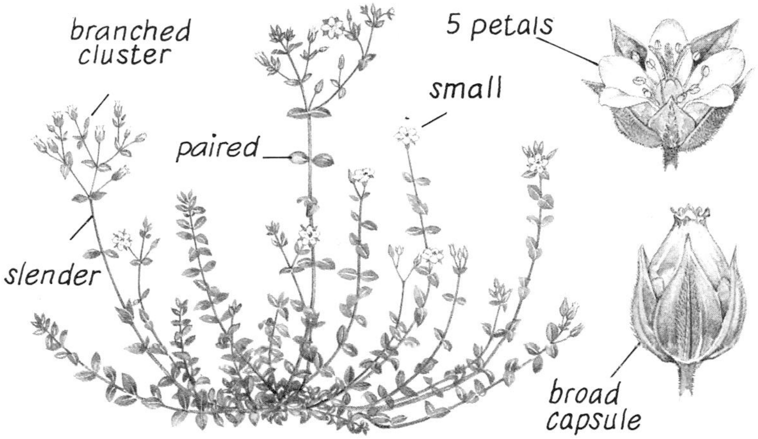

A low-growing and easily overlooked plant, with sprawling, untidy stems and small, white flowers. This colonizer of bare ground is apparently distasteful to browsing rabbits. *Status:* native; common throughout area. *Similar species:* the more delicate Slender Sandwort has smaller flowers and a narrower, straight-sided capsule. Three-nerved Sandwort has larger leaves and flowers with much longer stalks. Sea Sandwort, from the strand-line of sandy beaches, has fleshy leaves and almost petalless female flowers on different plants from the male.

1 Slender Sandwort *(A. leptoclados)*; **2** Three-nerved Sandwort *(Moehringia trinervia)*; **3** Sea Sandwort *(Honkenya peploides)*

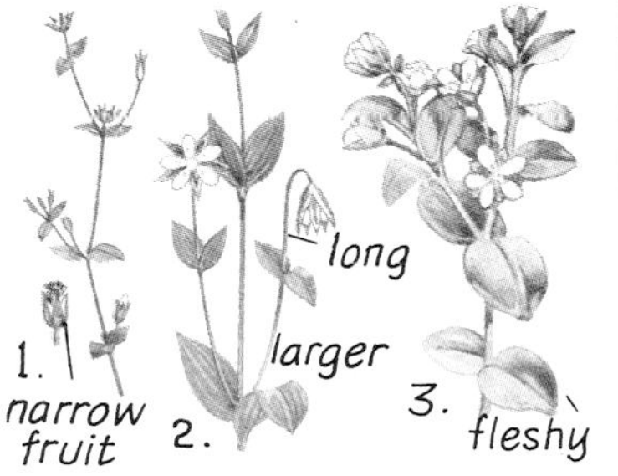

	THYME-LEAVED SANDWORT
Type	annual or biennial
Height	2.5–25cm
Habitat	arable fields, downs, cliffs, walls; sandy or chalky soil
Flowering	June–August
	STEMS AND LEAVES
Stem	slender, turning upwards
Root	fibrous
Hairs	roughly hairy throughout
Stipules	absent
Leaves	paired on opposite sides of stem, 2.5–8mm, oval, broadest below middle, grey-green, pointed, edge unbroken, broad-based
Leaf-stalk	mostly stalkless

	FLOWERS
Position	numerous, in branched heads
Bracts	present
Type	⚥
Size	5–8mm
Colour	white
Stalk	most longer than flowers
Sepals	5, 3–4.5mm, broadly spear-shaped, pointed
Petals	5, equal, oval, undivided, shorter than sepals
Stamens	10 or fewer
Stigmas	3
Ovary	1, 1-celled
	FRUIT
Type	single, capsule, opening by 6 teeth, oval, the sides curved
Size	*c*4mm
Seeds	many, 0.5–0.7mm, kidney-shaped, blackish, rough

Corn Spurrey *Spergula arvensis*

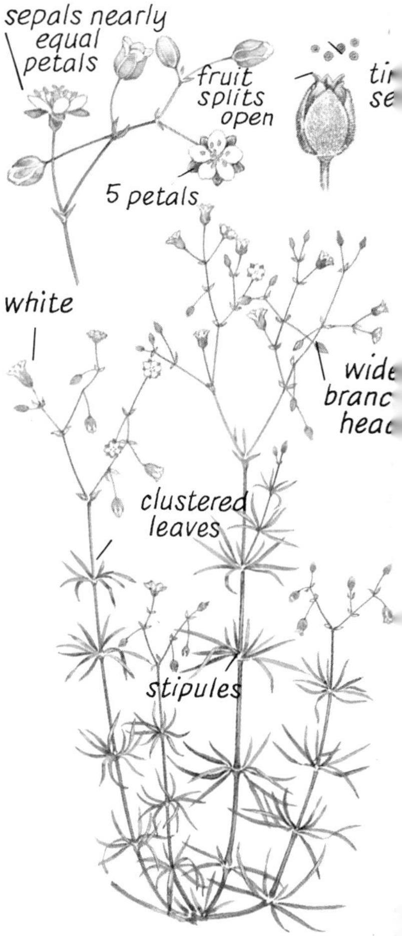

Leaves of this plant are paired but each bears such a conspicuous basal tuft of leaves that the plant seemingly has rings of leaves. Corn Spurrey can be a serious weed in farmland, although its seeds were once used for meal or animal-feed. *Status:* native; weed, common, most of area. *Similar species:* the smaller Pearlworts lack stipules. Procumbent Pearlwort has four petals shorter than the sepals, or lacks petals. Knotted Pearlwort has five petals about twice as long as its sepals. Annual Knawel has only the five sepals, with the ovary half sunken in the flower-base.

1 Procumbent Pearlwort *(Sagina procumbens)*; **2** Knotted Pearlwort *(S. nodosa)*; **3** Annual Knawel *(Scleranthus annuus)*

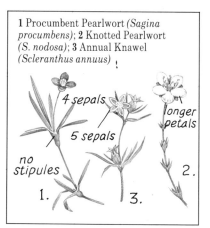

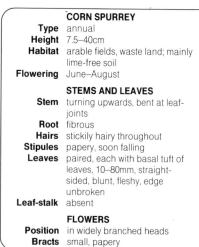

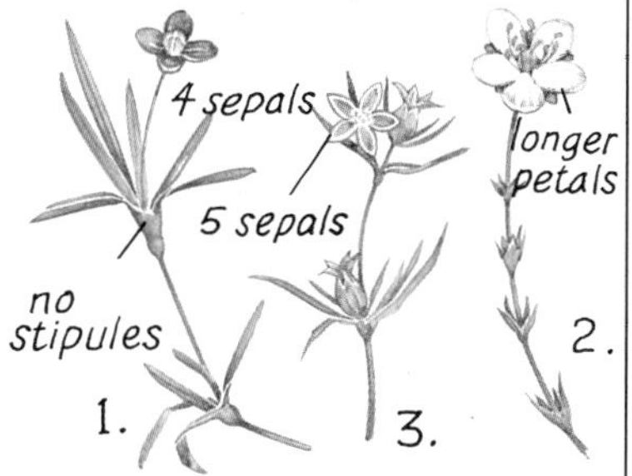

	CORN SPURREY
Type	annual
Height	7.5–40cm
Habitat	arable fields, waste land; mainly lime-free soil
Flowering	June–August
	STEMS AND LEAVES
Stem	turning upwards, bent at leaf-joints
Root	fibrous
Hairs	stickily hairy throughout
Stipules	papery, soon falling
Leaves	paired, each with basal tuft of leaves, 10–80mm, straight-sided, blunt, fleshy, edge unbroken
Leaf-stalk	absent
	FLOWERS
Position	in widely branched heads
Bracts	small, papery
Type	⚥
Size	4–7mm
Colour	white
Stalk	10–25mm, base bent back, turning upright in fruit
Sepals	5, 3–5mm, oval, edge narrowly papery
Petals	5, equal, oval, undivided, just longer than sepals
Stamens	10 or fewer
Stigmas	5, short
Ovary	1, 1-celled
	FRUIT
Type	single, capsule, opening by 5 teeth, egg-shaped
Size	5–6mm
Seeds	many, 1.2–1.5mm, round, often encircled by a wing, black, smooth or rough

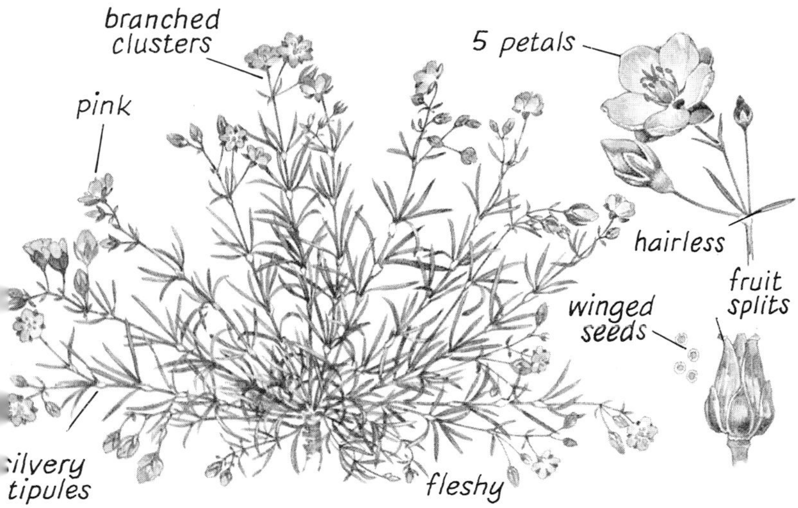

The fleshy shoots and attractive pink flowers of Sea-spurreys may be found on the drier parts of a salt-marsh, where flooding is restricted to exceptional high tides. *Status:* native; coasts throughout area. *Similar species:* no other species has all the seeds winged. Rock Sea-spurrey has dense, sticky hairs and grows on cliffs or among rocks. Lesser Sea-spurrey has smaller, deeper flowers and prefers drier parts of salt-marshes or salty places inland. Sand Spurrey has much smaller flowers and is often found on sandy soils inland.

1 Rock Sea-spurrey *(S. rupicola)*; **2** Lesser Sea-spurrey *(S. marina)*; **3** Sand Spurrey *(S. rubra)*

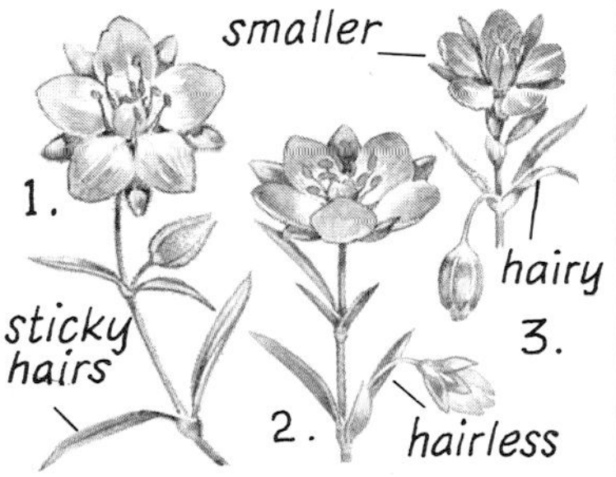

	GREATER SEA-SPURREY
Type	perennial
Height	10–35cm
Habitat	salt-marshes; mud or sand
Flowering	June–September
	STEMS AND LEAVES
Stem	many, low-growing, turning or angled upwards
Root	stout, branched stock
Hairs	hairless or sepals sometimes stickily hairy
Stipules	triangular, papery, silvery
Leaves	paired on opposite sides of stem, 10–25mm, straight-sided, fleshy, tip hard, blunt to sharp, edge unbroken
Leaf-stalk	absent

	FLOWERS
Position	in widely branched head
Bracts	mostly small
Type	⚥
Size	7.5–12mm
Colour	pink to whitish
Stalk	present
Sepals	5, 4–5mm, separate, blunt
Petals	5, 4.5–5.5mm, oval, blunt, edge not lobed
Stamens	usually 10
Stigmas	3
Ovary	1, 1-celled
	FRUIT
Type	single, capsule, splits into 3, withered sepals attached
Size	7–11mm
Seeds	*c*1.5mm, round, encircled by a pale wing

Red Campion *Silene dioica*

Typically a plant of the woodland margin, Red Campion is easily recognized by its rose-pink flowers and softly hairy leaves. This day-flowering Campion is usually pollinated by bees or hover-flies. *Status:* native, common except for parts of south. *Similar species:* Moss Campion is much smaller, with hairless leaves and grows on mountains. A plant of wet places, Ragged-Robin has deeply divided petals and hairless leaves. Sticky Catchfly has sticky stems just beneath each leaf and, like the previous species, capsules with five teeth.

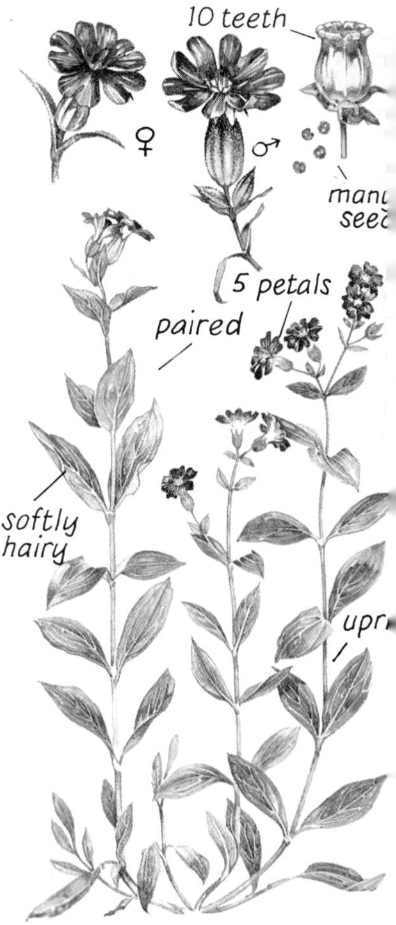

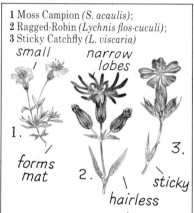

1 Moss Campion *(S. acaulis)*;
2 Ragged-Robin *(Lychnis flos-cuculi)*;
3 Sticky Catchfly *(L. viscaria)*

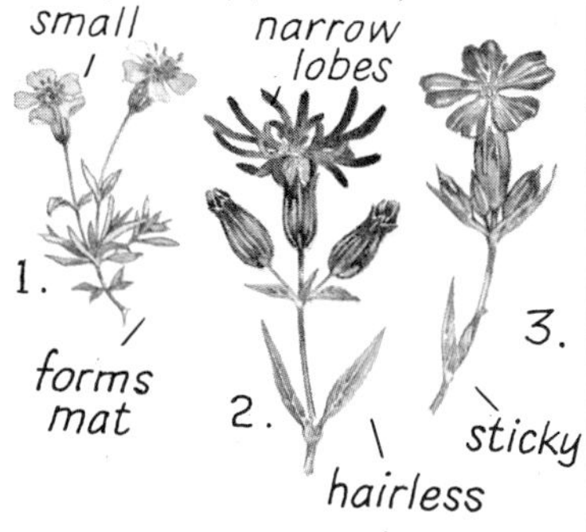

	RED CAMPION
Type	perennial
Height	20–90cm
Habitat	woods, hedgerows, cliffs or limestone screes; mostly lime-rich soil
Flowering	May–June
	STEMS AND LEAVES
Stem	turning upright
Root	slender, creeping stock
Hairs	soft, may be sticky above
Stipules	absent
Leaves	paired on opposite sides of stem, 40–100mm, oval or oblong, pointed, edge unbroken
Leaf-stalk	winged or upper stalkless
	FLOWERS
Position	numerous, branched head at stem-tip, ♂ and ♀ flowers on different plants
Bracts	present
Type	open during day, scentless
Size	18–25mm
Colour	rose-pink, rarely white
Stalk	5–15mm
Sepals	5, 12–17.5mm, joined into tube with pointed teeth
Petals	5, deeply 2-lobed with stalk-like base
Stamens	♂ with 10
Stigmas	♀ with 5
Ovary	1, 1-celled
	FRUIT
Type	1, capsule, opening by 10 curled back teeth, oval
Size	10–15mm
Seeds	many, black, kidney-shaped, rough with tiny outgrowths

Large, creamy-white flowers that open in the evening make the White Campion seem to glow in the dusk. Moths, drawn by the scent, pollinate the flowers. White Campion forms pink-flowered hybrids where it grows with Red Campion. *Status:* native or introduced to parts of west; common in most of the area. *Similar species:* several white-flowered Campions have only three stigmas. Bladder Campion and Sea Campion have swollen, bladder-like sepal-tubes, the latter species with cushion-like growth and few-flowered stems. Nottingham Catchfly has drooping flowers and smaller petals.

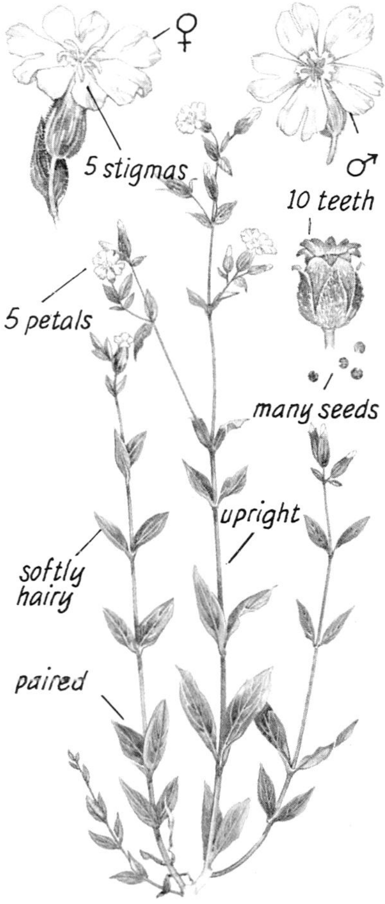

1 Bladder Campion *(S. vulgaris* subsp. *vulgaris)*; **2** Sea Campion *(S. vulgaris* subsp. *maritima)*; **3** Nottingham Catchfly *(S. nutans)*

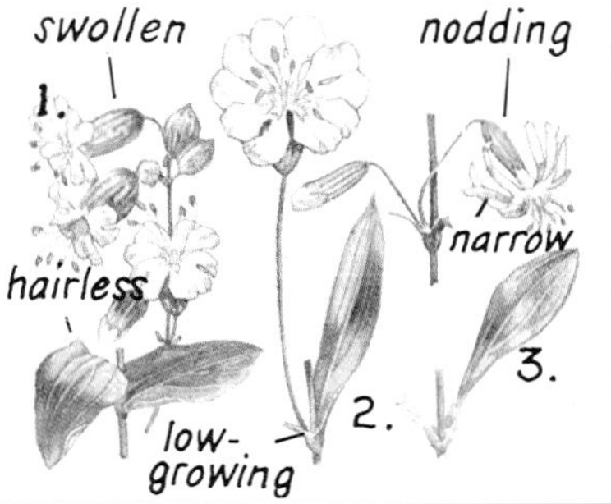

	WHITE CAMPION
Type	perennial
Height	30–100cm
Habitat	cultivated and waste ground, hedgerows
Flowering	May–September
	STEMS AND LEAVES
Stem	upright, mostly branched
Root	thick, almost woody stock
Hairs	soft, stickily hairy above
Stipules	absent
Leaves	paired on opposite sides of stem, 30–100mm, elliptical or spear-shaped, pointed, edge unbroken, base narrowed
Leaf-stalk	only on lower leaves
	FLOWERS
Position	few, in branched heads, ♂ and ♀ on different plants
Bracts	present
Type	day-flowering, slight scent
Size	25–30mm
Colour	white
Stalk	elongating in fruit
Sepals	5, 23–30mm, joined into tube with narrow teeth
Petals	5, deeply 2-lobed
Stamens	♂ with 10
Stigmas	♀ with 5
Ovary	1, 1-celled
	FRUIT
Type	single, capsule, opens by 10 teeth, egg-shaped
Size	*c*15mm
Seeds	numerous, 1.3–1.5mm, kidney-shaped, grey, rough

Soapwort *Saponaria officinalis*

Clumps of bluish foliage and large pink flowers enable Soapwort to be identified readily. Once an invaluable commodity, the plant was used for washing with long before soap, a usage that still persists in parts of the world. *Status:* native or naturalized in north. *Similar species:* plants with similar pinkish flowers include Cowherb, which has an inflated sepal-tube. Night-flowering Catchfly opens by night but the yellow-backed petals roll up in the morning. Corncockle, which has long sepals, was once abundant in cornfields but is now rare.

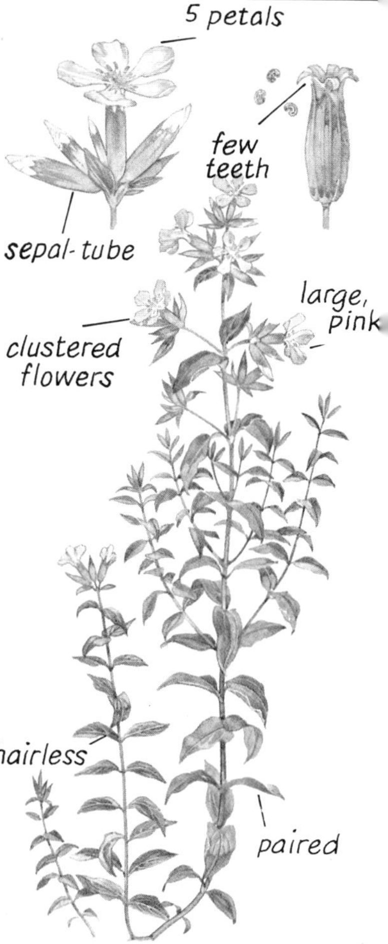

1 Night-flowering Catchfly *(Silene noctiflora)*; 2 Cowherb *(Vaccaria pyramidata)*; 3 Corncockle *(Agrostemma githago)*

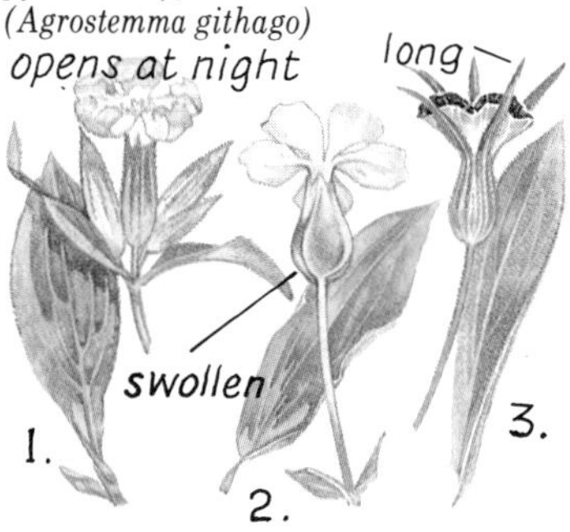

	SOAPWORT
Type	perennial
Height	30–90cm
Habitat	hedgerows, damp woods, grassy banks, roadsides, often near water or houses
Flowering	July–September
	STEMS AND LEAVES
Stem	upright or angled upwards, sometimes branched above
Root	stout rhizome and long, slender, underground stems
Hairs	more or less hairless
Stipules	absent
Leaves	paired on opposite sides of stem, 50–100mm, oval or elliptical, pointed, edge unbroken
Leaf-stalk	absent

	FLOWERS
Position	few, in heads at stem-tips
Bracts	present
Type	⚥
Size	*c*25mm
Colour	pink
Stalk	very short
Sepals	5, 18–20mm, joined into tube with short teeth
Petals	5, oval, tip rounded or notched, base stalk-like
Stamens	10
Stigmas	2, rarely 3
Ovary	1, 1-celled
	FRUIT
Type	single, capsule, almost oblong, opens by 4–5 teeth
Size	2–2.5mm
Seeds	many, *c*1.8mm, kidney-shaped, blackish, rough

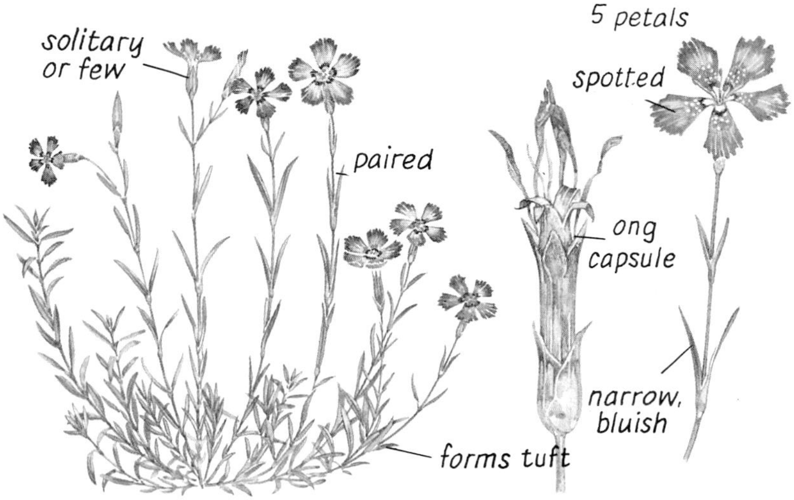

Slender stems and leaves make this plant almost invisible in grassland, until the opening flowers of intense pink herald its presence. Pinks have long been cultivated, and often differ greatly from their wild progenitors. *Status:* native; scattered localities in lowland parts of area. *Similar species:* Cheddar Pink, one of the rarest native species in Britain and specially protected by law, has larger, pale flowers. Deptford Pink has clustered flowers with slender bracts. Childing Pink has small heads of flowers, opening singly, enclosed by broad, papery scales.

1 Deptford Pink *(D. armeria)*; **2** Cheddar Pink *(D. gratianopolitanus)*; **3** Childing Pink *(Petrorhagia nanteuilii)*

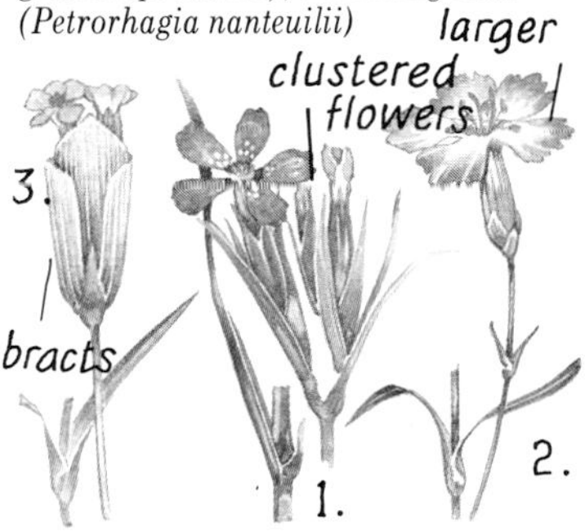

	MAIDEN PINK
Type	perennial
Height	15–45cm
Habitat	dry grassy places, fields, banks and hills
Flowering	June–September
	STEMS AND LEAVES
Stem	forming low tufts, turning upright to flower
Root	slender, creeping stock
Hairs	rough hairs on leaf-edges
Stipules	absent
Leaves	paired, 10–25mm, narrowly spear-shaped, bluish, pointed or lowest blunt, edge unbroken
Leaf-stalk	absent
	FLOWERS
Position	1–3, at stem-tips
Bracts	present
Type	⚥, scentless
Size	16–20mm
Colour	deep pink with pale spots or white, banded deep pink
Stalk	present
Sepals	5, 12–17mm, joined into tube, 2–4 scales at base
Petals	5, equal, broad, toothed, the base stalk-like
Stamens	10
Stigmas	2
Ovary	1, 1-celled
	FRUIT
Type	single, capsule, opening by 4 teeth, cylindrical
Size	*c*15mm
Seeds	many, 2–2.5mm, oval, flattened, black

White Water-lily *Nymphaea alba*

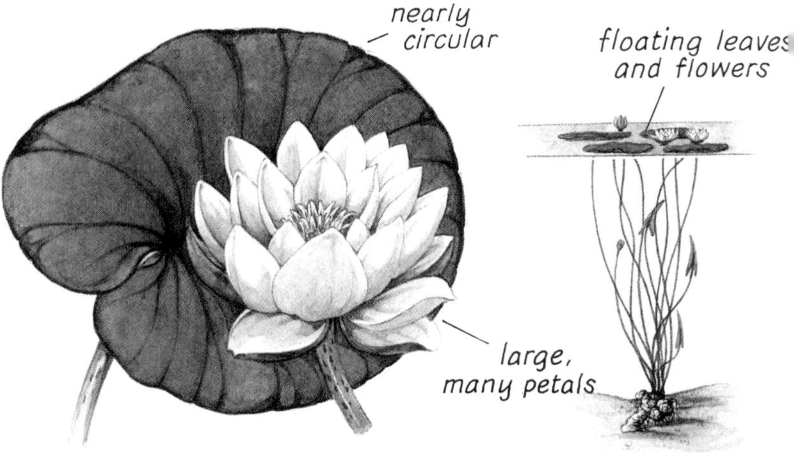

Large, white, cup-shaped flowers and nearly circular leaves floating on the water's surface easily identify the White Water-lily. Plants in the north-west often have much smaller flowers than elsewhere. *Status:* native; throughout area. *Similar species:* Yellow Water-lily has smaller flowers held above the water surface. The ripe fruit has an odd alcohol-like smell. Least Water-lily is even smaller and has non-overlapping petals. True to its name, Fringed Water-lily has fringed petals but also elongated stems, short leaf-stalks, and is a relative of the Gentians.

1 Yellow Water-lily *(Nuphar lutea)*; 2 Least Water-lily *(N. pumila)*; 3 Fringed Water-lily *(Nymphoides peltata)*

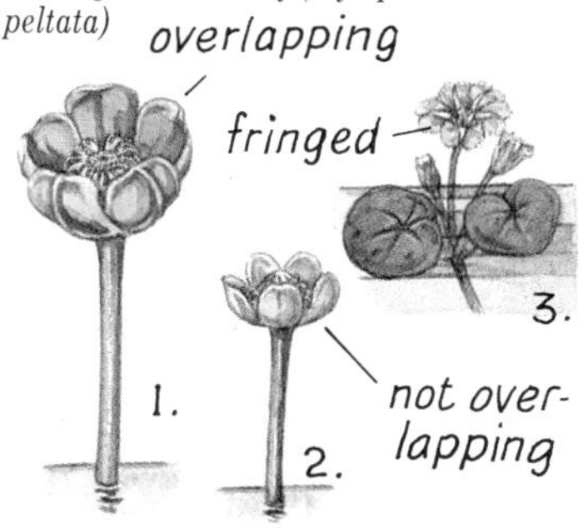

	WHITE WATER-LILY
Type	perennial
Height	underwater, up to 300cm
Habitat	lakes and ponds
Flowering	July–August
	STEMS AND LEAVES
Stem	short, forming a rhizome
Root	fleshy from rhizome
Hairs	absent
Stipules	present
Leaves	at base of plant, 100–300mm, nearly circular, floating, dark, glossy green above, often reddish below, rounded, edge unbroken, base forming deep cleft in circular outline
Leaf-stalk	up to 3m

	FLOWERS
Position	few
Type	⚥, floating, scented
Size	50–200mm
Colour	white
Stalk	up to 3m
Sepals	4, spear-shaped, whitish
Petals	20–25, spirally arranged
Stamens	numerous
Stigmas	many, forming radiating lines on top of ovary
Ovary	1, many-celled
	FRUIT
Type	single, spongy capsule, opens underwater, oval to nearly globular
Size	16–40mm
Seeds	numerous, *c*3mm, floating

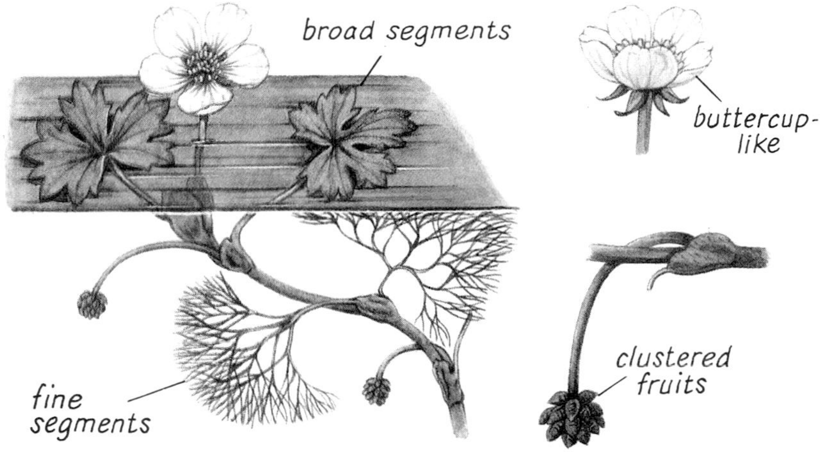

Dotted over the surface of a pond sometimes in great profusion, Water-crowfoot's white and yellow-centred flowers contrast to perfection the reflected blue of a summer's sky. This is a true amphibious plant, having mastered both land and water. Out of the water the leaves are lobed like those of Buttercups, but submerged leaves are finely divided. *Status:* native; most lowland areas. *Similar species:* species in flowing waters, like River Water-crowfoot and Thread-leaved Water-crowfoot, have only the finely divided leaves; Ivy-leaved Crowfoot has only the land form of leaf.

1 River Water-crowfoot *(R. fluitans)*; **2** Thread-leaved Water-crowfoot *(R. trichophyllus)*; **3** Ivy-leaved Crowfoot *(R. hederaceus)*

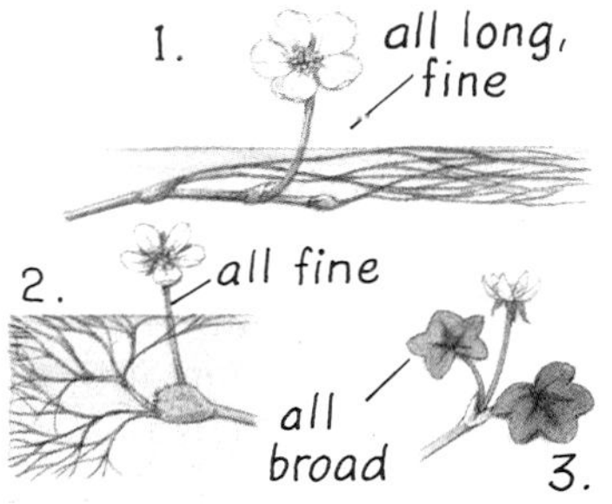

	COMMON WATER-CROWFOOT
Type	perennial or annual
Height	very variable
Habitat	ponds, slow streams or ditches
Flowering	May–June
	STEMS AND LEAVES
Stem	underwater or low-growing
Root	fibrous
Hairs	sparse, mainly on stipules and stalks of upper leaves
Stipules	present
Leaves	spirally arranged
Leaves 1	underwater, 30–60(–80)mm, with hair-like segments
Leaf-stalk	often shorter than blade
Leaves 2	floating, nearly circular, with 3–7 toothed lobes
Leaf-stalk	usually longer than blade

	FLOWERS
Position	1, opposite upper leaf
Bracts	absent
Type	⚥
Size	12–18mm
Colour	white with yellow base
Stalk	20–50mm
Sepals	usually 5
Petals	5, 5–10mm, equal
Stamens	13 or more
Stigmas	1 per ovary
Ovaries	numerous, 1-celled
	FRUIT
Type	numerous, nut-like, not opening, egg-shaped, short-beaked, hairy, in rounded head
Size	1.5–2mm
Seeds	1, not released

Meadow Buttercup *Ranunculus acris*

One of the most familiar summer flowers, Meadow Buttercup abounds in pastures everywhere. The rich yellow of the cup-shaped flowers is associated in folklore with the yellow butter from cattle that graze the pastures. *Status:* native; common, most of area. *Similar species:* two other Buttercups have a stalked middle lobe to the leaves. Creeping Buttercup has creeping, rooting stems, and Bulbous Buttercup has a bulb-like base to the stem and sepals bent downwards. Goldilocks Buttercup has basal leaves that are less divided, and often has petals missing.

1 Bulbous Buttercup *(R. bulbosus)*; 2 Creeping Buttercup *(R. repens)*; 3 Goldilocks Buttercup *(R. auricomus)*

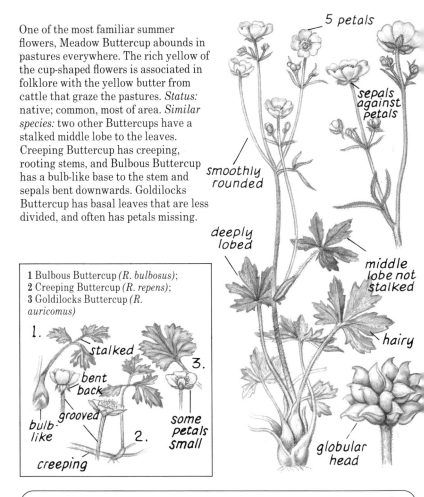

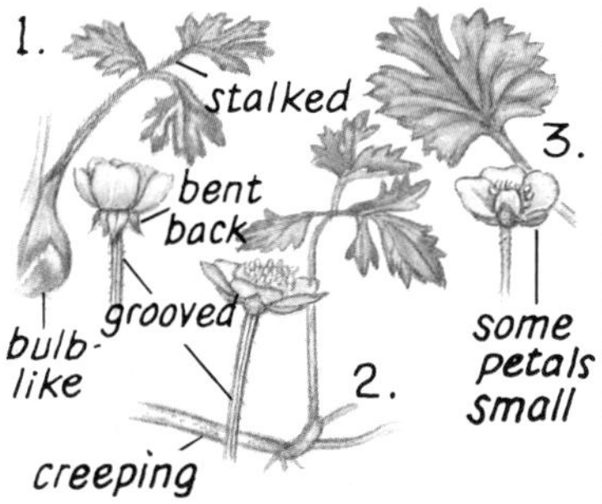

	MEADOW BUTTERCUP
Type	perennial
Height	15–100cm
Habitat	damp meadows, grassy places; lime-rich or neutral soils
Flowering	June– July
	STEMS AND LEAVES
Stem	upright, base hollow
Root	fibrous from stout stock
Hairs	pressed close on leaves, projecting on stem
Stipules	absent
Leaves	basal with 2–7 toothed lobes; stem-leaves scattered, upper narrowly lobed
Leaf-stalk	long or stalkless above

	FLOWERS
Position	numerous, in branched head from upper stem
Bracts	present
Type	mostly ⚥, cup-shaped
Size	18–25mm
Colour	glossy yellow or whitish
Stalk	longer than flower
Sepals	usually 5, oval, hairy, pressed against petals
Petals	usually 5, 6–11mm, rounded
Stamens	numerous
Stigmas	1 per ovary
Ovaries	numerous, 1-celled
	FRUIT
Type	many in rounded head, nut-like, not opening, egg-shaped, hooked beak, smooth
Size	2.5–3mm
Seeds	1, not released

Ranunculus sceleratus Celery-leaved Buttercup

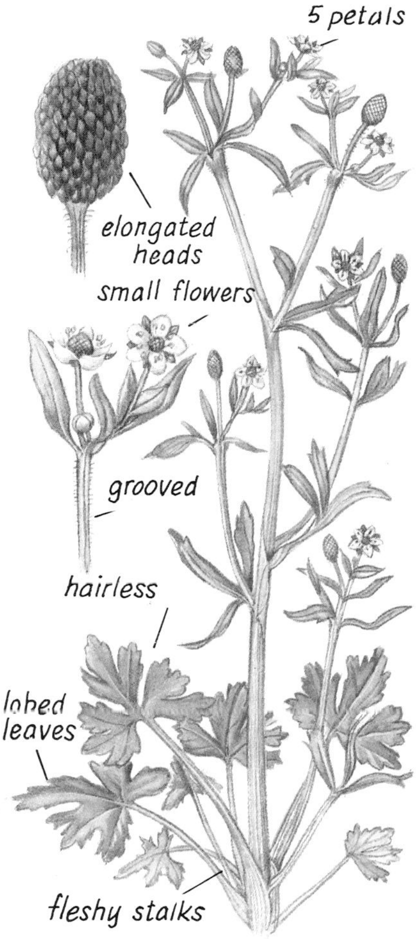

Lobed, glossy leaves with broad, fleshy leaf-stalks give a vague resemblance to Celery, which grows in similar damp places, and provide the plant with its common name. The flowers are much smaller than those of most common buttercups, and give way to unusually long heads of tiny fruits. *Status:* native; common, most of area. *Similar species:* Corn Buttercup has few spiny fruits. The hairy Small-flowered Buttercup has few, hooked fruits. A buttercup relative with much more elongated heads, which give the plant its common name, is the Mousetail.

1 Corn Buttercup *(R. arvensis)*; **2** Small-flowered Buttercup *(R. parviflorus)*; **3** Mousetail *(Myosurus minimus)*

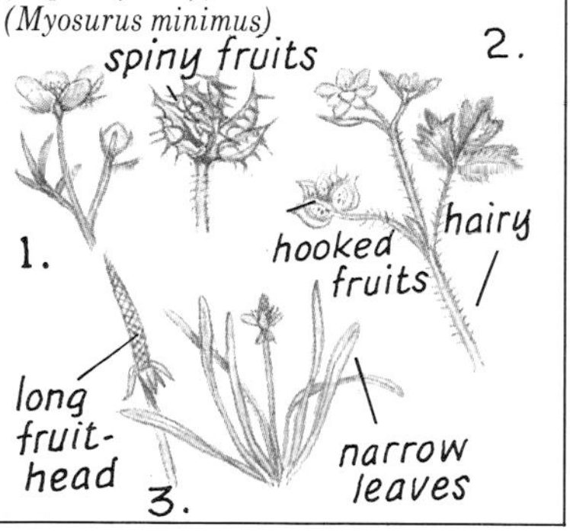

CELERY-LEAVED BUTTERCUP

- **Type** annual
- **Height** 20–60cm
- **Habitat** ponds, ditches or streams; damp soil or mud
- **Flowering** May–September

STEMS AND LEAVES

- **Stem** upright, stout, hollow
- **Root** fibrous
- **Hairs** more or less hairless
- **Stipules** absent
- **Leaves** spirally arranged around stem; lowest kidney-shaped, 3-lobed, each lobe toothed or lobed again; uppermost with narrow, unbroken lobes
- **Leaf-stalk** long, broad-based or absent above

FLOWERS

- **Position** numerous, in widely branched heads
- **Type** ⚥
- **Size** 5–10mm
- **Colour** pale yellow
- **Stalk** furrowed
- **Sepals** usually 5, bent downwards
- **Petals** 5, equal, narrowly oval, little longer than sepals
- **Stamens** numerous
- **Stigmas** 1 per ovary
- **Ovaries** numerous, 1-celled

FRUIT

- **Type** 70–250 in oblong head, nut-like, not opening, rounded, slightly beaked
- **Size** *c*1mm
- **Seeds** 1, not released

Lesser Celandine *Ranunculus ficaria* subsp. *ficaria*

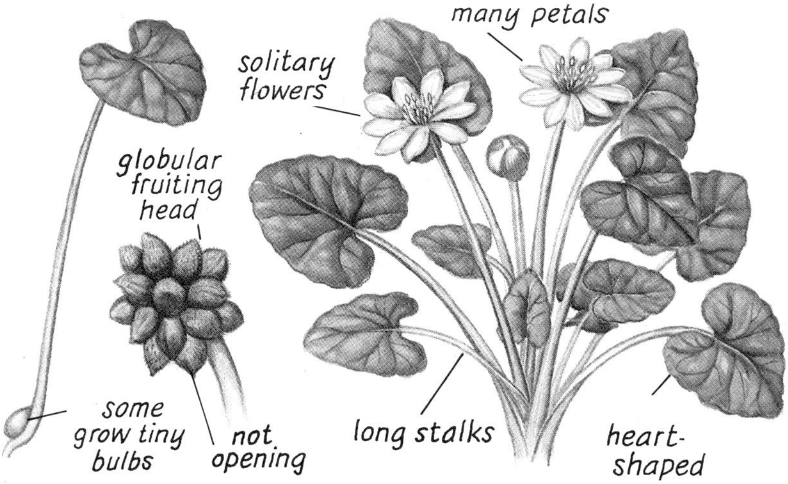

The rich yellow flowers open with the Spring sunshine, often in such great numbers that they carpet with gold a woodland floor or hedge-bank. Some plants have tiny swollen buds called bulbils at the base of the leaves, and all plants have small tubers through which they are able to last the Winter. *Status:* native, common throughout area. *Similar species:* Winter Aconite is similarly a Spring flower with numerous yellow petals, but differs in the collar-like bracts below the flower and the lobed leaves which grow only after flowering is finished.

Winter Aconite *(Eranthis hyemalis)*

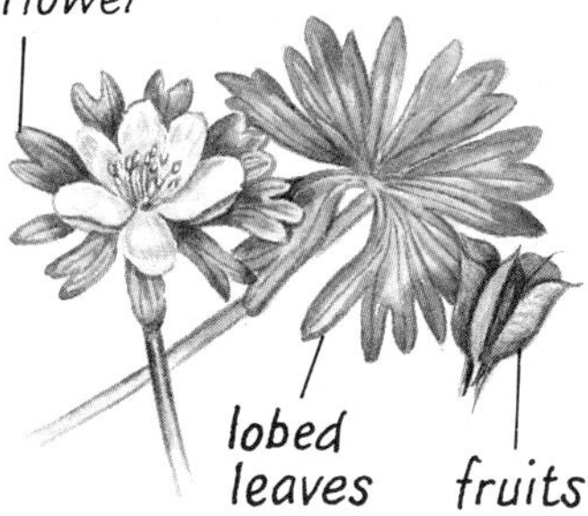

	LESSER CELANDINE
Type	perennial
Height	5–25cm
Habitat	woods, hedgerows, grassy places, stream-banks
Flowering	March–May
	STEMS AND LEAVES
Stem	angled upwards, base rooting
Root	fibrous, with many small, swollen tubers
Hairs	absent
Stipules	absent
Leaves	from base and spirally arranged around stem, 10–40mm, heart-shaped, blunt or rounded, edge shallowly toothed, base notched
Leaf-stalk	base broad, overlapping other stalks
	FLOWERS
Position	single, at tip of stem
Bracts	absent
Type	⚥
Size	20–30mm
Colour	bright, glossy yellow, fading nearly white
Stalk	much longer than flower
Sepals	3, oval
Petals	8–12, narrowly oval
Stamens	numerous
Stigmas	1 per ovary
Ovaries	numerous, 1-celled
	FRUIT
Type	many in rounded head, not opening, egg-shaped to globular, short-beaked
Size	up to 2.5mm
Seeds	1, not released

Common by streamsides and in damp meadows, this buttercup relative can be distinguished from the more usual kinds by the narrow leaves without lobes. The plant should be treated with care for it is acrid, like other Buttercups: leaves or roots ground with salt quickly blister the skin and, in the sixteenth century, such a preparation was used to treat sores caused by bubonic plague. *Status:* native; common throughout area. *Similar species:* Greater Spearwort is generally a taller plant, often over a metre tall, differing in the larger leaves and flowers.

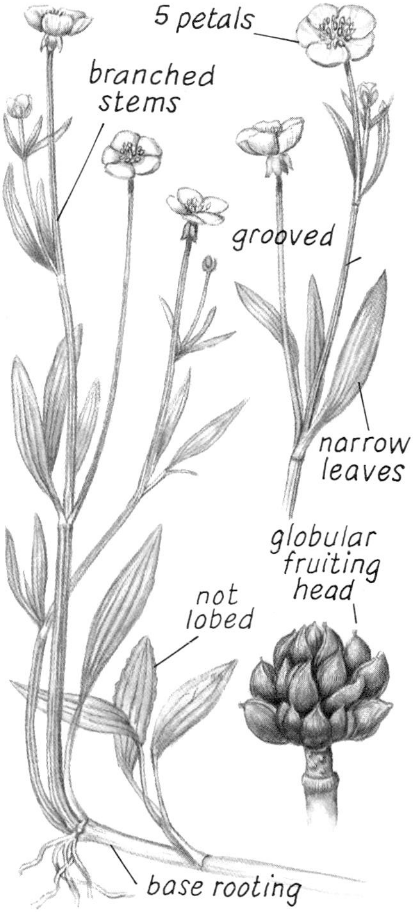

Greater Spearwort *(R. lingua)*

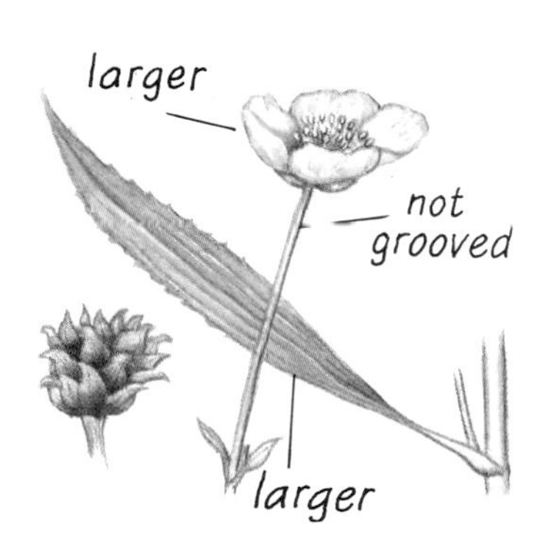

	LESSER SPEARWORT
Type	perennial
Height	8–50cm
Habitat	wet places
Flowering	May–September
	STEMS AND LEAVES
Stem	angled upwards, sometimes creeping and rooting
Root	fibrous
Hairs	more or less hairless
Stipules	absent
Leaves	spirally arranged on stem, 10–50mm, mostly spear-shaped or oval, rarely narrow, blunt to sharp, edge unbroken or toothed, base rounded, heart-shaped or tapered
Leaf-stalk	long below, absent above
	FLOWERS
Position	1 or few, in branched head at tip of stem
Type	⚥
Size	8–20mm, rarely 25mm
Colour	pale yellow, glossy
Stalk	present
Sepals	5, greenish yellow
Petals	5, equal, broadly oval to nearly circular
Stamens	numerous
Stigmas	1 per ovary
Ovaries	numerous, 1-celled
	FRUIT
Type	20–60 in rounded head, nut-like, not opening, egg-shaped, bluntly beaked tip, minutely pitted
Size	1–2mm
Seeds	1 per fruit, not separate

Green Hellebore *Helleborus viridis*

An imposing plant with large, hand-shaped leaves but, unusually for such a large-flowered species, the flowers are green and easily overlooked. The sepals are large and showy, whereas the petals are reduced to tubular structures which produce nectar. This is a close relative of the white-flowered Christmas Rose of gardens. *Status:* native or introduced in some places; scattered localities in southern half of the area. *Similar species:* Stinking Hellebore is easily distinguished by the smaller, more cup-shaped or almost globular flowers, edged with reddish purple.

Stinking Hellebore *(H. foetidus)*

	GREEN HELLEBORE
Type	perennial
Height	20–40cm
Habitat	woods and scrub; moist, lime-rich soils or scree
Flowering	March–April
	STEMS AND LEAVES
Stem	upright, little-branched
Root	stout, blackish stock
Hairs	absent or few above
Stipules	absent
Leaves	from base or scattered on stem, basal leaves usually 2, with 7–13 elliptical, finger-like, pointed lobes, edge toothed
Leaf-stalk	long or absent on stem-leaves
	FLOWERS
Position	2–4, in widely branched head at tip of stem
Type	⚥
Size	30–50mm
Colour	yellowish green
Stalk	slightly nodding
Sepals	5, equal, elliptical or oval, petal-like
Petals	9–12, much smaller than sepals, tubular, green
Stamens	numerous
Stigmas	1 per ovary
Ovaries	3–8, 1-celled
	FRUIT
Type	3–8, pod-like, splits down inner edge to release seeds
Size	*c*20mm
Seeds	numerous, with fleshy white ridge on one side

One of the most imposing plants of damp meadows in late Spring, but at its most luxuriant in wet woodland. Much folklore has been associated with the large, golden, cup-shaped flowers and the plant has been given many common names, including May-blobs and Kingcups. *Status:* native; common but rarer towards south. *Similar species:* Globeflower, named after the ball-shaped buds and young flowers, is a mountain plant of similar wet places. There is a double form grown in gardens, which has petal-like stamens.

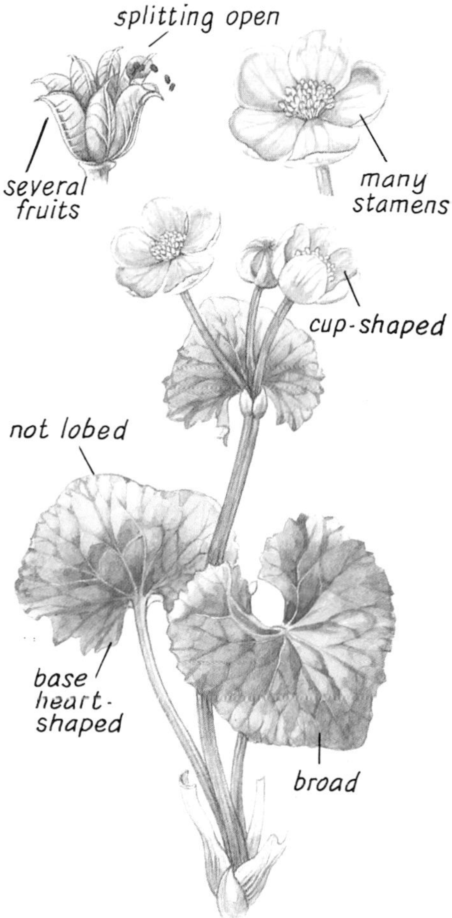

Globeflower *(Trollius europaeus)*

	MARSH-MARIGOLD
Type	perennial
Height	15–30mm, rarely 60mm
Habitat	ditches, damp woods, marshes; wet soils
Flowering	March–July
	STEMS AND LEAVES
Stem	upright or sometimes low-growing, hollow
Root	fibrous from thick, fleshy underground stem
Hairs	absent
Stipules	absent
Leaves	mostly at base of plant, few scattered around stem, kidney-shaped or triangular, tip rounded, edge toothed, base heart-shaped
Leaf-stalk	long or nearly stalkless stem-leaves

	FLOWERS
Position	few, wide-branched head from upper part of stem
Type	⚥
Size	16–50mm
Colour	bright golden-yellow, often tinged green beneath
Stalk	much longer than flower
Perianth	5–8 segments, 10–25mm, equal, rounded
Stamens	50–100
Stigmas	1 per ovary
Ovaries	5–15, 1-celled
	FRUIT
Type	5–15, pod-like, elongated, splitting along inner face, realeasing seeds
Size	9–18mm
Seeds	numerous, up to 2.5mm

Wood Anemone *Anemone nemorosa*

A Spring flower which often grows in such great profusion that it carpets the floor of woodland with delicate, many-petalled flowers of white, tinged and veined with purple. The main leaves arise from the ground only after flowering is completed. *Status:* native; often very common, throughout area. *Similar species:* Blue Anemone is grown for its beautiful blue flowers and often becomes naturalized. The native, summer-flowering Pasqueflower has larger, purple flowers and heads of long-plumed fruits. Pale Pasqueflower grows in mountains only in the east of the area.

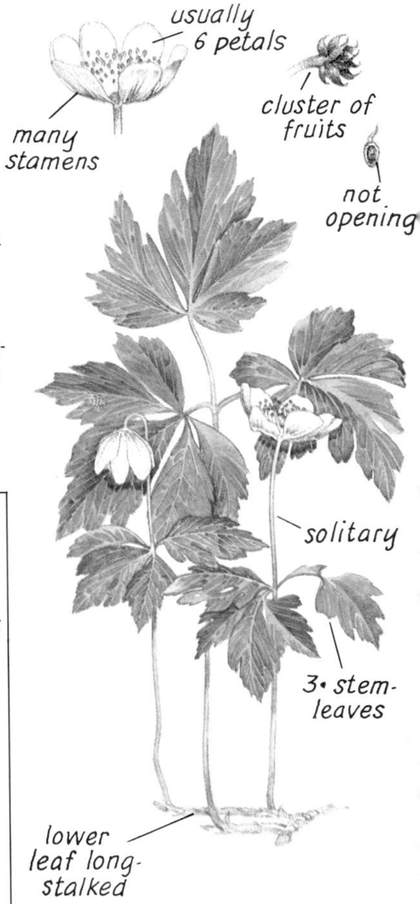

1 Blue Anemone *(A. apennina)*;
2 Pasqueflower *(Pulsatilla vulgaris)*;
3 Pale Pasqueflower *(P. vernalis)*

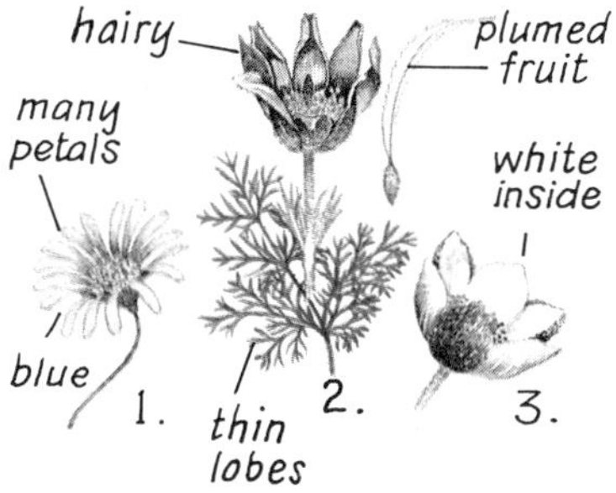

	WOOD ANEMONE
Type	perennial
Height	6–30cm
Habitat	deciduous woods; all but most acid or wet soils
Flowering	March–May
	STEMS AND LEAVES
Stem	upright, unbranched
Root	fibrous from thin, creeping underground stem
Hairs	absent or sparse on leaves
Stipules	absent
Leaves	3 around stem, 1–2 from base after flowering, 3-parted, with pointed, toothed lobes
Leaf-stalk	long or stem-leaves short
	FLOWERS
Position	single, from tip of stem
Bracts	absent
Type	⚥
Size	20–40mm
Colour	white, tinged and veined with purplish pink, rarely reddish purple
Stalk	long, upright or nodding
Perianth	5–9 segments, usually 6–7, equal, oblong-elliptical
Stamens	50–70
Stigmas	1 per ovary
Ovaries	10–30, 1-celled
	FRUIT
Type	10–30, nut-like, not opening, in pendulous, globular clusters, egg-shaped, beaked, downy
Size	4–4.5mm
Seeds	1 per fruit, not released

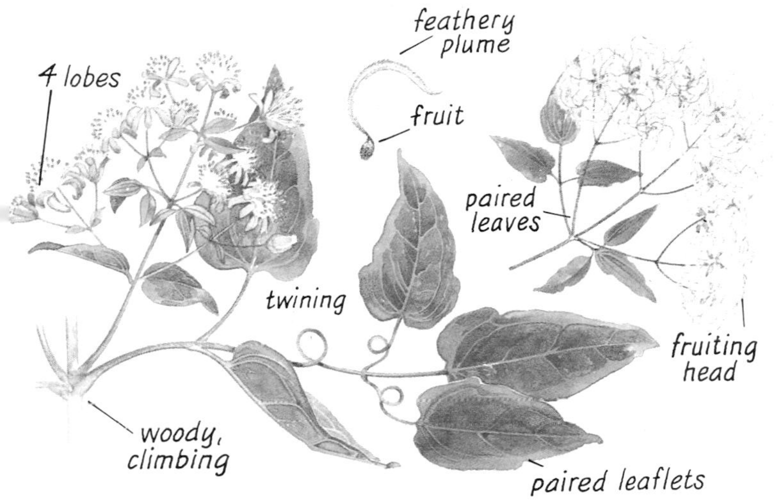

Draped over bushes or trees, this plant is perhaps most familiar when the cloud-like masses of white-plumed fruits earn another common name, 'Old Man's Beard'. The thick, rope-like stems loop and twist their way to the tree-tops, like tropical lianas. *Status:* native, southern half of area. *Similar species:* two species are native to the south-east of the area but are cultivated and sometimes escape. Alpine Clematis is a mountain plant with blue and white flowers. *Clematis recta* has non-climbing, annual stems and large heads of tiny, white, hawthorn-scented flowers.

1 Alpine Clematis *(C. alpina)*; **2** *C. recta*

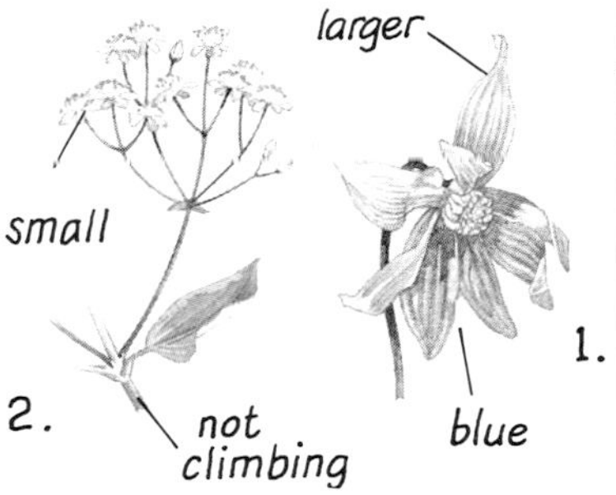

	TRAVELLER'S-JOY
Type	perennial
Height	up to 30m
Habitat	woods, scrub or hedgerows; mostly lime-rich soils
Flowering	July–August
	STEMS AND LEAVES
Stem	woody, vine-like, becoming very stout
Root	woody stock
Hairs	hairless except for flowers
Stipules	absent
Leaves	paired, either side of stem, 1–2 pairs of oval, pointed, toothed leaflets 30–100mm long, leaflet or tendril at tip, leaflets usually toothed, base rounded to heart-shaped
Leaf-stalk	twining
	FLOWERS
Position	many in broad head from tip of stem or leaf-base
Bracts	present
Type	⚥, fragrant
Size	*c*20mm
Colour	greenish white
Stalk	about equalling flower
Perianth	usually 4, hairy beneath
Stamens	numerous
Stigmas	1 per ovary
Ovaries	numerous, 1-celled
	FRUIT
Type	numerous, nut-like with long, whitish, feathery plume, not opening, in a rounded cluster
Size	*c*25mm
Seeds	1, not released

Columbine *Aquilegia vulgaris*

Columbine has unusual nodding flowers: all five of the petals are horn-shaped, each tip drawn out and curved over into a hollow spur. The spur contains a drop of sweet nectar, and it is this that attracts pollinating insects to the plant. *Status:* native but cultivated and often escaping. *Similar species:* Larkspur has only one spur and one pod-like fruit. Forking Larkspur differs in the wider branching, divided lower bracts and shorter fruit. The hooded or helmet-shaped purple flowers of Monk's-hood conceal the extremely poisonous nature of the plant.

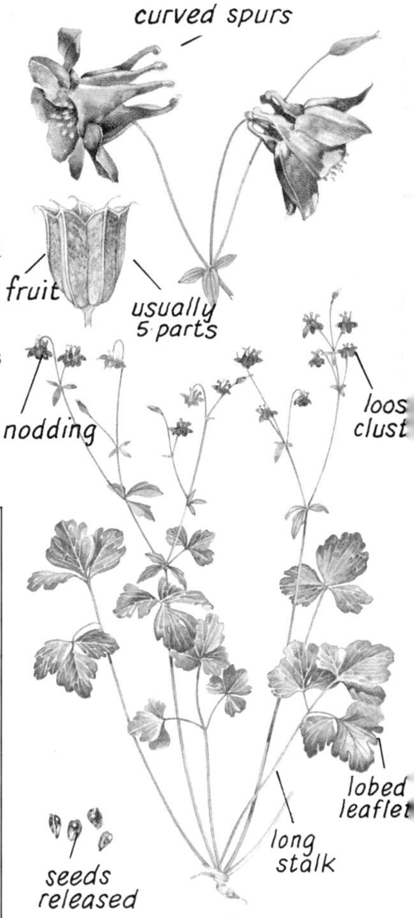

1 Forking Larkspur *(Consolida regalis)*; 2 Larkspur *(C. ambigua)*; 3 Monk's-hood *(Aconitum napellus)*

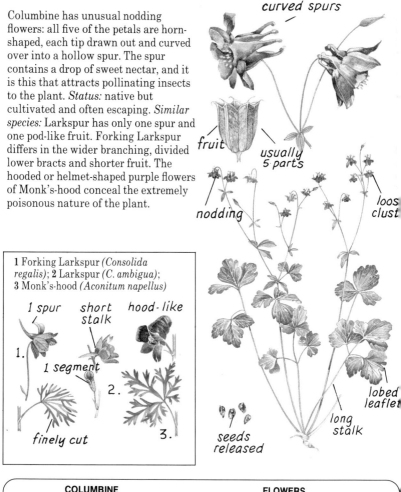

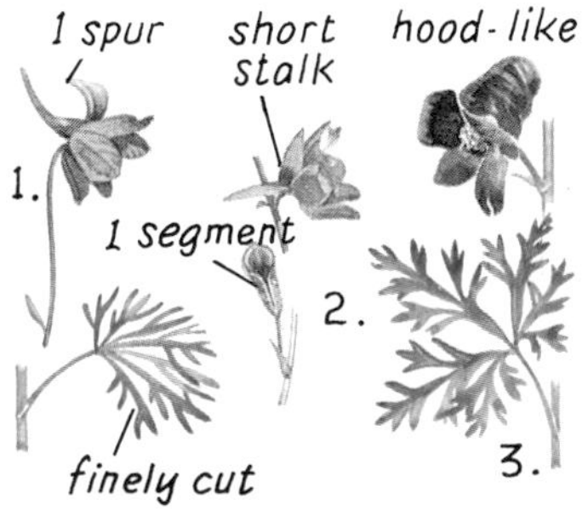

COLUMBINE	
Type	perennial
Height	40–100cm
Habitat	damp places on lime-rich soils, woods, fens
Flowering	May–June
	STEMS AND LEAVES
Stem	upright, branched above
Root	short, thick, stock
Hairs	hairless or softly hairy
Stipules	absent
Leaves	basal or scattered around stem, divided into blunt, irregularly 3-lobed, toothed, leaflets, bluish green above
Leaf-stalk	long, broad-based to absent on stem-leaves

FLOWERS	
Position	few, in loose cluster towards top of stem
Type	⚥
Size	30–50mm
Colour	blue, white or pink
Stalk	nodding
Sepals	5, 15–30mm, oval, pointed, coloured like petals
Petals	5, *c*30mm, oblong, with curved, spur-like base
Stamens	*c*50
Stigmas	1 per ovary
Ovaries	5, rarely 10, 1-celled
	FRUIT
Type	5, rarely 10, pod-like, opening along inner edge, upright
Size	15–25mm
Seeds	numerous, 2–2.5mm, globular, black, glossy

A stiffly upright plant of marshy places, forming clumps of rather coarse, dark leaves, cut into wedge-shaped leaflets. The most conspicuous feature of the fluffy flowers is the cluster of yellow stamens. *Status:* native, most of area except parts of north. *Similar species:* two species with smaller leaflets and nodding flowers are Lesser Meadow-rue, which has widely branched flower-heads, and Alpine Meadow-rue, which has unbranched spikes of flowers. Baneberry has a similar look in flower, though with coarse, toothed leaves, but it is easily distinguished in fruit by its black berries.

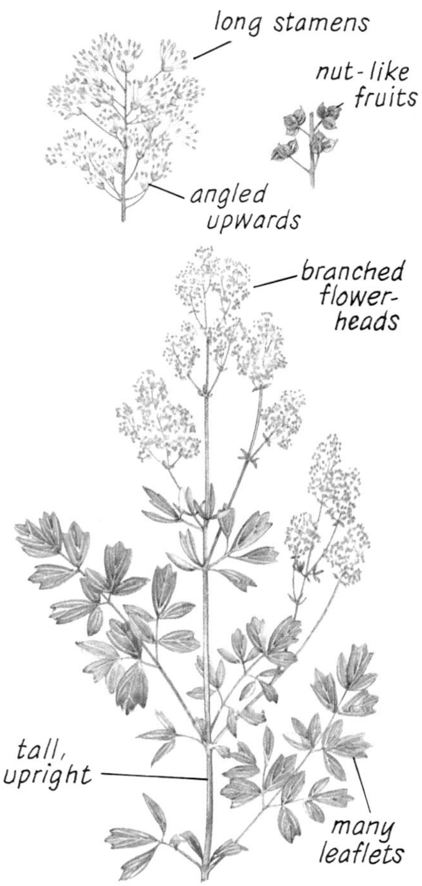

1 Lesser Meadow-rue *(T. minus)*;
2 Alpine Meadow-rue *(T. alpinum)*;
3 Baneberry *(Actaea spicata)*

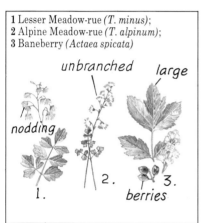

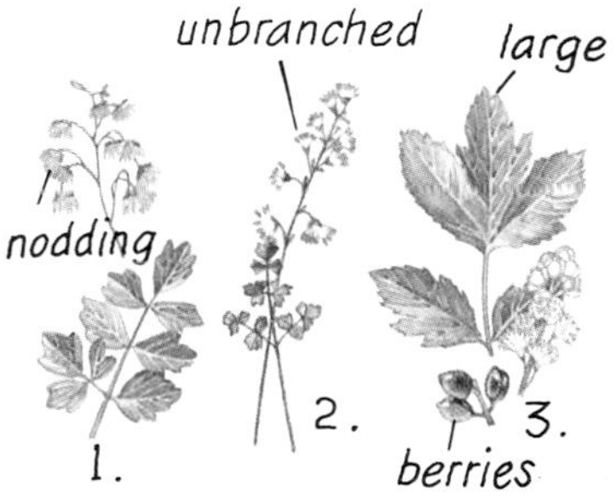

	COMMON MEADOW-RUE
Type	perennial
Height	50–100cm
Habitat	meadows, fens, stream-banks; wet soils
Flowering	July–August
	STEMS AND LEAVES
Stem	upright, little-branched
Root	from creeping, slender, underground stem
Hairs	more or less hairless
Stipules	present
Leaves	basal or spirally arranged around stem, divided 2–3 times, with oval to wedge-shaped leaflets, dark green above, tip bluntish, 3–4 lobed towards tip
Leaf-stalk	present or upper stalkless

	FLOWERS
Position	numerous in dense, branched heads
Bracts	present
Type	⚥, fragrant, upright
Size	6–10mm
Colour	whitish yellow
Stalk	about equalling flower
Perianth	4, 3–4mm, narrow
Stamens	numerous, yellow, held above flower
Stigmas	1 per ovary
Ovaries	few, 1-celled
	FRUIT
Type	few, nut-like, not opening, egg-shaped to ellipsoid with 6 ribs
Size	1.5–2.5mm
Seeds	1, not released

Common Poppy *Papaver rhoeas*

Poppies paint a new road verge or embankment a brilliant hue in their first year, but rapidly decline and after a few years exist only as seeds in the soil, waiting until the land is turned again. Once a common sight in cornfields, more effective seed cleaning and use of selective herbicides have made Poppies much rarer. *Status:* native; often very common, rare in parts of north. *Similar species:* two Poppies have elongated fruits: the Long-headed Poppy with a smooth fruit, and the Prickly Poppy with a spiny fruit. Opium Poppy has purplish flowers and much larger capsules.

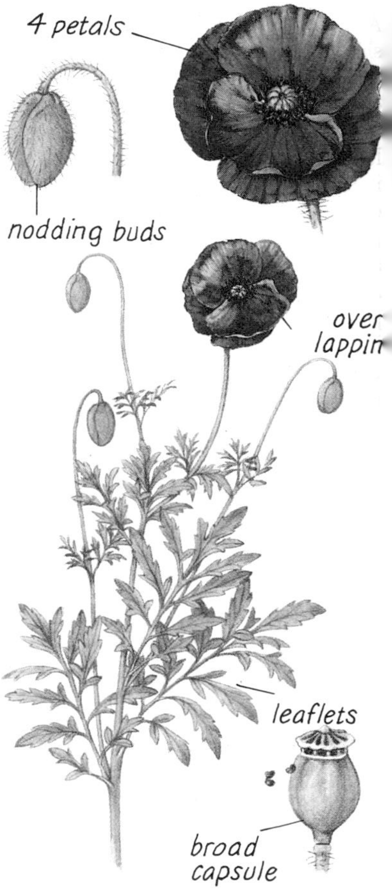

1 Long-headed Poppy *(P. dubium)*;
2 Prickly Poppy *(P. argemone)*;
3 Opium Poppy *(P. somniferum)*

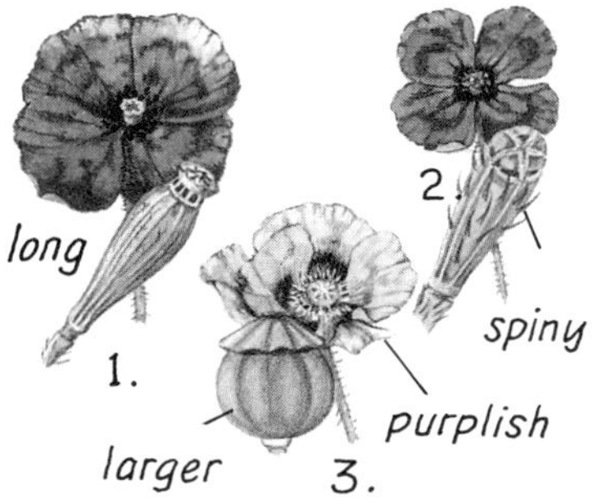

COMMON POPPY

Type annual
Height 20–60cm
Habitat newly dug and waste ground, arable fields
Flowering June–August

STEMS AND LEAVES

Stem upright, milky sap
Root slender taproot
Hairs stiff, outward-pointing
Stipules absent
Leaves at base or spirally around stem, 30–150mm, cut into narrow lobes or leaflets, upper leaves mostly 3-lobed, pointed, toothed
Leaf-stalk present or upper stalkless

FLOWERS

Position single, from base of leaf
Bracts absent
Type ⚥
Size 70–100mm
Colour scarlet, rarely pink or white, usually with blackish blotch at base
Stalk longer than flower
Sepals 2, bristly, soon falling
Petals 4, 20–40mm, rounded, crumpled, soon falling
Stamens numerous, anthers bluish
Stigmas 8–12, forming radiating bands on top of ovary
Ovary 1, with 8–12 cells

FRUIT

Type 1, capsule, opens by ring of pores at top, nearly globular, smooth
Size 10–20mm
Seeds many, *c*1mm, blackish

A striking plant of coastal dunes and shingle banks, with large yellow flowers held above blue-green foliage. Its curved, horn-like fruits, unlike those of the cornfield Poppies, split open lengthways leaving the seeds embedded in a middle wall. *Status:* native, most coasts. *Similar species:* Welsh Poppy, a plant of inland, mostly mountainous, areas, has leaves that are more divided, and much shorter fruits which open by pores like common Poppies. This species is related to the magnificent blue Himalayan Poppy, which is cultivated in gardens.

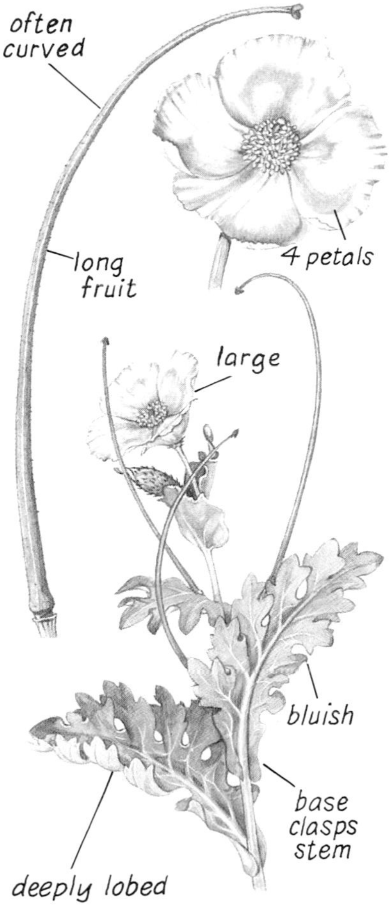

Welsh Poppy *(Meconopsis cambrica)*

	YELLOW HORNED-POPPY
Type	perennial or biennial
Height	30–90cm
Habitat	mainly dunes or shingle banks by sea
Flowering	June–September
	STEMS AND LEAVES
Stem	upright, branched, with yellow sap when cut
Root	thick tap-root
Hairs	rather sparse, rough
Stipules	absent
Leaves	from base or scattered around stem, 150–350mm, bluish green, tip blunt, edge lobed and toothed, often wavy
Leaf-stalk	present or absent on upper leaves
	FLOWERS
Position	single, from base of leaf
Bracts	absent
Type	⚥
Size	60–90mm
Colour	yellow
Stalk	short
Sepals	2, separate, soon falling
Petals	4, almost equal, nearly circular
Stamens	numerous, yellow
Stigmas	2, nearly stalkless
Ovary	1, 2-celled
	FRUIT
Type	1, capsule, 2 sides splitting almost to base, long, thin, usually curved
Size	150–300mm
Seeds	numerous, minutely pitted

Greater Celandine *Chelidonium majus*

The flowers of Greater Celandine look like tiny yellow Poppies, but its fruits appear more like those of the Cresses and Cabbages. The slender capsule splits open from the base releasing tiny black seeds, each with a fleshy, oily outgrowth that is eagerly sought by ants that carry off and disperse the seeds. The plant was formerly widely used for the treatment of sore or cloudy eyes, although the bright orange sap is acrid and poisonous. External application of the sap was used to treat warts, corns and ringworm, although it will equally damage any skin that it touches. In Russia, the plant has been used as an anti-cancer drug. The native distribution of Greater Celandine has been obscured by innumerable escapes from cultivation; it is now found in gardens mostly as a weed. *Status:* native or introduced in some localities; common, throughout area. (There are no similar species.)

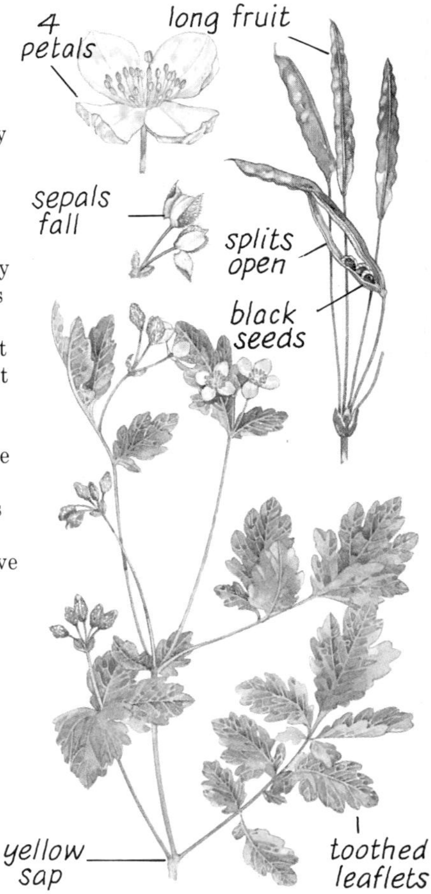

	GREATER CELANDINE
Type	perennial
Height	30–90cm
Habitat	banks and walls, often near houses
Flowering	May–August
	STEMS AND LEAVES
Stem	upright, branched, with orange sap
Root	woody stock, covered with fibres from old leaf-bases
Hairs	sparse
Stipules	absent
Leaves	at base of plant or scattered around stem, cut into 2–3 pairs of leaflets with leaflet at tip, blunt, edge with rounded teeth
Leaf-stalk	long below, absent above
	FLOWERS
Position	2–6, from tip of stem
Bracts	present
Type	⚥
Size	20–25mm
Colour	bright yellow
Stalk	about equalling flower
Sepals	2, separate, soon falling, hairy
Petals	4, up to 10mm, oval, broadest above middle
Stamens	numerous, yellow
Stigma	1, 2 lobes on short style
Ovary	1, 1-celled
	FRUIT
Type	1, capsule, splitting from bottom, narrow
Size	30–50mm
Seeds	many, 1.5–2mm, black with fleshy, white outgrowth

This plant's name suggests a smoky nature, inspired partly by the look of finely divided, greyish leaves on widely branched stems and the tiny, dull purple flowers. Fumitory also has an acrid smell to the root and the sap makes eyes weep. *Status:* native; common throughout most of area. *Similar species:* White Ramping-fumitory has climbing stems, broader leaf-segments and larger, white flowers, tipped with purple. Corydalis species have many-seeded pods. Yellow Corydalis has bright yellow flowers, and Climbing Corydalis climbs and has small, creamy-white flowers.

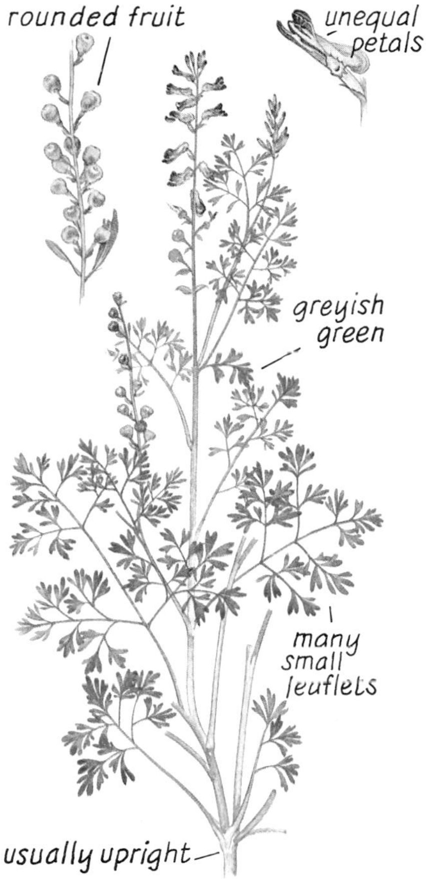

1 White Ramping-fumitory *(F. capreolata)*; **2** Yellow Corydalis *(Corydalis lutea)*; **3** Climbing Corydalis *(C. claviculata)*

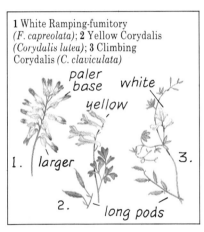

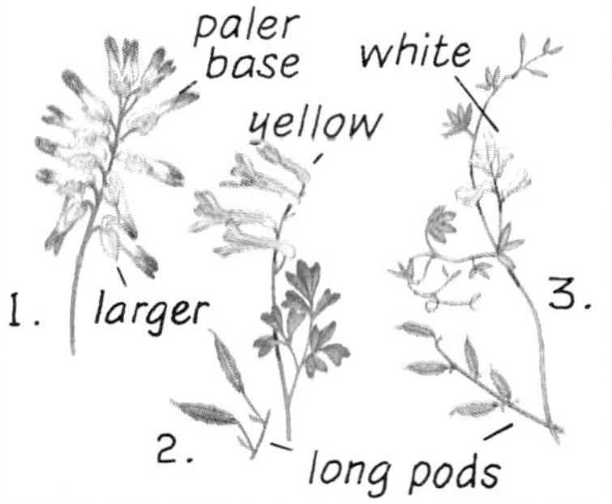

	COMMON FUMITORY
Type	annual
Height	12–40cm
Habitat	cultivated ground; mostly light soils
Flowering	May–October
	STEMS AND LEAVES
Stem	nearly upright or climbing
Root	slender tap-root
Hairs	hairless
Stipules	absent
Leaves	spirally arranged, 20–100mm, many spear-shaped or oblong, bluish lobes
Leaf-stalk	present, lower broad-based
	FLOWERS
Position	10–40, in crowded spike from opposite leaf-base
Bracts	narrow, pointed, shorter than flower-stalk
Type	⚥
Size	7–9mm
Colour	pink with blackish-purple tips to inner petals
Stalk	shorter than flowers
Sepals	2, 2–3.5mm, oval, toothed at base, soon falling
Petals	4, unequal, inner pair joined, hidden by larger, outer pair
Stamens	2
Stigma	1, 2-lobed
Ovary	1, 1-celled
	FRUIT
Type	1, nut-like, not opening, globular, blunt or notched
Size	2–2.5mm
Seeds	1, not released

Garlic Mustard *Alliaria petiolata*

A fresh-looking plant in late Spring, when heads of snow-white flowers and broad, pale green leaves contrast starkly with the gathering shade of the woodland or hedgerow. A garlic-like aroma advertises its presence. *Status:* native; common except in some northern parts. *Similar species:* Honesty, a common garden escapee, has larger, purplish or white flowers. Its nearly circular fruits split revealing a silvery inner wall. Perennial Honesty, with fruits more pointed, is native to the east of the area. The fragrant Dame's-violet has slender fruits and narrower leaves.

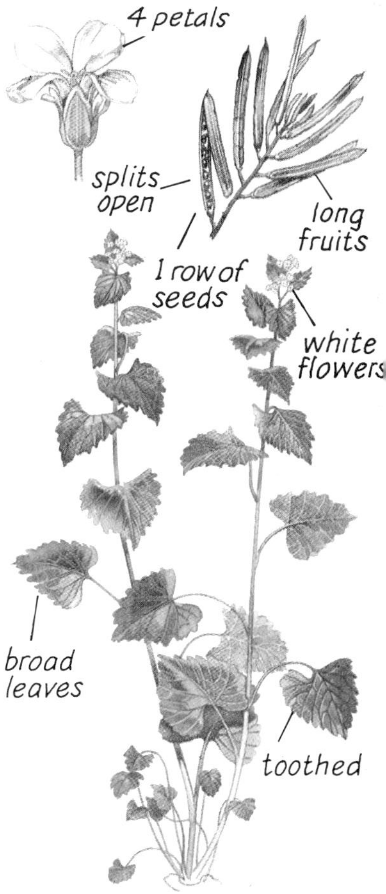

1 Honesty *(Lunaria annua)*;
2 Perennial Honesty *(L. rediviva)*;
3 Dame's-violet *(Hesperis matronalis)*

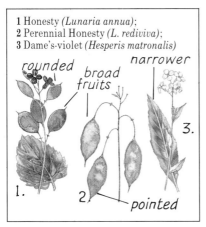

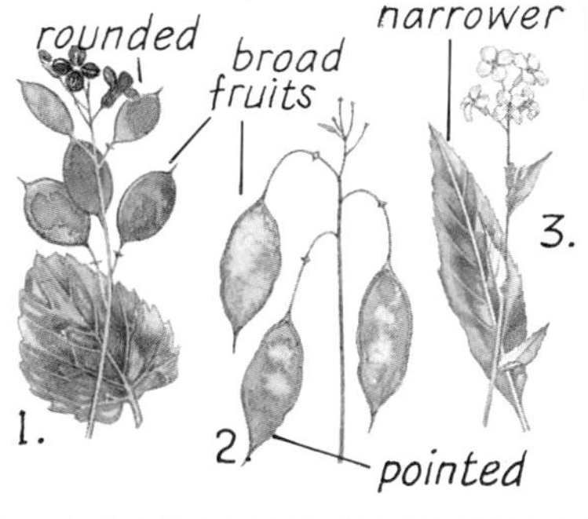

	GARLIC MUSTARD
Type	biennial or perennial
Height	20–120cm
Habitat	woods, hedgerows, by walls; mostly lime-rich soils
Flowering	April–June
	STEMS AND LEAVES
Stem	upright, usually branched
Root	whitish tap-root, fibrous roots produce new shoots
Hairs	sparse to hairless above
Stipules	absent
Leaves	basal or spirally around stem, 30–120mm, kidney-shaped to triangular, garlic-smelling, wavy or toothed, base heart-shaped
Leaf-stalk	long below, short above

	FLOWERS
Position	*c*30 in head at stem-tip
Bracts	absent
Type	⚥
Size	5–10mm
Colour	white
Stalk	2.5–13mm
Sepals	4, 2.5–3.5mm, oval, whitish
Petals	4, 4–6mm, rounded, base stalk-like
Stamens	6
Stigma	1
Ovary	1, 2-celled
	FRUIT
Type	1, pod-like, slender, straight, sides 3-veined, splits from base to top, seeds in 1 row
Size	35–60mm
Seeds	3–18, *c*3mm, angular, black

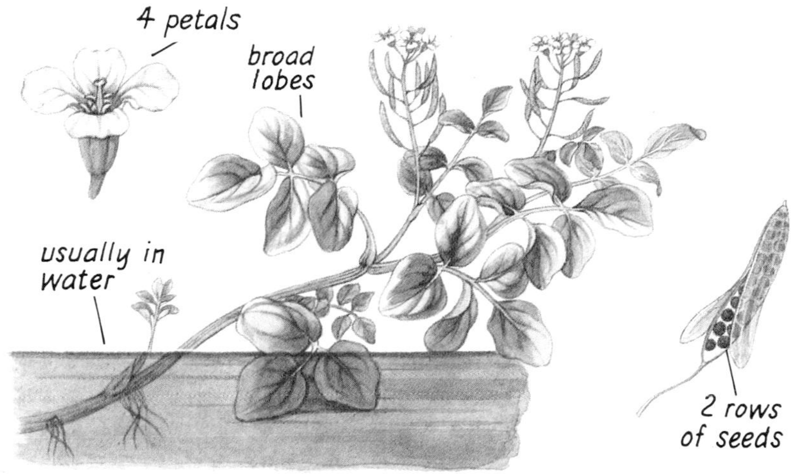

Best known as a salad plant or garnish with hot-tasting leaves, Water-cress is a species of the Cabbage family which normally grows in shallow water. Fleshy, hollow stems bear dark green leaves, paired leaflets and spikes of white, four-petalled flowers. Plants from stagnant water or where sheep graze should not be eaten because of the parasitic liver-fluke, which also attacks humans. *Status:* native; lowland, throughout area. *Similar species:* Narrow-fruited Water-cress often has leaves tinged with purple, especially in Autumn, and narrow fruits with a single row of seeds.

Narrow-fruited Water-cress *(N. microphyllum)*

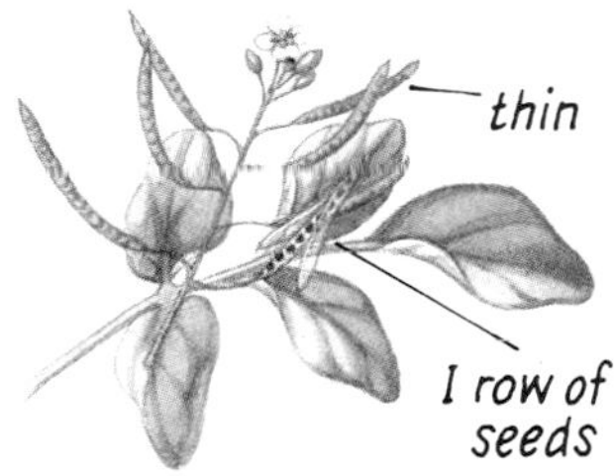

	WATER-CRESS
Type	perennial
Height	10–60cm
Habitat	ditches, streams, rivers; wet soil or shallow water
Flowering	May–October
	STEMS AND LEAVES
Stem	low-growing, turning upright, rooting, often floating, hollow
Root	branched, creeping stock
Hairs	absent
Stipules	absent
Leaves	spirally arranged, 1–4 pairs of leaflets, leaflet at tip, each elliptical to circular, blunt, edge unbroken or partly toothed
Leaf-stalk	present or absent above

	FLOWERS
Position	many, in spike-like heads
Bracts	absent
Type	⚥
Size	4–6mm
Colour	white
Stalk	8–12mm
Sepals	4, alternating with petals
Petals	4, equal, rounded with stalk-like base
Stamens	6
Stigma	1, sometimes 2-lobed
Ovary	1, 2-celled
	FRUIT
Type	1, pod-like, level or curving upwards, sides swollen with faint mid-vein, seeds in 2 rows
Size	13–18mm
Seeds	many, *c*2mm, egg-shaped, shallowly pitted

Hedge Mustard *Sisymbrium officinale*

Commonly growing close to roads and tracks, plants of Hedge Mustard often have a dusty, neglected look. Almost stalkless fruits are held stiffly upright, pressed close to the stems, and give a spidery look. Hedge Mustard was formerly used in cough medicines and was also eaten in salads, soups and omelettes. *Status:* native; common, most of area. *Similar species:* Tall Rocket has more leaflets or lobes, the upper very narrow, and longer, stalked fruits. Flixweed has leaves cut into very many small lobes. Treacle Mustard has undivided leaves covered with odd short-stalked, T-shaped hairs.

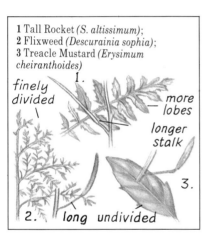

1 Tall Rocket *(S. altissimum)*; **2** Flixweed *(Descurainia sophia)*; **3** Treacle Mustard *(Erysimum cheiranthoides)*

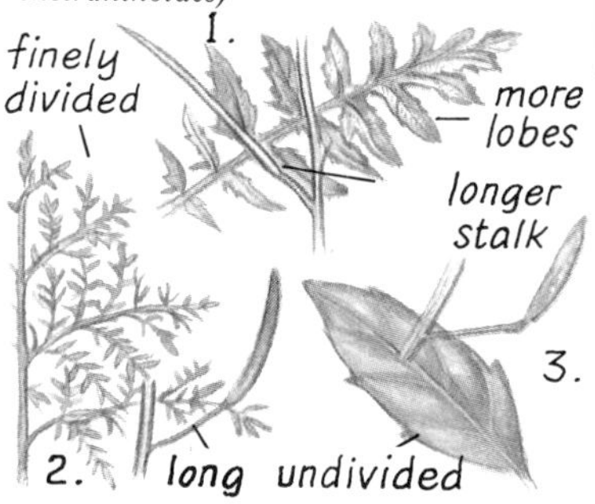

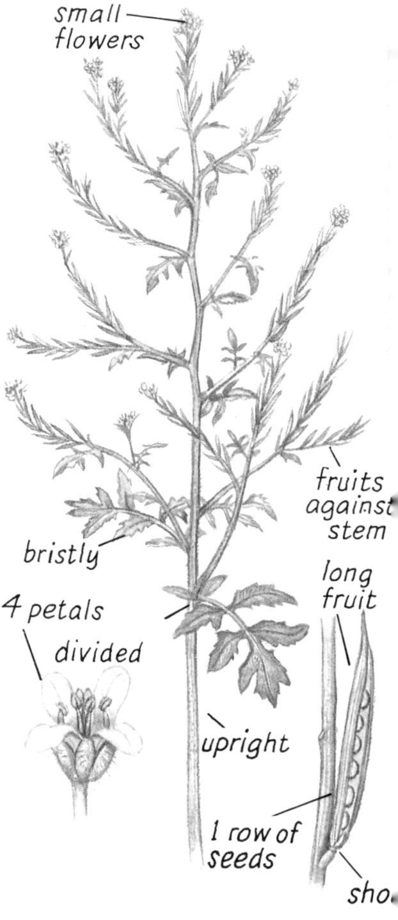

	HEDGE MUSTARD
Type	annual
Height	30–90cm
Habitat	waste ground, arable fields, hedgebanks
Flowering	June–July
	STEMS AND LEAVES
Stem	upright, branched above
Root	slender tap-root
Hairs	bristly, pointing down on stems
Stipules	absent
Leaves	basal or scattered around stem, 50–80mm, cut into 1–5 pairs of narrow, toothed lobes, broad lobe at tip
Leaf-stalk	present or absent above
	FLOWERS
Position	many, in spike at stem-tip
Bracts	absent
Type	⚥
Size	3–3.5mm
Colour	pale yellow
Stalk	1–2mm
Sepals	4, 1.5–2mm, oblong, blunt
Petals	4, 2–4mm, equal, oblong, rounded, base stalk-like
Stamens	6, 4 long, 2 short
Stigma	1
Ovary	1, 2-celled
	FRUIT
Type	1, pod-like, held close to stem, sides hairy, 3-veined, splits from base, slender, seeds in 1 row
Size	10–15mm
Seeds	10–20, *c*1mm, egg-shaped, orange-brown

This robust, virtually hairless species of the Cabbage family grows in wet places and has broad heads of yellow, four-petalled flowers. *Status:* native, most of area except parts of north. *Similar species:* Northern Yellow-cress has much shorter fruits. Winter-cresses have a rounded lobe at the leaf-tip, fruits with a distinct middle vein on each side, and seeds in one row. Winter-cress is sometimes used like Water-cress in salads or boiled like spinach; this species has toothed upper leaves. American Winter-cress has lobed upper leaves and fruits twice as long.

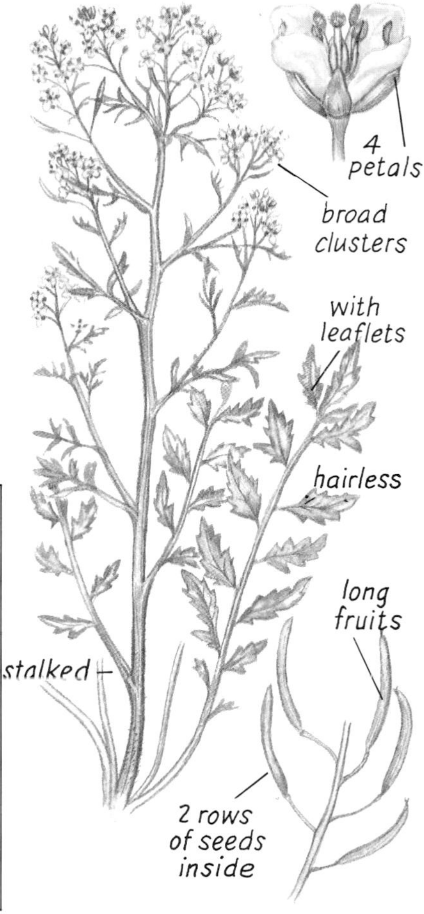

1 Northern Yellow-cress *(R. islandica)*; **2** Winter-cress *(Barbarea vulgaris)*; **3** American Winter-cress *(B. verna)*

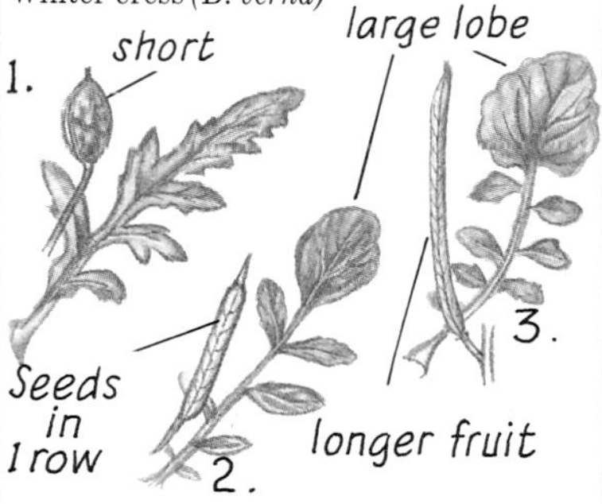

	CREEPING YELLOW-CRESS
Type	perennial
Height	20–50cm
Habitat	damp ground or where water stands in winter
Flowering	June–August
	STEMS AND LEAVES
Stem	upright, branched, angled
Root	fibrous, from creeping, underground stems
Hairs	more or less hairless
Stipules	absent
Leaves	spirally arranged, lower leaves with oblong or spear-shaped, toothed leaflets either side, leaflet at tip, upper leaves lobed
Leaf-stalk	present or absent above

	FLOWERS
Position	spikes in branched head
Bracts	absent
Type	⚥
Size	*c*5mm
Colour	yellow
Stalk	5–12mm
Sepals	4, alternating with petals
Petals	4, 4–5mm, equal, oval, rounded, base stalk-like
Stamens	6
Stigma	1, slightly 2-lobed
Ovary	1, 2-celled
	FRUIT
Type	1, pod-like, thin, sides swollen, scarcely veined, seeds mostly in 2 rows
Size	9–18mm
Seeds	many, *c*0.7mm, red-brown

Cuckooflower *Cardamine pratensis*

Attractive lavender flowers, opening at a time of the year when the cuckoo starts to call, mark out the clumps of Cuckooflower in a meadow or by a stream. The seeds are effectively dispersed by the pod, which splits open suddenly, hurling the seeds from the plant. *Status:* native; throughout region. *Similar species:* Large Bitter-cress has purple anthers. Explosive fruits are also found in two small-flowered species, making them troublesome in gardens. The annual Hairy Bitter-cress mostly has four stamens, whereas Wavy Bitter-cress has six and is usually perennial.

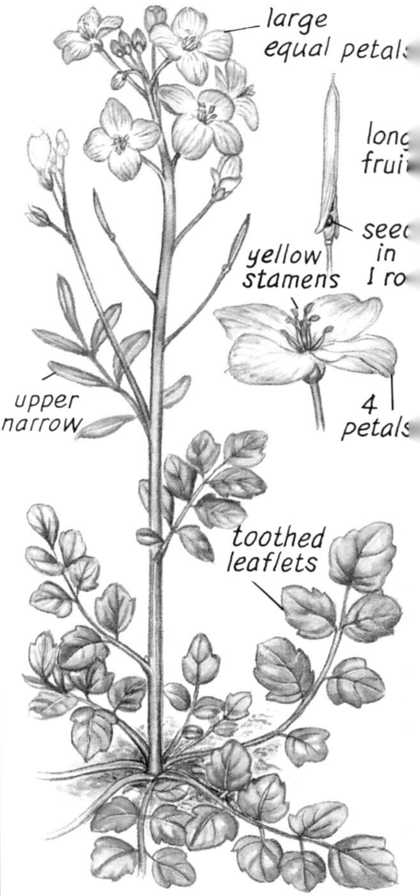

1 Large Bitter-cress *(C. amara)*;
2 Hairy Bitter-cress *(C. hirsuta)*;
3 Wavy Bitter-cress *(C. flexuosa)*

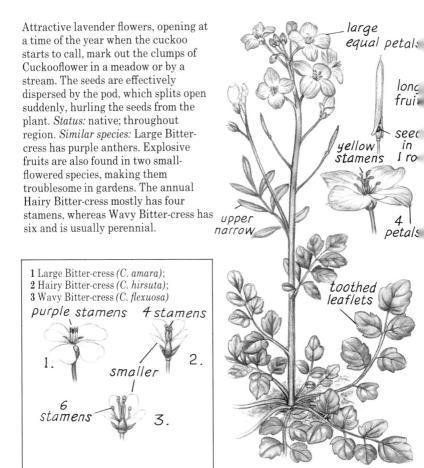

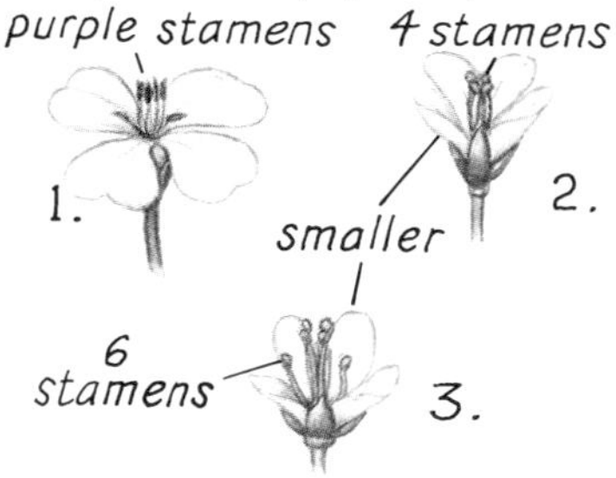

CUCKOOFLOWER

Type perennial
Height 15–60cm
Habitat meadows or streams; damp soil or shallow water
Flowering April–June

STEMS AND LEAVES

Stem upright, usually unbranched
Root short, nearly horizontal stock, many fibrous roots
Hairs sparse, on leaves
Stipules absent
Leaves basal or spirally arranged, lower with broad, toothed leaflets, upper leaves with narrow, unbroken leaflets
Leaf-stalk present

FLOWERS

Position 7–20, in rounded heads which elongate in fruit
Bracts absent
Type ⚥
Size 12–18mm
Colour lilac, rarely white
Stalk 8–25mm
Sepals 4, 3–4mm, papery edges, tip violet
Petals 4, 8–13mm, equal, oval, often notched, base stalk-like
Stamens 4–6
Stigma 1, sometimes 2-lobed
Ovary 1, 2-celled

FRUIT

Type 1, pod-like, suddenly coils open, slender, seeds in 1 row
Size 25–40mm
Seeds numerous, *c*2mm, oblong

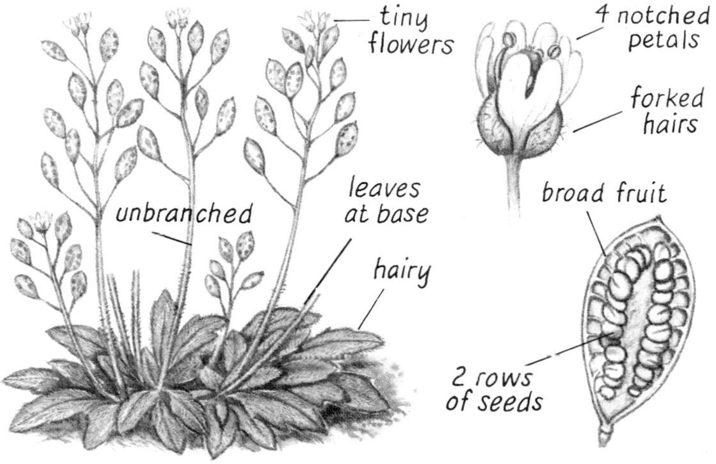

A diminutive plant of dry, often shallow or sandy soil, that has a rosette of leaves densely covered with odd Y-shaped or branched hairs. The short, flattened fruits quickly ripen and split open, revealing a silvery inner wall and two rows of seeds. *Status:* native, most of area except for parts of north. *Similar species:* several species from dry places lack the notch in the petals. Wall Whitlowgrass has taller, leafy stems. Much longer fruits are a feature of Thale Cress, which has cylindrical fruits, and Hairy Rock-cress, which has flattened fruits and winged seeds.

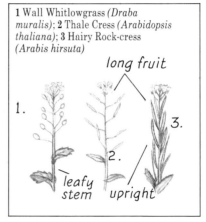

1 Wall Whitlowgrass *(Draba muralis)*; **2** Thale Cress *(Arabidopsis thaliana)*; **3** Hairy Rock-cress *(Arabis hirsuta)*

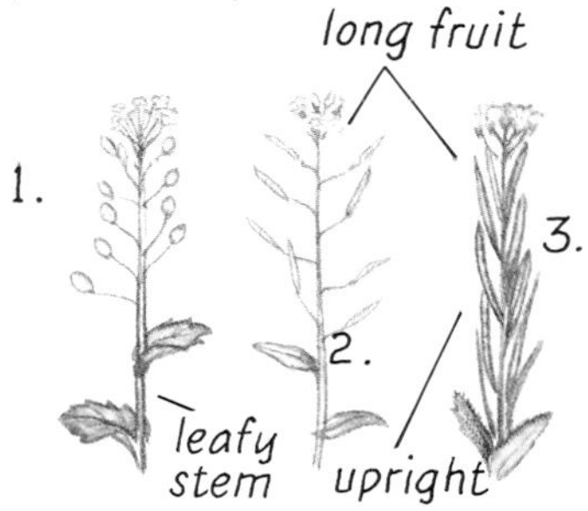

	COMMON WHITLOWGRASS
Type	annual
Height	2–20cm
Habitat	dry places, often among rocks or on walls
Flowering	March–June
	STEMS AND LEAVES
Stem	straight or base branched
Root	fibrous
Hairs	dense, forked or star-shaped
Stipules	absent
Leaves	in rosette at base, 10–15mm, elliptical or spear-shaped, pointed, edge unbroken or 1–2 teeth
Leaf-stalk	broad
	FLOWERS
Position	in a rounded head, elongating in fruit
Bracts	absent
Type	⚥
Size	3–6mm
Colour	white, some tinged red
Stalk	1.5–6mm
Sepals	4, 1.5–2.5mm
Petals	4, 1.5–6mm, equal, deeply notched, base stalk-like
Stamens	6, 4 long, 2 short
Stigma	1
Ovary	1, 2-celled
	FRUIT
Type	1, pod-like, oval, usually broadest above middle, flattened, sides split leaving broad inner wall, seeds in 2 rows
Size	3–9mm
Seeds	40–60, 0.3–0.4mm, flattened

Common Scurvygrass *Cochlearia officinalis*

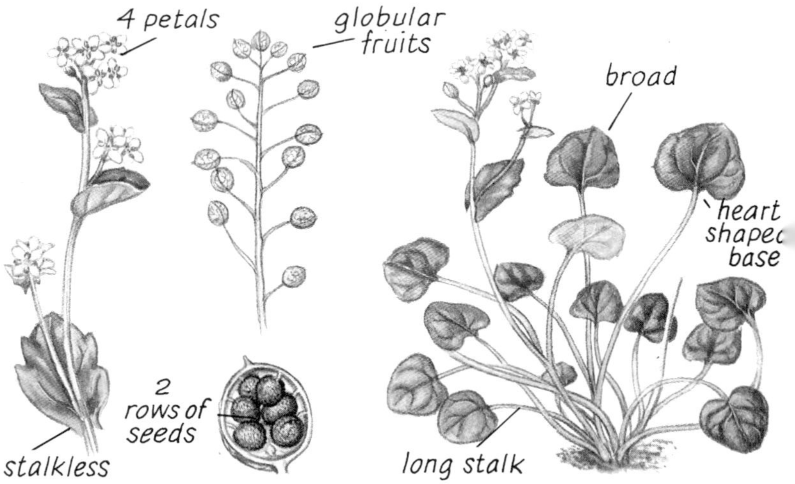

A distinctive feature of sea-cliffs, shingle banks or the upper limits of salt-marshes, this low-growing plant has rather succulent, mostly kidney-shaped leaves and white, four-petalled flowers. Rich in Vitamin C, its leaves were used to combat scurvy, a disease once prevalent in sailors and caused by deficiency of the vitamin. *Status:* native; most coastal areas. *Similar species:* Danish Scurvygrass has smaller flowers and mostly stalked stem-leaves. English Scurvygrass has a tapered base to the lower leaves, and flattened fruits.

1 Danish Scurvygrass *(C. danica)*; **2** English Scurvygrass *(C. anglica)*

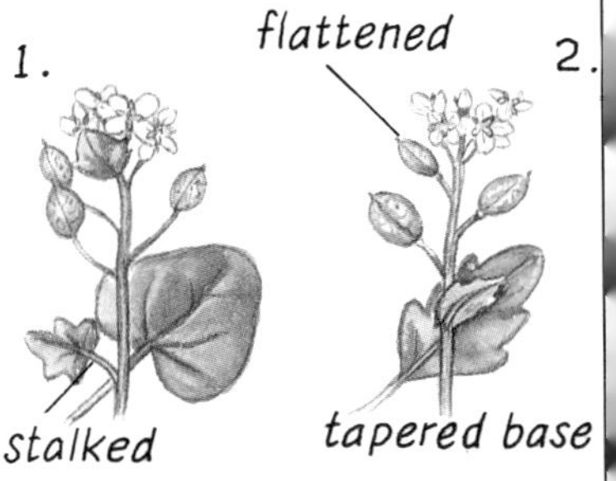

	COMMON SCURVYGRASS
Type	biennial or perennial
Height	5–50cm
Habitat	sea-cliffs, drier parts of salt-marshes, mountains
Flowering	May–August
	STEMS AND LEAVES
Stem	low or angled upwards
Root	long, stout tap-root
Hairs	hairless
Stipules	absent
Leaves	basal *c*15mm, nearly circular, fleshy, blunt, edge usually unbroken, base heart-shaped; stem-leaves scattered, narrower, edge wavy or toothed, base clasps stem
Leaf-stalk	longer than blade on basal leaves, absent above

	FLOWERS
Position	in elongated head
Bracts	absent
Type	⚥, fragrant
Size	8–10mm
Colour	white, rarely tinged lilac
Stalk	4–7
Sepals	4
Petals	4, oblong, base stalk-like
Stamens	6
Stigma	1
Ovary	1, 2-celled
	FRUIT
Type	1, pod-like, globular, each side splits open, seeds in 2 rows on inner wall
Size	3–7mm
Seeds	2–32, 1.5–2mm, egg-shaped, reddish brown

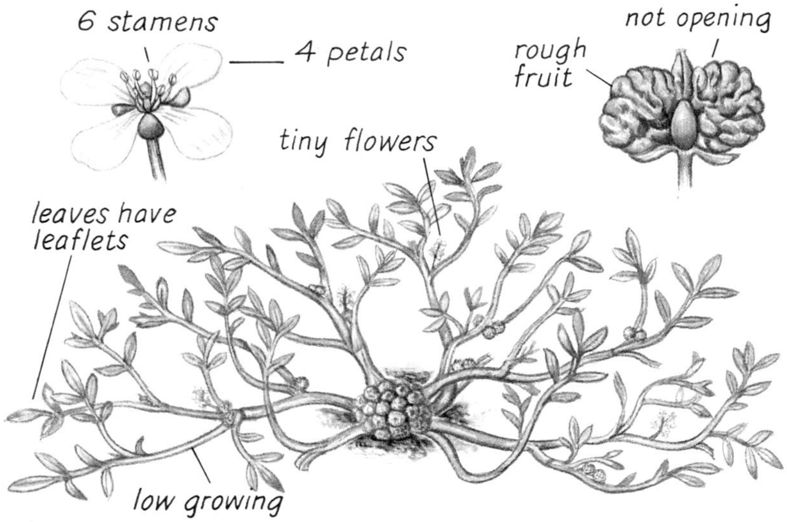

An undistinguished plant of trampled ground, Swine-cress is common by paths and other tracks but is easily overlooked because the flowers are minute. These flowers are pollinated automatically so the plant can set a full complement of seed regardless of the weather or presence of insects. *Status:* native; common mainly in south of region. *Similar species:* Lesser Swine-cress has only two stamens and smaller, almost smooth fruits notched at the tip, and a longer stalk.

Lesser Swine-cress *(C. didymus)*

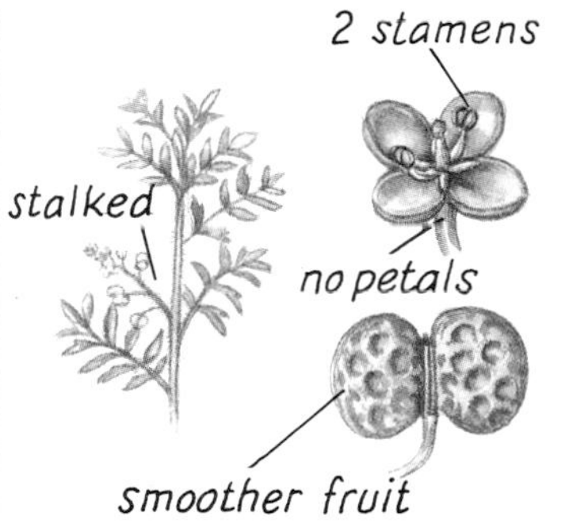

SWINE-CRESS

Type	annual or biennial
Height	5–30cm
Habitat	waste ground, particularly where trampled
Flowering	June–September

STEMS AND LEAVES

Stem	low-growing, branched, main stem short
Root	slender tap-root
Hairs	absent
Stipules	absent
Leaves	spirally around stem, with spear-shaped or oval, pointed segments or leaflets, lower leaflets sometimes toothed or lobed
Leaf-stalk	long below, short above

FLOWERS

Position	crowded clusters at tip of main stem, elongated heads opposite upper leaves
Bracts	absent
Type	⚥
Size	*c*2.5mm
Colour	white
Stalk	1.5–3mm
Sepals	4, shorter than petals
Petals	4 or 0, 1–1.5mm, equal, oblong, base stalk-like
Stamens	6
Stigma	1
Ovary	1, 2-celled

FRUIT

Type	1, not opening, nearly kidney-shaped, roughly ridged
Size	*c*2.5 × 3–4mm
Seeds	2, 2–2.5mm, not released

Gold-of-pleasure *Camelina sativa*

A slender plant with narrow, arrow-shaped leaves and branched heads of four-petalled, golden-yellow flowers. It was formerly common as a weed among many crops. The seeds are similar in size and shape to those of Flax and were probably spread when Flax was more widely cultivated. Gold-of-pleasure was also cultivated in its own right, for the seeds yield an edible oil. *Status:* introduced, occasionally naturalized; scattered through area, mainly in south-east. *Similar species:* Woad has pendulous, oblong fruits and was formerly cultivated for a blue dye extracted from its leaves.

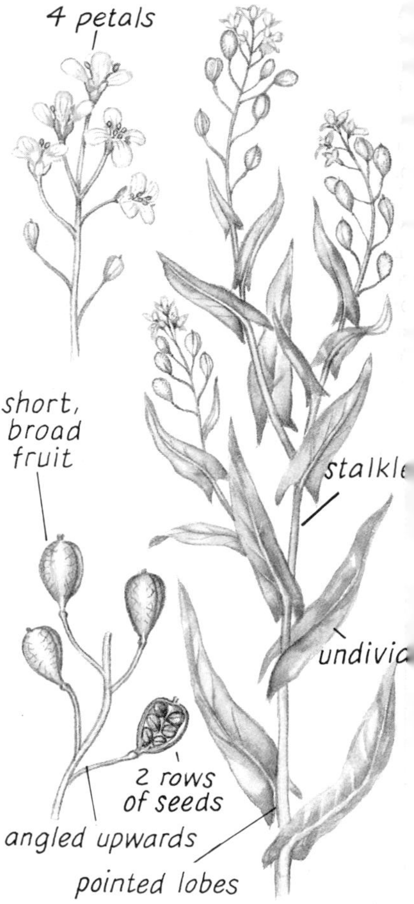

Woad *(Isatis tinctoria)*

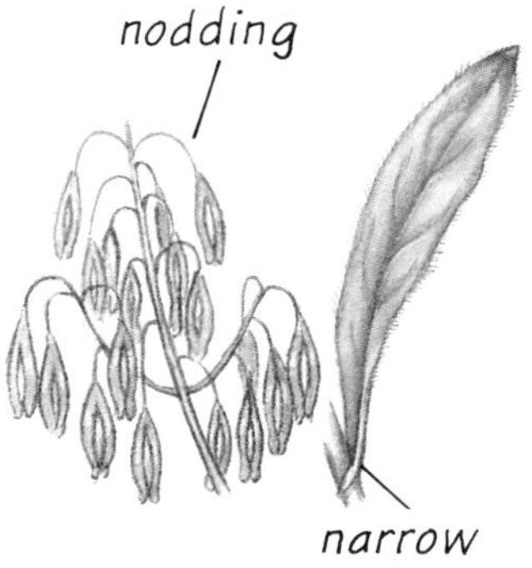

	GOLD-OF-PLEASURE
Type	annual
Height	30–80cm
Habitat	arable fields, especially of corn, flax and lucerne
Flowering	June–September
	STEMS AND LEAVES
Stem	upright, branched above
Root	slender, yellow tap-root
Hairs	sometimes hairy
Stipules	absent
Leaves	spirally arranged on stem, lower oblong or spear-shaped, edge unbroken, toothed or rarely lobed, base tapered; upper with pointed basal lobes clasping stem
Leaf-stalk	absent

	FLOWERS
Position	many, in branched heads
Bracts	absent
Type	⚥
Size	width *c*3mm
Colour	yellow
Stalk	up to 25mm in fruit
Sepals	4, upright
Petals	4, up to 5mm, equal, rounded, base stalk-like
Stamens	6
Stigma	1
Ovary	1, 2-celled
	FRUIT
Type	1, pod-like, egg-shaped, each swollen side splits away leaving 2 rows of seeds on middle wall
Size	6–9mm
Seeds	8–24, 1–2mm, egg-shaped

A robust plant with dark green, finely toothed, crinkly leaves, sometimes half a metre long. This is the same species as the cultivated plant used for making the hot and pungent horseradish sauce, commonly to accompany roast beef, prepared from peeled and grated roots. The aroma of the sauce is given off when a leaf is lightly crushed. *Status:* introduced; widely naturalized, most of region. *Similar species:* Dittander has broad, toothed leaves, although mostly smaller and not crinkled. Its hairy fruits, containing only two seeds, are produced in abundance whereas those of Horse-radish rarely develop.

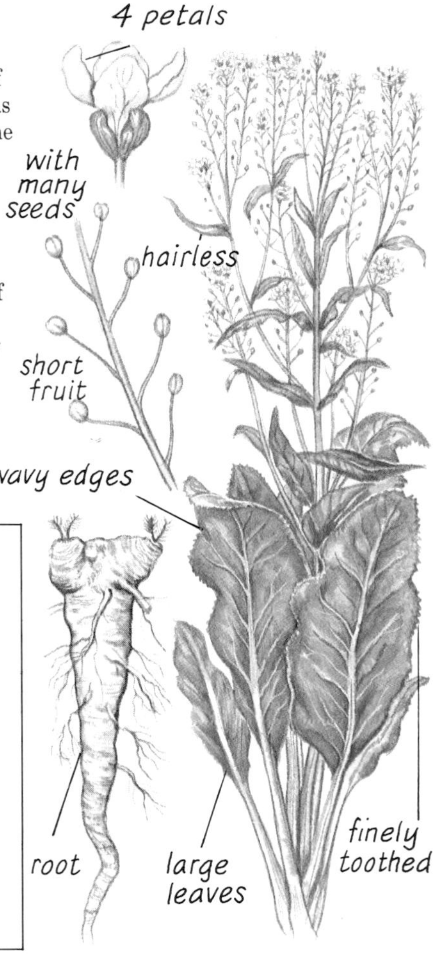

Dittander *(Lepidium latifolium)*

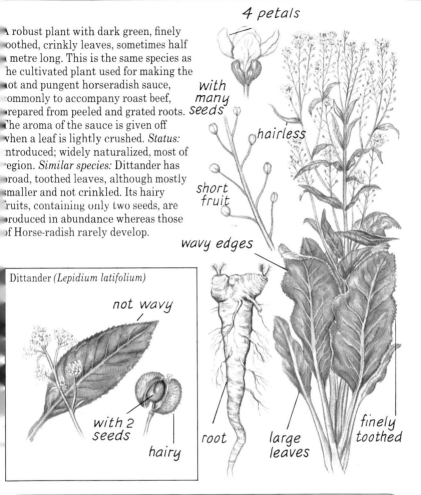

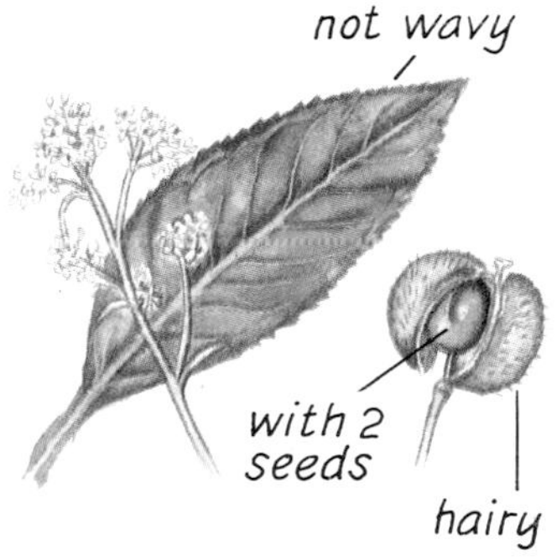

	HORSE-RADISH
Type	perennial
Height	up to 125cm
Habitat	fields, stream banks, waste places
Flowering	May–June
	STEMS AND LEAVES
Stem	upright, leafy, branched
Root	thick stock, sometimes branched, long tap-root
Hairs	absent
Stipules	absent
Leaves	basal or scattered on stem, basal 300–500mm, oval or oblong, blunt, fine-toothed, crinkled, some lobed; stem-leaves elliptical or spear-shaped, pointed
Leaf-stalk	to 300mm or absent above

	FLOWERS
Position	many, in branched head
Bracts	absent
Type	⚥
Size	8–9mm
Colour	white
Stalk	up to 200mm
Sepals	4, *c*3mm
Petals	4, 5–7mm, equal, oval, base stalk-like
Stamens	6, 4 long, 2 short
Stigma	1, slightly 2-lobed
Ovary	1, 2-celled
	FRUIT
Type	single, pod-like, rarely matures, globular, sides split, seeds in 2 rows
Size	4–6mm
Seeds	16–24, egg-shaped

Shepherd's-purse *Capsella bursa-pastoris*

A widespread weed often found in gardens and waste places, distinguished by small, heart-shaped fruits. A preparation from the leaves has long been used against inflammation and bleeding, and is still found in some medicines. *Status:* native; common throughout area. *Similar species:* Shepherd's Cress has two petals much smaller than the other two. Species differing in having one-seeded fruits include Smith's Pepperwort, which has narrower fruits winged at the top, and Hoary Cress which has larger, flatter-topped flower-heads and fruits that do not open.

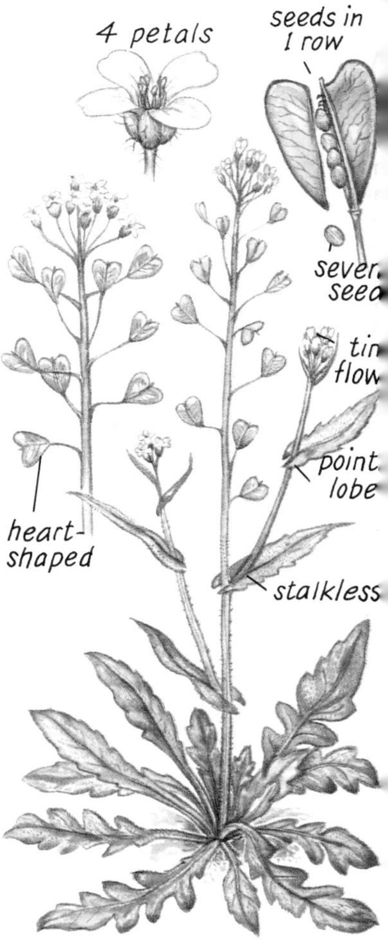

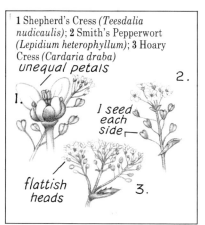

1 Shepherd's Cress *(Teesdalia nudicaulis)*; **2** Smith's Pepperwort *(Lepidium heterophyllum)*; **3** Hoary Cress *(Cardaria draba)*

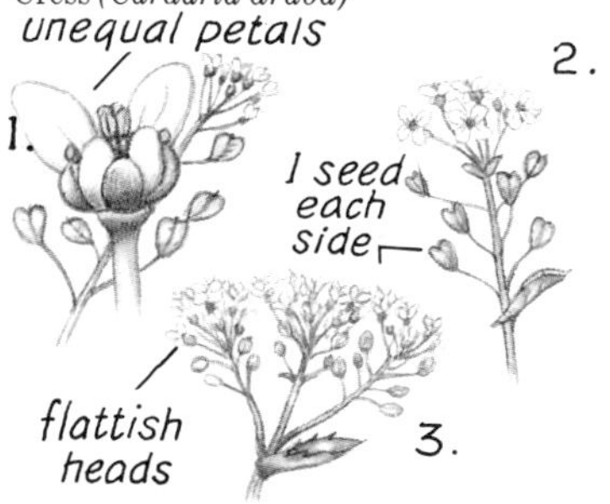

	SHEPHERD'S-PURSE
Type	annual or biennial
Height	3–40cm
Habitat	cultivated land, road and path-sides, waste places
Flowering	January–December
	STEMS AND LEAVES
Stem	upright or angled upwards
Root	slender tap-root
Hairs	hairless or sparsely hairy
Stipules	absent
Leaves	basal rosette, few on stem; lowest spear-shaped, broad near tip, lobed; stem-leaves toothed or unbroken, 2 pointed lobes clasp stem
Leaf-stalk	only on lowest leaves

	FLOWERS
Position	in elongated heads
Bracts	absent
Type	⚥
Size	width *c*2.5mm
Colour	white
Stalk	lengthening in fruit
Sepals	4, *c*1.5mm, upright
Petals	4, 2–3mm, oval, tip notched, base stalk-like
Stamens	6, sometimes absent
Stigma	1, on short stalk
Ovary	1, 2-celled
	FRUIT
Type	1, heart-shaped or triangular, tip notched, sides part leaving 1 row of seeds on thin inner wall
Size	6–9mm
Seeds	12–24, 0.8–1mm, oblong to egg-shaped, pale brown

A weed with rounded, broadly winged fruits that have led to its common name. Although the fruits are a little like those of Honesty, when they split the middle wall is much narrower and less attractive. Field Penny-cress can grow in such great quantity on farmland that it becomes a serious pest. *Status:* native or introduced; most of area. *Similar species:* Perfoliate Penny-cress has narrowly winged, heart-shaped fruits. Alpine Penny-cress is a mountain plant with smaller, untoothed leaves and triangular fruits with a spike at the tip.

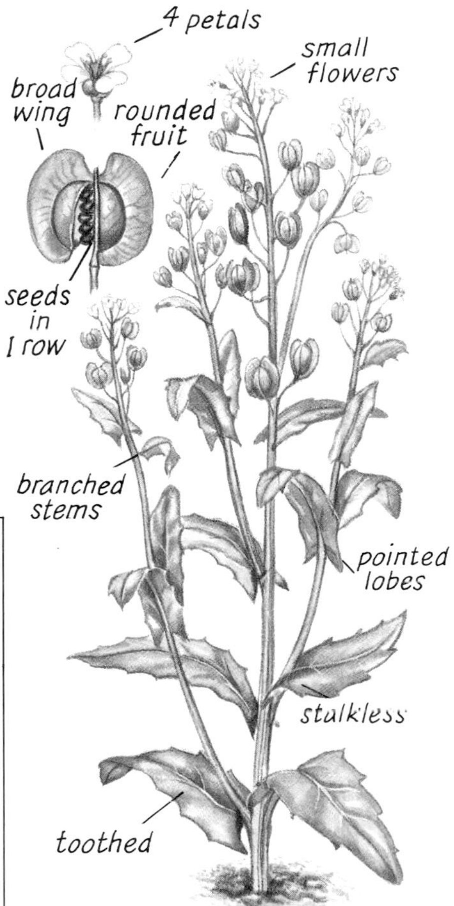

1 Alpine Penny-cress *(T. alpestre)*;
2 Perfoliate Penny-cress *(T. perfoliatum)*

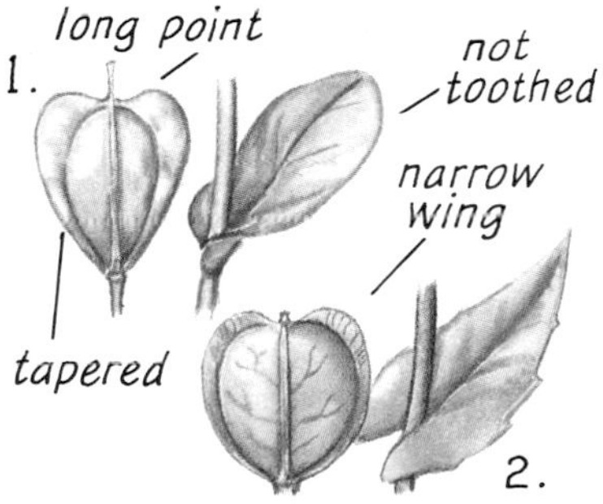

	FIELD PENNY-CRESS
Type	annual
Height	10–60cm
Habitat	arable fields or waste places
Flowering	May–July
	STEMS AND LEAVES
Stem	upright, branched above
Root	slender tap-root
Hairs	absent
Stipules	absent
Leaves	spirally arranged on stem, spear-shaped to oval, most sparsely toothed; 2 pointed lobes at base of upper leaves clasp stem
Leaf-stalk	only lowest stalked

	FLOWERS
Position	elongated heads
Bracts	absent
Type	⚥
Size	4–6mm
Colour	white
Stalk	lengthening in fruit
Sepals	4, 1.5–2mm, narrow
Petals	4, 3–4mm, equal, base stalk-like
Stamens	6, 4 long, 2 short
Stigma	1, slightly 2-lobed
Ovary	1, 2-celled
	FRUIT
Type	1, pod-like, circular, flattened, edge wing-like, notched, sides split away leaving seeds in 1 row on narrow inner wall
Size	12–22mm
Seeds	10–16, 1.5–2mm, ridged

Black Mustard *Brassica nigra*

A tall plant with smooth, bluish upper leaves and wide-branched stems bearing heads of yellow, 4-petalled flowers. It is cultivated for mustard, made from the ground seeds. *Status:* native near coast, mostly escaped elsewhere; commonest in south. *Similar species:* the fields of yellow commonly seen are mostly a form of Rape, grown for an edible oil extracted from the seeds. Rape has stalkless upper leaves as does Wild Turnip, which has mostly bristly, green leaves, and Wild Cabbage, which has hairless, bluish leaves, and has given rise to cultivated Cabbage, Cauliflower and Broccoli.

1 Wild Turnip *(B. rapa)*; **2** Rape *(B. napus)*; **3** Wild Cabbage *(B. oleracea)*

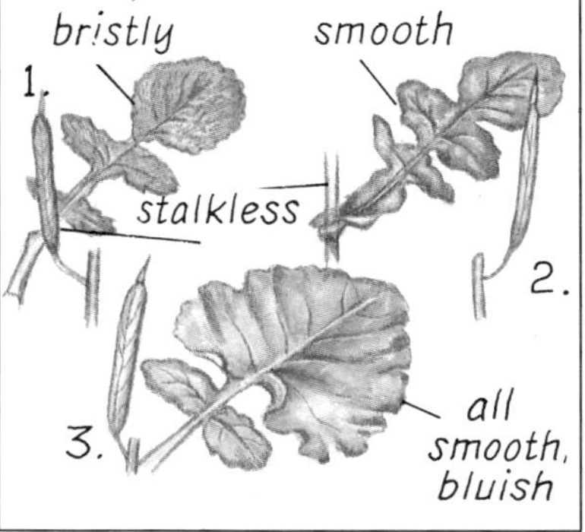

	BLACK MUSTARD
Type	annual
Height	up to 100cm
Habitat	cliffs by sea, stream banks, waste places
Flowering	May–August
	STEMS AND LEAVES
Stem	rather stout, much-branched
Root	slender tap-root
Hairs	bristly below, hairless above
Stipules	absent
Leaves	scattered, to 160mm, bluish, lower broad, 1–3 pairs of lobes, large lobe at tip; upper narrow, edge wavy or unbroken
Leaf-stalk	present

	FLOWERS
Position	many, short heads elongate
Bracts	absent
Type	⚥
Size	8–10mm
Colour	bright yellow
Stalk	shorter than flower
Sepals	4, 4–5mm
Petals	4, 7–9mm, base stalk-like
Stamens	6
Stigma	1, slightly 2-lobed
Ovary	1, 2-celled
	FRUIT
Type	1, pod-like, 4-angled, upright, tip beak-like, sides split away leaving seeds in 1 row
Size	12–20mm
Seeds	4–10, nearly globular

\ coarse, bristly plant with the ypically cross-shaped flowers of species of the Cabbage family. The fruits are listinctive, with a long, conical beak at he tip. Young leaves and buds can be eaten, or seeds used like mustard, but his plant is a pest to farmers in that it nfests fields and its seeds can survive or half a century. *Status:* probably native; throughout area. *Similar species:* White Mustard has fruits with a curved, flatter beak, up to eight seeds, and is grown for mustard and cress. Annual Wall-rocket has short-beaked ruits with many seeds in two rows.

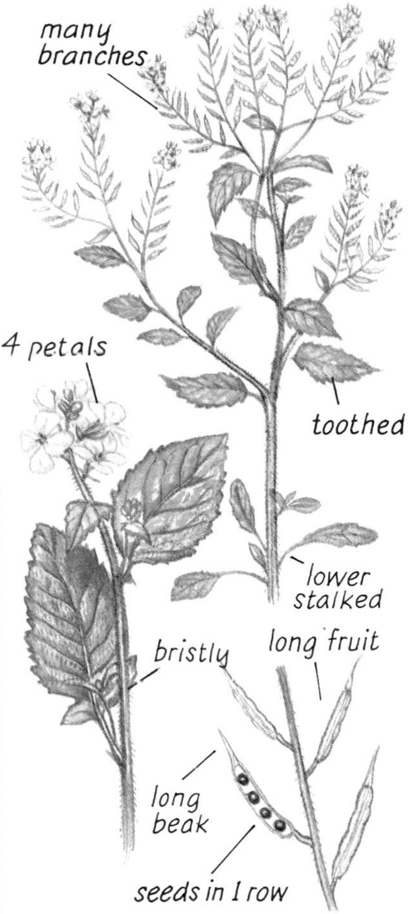

1 White Mustard *(S. alba)*; **2** Annual Wall-rocket *(Diplotaxis muralis)*

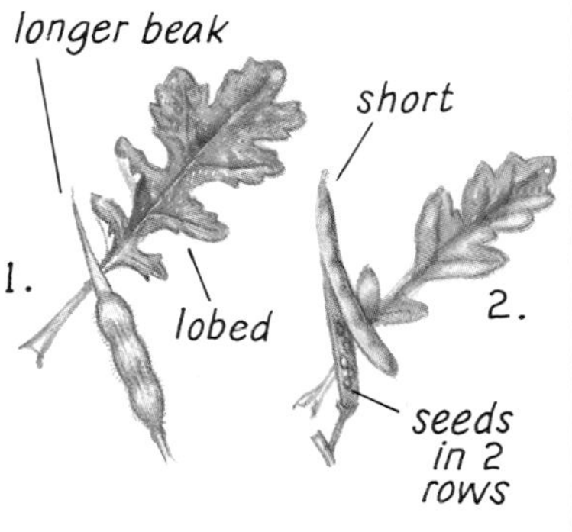

	CHARLOCK
Type	annual
Height	30–80cm
Habitat	arable land; especially lime-rich and clay soils
Flowering	May–July
	STEMS AND LEAVES
Stem	upright, usually branched
Root	slender tap-root
Hairs	stiffly hairy, sometimes hairless above
Stipules	absent
Leaves	scattered on stem, to 200mm; lower with few, small lobes and large, toothed lobe at tip; upper with edge coarsely toothed
Leaf-stalk	on lower leaves only

	FLOWERS
Position	numerous, elongated heads
Bracts	absent
Type	⚥
Size	12–17mm
Colour	bright yellow
Stalk	about equalling flower
Sepals	4, spreading apart
Petals	4, 9–12mm, base stalk-like
Stamens	6, 4 long, 2 short
Stigma	1, slightly 2-lobed
Ovary	1, 2-celled
	FRUIT
Type	1, pod-like, usually hairless, tip long, conical, beak-like, swollen sides split away, seeds in 1 row
Size	25–40mm
Seeds	8–24, *c*3mm, globular, reddish brown

Sea Rocket *Cakile maritima*

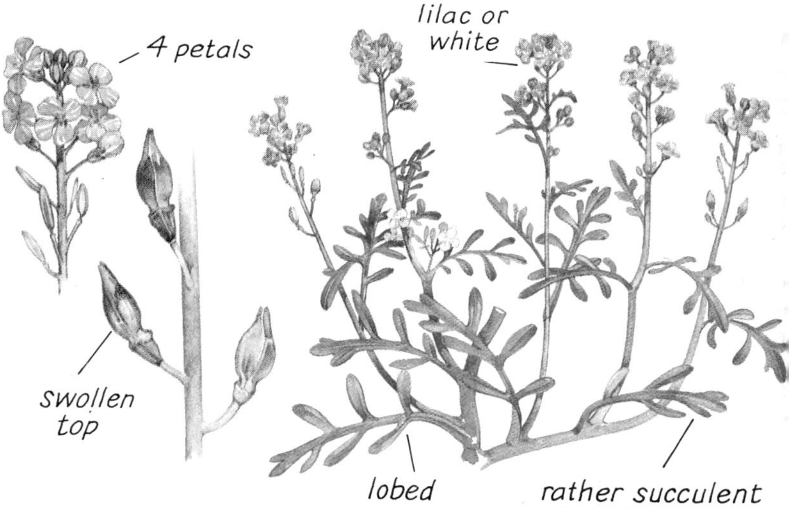

A common and distinctive plant of the drift-line of sandy or shingle sea-shores, usually with succulent, lobed leaves and lilac flowers. At the top of each short fruit is a corky-walled segment which breaks away with its single seed, to float in the sea while wind and tide carry it to some distant shore. *Status:* native; all round coasts. *Similar species:* several other species of the Cabbage family grow on the shore. Sea Stock has greyish, hairy, scarcely lobed leaves and slender fruits. Sea-kale has large, wavy-edged leaves and branched heads of pale flowers.

1 Sea Stock *(Matthiola sinuata)*; **2** Sea-kale *(Crambe maritima)*

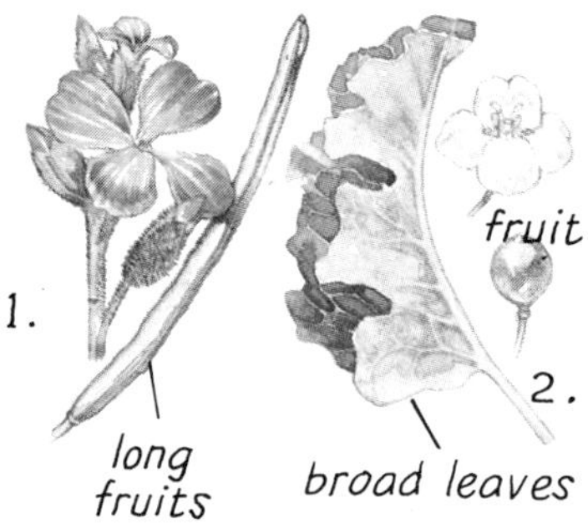

	SEA ROCKET
Type	annual
Height	15–45cm
Habitat	drift-lines of sand and shingle beaches
Flowering	June–August
	STEMS AND LEAVES
Stem	low-growing or angled upwards, branched
Root	slender tap-root
Hairs	absent
Stipules	absent
Leaves	spirally arranged, 30–60mm, lower mostly with oblong, rarely toothed lobes; upper with few or no lobes
Leaf-stalk	only on lower leaves
	FLOWERS
Position	numerous, crowded in short spike at branch-tip
Bracts	absent
Type	⚥
Size	8–12mm
Colour	purple, lilac or white
Stalk	about equalling flower
Sepals	4, 3–5mm, upright
Petals	4, 6–10mm, base stalk-like
Stamens	6
Stigma	1
Ovary	1, 2-celled
	FRUIT
Type	1, pod-like, not opening, upper part pointed, corky-walled, breaking off when ripe; lower part remains on plant
Size	10–25mm
Seeds	1–2, 4–5mm, smooth

\ bristly-leaved plant with variably ·oloured, cross-shaped flowers, but :ommonly pale yellow veined with lilac. 'he slender fruits are distinctive, being trongly constricted between the seeds. *Status:* mostly native, introduced in ıorth; common weed, throughout area. *Similar species:* Sea Radish is a coastal ·lant with more numerous, crowded eaflets and the short-beaked fruit has ·ven narrower sections between the eeds. The cultivated Radish is a related pecies which has the swollen, edible ap-root and fruits lacking constrictions ·etween the seeds.

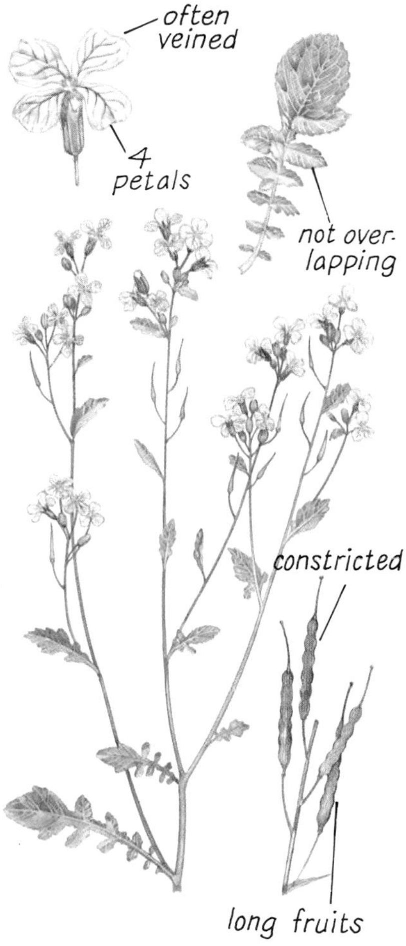

Sea Radish *(R. maritimus)*

WILD RADISH

Type annual
Height 20–60cm
Habitat arable fields, waste ground; mainly lime-free soil
Flowering May–September

STEMS AND LEAVES

Stem upright, hardly branched
Root slender, whitish tap-root
Hairs bristly throughout
Stipules absent
Leaves scattered on stem, lower with 1–4 pairs of wide-spaced lobes and large top lobe, edge toothed; upper smaller, lobed or toothed
Leaf-stalk present

FLOWERS

Position many, in head at stem-tip
Bracts absent
Type ⚥
Size 15–22mm
Colour yellow, lilac or white, most with darker veins
Stalk 10–50mm
Sepals 4, 5–10mm, upright
Petals 4, 12–20mm, base stalk-like
Stamens 6, 4 long, 2 short
Stigma 1
Ovary 1, 2-celled

FRUIT

Type 1, pod-like, narrowed between seeds, thick walls, tip narrow, seedless, beak-like, fruit breaks into 1-seeded segments
Size 30–90mm
Seeds 3–8, 1.5–3mm, rounded

Weld *Reseda luteola*

A tall, stiffly upright plant with slender spikes of greenish-yellow flowers above narrow, wavy-edged, dark green leaves. This is the plant for centuries used by dyers to produce a bright yellow dye, and Dyer's Rocket is an alternative common name. It is a relative of the Mignonette of gardens, grown for its scented flowers. *Status:* native; throughout area, but rarer in north and west. *Similar species:* Wild Mignonette is a smaller, branched plant with deeply lobed leaves. Corn Mignonette is similar but has white flowers and ripe fruits that hang down.

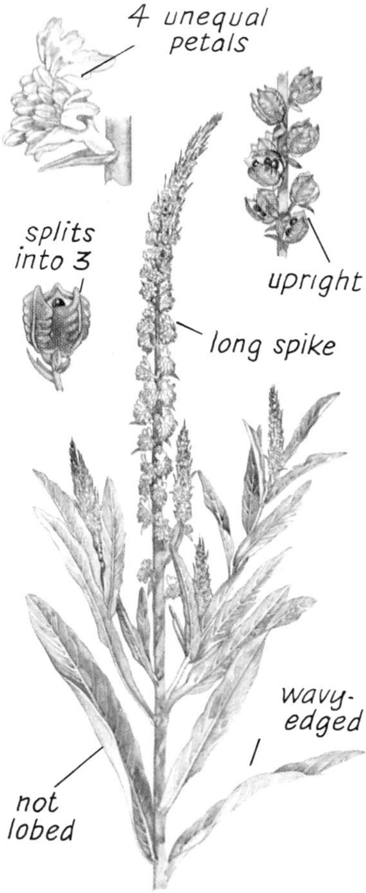

1 Wild Mignonette *(R. lutea)*; **2** Corn Mignonette *(R. phyteuma)*

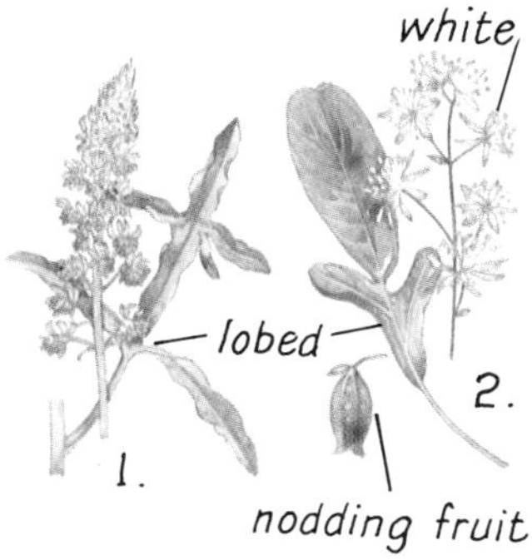

	WELD
Type	biennial
Height	50–150cm
Habitat	waste or arable ground, walls; often lime-rich soil
Flowering	June–August
	STEMS AND LEAVES
Stem	upright, ribbed, hollow, hardly branched
Root	tap-root
Hairs	more or less hairless
Stipules	with sticky hairs
Leaves	forming rosette in first year, lance-shaped, 25–120mm, edge unbroken, wavy, upper oblong, spirally arranged
Leaf-stalk	only on some upper leaves

	FLOWERS
Position	many in spike-like clusters
Bracts	present
Type	⚥
Size	4–5mm
Colour	yellowish-green
Stalk	*c*1mm
Sepals	4, remaining in fruit
Petals	3–5, mostly 4, front petal slender, others cut into 3 or more lobes
Stamens	20–25
Stigmas	3
Ovary	1, 1-celled
	FRUIT
Type	1, capsule, nearly globular, tip opens by 3 teeth
Size	5–6mm
Seeds	numerous, 0.8–1mm, black, smooth, glossy

A rosette of leaves fringed with hairs, each tipped with a glistening, sticky, red droplet identifies the Sundew. The hairs are capable of movement and, tentacle-like, curve round to embrace an insect trapped by the sticky droplets. An enzyme-rich fluid is secreted and the leaf digests the hapless insect. *Status:* native; scattered throughout area. *Similar species:* two other Sundews have elongated leaves: the Great Sundew, which has a long stalk bearing the flowers well above the leaves, and the Oblong-leaved Sundew, which has a much shorter stalk about equalling the leaves.

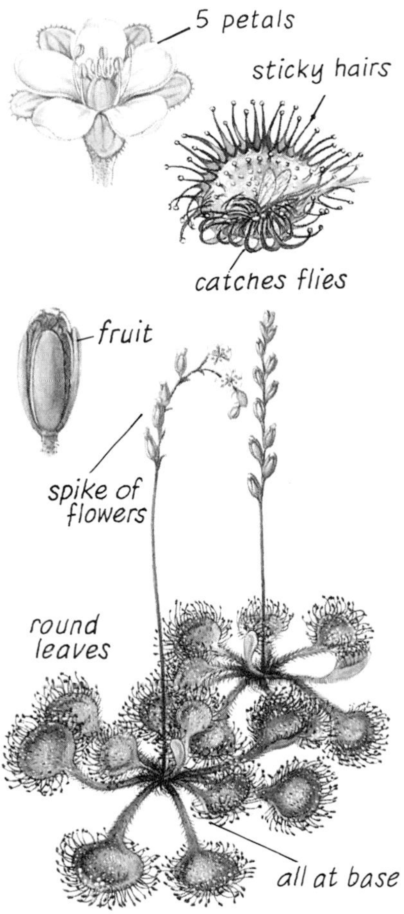

1 Great Sundew *(D. anglica)*;
2 Oblong-leaved Sundew *(D. intermedia)*

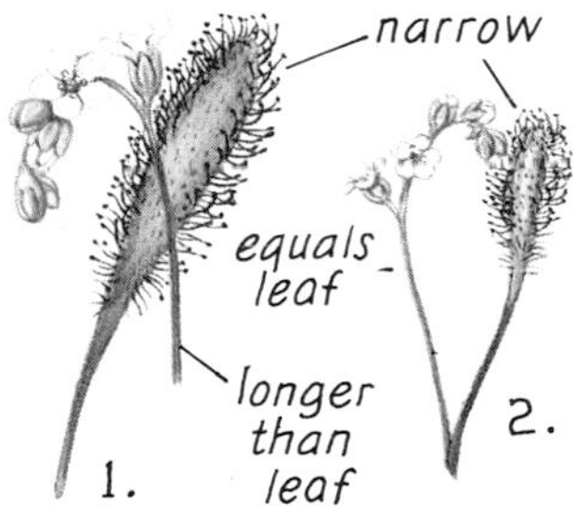

	ROUND-LEAVED SUNDEW
Type	perenial
Height	6–25cm
Habitat	bogs or by water on heaths and moors; acid soil
Flowering	June–August
	STEMS AND LEAVES
Stem	slender, mostly leafless
Root	fibrous
Hairs	on leaf-blades, gland-tipped, longest on edges
Stipules	fringed
Leaves	rosette at base, blade to 10mm, circular, nearly horizontal, edge unbroken, fringed with tentacle-like hairs
Leaf-stalk	15–30mm, hairy

	FLOWERS
Position	6–10, in curved, spike-like head
Bracts	absent
Type	⚥
Size	*c*5mm
Colour	white
Stalk	shorter than flower
Sepals	5, blunt, toothed
Petals	5, equal, oval, broadest above middle, tip blunt
Stamens	5
Stigmas	6, on 3 forked styles
Ovary	1, 1-celled
	FRUIT
Type	1, capsule, covered by remains of flower, splits to release seeds
Size	6–8mm
Seeds	many, long, slender, winged from both sides

Orpine *Sedum telephium*

A broad-leaved, succulent plant with rounded, dense heads of purple flowers. It is related to the 'Ice Plant' of gardens, and is similarly popular with bees. *Status:* native; scattered over much of area but rarer in the north. *Similar species:* Roseroot is a mountain plant with similar foliage but yellowish, 4-petalled flowers on male or female plants. Though with a very different shape of leaf, Navelwort has flowers and fruits of similar structure but with petals joined into a tube. It is common on walls and banks in the west.

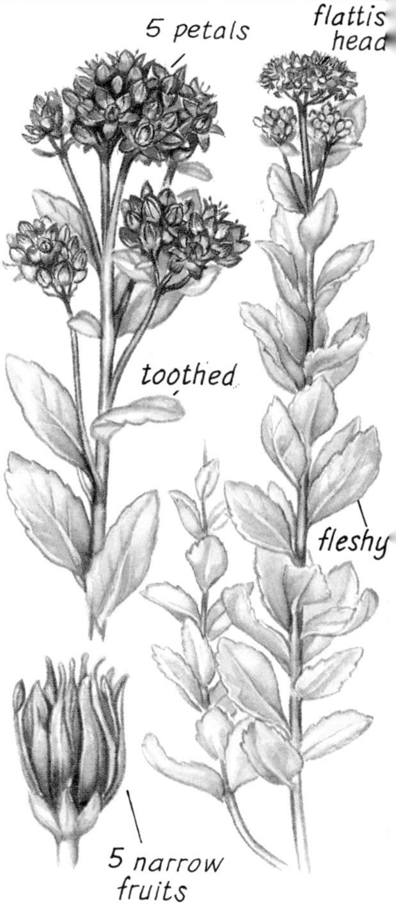

1 Roseroot *(Rhodiola rosea)*;
2 Navelwort *(Umbilicus rupestris)*

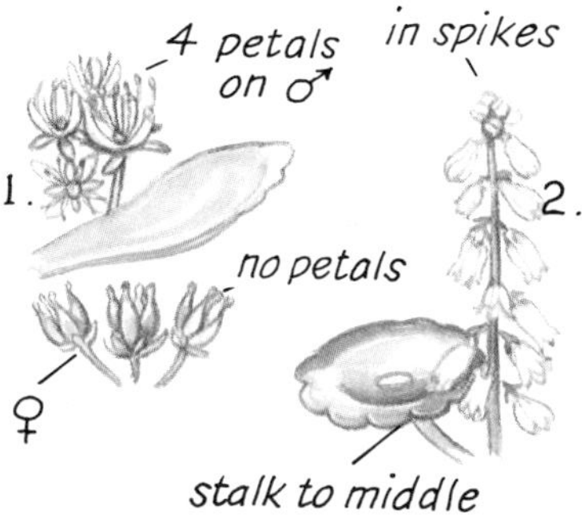

	ORPINE
Type	perennial
Height	20–60cm
Habitat	woods and hedgerows
Flowering	July–September
	STEMS AND LEAVES
Stem	upright, hardly branched, usually several
Root	stout, carrot-like tubers
Hairs	absent
Stipules	absent
Leaves	spirally placed on stem, 20–80mm, oval or oblong, bluish, often red-tinged, fleshy, blunt, toothed, base wedge-shaped or rounded
Leaf-stalk	mostly stalkless
	FLOWERS
Position	many, crowded in rounded head at tips of stems
Bracts	present
Type	⚥
Size	9–12mm
Colour	reddish purple
Stalk	shorter than flower
Sepals	5, shorter than petals, spear-shaped, pointed
Petals	5, 3–5mm, spear-shaped, pointed
Stamens	10
Stigmas	1 to each ovary
Ovaries	5, 1-celled
	FRUIT
Type	5, pod-like, upright, slender, splitting to release seeds
Size	5–7mm
Seeds	numerous, small, elongated

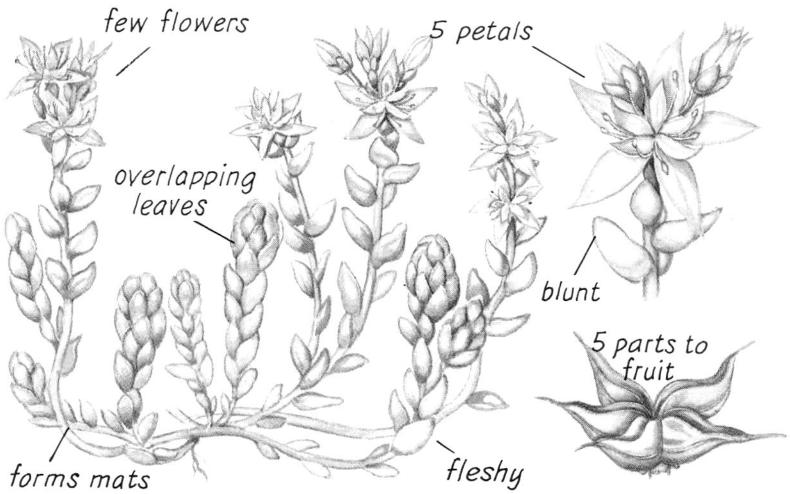

This dwarf, succulent plant of dry, sunny places, has small, overlapping leaves and short stems forming mats. It is common on walls, rocks, cindery edges of railway tracks, or even old roofs. The leaves are hot-tasting, hence the common name. *Status:* native; most of area except parts of north. *Similar species:* Reflexed Stonecrop is larger with longer, pointed leaves and flattish heads of yellow flowers. Two white-flowered species are English Stonecrop, which has tiny leaves and few flowers, and White Stonecrop, which has oblong leaves and broad heads of tiny flowers.

1 Reflexed Stonecrop *(S. reflexum)*; 2 English Stonecrop *(S. anglicum)*; 3 White Stonecrop *(S. album)*

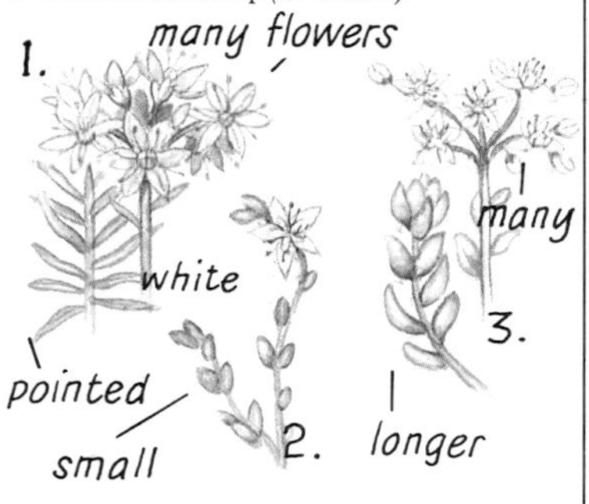

	BITING STONECROP
Type	perennial
Height	2–10cm
Habitat	dunes, shingle, dry grassy places, walls
Flowering	June–July
	STEMS AND LEAVES
Stem	creeping, numerous, forms mats, turning upwards
Root	fibrous
Hairs	absent
Stipules	absent
Leaves	spirally around stem, 3–5mm, nearly triangular, broad-based, thick, succulent, mostly overlapping, blunt, edge unbroken
Leaf-stalk	absent

	FLOWERS
Position	2–4 per branch, few branches near stem-tip
Bracts	present
Type	⚥
Size	*c*12mm
Colour	bright yellow
Stalk	nearly stalkless
Sepals	5, oval, blunt-tipped
Petals	5, 8–9mm, spear-shaped, pointed, spreading apart
Stamens	10
Stigmas	1 per ovary
Ovaries	5, 1-celled
	FRUIT
Type	5, pod-like, pointed, spread apart, top splits
Size	5–6mm
Seeds	many, *c*1mm, egg-shaped

Meadow Saxifrage *Saxifraga granulata*

A delightful meadow plant with snow-white flowers and lobed, kidney-shaped leaves. At the base are tiny bulb-like buds, which serve to propagate the plant. A double form is sometimes grown in gardens. *Status:* native; scattered localities, mainly east of area. *Similar species:* two mountain species are Starry Saxifrage, its rosettes of leaves found especially where water seeps over rocks, and Mossy Saxifrage, which forms moss-like cushions on rocks. Rue-leaved Saxifrage is a small annual plant of dry, mainly lowland places, its leaves often tinged with red.

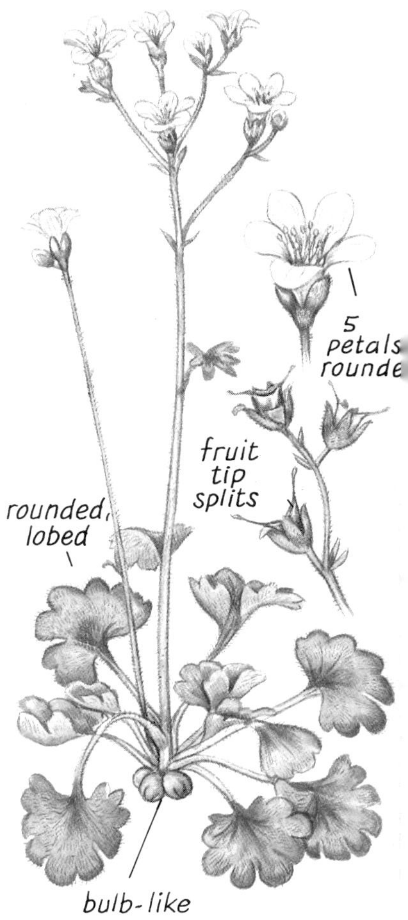

1 Starry Saxifrage *(S. stellaris)*;
2 Mossy Saxifrage *(S. hypnoides)*;
3 Rue-leaved Saxifrage *(S. tridactylites)*

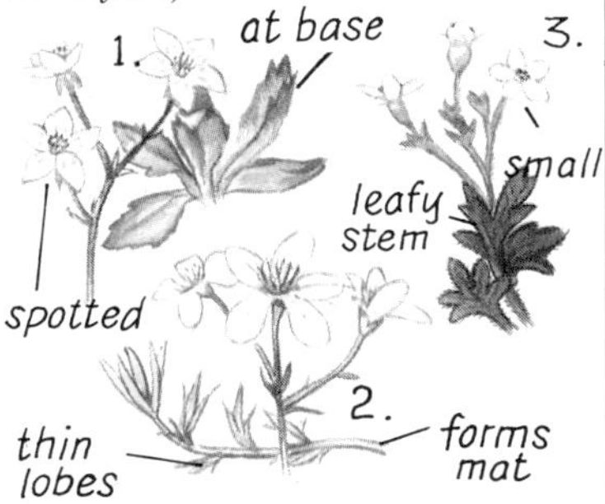

	MEADOW SAXIFRAGE
Type	perennial
Height	10–50cm
Habitat	dryish grassland; all but acid soils
Flowering	April–June
	STEMS AND LEAVES
Stem	single, upright
Root	fibrous, bulb-like buds from base of lowest leaves
Hairs	scattered, long, white, stickily hairy above
Stipules	absent
Leaves	rosette at base, few on stem, blade 5–30mm, most kidney-shaped, lobed; upper sharply toothed, base wedge-shaped
Leaf-stalk	longer than blade or short on stem-leaves

	FLOWERS
Position	2–12, in widely branched head at tip of stem
Bracts	small, slender
Type	⚥
Size	10–15mm
Colour	white
Stalk	4–20mm, stickily hairy
Sepals	5, oval, tip blunt
Petals	5, 10–17mm, oval
Stamens	10
Stigmas	2, on long styles
Ovary	1, 2-celled
	FRUIT
Type	1, capsule, egg-shaped, splits along upper edge
Size	6–8mm
Seeds	many, egg-shaped, rough

Chrysoplenium oppositifolium Opposite-leaved Golden-saxifrage

A plant of shady banks, among tree-roots or beneath boulders, brightening the gloom with a yellowish colour to the entire top of the plant. The rounded leaves are rather succulent, and are sometimes eaten in the mountains of north-eastern France. *Status:* native; common, most of area. *Similar species.* Alternate-leaved Golden-saxifrage differs in its creeping, underground, scaly stems, from which most of the kidney-shaped leaves arise. Most flowering stems have only a single leaf, but if there are more they are not paired.

Alternate-leaved Golden-saxifrage
(C. alternifolium)

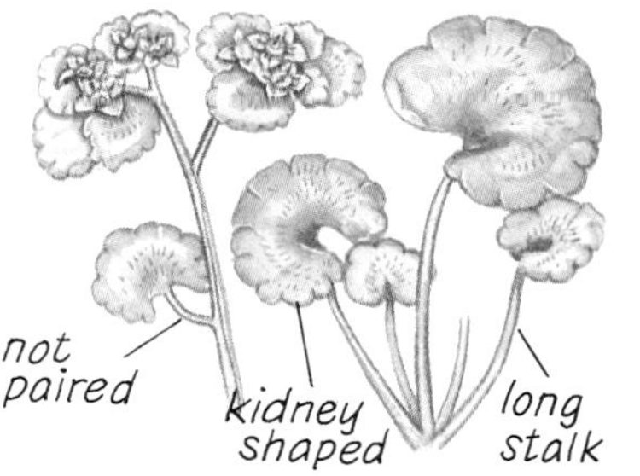

OPPOSITE-LEAVED GOLDEN-SAXIFRAGE

Type perennial
Height 5–15cm
Habitat wet, shady places, often by streams or springs
Flowering April–July

STEMS AND LEAVES

Stem low-growing, rooting, forming large patches, turning upwards to flower
Root fibrous
Hairs scattered, pressed close to lower leaves, upper leaves hairless
Stipules absent
Leaves paired on opposite sides of stem, 10–20mm, circular, blunt, edge unbroken or with shallow, rounded teeth, base square or broadly wedge-shaped
Leaf-stalk about equalling blade, upper shorter

FLOWERS

Position few, in flattish heads
Bracts leaf-like, greenish yellow
Type ⚥
Size 3–4mm
Colour greenish yellow
Stalk absent
Sepals 4–5, oval to triangular
Petals absent
Stamens 8
Stigmas 2, on separate styles
Ovary 1, 1-celled

FRUIT

Type 1, capsule, splits down centre
Size 5–6mm
Seeds many, blackish, rough

Grass-of-Parnassus *Parnassia palustris*

This beautiful, honey-scented, moorland flower is not at all grass-like but has long-stemmed, white, cup-shaped flowers, delicately veined with green, and a tuft of heart-shaped leaves. It was formerly found more widely on marshy ground, but its range has been restricted by drainage and 'improvement' of land. Five of the stamens have been transformed into special structures, fringed with glistening drops, which attract insects with the false promise of abundant nectar. These structures distinguish the species from those of the Saxifrage family, which otherwise have a rather similar structure to the flowers. Grass-of-Parnassus has been used in the past to treat liver and nervous complaints. *Status:* native; widespread but rather scattered, rarer in south. (There are no similar species.)

	GRASS-OF-PARNASSUS
Type	perennial
Height	10–30cm
Habitat	marshes and moors; wet ground
Flowering	July–October
	STEMS AND LEAVES
Stem	upright, straight
Root	short, upright stock
Hairs	hairless
Stipules	absent
Leaves	most basal, 10–50mm, heart-shaped, bluish green, often red-spotted beneath, sharpish, edge unbroken; 1 stem-leaf near base of flowering stem
Leaf-stalk	longer than blade, absent on stem-leaf
	FLOWERS
Position	single, on long stalk from base of single stem-leaf
Bracts	absent
Type	⚥
Size	15–30mm
Colour	white, grey-green veins
Stalk	much longer than flower
Sepals	5, spear-shaped
Petals	5, 7–12mm, equal, oval, tip notched
Stamens	5, with 5 modified stamens fringed with sticky drops
Stigmas	4, not stalked
Ovary	1, 1-celled except at base
	FRUIT
Type	1, capsule, egg-shaped, 4 grooves, splits into 4
Size	15–20mm
Seeds	many, 1.5–2mm, oblong

Often forming large clumps, especially in damp meadows, with frothy heads of creamy-white, sweetly scented flowers, Meadowsweet was formerly used as a sort of air-freshener, strewn on the floor of houses. The flowers were used to flavour mead and to make herbal teas. *Status:* native; common throughout the area. *Similar species:* Meadowsweet has twisted clusters of fruits, but the related Dropwort has straight fruits. This species – which is resident in drier, lime-rich soils – has more numerous, smaller leaflets and fewer, larger flowers in each head.

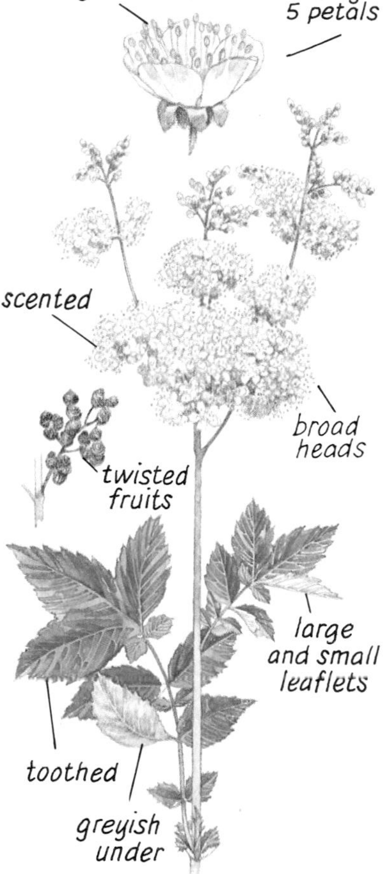

Dropwort *(F. vulgaris)*

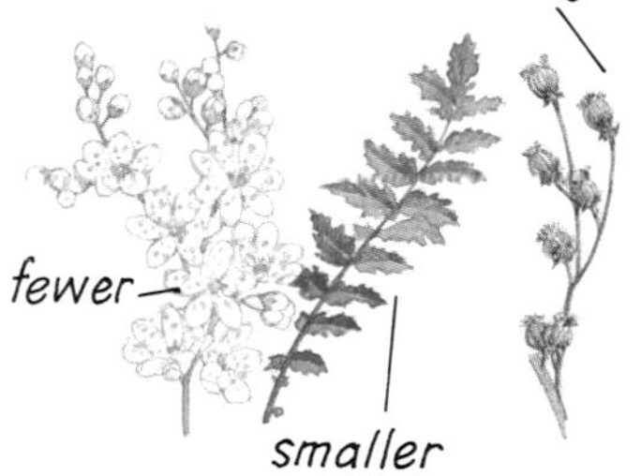

	MEADOWSWEET
Type	perennial
Height	60–120cm
Habitat	meadows, marshes, fens, by rivers, streams; wet ground
Flowering	June–September
	STEMS AND LEAVES
Stem	upright, scarcely branched
Root	fibrous from pink rhizome
Hairs	mostly hairless, dense grey hairs beneath leaves
Stipules	absent
Leaves	on alternate sides of stem, 300–600mm, up to 5 pairs of main leaflets, smaller leaflets between, 3-lobed leaflet at tip, dark green above, greyish below, pointed, coarse teeth with finer teeth
Leaf-stalk	present

	FLOWERS
Position	many, in branched heads
Bracts	absent
Type	⚥
Size	5–10mm
Colour	creamy white
Stalk	shorter than flower
Sepals	usually 5, triangular, bent back, downy
Petals	usually 5, 2–5mm, oval
Stamens	20–40
Stigmas	1 per ovary
Ovaries	6–10, 1-celled
	FRUIT
Type	6–10, not opening, twisted together spirally, hairless
Size	*c*2mm
Seeds	2 per fruit, not released

Cloudberry *Rubus chamaemorus*

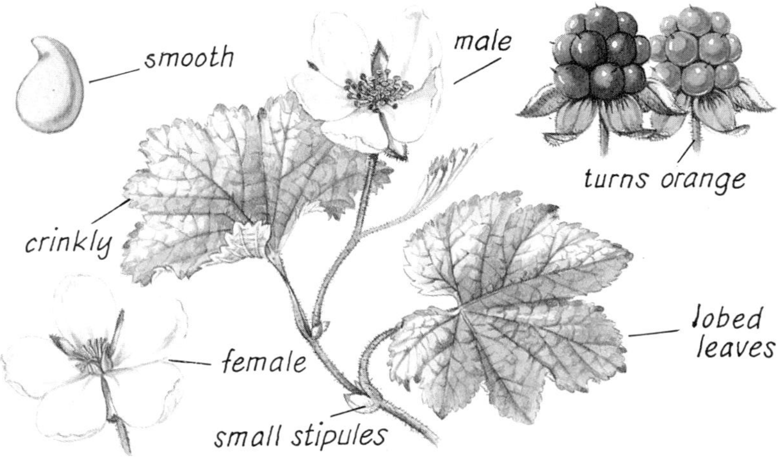

Cloudberry is a rather surprising plant, producing its succulent, raspberry-like fruits on short, herb-like stems near ground level instead of the shrubby growth normally associated with such fruits. The leaves are also unusual in that they have radiating lobes and a rather crinkly texture. *Status:* native; common in some mountain areas, absent from much of the south. *Similar species:* Stone Bramble is a plant of rocky places, usually in woodland shade, and differs from Cloudberry in having leaves divided into three leaflets and scarlet ripe fruits.

one Bramble *(R. saxatilis)*

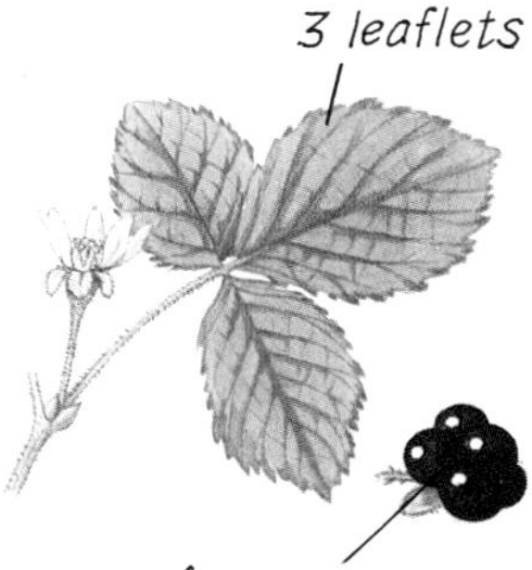

	CLOUDBERRY
Type	perennial
Height	5–20cm
Habitat	mountains, moors and bogs; damp ground
Flowering	June–August
	STEMS AND LEAVES
Stem	flowering stems upright, replaced each year
Root	long, creeping rhizome
Hairs	short
Stipules	oval, papery
Leaves	on alternate sides of stem, 15–80mm, few, rounded, with 5–7 triangular, blunt, toothed lobes, base heart-shaped
Leaf-stalk	10–70
	FLOWERS
Position	single, at stem-tip, ♂ and ♀ flowers on separate plants
Bracts	absent
Type 1	♂ with numerous stamens
Type 2	♀ with 1 stigma per ovary
Size	18–30mm
Colour	white
Stalk	present
Sepals	5, shorter than petals, oval, pointed
Petals	5, 8–15mm, oval, blunt
Ovaries	few, 1-celled
	FRUIT
Type	few, berry-like segments in a rounded cluster with middle attached when shed, turns red, then orange
Size	cluster 15–20mm
Seeds	1 per fruit, not released

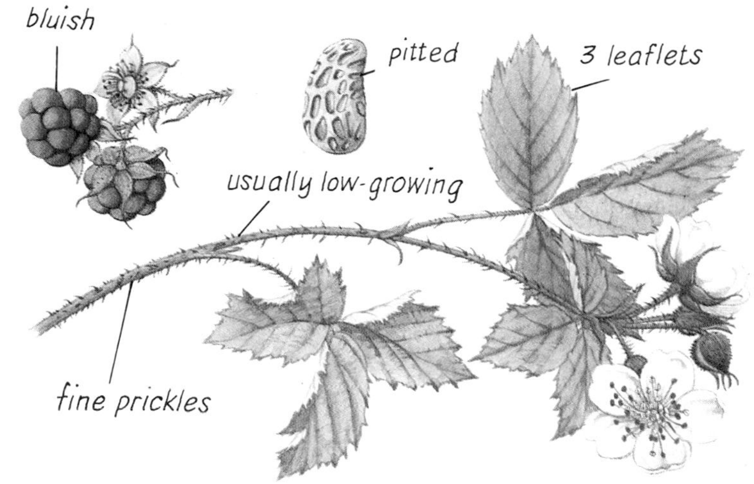

Commonly an understorey plant of woodland, it has low, arching, spiny stems, rooting at the tip, making hoop-like obstacles to trip up the unwary. This is one of the smaller Brambles, with few fruit-segments developing from each flower. *Status:* native; widespread, commonest in south. *Similar species:* Bramble is a name given to many species, differing in details of stem-angles, prickles, hairs or leaf-shape, and requiring considerable expertise for accurate identification. Raspberry differs by its paired leaflets and red fruits of which the centre usually stays on the plant.

1 Bramble *(R. fruticosus* agg.*)*;
2 Raspberry *(R. idaeus)*

	DEWBERRY
Type	perennial
Height	up to 45cm
Habitat	scrub, woodland, grassland; mostly lime-rich soil
Flowering	June–September
	STEMS AND LEAVES
Stem	arching, tip roots, not angled, sparsely prickly, waxy, lasts 2 years, flowers in second
Root	fibrous
Hairs	sparse, mainly above
Stipules	spear-shaped, on leaf-stalk
Leaves	scattered around stem, 3 oval or diamond-shaped, toothed or lobed leaflets
Leaf-stalk	present

	FLOWERS
Position	few, in branched head from stem-tip or leaf-base
Bracts	absent
Type	⚥
Size	20–25mm
Colour	white or pink-tinged
Stalk	slender, sparsely prickly
Sepals	5, long-pointed, white-edged
Petals	5, nearly circular, equal
Stamens	numerous
Stigmas	1 per ovary
Ovaries	2–5, rarely to 20, 1-celled
	FRUIT
Type	2–5, rarely to 20, berry-like parts, black, whitish, waxy covering; base stays with segments when shed
Size	8–18mm
Seeds	single, not released

Dog-rose *Rosa canina*

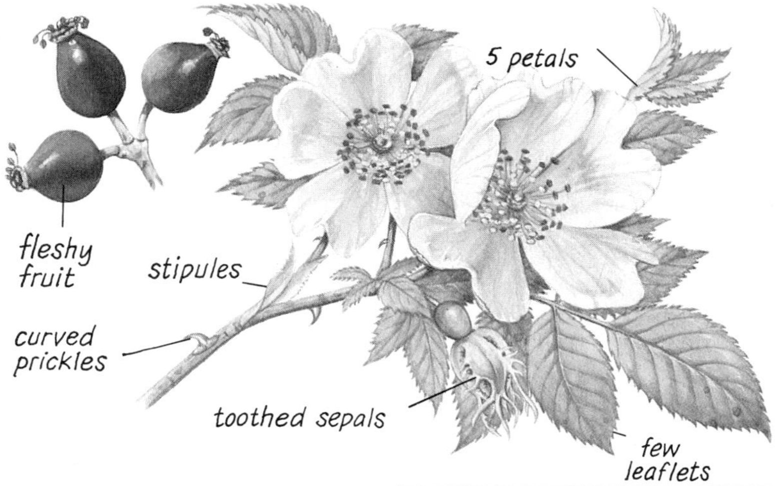

One of the most familiar of all wild flowers, abounding in hedgerows and adorning them with its delicately scented, shell-pink flowers. In the autumn, red, berry-like fruits or hips are attractive. Children are still given rose-hip syrup, which is rich in Vitamin C. *Status:* native; common through most of area but rarer in parts of north. *Similar species:* there are many forms and species of wild Rose. Harsh Downy-rose, which has hairy leaves and fruits, has straight prickles. Sweet-briar has sticky, apple-scented hairs beneath the leaves and the sepals stay on the ripening fruit.

1 Harsh Downy-rose *(R. tomentosa)*;
2 Sweet-briar *(R. rubiginosa)*

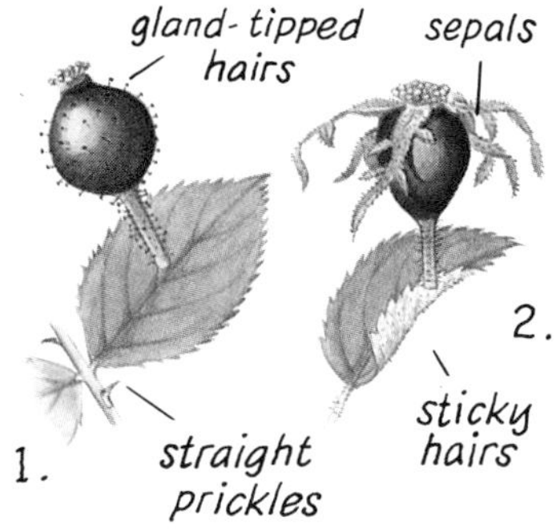

	DOG-ROSE
Type	perennial
Height	100–300cm
Habitat	woods, scrub, hedges
Flowering	June–July
	STEMS AND LEAVES
Stem	arching, with strongly curved or hooked prickles
Root	woody stock
Hairs	absent or sometimes short hairs beneath leaves
Stipules	long, broad, on leaf-stalk
Leaves	on alternate sides of stem, with 2–3 pairs of oval or elliptical, toothed leaflets, each 15–40mm
Leaf-stalk	present

	FLOWERS
Position	1–4, at ends of stems
Bracts	broad
Type	⚥
Size	15–25mm, rarely 50mm
Colour	pink or white
Stalk	5–20mm
Sepals	5, lobed, bent back, falling in fruit
Petals	5, 20–25mm
Stamens	numerous
Stigmas	many in conical head
Ovaries	numerous, 1-celled
	FRUIT
Type	1, berry-like, egg-shaped or ellipsoidal, outer layer formed from flower-base, contains nut-like fruits, scarlet, smooth
Size	10–20mm
Seeds	1 to each nut-like fruit, not released

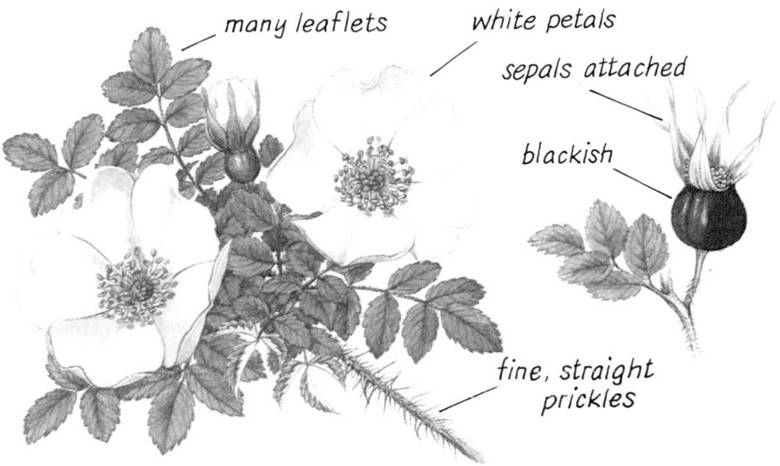

This dainty little Rose is most common near the sea, spreading by suckers to cover large areas on old dunes and heaths. The plant is easily recognized: the fruits are almost black, instead of the red of other species. The leaves have small, toothed leaflets and resemble those of Salad Burnet or Burnet Saxifrage. *Status:* native; absent from extreme north, most common by coast. *Similar species:* Field-rose is a more robust white-flowered species, and has larger, broader leaflets up to 20mm across and styles joined forming a beak-like tip to the fruit.

Field-rose *(R. arvensis)*

	BURNET ROSE
Type	shrub
Height	10–40mm, rarely 100mm
Habitat	mainly coastal, dunes, heaths, or on limestone
Flowering	May–July
	STEMS AND LEAVES
Stem	upright, with many straight prickles or bristles
Root	from creeping underground stems
Hairs	more or less absent
Stipules	narrow, lobed at tip
Leaves	on alternate sides of stem, 3–5 pairs of leaflets, leaflet at tip, each 5–20mm, oval to circular, blunt, edge toothed
Leaf-stalk	absent

	FLOWERS
Position	single, at tip of stem
Bracts	absent
Type	⚥
Size	20–40mm
Colour	creamy white, rarely pink
Stalk	15–25mm
Sepals	5, 10–18mm, narrow, not toothed
Petals	5, 10–20mm, rarely 25mm, broad, notched
Stamens	numerous
Stigmas	1 per ovary, forming rounded head
Ovaries	numerous, 1-celled
	FRUIT
Type	single, globular, blackish, leathery or scarcely fleshy
Size	10–15mm
Seeds	not released

Agrimony *Agrimonia eupatoria*

A stiffly upright plant, with slender spikes of yellow flowers and rather coarse leaves with leaflets of varying size. The nodding fruits have a ring of hooked spines, which may catch in an animal's fur, thus effecting dispersal. Agrimony once had many uses, including as an antidote for snake-bite and to give relief from colds, in the form of a wine with oranges, lemons, and ginger. *Status:* native; most of area except parts of north. *Similar species:* Fragrant Agrimony is rarer, more robust, and has sweetly scented flowers; the lowest spines of the fruit are bent backwards.

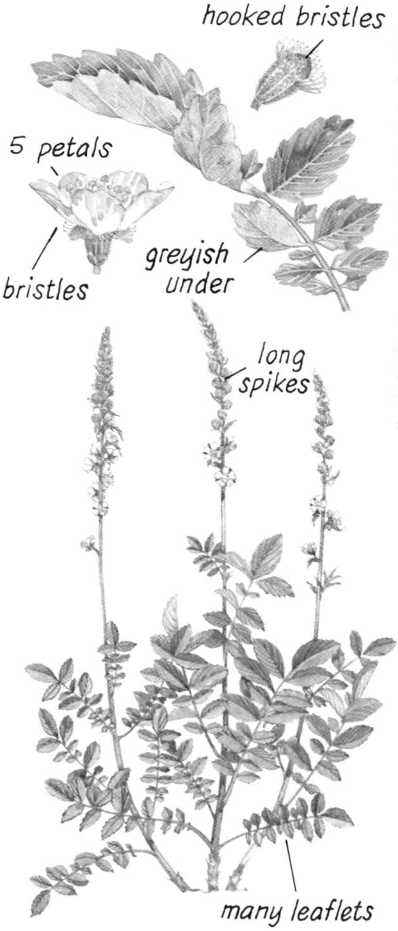

Fragrant Agrimony *(A. procera)*

	AGRIMONY
Type	perennial
Height	30–60cm
Habitat	grassy places, hedgebanks, fields and road-verges
Flowering	June–August
	STEMS AND LEAVES
Stem	upright, mostly unbranched
Root	rhizome
Hairs	gland-tipped on stems, grey-woolly beneath leaves
Stipules	leaf-like
Leaves	on alternate sides of stem, most near base, 3–6 main pairs of elliptical, coarse-toothed leaflets, 20–60mm long, small leaflets between, leaflet at tip; upper leaves with few leaflets
Leaf-stalk	short

	FLOWERS
Position	many, in spike at stem-tip
Bracts	present, lower 3-lobed
Type	⚥
Size	5–8mm
Colour	golden yellow
Stalk	1–3mm, shorter than flower
Sepals	5, oval, pointed
Petals	5, oval
Stamens	10–20
Stigmas	1 per ovary
Ovaries	1–2, 1-celled
	FRUIT
Type	single, conical, hard wall encloses 1–2 nut-like fruits, grooved, ring of hooked spines near top
Size	6–7mm
Seeds	not released

A tall plant with long, bare stalks ending in mahogany-red, oblong heads of petal-less flowers with tassel-like stamens. Its leaves were used to staunch bleeding. *Status:* native; common, throughout area except for parts of north. *Similar species:* Salad Burnet is smaller, with rounder heads. Its cucumber-flavoured leaves were used in salads or cooling drinks. Pirri-pirri-bur and related plants, naturalized in Britain and Ireland, arrived from New Zealand and Australia in wool waste or as garden plants. Barbed spines on the fruit stick to fur or wool.

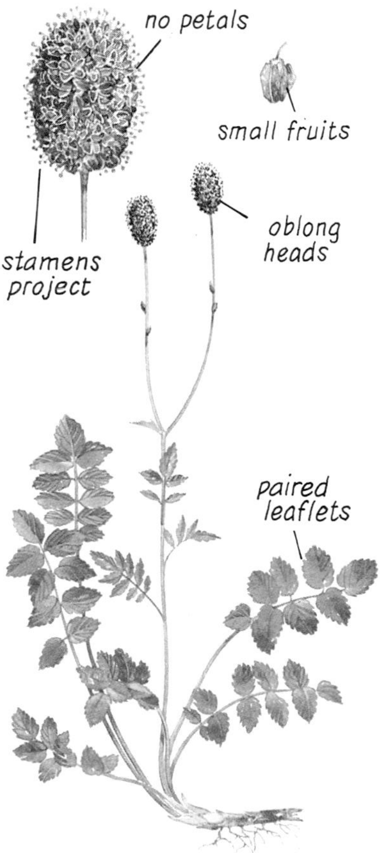

1 Salad Burnet *(S. minor)*; 2 Pirri-pirri-bur *(Acaena novae-zelandiae)*

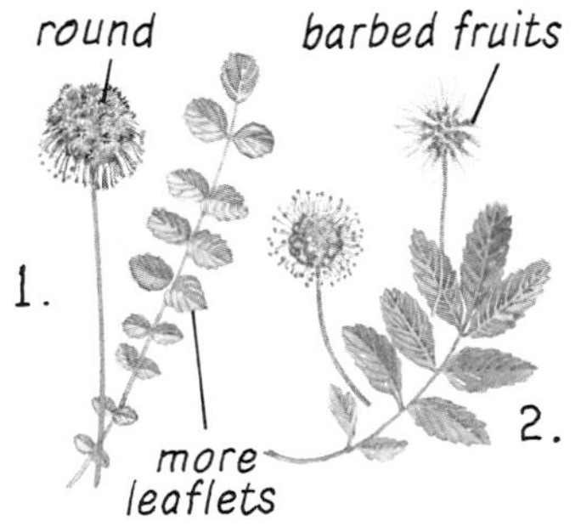

	GREAT BURNET
Type	perennial
Height	30–100cm
Habitat	grassy places; damp soils
Flowering	June–September
	STEMS AND LEAVES
Stem	upright, branched above
Root	thick rootstock
Hairs	absent
Stipules	lower papery, upper like leaflets, toothed
Leaves	on alternate sides of stem, lower with 3–7 pairs of oval or oblong leaflets, leaflet at tip, each 20–40mm, blunt, edge toothed, base heart-shaped; upper few, smaller
Leaf-stalk	present
	FLOWERS
Position	10–20 in oblong head, 10–30mm long, from stem-tip
Bracts	2–3 beneath each flower
Type	⚥
Size	4–5mm
Colour	dull purplish red
Stalk	absent
Sepals	4, *c*3mm, coloured
Petals	absent
Stamens	4, long, crimson
Stigmas	1 per flower
Ovary	1, 1-celled
	FRUIT
Type	10–20 in head, nut-like, 4-winged, not opening, each encloses single seed
Size	*c*4mm
Seeds	1, not released

Mountain Avens *Dryas octopetala*

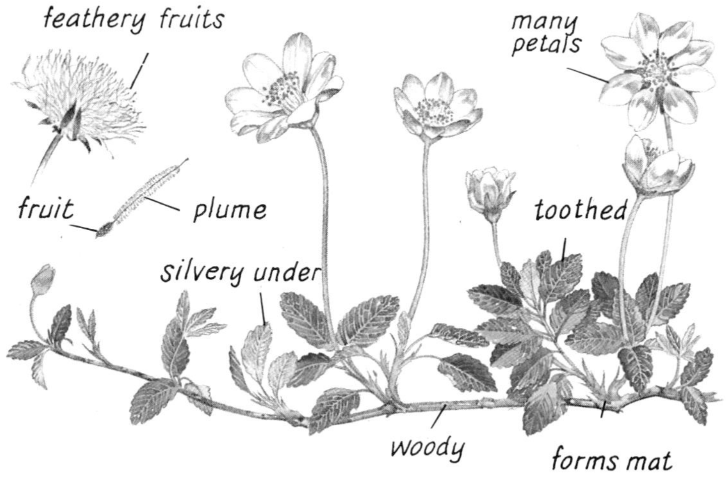

Wiry stems of Mountain Avens support a tough mat of dark green foliage which carpets rocky places or hangs down cliffs. In Summer it is dotted with anemone-like flowers of white petals encircling a boss of golden stamens. Later, it has feathery, plumed fruits like those of the distantly related Pasqueflower and Traveller's Joy. A mountain plant in the south of the area, it is found by the Atlantic shore in the north-west. This is mainly an Arctic plant, elsewhere being a relict from the last Ice Age when it covered large expanses south of the ice-sheet. Mountain Avens is often cultivated as a rockery plant in gardens, and is propagated by layering young shoots or from seed. Uses for the plant include infusion as a stomach tonic and a gargle to treat infections of the mouth and throat. *Status:* native; mountains towards south, more common at low altitudes towards Arctic. (There are no similar species.)

	MOUNTAIN AVENS
Type	perennial
Height	low-growing
Habitat	rock crevices, mountain ledges, sometimes near sea-level; base-rich rocks
Flowering	June–July
	STEMS AND LEAVES
Stem	up to 50cm long, woody, twisted, much-branched
Root	creeping
Hairs	dense, white beneath leaves, hairless above, flower-stalks and sepals with gland-tipped hairs
Stipules	papery, brownish
Leaves	on alternate sides of stem, 5–40mm, oblong or oval, evergreen, blunt, toothed, base squarish
Leaf-stalk	present
	FLOWERS
Position	single, from base of leaf
Bracts	absent
Type	⚥
Size	25–40mm
Colour	white
Stalk	20–80mm, upright
Sepals	7–10, oblong
Petals	8–16, 7–17mm, oblong
Stamens	numerous
Stigmas	1 per ovary
Ovaries	numerous
	FRUIT
Type	numerous in cluster, nut-like at base, with long, feathery, whitish plume
Size	20–30mm
Seeds	not released

Shady places are home to the small yellow, upturned flowers and hooked, animal-dispersed fruits of Wood Avens. In gardens it is awkward to remove because the brittle stems snap, leaving the roots. Faintly clove-scented, the roots were once used to flavour ale or as an insect-repellent. *Status:* native; most of area except parts of north. *Similar species:* Water Avens, in wet places, has larger, nodding, orange-pink flowers. Hybrid Avens grows near Wood Avens, with intermediate but often very variable flowers. Marsh Cinquefoil has reddish sepals and slender, purple petals.

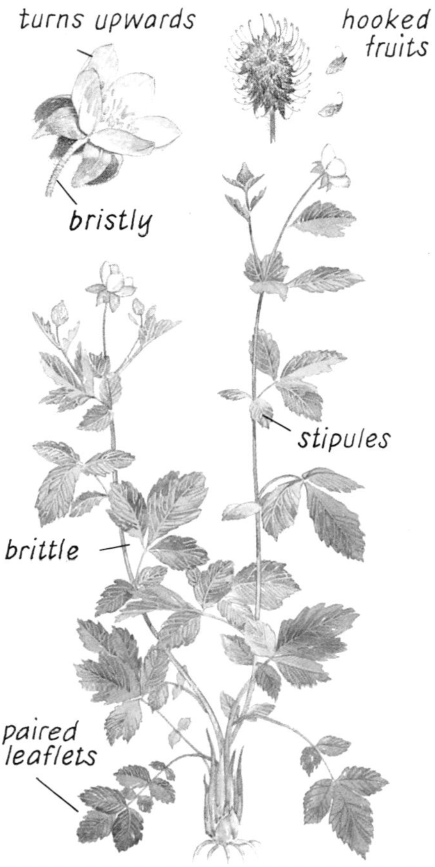

1 Water Avens *(G. rivale)*; **2** Hybrid Avens *(G. × intermedium)*; **3** Marsh Cinquefoil *(Potentilla palustris)*

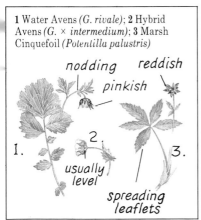

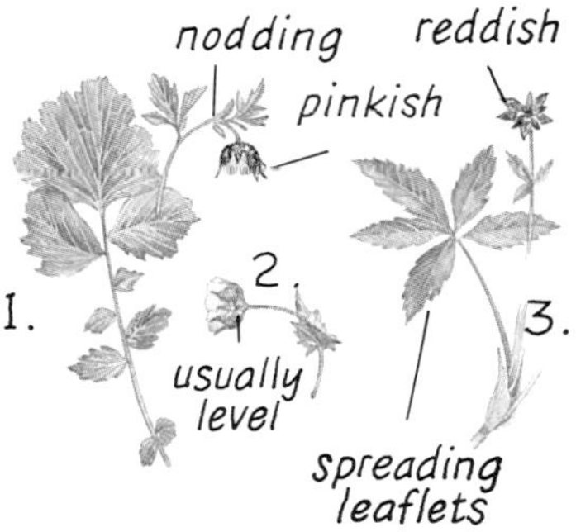

	WOOD AVENS
Type	perennial
Height	20–60cm
Habitat	shady places, woods, hedges; damp, rich soils
Flowering	June–August
	STEMS AND LEAVES
Stem	mostly upright, brittle
Root	fibrous from short stock
Hairs	short, rather bristly
Stipules	lower as row of bristles; upper toothed, leaflet-like
Leaves	basal or on alternate sides of stem; lower with 2–4 unequal pairs of leaflets, leaflet at tip, each 5–80mm, blunt, toothed, base wedge-shaped; upper with 3 leaflets or lobes
Leaf-stalk	present
	FLOWERS
Position	2–5, in wide-branched heads
Bracts	present
Type	⚥
Size	10–15mm
Colour	yellow
Stalk	longer than flower, upright
Sepals	5, oval, pointed
Petals	5, 5–9mm, oval, blunt
Stamens	numerous
Stigmas	1 per ovary
Ovaries	numerous, 1-celled
	FRUIT
Type	numerous in small head, nut-like, egg-shaped, tip hooked
Size	3–6mm
Seeds	not released

Tormentil *Potentilla erecta*

Four-petalled, buttercup-like flowers of Tormentil are a common sight on heaths or other grassy places. Its dried roots have many uses including treating mouth infections or sunburn, and provide a red dye. Tormentil is a larval food of the Grizzled Skipper butterfly. *Status:* native; common, throughout area. *Similar species:* stems of Creeping Cinquefoil run along the ground, regularly sending up long-stalked leaves and single flowers. Silverweed grows in the same way but its numerous, paired leaflets are silvery beneath. The silvery leaves of Hoary Cinquefoil look more like those of Tormentil.

1 Creeping Cinquefoil *(P. reptans)*; **2** Silverweed *(P. anserina)*; **3** Hoary Cinquefoil *(P. argentea)*

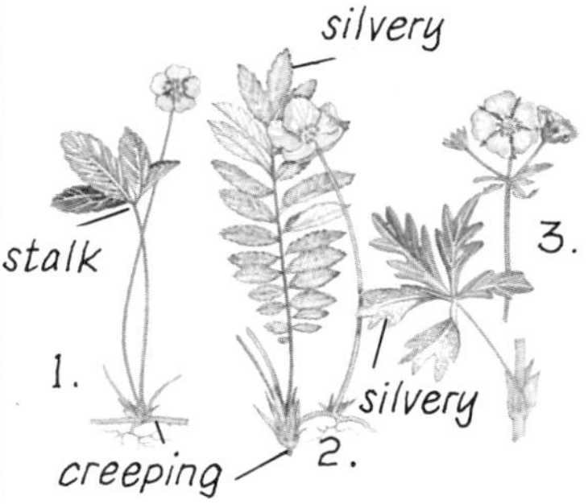

	TORMENTIL
Type	perennial
Height	10–30cm, rarely 50cm
Habitat	grassland, heaths, wood clearing; mainly acid soil
Flowering	June–September

	STEMS AND LEAVES
Stem	low-growing to nearly upright, slender, branched
Root	thick, woody stock
Hairs	short, pressed to surface
Stipules	like leaflets, lobed
Leaves	basal or on alternate sides of stem, with 3 or rarely 5 leaflets; lower 5–10mm, blunt, toothed; upper 10–20mm, narrower, lobed or toothed above
Leaf-stalk	long below, absent above

	FLOWERS
Position	numerous in branched head
Bracts	leaf-like, upper undivided
Type	⚥
Size	7–15mm
Colour	yellow
Stalk	much longer than flower
Sepals	4, 3–5mm, spear-shaped, pointed, surrounded by bract-like structures
Petals	4, 3–6mm, tip notched
Stamens	14–20
Stigmas	1 per ovary
Ovaries	4–8, rarely to 20, 1-celled
	FRUIT
Type	mostly 4–8 in rounded head, nut-like, egg-shaped, rough
Size	*c*2mm
Seeds	not released

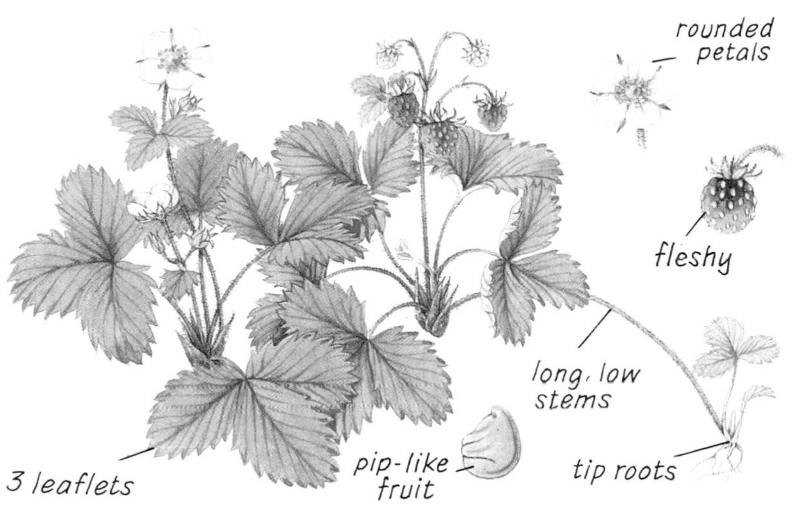

Like a diminutive version of the Garden Strawberry, the fruits of the Wild Strawberry are less succulent but full of flavour. Plants spread by low, arching stems called runners. The fleshy part of a Strawberry is derived from the swollen base of the flower, the fruits proper being the yellowish pips on the surface. *Status:* native; common throughout area. *Similar species:* Hautbois Strawberry, mainly from the east of the area, is larger and has fruits devoid of pips at the base. Garden Strawberry is commonly naturalized. Barren Strawberry lacks the fleshy base to the nut-like fruits.

1 Hautbois Strawberry *(F. moschata)*; **2** Garden Strawberry *(F. × ananassa)*; **3** Barren Strawberry *(Potentilla sterilis)*

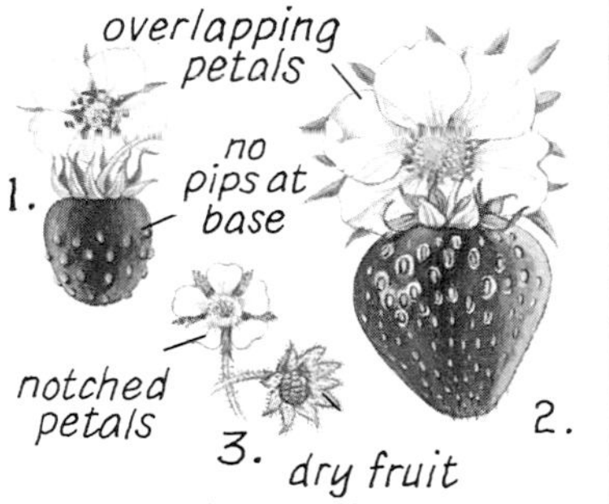

	WILD STRAWBERRY
Type	perennial
Height	5–30cm
Habitat	shady places, woods, hedgerows, grassland; mainly lime-rich soils
Flowering	April–July
	STEMS AND LEAVES
Stem	nearly upright or low, arching and rooting
Root	thick, woody stock
Hairs	spreading out on stem, silky under leaves
Stipules	papery, often purplish
Leaves	basal or on alternate sides of stem, with 3 leaflets, each 10–60mm, oval, blunt, toothed
Leaf-stalk	long

	FLOWERS
Position	few, in branched head
Bracts	leaf-like, upper undivided
Type	⚥
Size	12–18mm
Colour	white
Stalk	longer than flower
Sepals	5, 3–6mm, oval, pointed, bent back in fruit, 5 extra bract-like parts
Petals	5, 5–7mm, oval, blunt
Stamens	*c*20
Stigmas	1 per ovary
Ovaries	numerous, 1-celled
	FRUIT
Type	egg-shaped or spherical, red, juicy base, mainly tiny, nut-like fruits on surface
Size	10–20mm
Seeds	1 per fruit, not released

Hairy Lady's-mantle *Alchemilla filicaulis* subsp. *vestita*

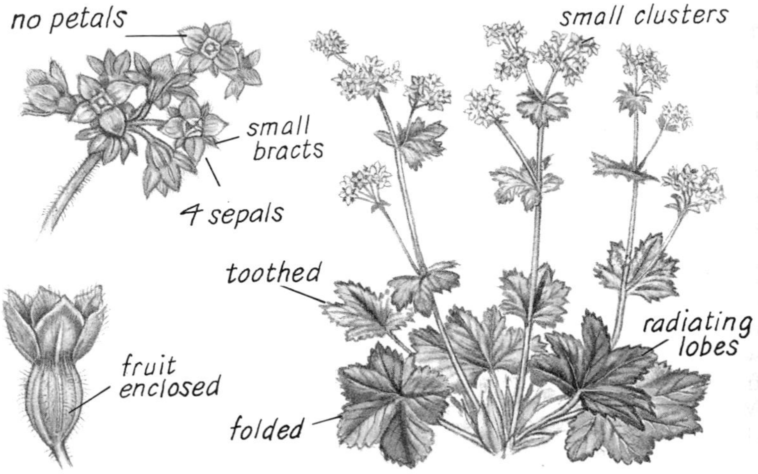

Although its flowers are inconspicuous, the broad leaves of this plant are lobed with fan-like folds, for which it is often grown in gardens. Water-droplets are exuded by the leaves when the air humidity is high, usually before the morning sun touches them. *Status:* native; most of area but rarer in south. *Similar species:* one of the more distinct of many related species is Alpine Lady's-mantle, its narrowly lobed leaves silvery beneath. Parsley-piert is a much smaller, annual plant of waste or cultivated ground. Sibbaldia has leaves cut into leaflets and usually has narrow, yellow petals.

1 Alpine Lady's-mantle *(A. alpina)*;
2 Parsley-piert *(Aphanes arvensis)*;
3 Sibbaldia *(Sibbaldia procumbens)*

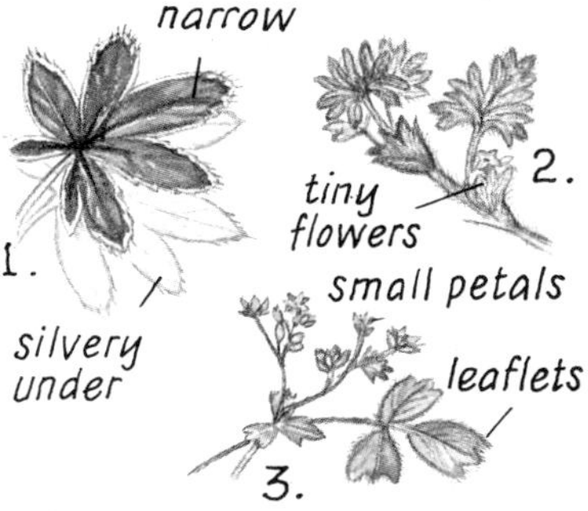

	HAIRY LADY'S-MANTLE
Type	perennial
Height	5–45cm
Habitat	open woods, rock-ledges, grassland; damp lime-rich or neutral soil
Flowering	June–September
	STEMS AND LEAVES
Stem	turning or angled upwards
Root	thick, woody stock
Hairs	rather dense, projecting
Stipules	papery, often purple-tinged
Leaves	basal or few on alternate sides of stem; lower 10–150mm, circular or kidney-shaped with 7–9 toothed lobes, notch between lobes wide; upper smaller, with fewer lobes
Leaf-stalk	long below, short above

	FLOWERS
Position	in small clusters on near stem-tips
Bracts	leaf-like, toothed
Type	⚥
Size	3–4mm
Colour	green
Stalk	shorter than flower
Sepals	4, oval, broad-based
Petals	absent
Stamens	4, between sepals
Stigma	1, club-shaped
Ovary	1, 1-celled
	FRUIT
Type	1, nut-like, enclosed by base of flower, not opening
Size	2–3mm
Seeds	1, not released

These bushy plants form such large colonies by the sea that they appear to be a long-established native species. But they and most other Lupins have been introduced recently from North America. Seeds are flung from the explosive seed pods which, on a hot day, sound like the rattle of gunfire. *Status:* introduced; coastal areas of Britain and Ireland. *Similar species:* Garden Lupin and its hybrids are often found by roads or railways. Stems bear blue, pink or white flowers and die back after fruiting. Sweet Lupin is a Mediterranean annual, naturalized in the south of the area.

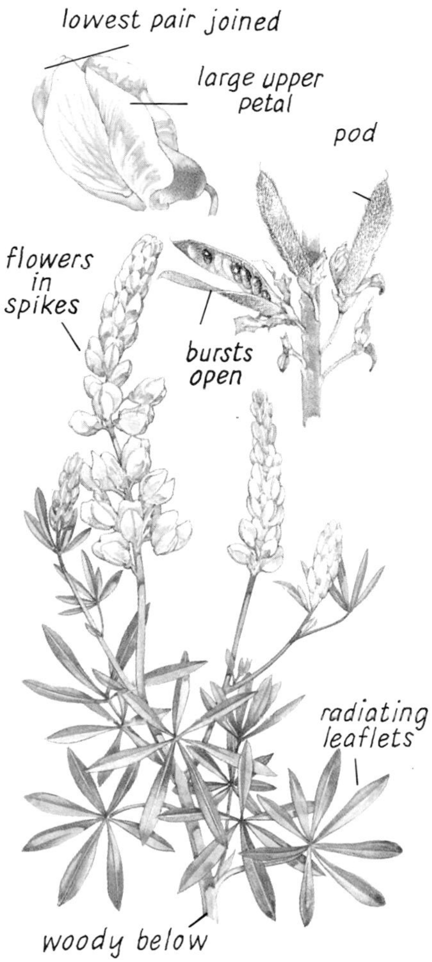

1 Garden Lupin *(L. polyphyllus)*;
2 Sweet Lupin *(L. luteus)*

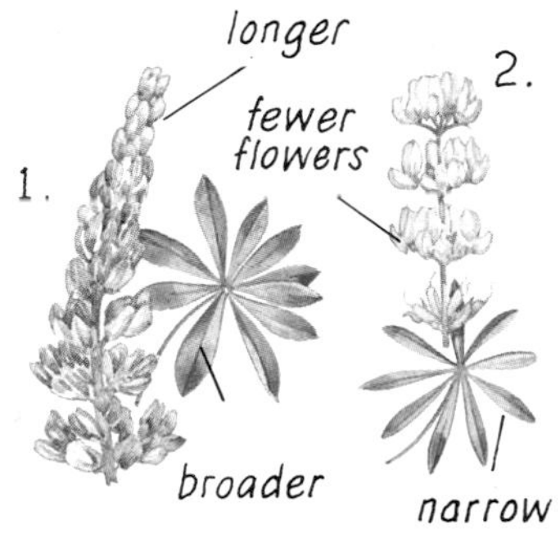

	TREE LUPIN
Type	shrub
Height	up to 300cm
Habitat	shingle banks, waste ground
Flowering	June–September
	STEMS AND LEAVES
Stem	much-branched, woody below
Root	fibrous from stout stock
Hairs	leaves hairless above, silky below
Stipules	joined to leaf-stalk
Leaves	on alternate sides of stem, 7–11 radiating, spear-shaped leaflets, each 20–60mm, pointed
Leaf-stalk	about equalling leaflets
	FLOWERS
Position	numerous, spirally arranged in spike at stem-tip, stalk of spike 4–10cm
Bracts	absent
Type	⚥, scented
Size	14–17mm
Colour	yellow, rarely white or tinged with blue
Stalk	shorter than flower
Sepals	joined into 2-lipped tube
Petals	5, 14–17mm, lowest pair joined, overlapped by 2 side petals, upper largest
Stamens	10, joined at base
Stigma	1, on curved style
Ovary	1, 1-celled
	FRUIT
Type	1, pod, hairy, splits open, flicks seeds out
Size	*c*80mm
Seeds	8–12, 4–5mm, ellipsoidal

Tufted Vetch *Vicia cracca*

An elegant plant, climbing high through tall grass or hedgerow by means of branched tendrils at the tips of ladder-like leaves. The slender spires of small pea-flowers open a rather pale purple but fade deep violet-blue. *Status:* native; common, throughout area. *Similar species:* Bush Vetch is less robust, and has smaller, short-stalked spikes of duller purple flowers. Two related species frequent wooded or rocky places: Wood Vetch has fewer, larger flowers and toothed stipules; Wood Bitter-vetch lacks a tendril at the leaf-tip.

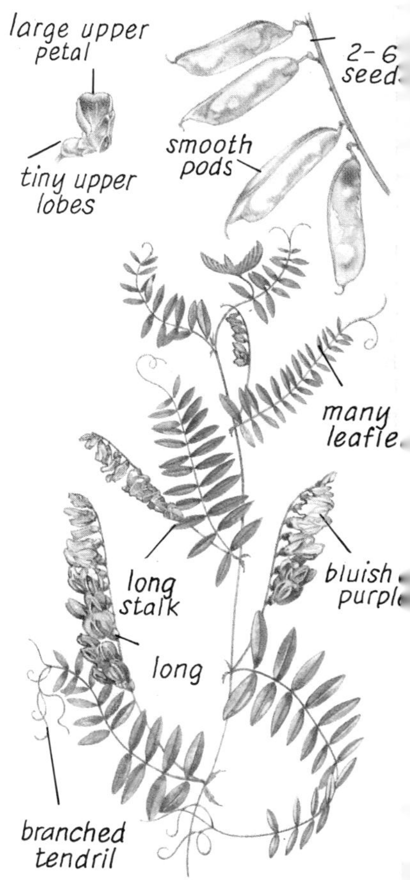

1 Bush Vetch *(V. sepium)*; **2** Wood Vetch *(V. sylvatica)*; **3** Wood Bitter-vetch *(V. orobus)*

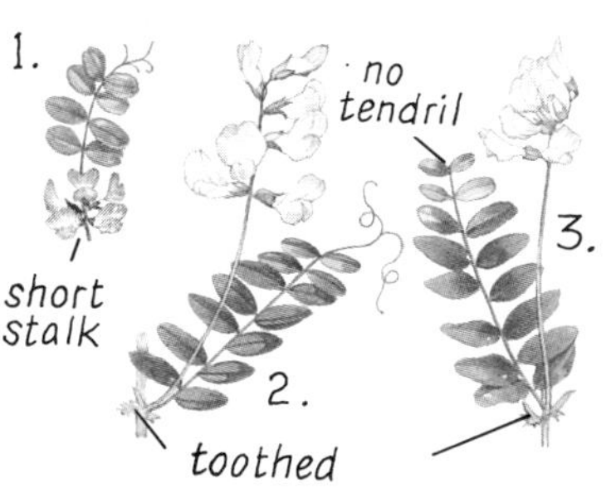

	TUFTED VETCH
Type	perennial
Height	60–200cm
Habitat	among grass or bushes
Flowering	June–August
	STEMS AND LEAVES
Stem	climbing by tendrils
Root	fibrous, with tiny nodules
Hairs	pressed close against leaves or absent
Stipules	half arrow-shaped, not toothed
Leaves	on alternate sides of stem, branched tendril at tip, 6–15 pairs of leaflets, each 5–30mm, spear-shaped, pointed
Leaf-stalk	almost absent
	FLOWERS
Position	10–40, in long-stalked, dense spike from leaf-base
Bracts	absent
Type	⚥
Size	10–12mm
Colour	pale purple, turning blue
Stalk	much shorter than flower
Sepals	5, 2–4mm, joined into tube at base, upper teeth short
Petals	5, 10–12mm, lowest pair joined, side pair overlap lower, upper largest
Stamens	10, 9 joined at base
Stigma	1, with hairy style
Ovary	1, 1-celled
	FRUIT
Type	1, pod, oblong, smooth, splits lengthwise into 2
Size	10–20mm
Seeds	2–6, *c*3mm, orbicular

Vicia hirsuta Hairy Tare

Tares have caused farmers problems for thousands of years, reducing yields and making harvesting difficult, and are mentioned as such in the Bible. Slender stems climb with twining tendrils, to bear tiny flowers and pods amidst fields of grain. *Status:* native, throughout area. *Similar species:* other Tares have short, unequal sepal-teeth. Smooth Tare has one or two flowers on a stalk and smooth, mostly four-seeded pods. Slender Tare has small flower-heads and pods usually with five or six seeds. Birdsfoot has a leaf-like bract just below the flowers, and curved, jointed pods.

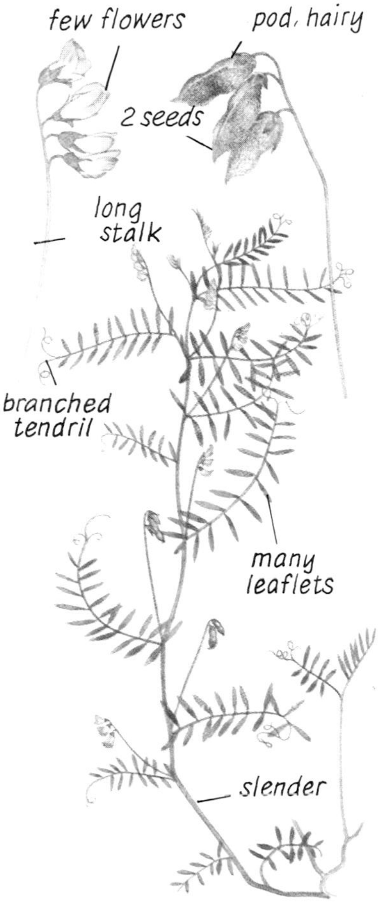

1 Smooth Tare *(V. tetrasperma)*;
2 Slender Tare *(V. tenuissima)*;
3 Birdsfoot *(Ornithopus perpusillus)*

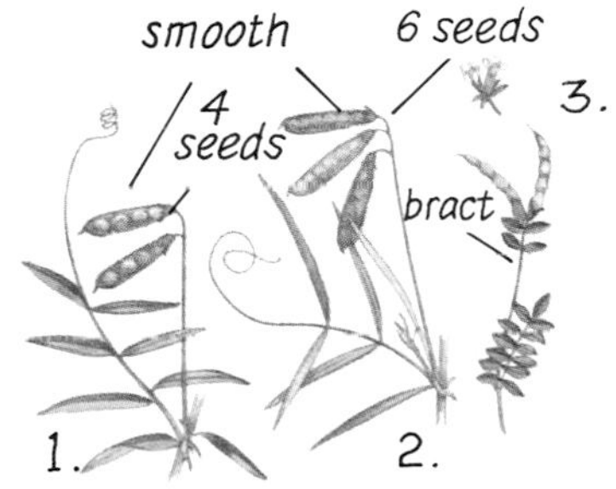

	HAIRY TARE
Type	annual
Height	20–30cm, rarely 70cm
Habitat	cultivated ground, grassy places
Flowering	May–August
	STEMS AND LEAVES
Stem	climbing, slender
Root	fibrous, with tiny nodules
Hairs	nearly hairless
Stipules	often lobed
Leaves	on alternate sides of stem, branched tendril at tip, 4–10 pairs of leaflets, each 5–12mm, narrowly oblong, tip squarish or notched
Leaf-stalk	mostly absent

	FLOWERS
Position	1–9, in short spike from leaf-base, stalk 10–30mm
Bracts	absent
Type	⚥
Size	2–4mm, rarely 5mm
Colour	dull white or purplish
Stalk	shorter than flower
Sepals	5, *c*2mm, bases joined, teeth equal, longer than tube
Petals	5, 4–5mm, lowest 2 joined, 2 side petals overlap lower
Stamens	10, 9 joined at base
Stigma	1, style hairless or hairy
Ovary	1, 1-celled
	FRUIT
Type	1, pod, splits lengthwise, oblong, hairy, black
Size	6–11 × 3–5mm
Seeds	usually 2, *c*1mm, round

Common Vetch *Vicia sativa*

This common plant twines its way through grass, bearing rather small but bright pea-flowers. There are two forms: one native, with rather pointed leaflets, small flowers and straight pods; the other, a crop or naturalized, with mostly notched leaflets, larger flowers and pods narrowed between the seeds. *Status:* native or introduced; throughout area. *Similar species:* Spring Vetch has smaller flowers and rough seeds. Two species lack tendrils and have a long stalk bearing the flowers: Bitter-vetch has several pairs of leaflets, and Grass Vetchling has odd, grass-like leaves.

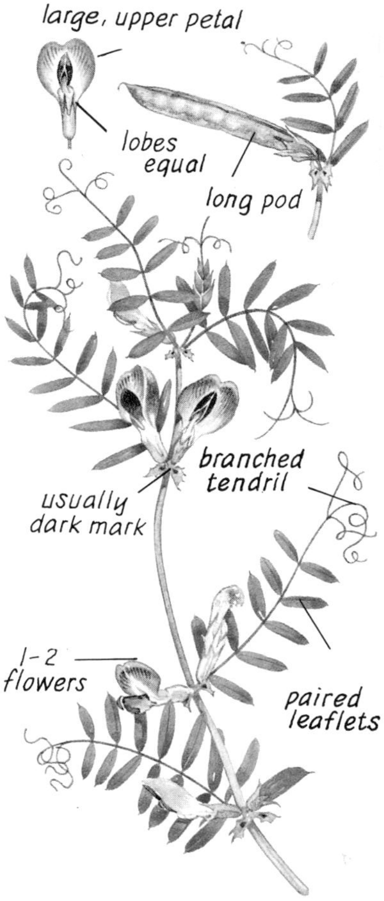

1 Spring Vetch *(V. lathyroides)*;
2 Bitter-vetch *(Lathyrus montanus)*;
3 Grass Vetchling *(L. nissolia)*

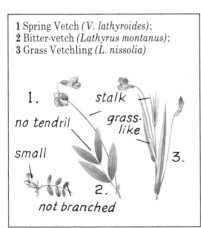

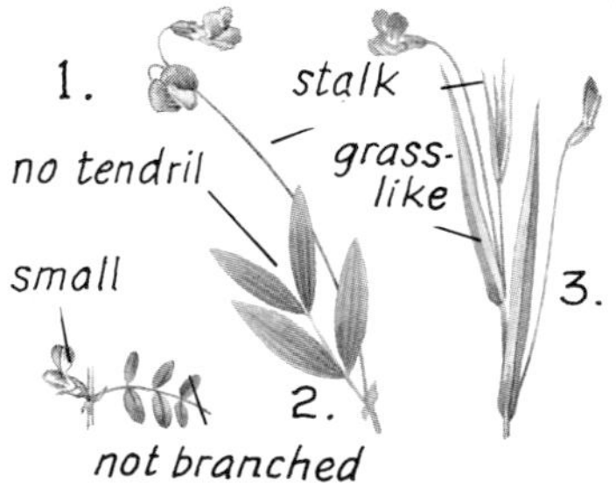

	COMMON VETCH
Type	annual
Height	15–120cm
Habitat	hedges, grassy places
Flowering	May–September
	STEMS AND LEAVES
Stem	climbing or trailing
Root	fibrous, with tiny nodules
Hairs	short, throughout
Stipules	usually toothed, with blackish mark
Leaves	on alternate sides of stem, branched tendril at tip, 4–8 pairs of leaflets, each 6–20mm, tip pointed, blunt or notched
Leaf-stalk	short
	FLOWERS
Position	1–2, at leaf-base
Bracts	absent
Type	⚥
Size	10–30mm
Colour	purplish magenta
Stalk	shorter than flower
Sepals	5, 6–12mm, equal, bases joined, teeth equal to tube
Petals	5, 10–30mm, lowest pair joined, side pair overlap lower, upper largest
Stamens	10, 9 joined at base
Stigma	1, style hairy
Ovary	1, 1-celled
	FRUIT
Type	1, pod, splits lengthwise, narrowly oblong, tip beaked
Size	25–80mm
Seeds	4–12, 2–6.5mm, globular, smooth, mottled

Restharrow's pretty pink pea-flowers are found in dry grassy places, especially chalk-grassland. Tough, matted, underground stems of Restharrow literally arrested the harrow of ox-drawn ploughs. Farmers disliked the plant also because it gave an unpleasant taint to cow's milk, yet the underground stems were sometimes cut for chewing like Wild Liquorice. *Status:* native; most of area, rarer in north. *Similar species:* Spiny Restharrow has spine-tipped stems, with two lines of hairs. Large Yellow-restharrow, from the south of the area, is a much stickier plant, its yellow flowers pencilled red.

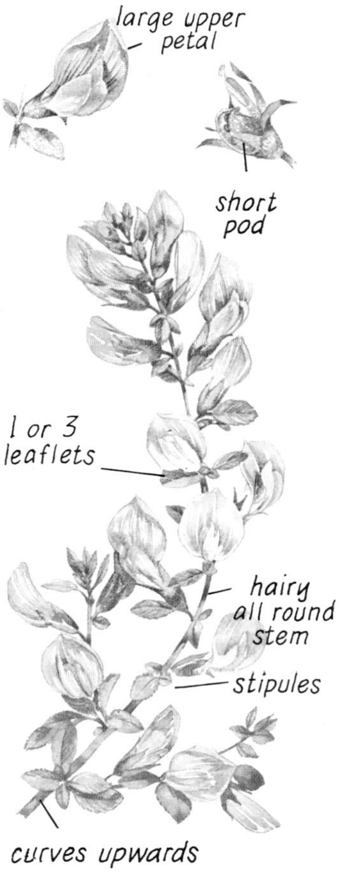

1 Spiny Restharrow *(O. spinosa)*; 2 Large Yellow-restharrow *(O. natrix)*

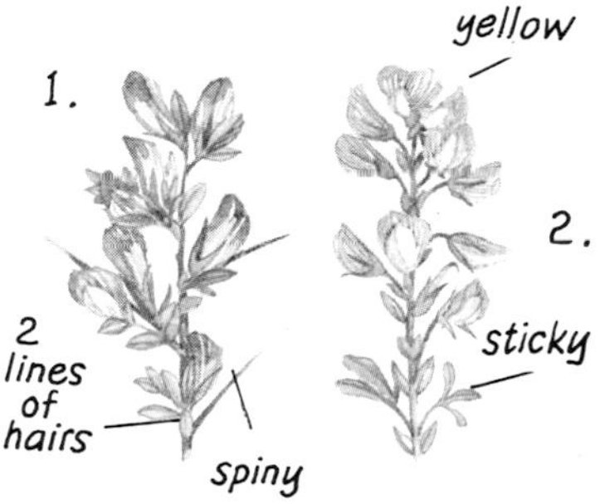

	COMMON RESTHARROW
Type	perennial
Height	30–60cm
Habitat	grassy places; dry, often lime-rich soils
Flowering	June–September
	STEMS AND LEAVES
Stem	low-growing or angled upwards, woody, rooting below
Root	creeping underground stem
Hairs	long or short and sticky, hairy all round stems
Stipules	toothed, bases clasp stem
Leaves	on alternate sides of stem, each up to 20mm, with 1–3 leaflets, tip blunt, edge toothed
Leaf-stalk	3–5mm, shorter than leaf
	FLOWERS
Position	1–2 at leaf-base
Bracts	leaf-like
Type	☿
Size	10–20mm
Colour	pink or purple
Stalk	much shorter than flower
Sepals	5, bases joined, teeth equal, longer than tube, enlarged in fruit
Petals	5, 7–20mm, lowest pair joined, side pair overlap lower, upper largest, broad
Stamens	10, bases joined
Stigma	1, style long, hairless
Ovary	1, 1-celled
	FRUIT
Type	1, pod, splits lengthwise, shorter than sepals, oblong
Size	5–7mm
Seeds	1–4, 2–3mm, globular, rough

Meadow Vetchling *Lathyrus pratensis*

A common plant of meadows and grassy edges of roads or paths, it has clusters of rich yellow pea-flowers. Specialized nodules on its roots turn nitrogen from the air into a form which enriches the pasture. *Status:* native; throughout area. *Similar species:* Yellow Vetchling is a rather rare native annual in dry, sandy or chalky places in the south of the area, although it is sometimes introduced further north. Its 'leaves' are the broad, arrow-shaped stipules, the true leaves being reduced to tendrils. Yellow-vetch has short-stalked, solitary flowers at the base of leaves with many paired leaflets.

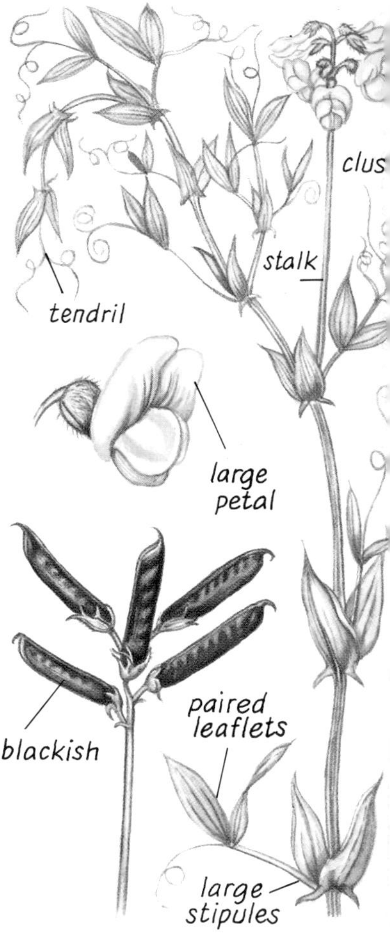

1 Yellow Vetchling *(L. aphaca)*;
2 Yellow-vetch *(Vicia lutea)*

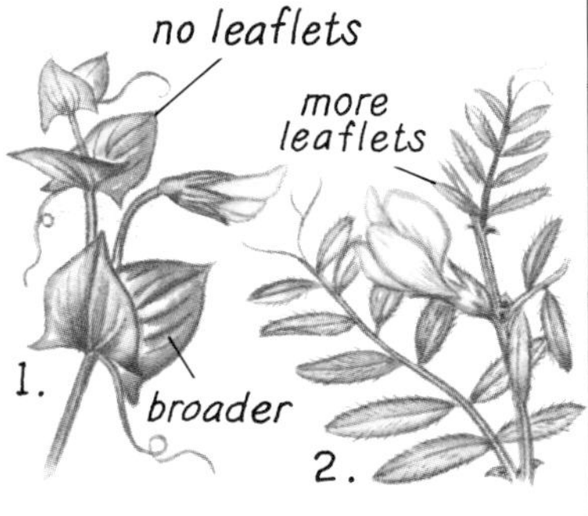

	MEADOW VETCHLING
Type	perennial
Height	30–120cm
Habitat	grassland, scrub
Flowering	May–August
	STEMS AND LEAVES
Stem	climbs or trails, angled
Root	fibrous, with tiny nodules
Hairs	short, throughout plant
Stipules	10–25mm, arrow-shaped
Leaves	on alternate sides of stem, tendril at tip sometimes branched, 1 pair of leaflets, each 10–30mm, spear-shaped, pointed
Leaf-stalk	about equalling leaflets
	FLOWERS
Position	5–12, in long-stalked head from leaf-base
Bracts	minute
Type	⚥
Size	15–18mm
Colour	yellow, greenish veins
Stalk	shorter than flower
Sepals	5, bases joined, teeth equalling tube
Petals	5, 11–18mm, lowest pair joined, side pair overlap lower, upper largest
Stamens	10, 9 joined at base
Stigma	1, hairy on one side
Ovary	1, 1-celled
	FRUIT
Type	1, pod, splits lengthwise, oblong, blackish
Size	25–35mm
Seeds	5–10, 3–4mm, globular, smooth

This exotic-looking plant has long-stalked heads of pink pea-flowers, similar to the cultivated Sweet Pea. Its leaves have two narrow leaflets and a tendril enabling the plant to scramble over surrounding vegetation. *Status:* native; scattered through area except extreme north. *Similar species:* two southern species are sometimes naturalized further north. Broad-leaved Everlasting-pea has broader leaves and stipules. Tuberous Pea has narrow, angled stems, swollen tubers and crimson flowers. The low-growing Sea Pea has several pairs of broad leaflets and grows on dunes, shingle beaches or, rarely, lake-shores.

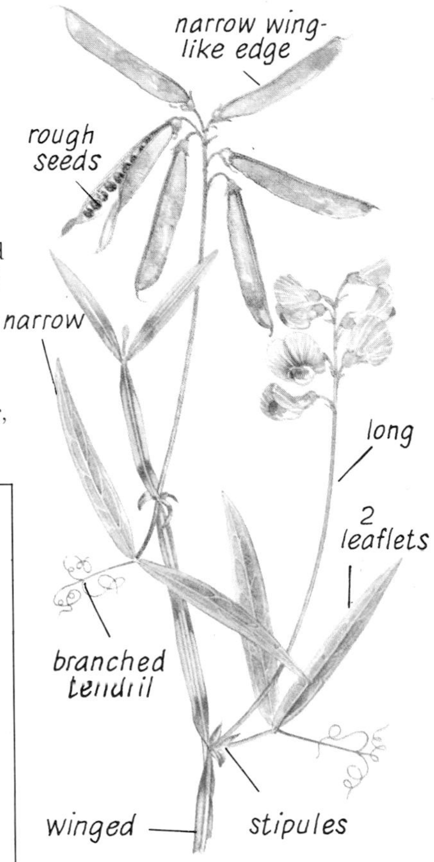

1 Broad-leaved Everlasting-pea *(L. latifolius)*; **2** Tuberous Pea *(L. tuberosus)*; **3** Sea Pea *(L. japonicus)*

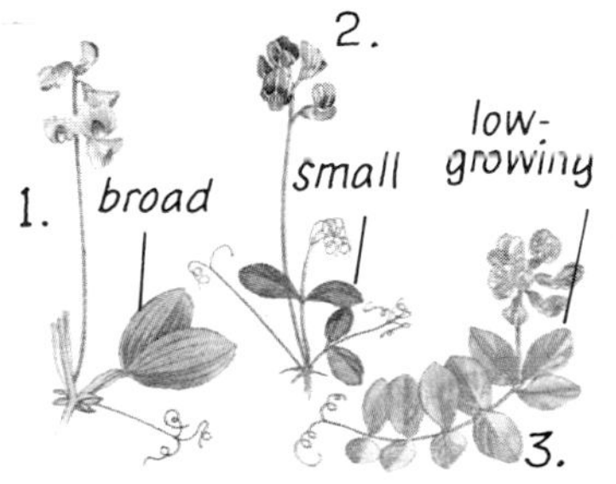

	NARROW-LEAVED EVERLASTING-PEA
Type	perennial
Height	100–200cm
Habitat	woods, scrub, hedges, railway embankments
Flowering	June–August
	STEMS AND LEAVES
Stem	climbing, broadly winged
Root	fibrous, with tiny nodules
Hairs	absent
Stipules	up to 20mm, slender, pointed, narrow basal lobe
Leaves	on alternate sides of stem, branched tendril at tip, 2 leaflets, each 70–150mm, narrowly elliptical or spear-shaped, bluish, pointed
Leaf-stalk	shorter than leaflets

	FLOWERS
Position	3–12 in head on stalk 100–200mm long, from leaf-base
Bracts	small, pointed
Type	⚥
Size	15–17mm
Colour	rosy pink
Stalk	shorter than flower
Sepals	5, unequal, bases joined, teeth shorter than tube
Petals	5, 12–17mm, lowest pair joined, side pair overlap lower
Stamens	10, 9 joined at base
Stigma	1, style curved, hairy
Ovary	1, 1-celled
	FRUIT
Type	1, pod, splits lengthwise, oblong, top edge winged
Size	50–70mm
Seeds	8–14, 5–6mm, globular, rough

Lucerne *Medicago sativa*

An important crop, often grown for the tiny nodules on the roots, in which bacteria turn nitrogen from the air into nitrates. These are essential for plant growth and enrich the soil in a way similar to fertilizers. *Status:* introduced; most of area except extreme north. *Similar species:* several native plants have yellow flowers and tightly coiled, spiny fruits. Spotted Medick, with dark-spotted leaves, has three grooves on the edge of each coil of the fruit. Toothed Medick lacks spots and has only two grooves. Bur Medick has hairy leaves and tiny fruits, bristling with fine spines.

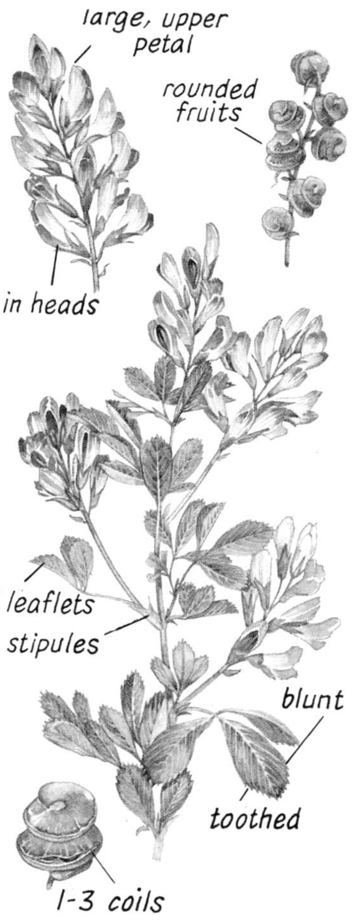

1 Spotted Medick *(M. arabica)*;
2 Toothed Medick *(M. polymorpha)*;
3 Bur Medick *(M. minima)*

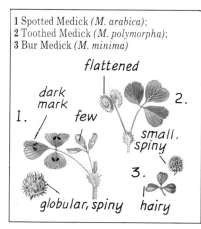

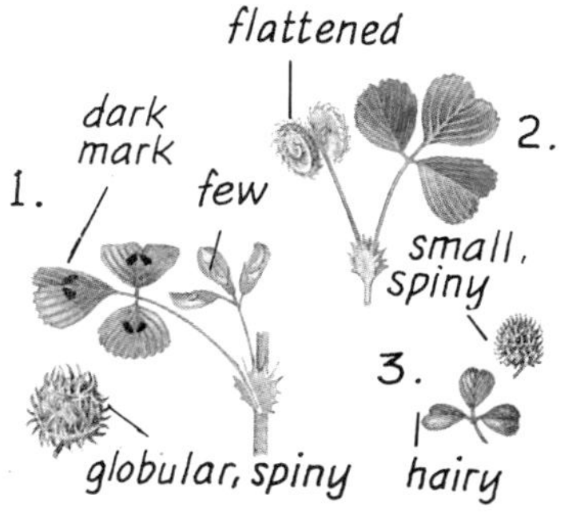

	LUCERNE
Type	perennial
Height	30–90cm
Habitat	waste and grassy places
Flowering	June–July
	STEMS AND LEAVES
Stem	upright or angled upwards
Root	deep, with tiny nodules
Hairs	short, on whole plant
Stipules	narrowly spear-shaped, toothed, on leaf-stalk
Leaves	on alternate sides of stem, 3 leaflets, each to 30mm, broadest near tip, blunt except for fine point, toothed above
Leaf-stalk	usually shorter than leaf
	FLOWERS
Position	5–40, in spike with stalk about equalling leaf
Bracts	small, slender
Type	⚥
Size	7–12mm
Colour	purple
Stalk	shorter than flower
Sepals	5, equal, bases joined, teeth about equalling tube
Petals	5, 6–12mm, lowest pair joined, side pair overlap lower, upper largest
Stamens	10, 9 joined at base
Stigma	1, club-shaped
Ovary	1, 1-celled
	FRUIT
Type	1, pod, rarely splitting, in spiral of 1–3 turns
Size	4–6mm
Seeds	10–20, 2–3mm, smooth

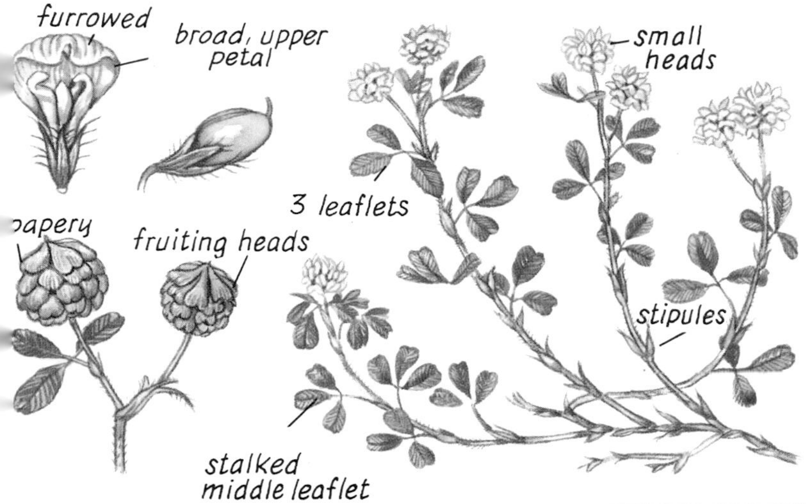

Hop Trefoil is a small, clover-like plant with tiny yellow flower-heads, and is common in short grass. The fruiting heads look like diminutive hops, owing to the dry petals which remain attached. *Status:* native; very common, most of area. *Similar species:* Lesser Trefoil has smaller fruiting heads, the dark brown upper petals lacking grooves but folded over the pod. Slender Trefoil has stalkless middle leaflets and very few flowers in a head. In flower, Black Medick is often mistaken for Hop Trefoil but has coiled black pods without remains of flowers.

1 Lesser Trefoil *(T. dubium)*; **2** Slender Trefoil *(T. micranthum)*; **3** Black Medick *(Medicago lupulina)*

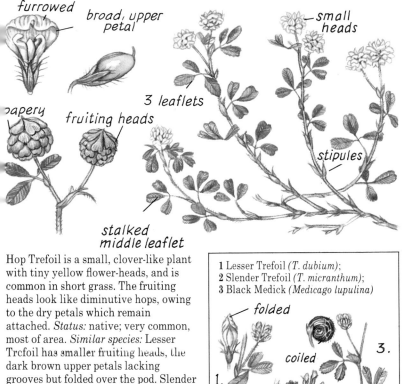

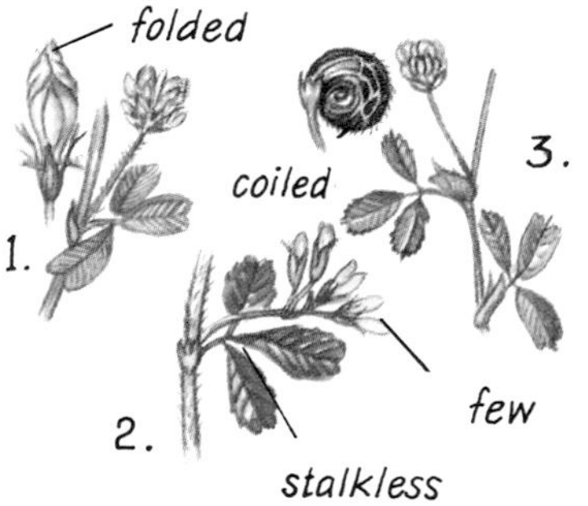

	HOP TREFOIL
Type	annual
Height	5–35cm, rarely to 50cm
Habitat	grassy places; dryish soil
Flowering	June–September
	STEMS AND LEAVES
Stem	upright or angled upwards
Root	fibrous, with tiny nodules
Hairs	over whole plant
Stipules	oval, joined to leaf-stalk, not toothed
Leaves	on alternate sides of stem, with 3 leaflets, the end one stalked, each 6–10mm, tip blunt or notched, edge toothed
Leaf-stalk	shorter than leaflets
	FLOWERS
Position	20–30, in head from leaf-base, stalk about equals leaf
Bracts	absent
Type	⚥
Size	4–6mm
Colour	yellow, turning pale brown
Stalk	very short
Sepals	5, unequal, bases joined, teeth about equal tube
Petals	5, 3–6mm, remaining in fruit, lowest pair joined, side pair overlap lower, upper broad, becomes grooved
Stamens	10, 9 joined at base
Stigma	1, with curved style
Ovary	1, 1-celled
	FRUIT
Type	1, egg-shaped pod, not opening
Size	2–2.5mm
Seeds	1, 1–1.5mm, yellow

Hare's-foot Clover *Trifolium arvense*

A slender, short-lived annual, often covering large areas on sand-dunes in early Summer. Attractive, pink, softly hairy flower-heads give the plant its common name. In fruit, the reddish, bristle-like sepal-teeth project from the head like a miniature bottle-brush. *Status:* native; scattered, most common in south and east. *Similar species:* the cultivated Crimson Clover is more robust, and has crimson petals, although a rarer pale form on cliff-tops is native. Two low-growing species are Knotted Clover, which has stalkless flower-heads, and Strawberry Clover, which has an inflated, reddish sepal-tube in fruit.

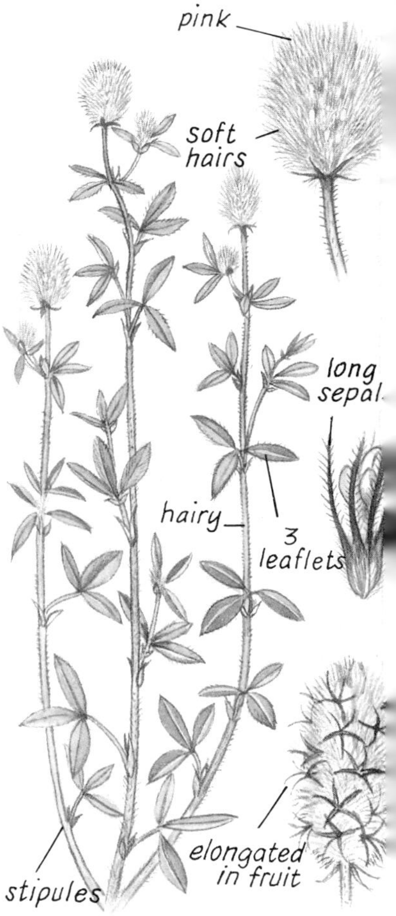

1 Crimson Clover *(T. incarnatum)*;
2 Knotted Clover *(T. striatum)*;
3 Strawberry Clover *(T. fragiferum)*

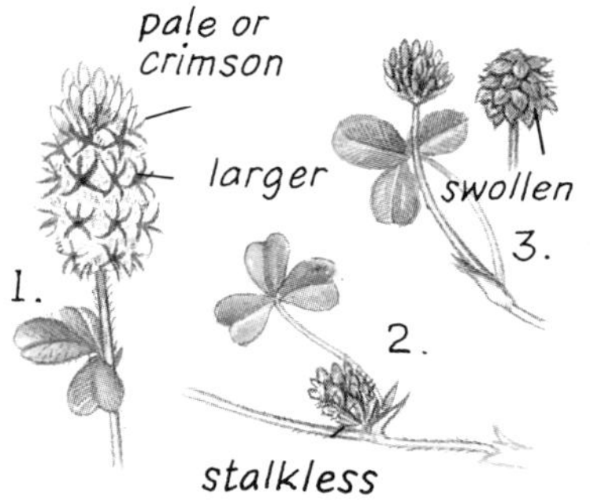

	HARE'S-FOOT CLOVER
Type	annual or biennial
Height	5–40cm
Habitat	arable fields, pastures, dunes; dry, sandy soil
Flowering	June–September
	STEMS AND LEAVES
Stem	upright or angled upwards
Root	fibrous, with tiny nodules
Hairs	soft, downy, white or pink, dense on sepals
Stipules	oval, bristle-like tip
Leaves	on alternate sides of stem, with 3 leaflets, each 10–15, oblong, blunt or sharpish
Leaf-stalk	to 10mm, upper stalkless
	FLOWERS
Position	numerous, in stalked, cylindrical heads to 25mm, from stem-tip or leaf-base
Bracts	absent
Type	⚥
Size	3.5–7mm
Colour	white or pink
Stalk	almost absent
Sepals	5, about equal, bases joined, bristle-like teeth, reddish, longer than tube and petals
Petals	5, remaining in fruit, 2.5–7mm, lower 2 joined, side 2 overlapping, upper largest
Stamens	10, 9 joined at base
Stigma	1, style-tip curved
Ovary	1, 1-celled
	FRUIT
Type	1, pod, egg-shaped
Size	1–1.5mm
Seeds	1, *c*0.8mm, egg-shaped

The familiar Clover of pasture, grown to feed livestock and to enrich the pasture by virtue of tiny nodules on its roots. Many vigorous forms, often with paired heads, have been bred and frequently escape from fields. Clover leaflets fold up at night or in rain. The flowers are important to bee-keepers as a nectar-source. *Status:* native or planted; often very common, most of area. *Similar species:* Zigzag Clover has rather twisting stems; the base of the sepals is hairless. Species with white or pink flowers include White Clover, which has creeping, rooting stems, and Alsike Clover which has upright stems.

1 Zigzag Clover *(T. medium)*; **2** White Clover *(T. repens)*; **3** Alsike Clover *(T. hybridum)*

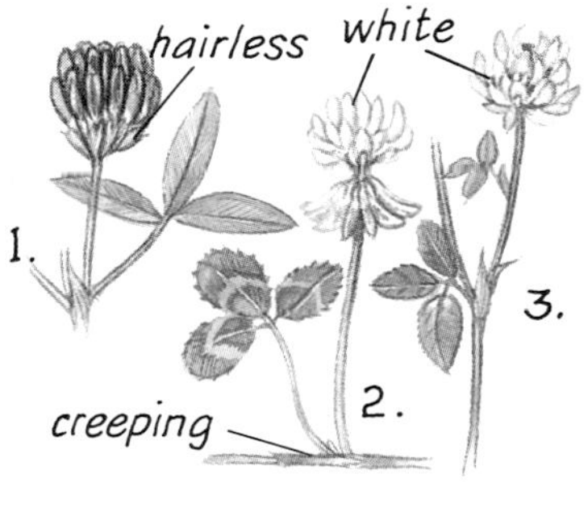

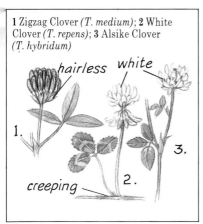

	RED CLOVER
Type	perennial
Height	5–100cm
Habitat	grassy places; mostly rich, moist soil
Flowering	May–September
	STEMS AND LEAVES
Stem	upright or turns upright
Root	fibrous, with tiny nodules
Hairs	short, often sparse above
Stipules	oblong, bases joined, end triangular, tip slender
Leaves	on alternate sides of stem, 3 leaflets, each 10–30mm, mostly elliptical, with V-shaped, white mark, blunt
Leaf-stalk	lower longer than leaves
	FLOWERS
Position	many in rounded, stalkless head, 20–40mm, at stem-tip
Bracts	2 tiny leaves with broad stipules beneath head
Type	⚥
Size	12–15mm
Colour	usually pinkish purple
Stalk	absent
Sepals	5, bases joined, tube 10-ribbed, hairy, teeth thin
Petals	5, 10–15mm, attached in fruit, lower 2 joined, side 2 hide lower, upper broad
Stamens	10, 9 joined at base
Stigma	1, style-tip curved
Ovary	1, 1-celled
	FRUIT
Type	1, pod, egg-shaped, tip breaks off, hairless
Size	2–2.5mm
Seeds	1, 1.5–2mm, notched

Tall Melilot *Melilotus altissima*

A tall, bushy plant with many branched stems bearing slender, spiky flower-heads. The whole plant has an aroma of new-mown hay, especially when dried. Melilots were once used to treat blisters, swellings and sore eyes. *Status:* native or introduced in west; most of area. *Similar species:* other Melilots have hairless fruits. White Melilot is easily identified by the white petals. Ribbed Melilot has short lower petals and blunt, ridged, brown ripe pods. Small Melilot has tiny flowers and smaller, olive-green ripe pods.

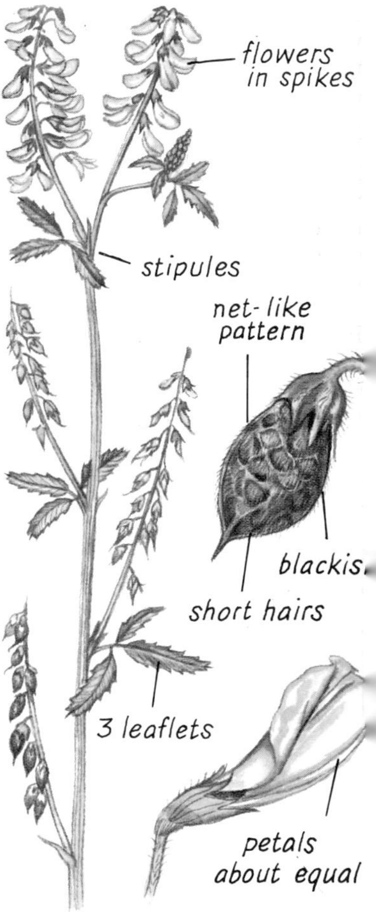

1 White Melilot *(M. alba)*; **2** Ribbed Melilot *(M. officinalis)*; **3** Small Melilot *(M. indica)*

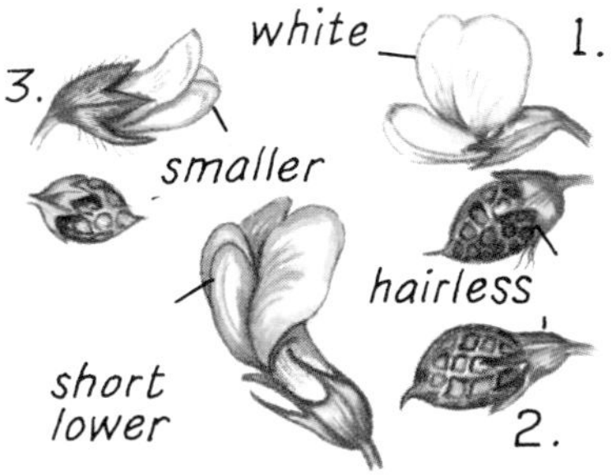

	TALL MELILOT
Type	biennial or perennial
Height	60–150cm
Habitat	grassland, wood clearings; damp, sometimes salty soil
Flowering	June–August
	STEMS AND LEAVES
Stem	upright, branched
Root	fibrous, with tiny nodules
Hairs	under leaves, on sepals
Stipules	slender, bristle-like
Leaves	on alternate sides of stem, with 3 leaflets, each 15–30mm, oblong or oval, blunt, edge toothed
Leaf-stalk	shorter than leaflets
	FLOWERS
Position	many, in stalked head, 20–50mm, from leaf-base
Bracts	hair-like
Type	⚥
Size	5–6mm
Colour	yellow
Stalk	shorter than flower
Sepals	5, bases joined, teeth longer than tube
Petals	5, 5–6mm, about equal, lower 2 joined, side 2 overlap, upper broad
Stamens	10, 9 joined
Stigma	1, style long, curved
Ovary	1, 1-celled
	FRUIT
Type	1, egg-shaped pod, most not opening, net-like pattern, hairy, pointed, black
Size	5–6mm
Seeds	2, 2–2.5mm, notched

A plant of sunny, grassy places, with wiry stems bearing yellow pea-flowers tipped or streaked with red. Of its many common names, 'Eggs and bacon' recalls the yellow and red flowers. The leaves are food to the larvae of the Silver-studded Blue butterfly and the Six-spot Burnet moth. *Status:* native; throughout area. *Similar species:* Greater Bird's-foot-trefoil, of wetter places, has tall, upright, hollow stems and creeping underground stems. Horseshoe Vetch has many leaflets and wavy pods that break into horseshoe-shaped segments. Dragon's-teeth has larger flowers and pods with 4, wing-like angles.

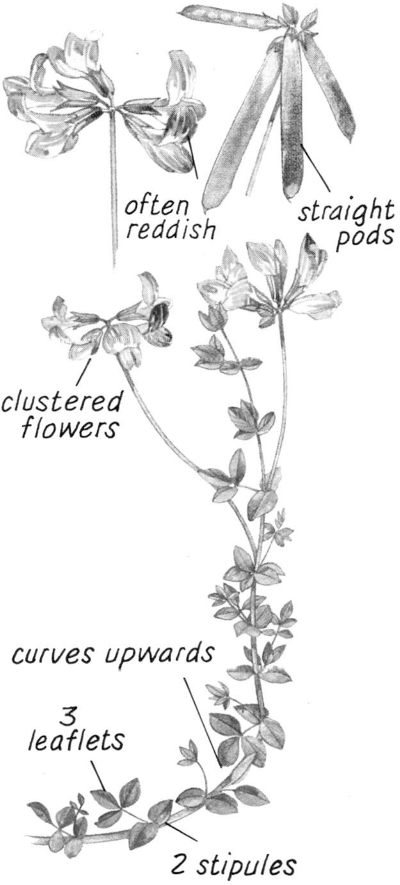

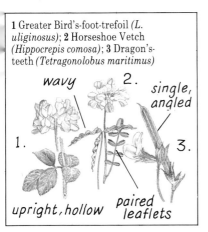

1 Greater Bird's-foot-trefoil *(L. uliginosus)*; **2** Horseshoe Vetch *(Hippocrepis comosa)*; **3** Dragon's-teeth *(Tetragonolobus maritimus)*

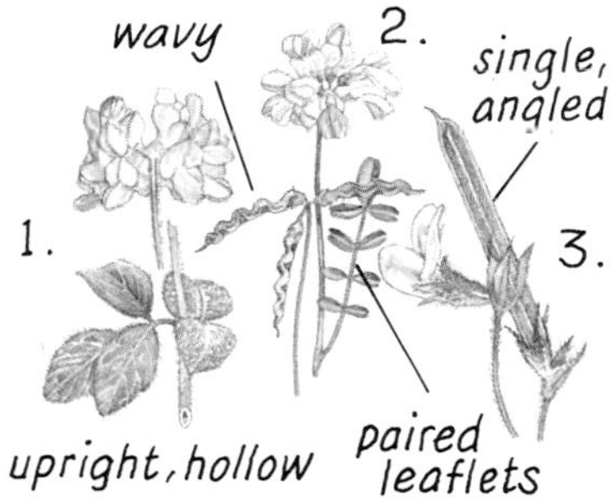

	COMMON BIRD'S-FOOT-TREFOIL
Type	perennial
Height	10–40cm
Habitat	grassy places
Flowering	June–September
	STEMS AND LEAVES
Stem	low-growing, tips turn up
Root	stout, woody stock
Hairs	hairless or rarely hairy
Stipules	minute
Leaves	on alternate sides of stem, 5 leaflets, lower 2 stipule-like, each 3–10mm, oval, blunt, edge unbroken
Leaf-stalk	very short
	FLOWERS
Position	2–8 in short head, stalk up to 80mm, from leaf-base
Bracts	divided into 3
Type	⚥
Size	10–16mm
Colour	yellow, often tinged or veined with red
Stalk	shorter than flowers
Sepals	5, equal, bases joined, teeth about equal tube
Petals	9–16mm, lower 2 joined, side 2 overlap, upper largest
Stamens	10, 9 joined at base
Stigma	1, style long, straight
Ovary	1, 1-celled
	FRUIT
Type	1, pod, splits lengthwise, cylindrical, straight; partitions between seeds
Size	15–30mm
Seeds	many, 1–1.5mm, kidney-shaped

Kidney Vetch *Anthyllis vulneraria*

A plant of sunny, grassy places, especially the short turf around tops of sea-cliffs. The flower-heads often have a dual nature, one half in flower, the other in bud or fruit. *Status:* native; widespread, most of area, most common by coast. *Similar species:* several pea-flowered species have more elongated flower-heads. Wild Liquorice has cream-coloured flowers and long, curved, hairless pods. Two yellow-flowered species that have swollen, hairy pods are Yellow Alpine Milk-vetch (tiny sepal-teeth and ellipsoidal pods) and Wild Lentil (oval, membranous pods and sepal-teeth about half as long as the tube).

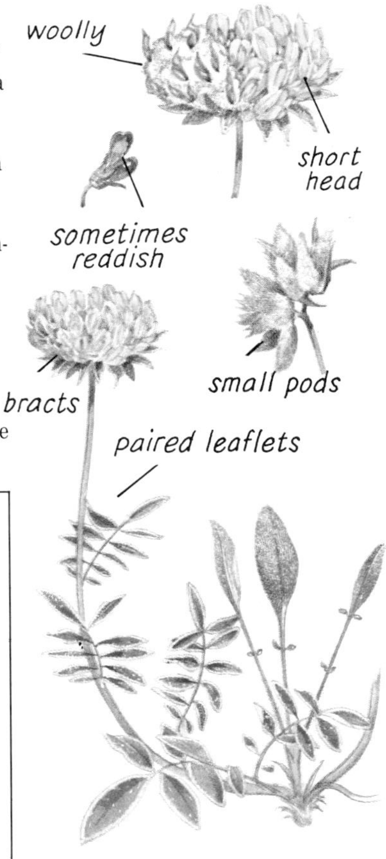

1 Wild Liquorice *(Astragalus glycyphyllos)*; 2 Yellow Alpine Milk-vetch *(A. frigidus)*; 3 Wild Lentil *(A. cicer)*

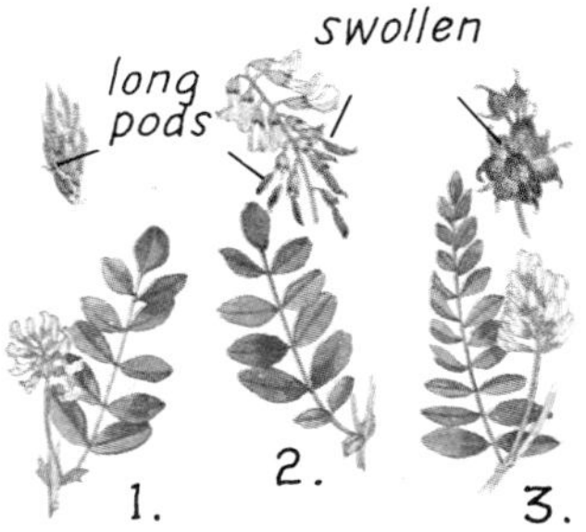

	KIDNEY VETCH
Type	perennial, rarely annual
Height	5–60cm
Habitat	grassy places; dry, often lime-rich soils
Flowering	June–September
	STEMS AND LEAVES
Stem	upright or turns upright
Root	fibrous, with tiny nodules
Hairs	short, silky
Stipules	small, soon fall
Leaves	on alternate sides of stem, to 140mm, mostly 5–15 oval to oblong leaflets, that at tip often largest, lower scattered, upper paired
Leaf-stalk	short or absent
	FLOWERS
Position	numerous, in dense, mostly paired, long-stalked heads

Bracts	2, leafy, several leaflets
Type	⚥
Size	12–15mm
Colour	yellow, rarely tinged red
Stalk	mostly absent
Sepals	5, bases joined, inflated, woolly, teeth short, unequal
Petals	5, 10–15mm, lowest pair joined, side pair overlap lower, upper largest
Stamens	10, 9 joined at base
Stigma	1, club-shaped
Ovary	1, 1-celled
	FRUIT
Type	1 nearly globular pod, not opening, sepals persist
Size	*c*3mm
Seeds	1–2, 2–2.5mm, notched

A spectacular plant to find in a pasture or grassy verge on a chalky hillside, its bright pink flowers lined with purple. A network of ridges and spines covers the unusual pods. The common name, borrowed from the French, simply means that this makes wholesome hay. *Status:* probably introduced; mainly southern. *Similar species:* several plants with pink or purplish pea-flowers have longer pods lacking teeth. Purple Milk-vetch has short stems and dense heads of purple flowers. Crown Vetch has a ring of pink flowers and the long pods break into segments. Goat's-rue is bushy, with lilac or white flowers.

1 Purple Milk-vetch *(Astragalus danicus)*; 2 Crown Vetch *(Coronilla varia)*; 3 Goat's-rue *(Galega officinalis)*

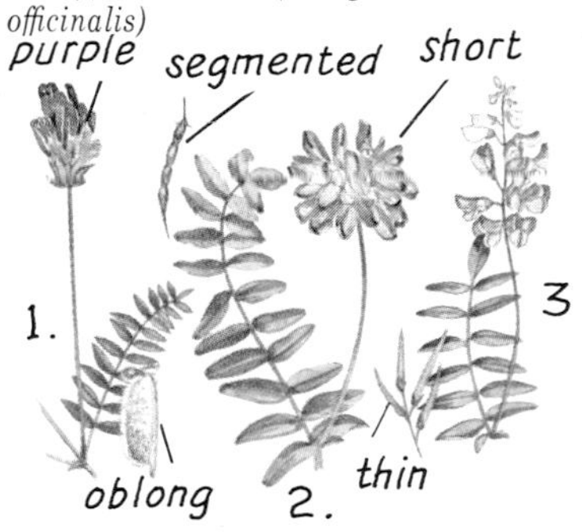

	SAINFOIN
Type	perennial
Height	30–60cm
Habitat	grassland; lime-rich soils
Flowering	June–August
	STEMS AND LEAVES
Stem	upright
Root	fibrous, with tiny nodules
Hairs	short, sparse
Stipules	oval, papery
Leaves	on alternate sides of stem, oblong or oval leaflets in 6–12 pairs, one at tip, each 10–30mm, not toothed
Leaf-stalk	short
	FLOWERS
Position	up to 50 in long-stalked, spike-like head from leaf-base
Bracts	minute
Type	⚥
Size	10–12mm
Colour	pink or red, purple veins
Stalk	much shorter than flower
Sepals	5, 5–8mm, bases joined into tube, teeth very narrow, longer than tube
Petals	5, 4–12mm, lower 2 joined, side 2 tiny, upper broad
Stamens	10, 9 joined at base
Stigma	1
Ovary	1, 1-celled
	FRUIT
Type	1, short pod, not opening, with network of ridges and bumps, 6–8 teeth on edge
Size	6–8mm
Seeds	1, not released

Wood-sorrel *Oxalis acetosella*

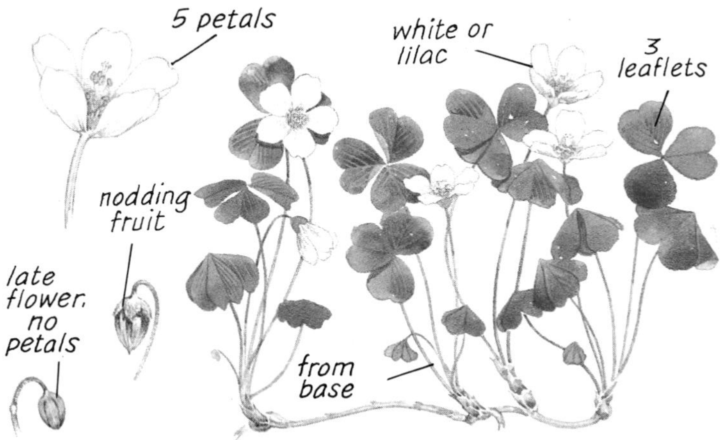

The delicate white flowers and clover-like leaves of Wood-sorrel carpet the floor of many deciduous woods in Spring. At night and in wet weather, the leaflets fold together. An elastic coat to the seeds enables them to be shot from the capsule. Most seeds develop from late, petal-less flowers. *Status:* native; throughout area. *Similar species:* several yellow-flowered species are naturalized. Procumbent Yellow-sorrel has slender, trailing, rooting stems; Upright Yellow-sorrel has thick, upright stems. Bermuda-buttercup, with large heads of flowers, occurs in the south-west.

1 Procumbent Yellow-sorrel *(O. corniculata)*; **2** Bermuda-buttercup *(O. pes-caprae)*; **3** Upright Yellow-sorrel *(O. europaea)*

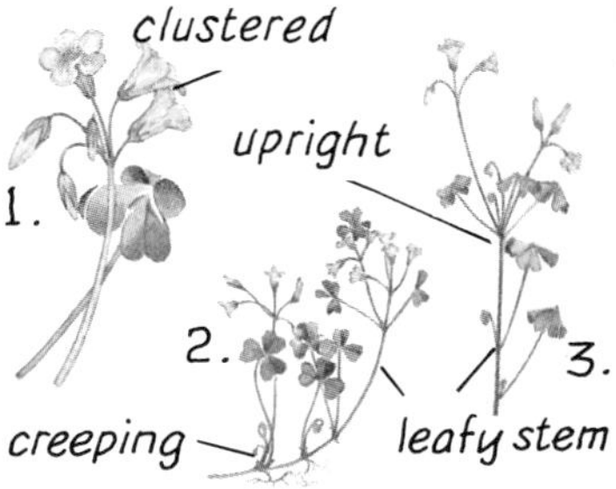

WOOD-SORREL

Type perennial
Height 5–15cm
Habitat woods, hedgerows, among rocks; mostly acid soils
Flowering April–May

STEMS AND LEAVES

Stem flowering stem upright
Root fibrous from slender, scaly, underground stem
Hairs sparse, pressed to surface
Stipules absent
Leaves at base of plant, with 3 leaflets, each 10–20mm, heart-shaped, yellowish green, notched, edge unbroken
Leaf-stalk 50–150mm

FLOWERS

Position single, at stem-tip
Bracts 2, small, at middle of stem
Type 1 ⚥, cup-shaped
Type 2 late, no petals, not opening
Size 15–30mm
Colour white, rarely lilac or purple, lilac veins
Stalk longer than flower
Sepals 5, 3–4mm, equal, oblong
Petals 5, 8–16mm, equal, notched
Stamens 10, 2 rings of 5
Stigmas 5
Ovary 1, 1-celled

FRUIT

Type 1, capsule, 5-ridged
Size 4–7mm
Seeds many, 2–2.5mm, egg-shaped, ridged, with fleshy coat

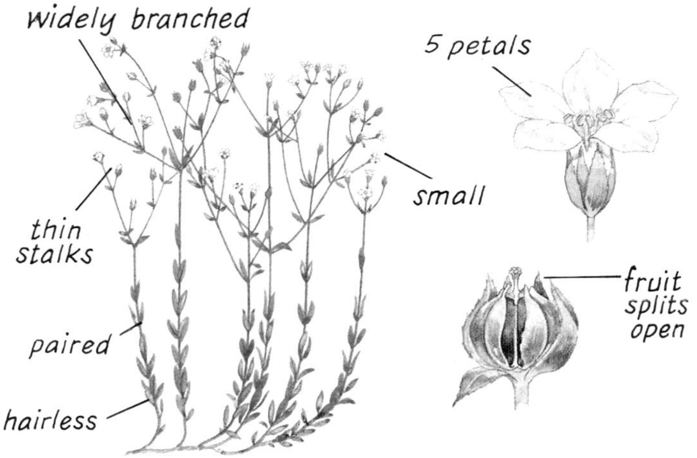

An appropriate common name for such a delicate plant, the tiny flowers seeming to float as the hair-like, dark stems are lost against the background. The plant has had many uses, one being indicated in the alternative common name 'Purging Flax'. Fairy Flax is related to the cultivated flaxes, which are the source of linen. *Status:* native; throughout area. *Similar species:* Allseed is a smaller plant which has four tiny petals and toothed sepals. Two blue-flowered species resemble the cultivated Flax: Pale Flax has pointed sepals, and Perennial Flax has blunt sepals.

1 Pale Flax *(L. bienne)*; **2** Perennial Flax *(L. perenne)*; **3** Allseed *(Radiola linoides)*

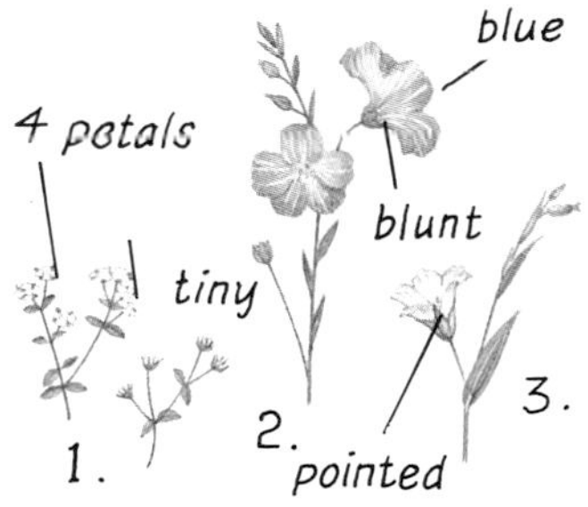

	FAIRY FLAX
Type	annual
Height	5–25cm
Habitat	grassy places, moors, dunes; dry, often lime-rich soils
Flowering	June–September
	STEMS AND LEAVES
Stem	1 or few, slender, wiry, upright, often blackish
Root	fibrous
Hairs	absent
Stipules	absent
Leaves	paired, either side of stem, 5–12mm, oblong to spear-shaped, most blunt, edge unbroken, base wedge-shaped or rounded
Leaf-stalk	absent
	FLOWERS
Position	many, wide-branched head
Bracts	slender, lowest leaf-like
Type	⚥, nodding in bud
Size	5–7mm
Colour	white
Stalk	5–10mm, hair-like
Sepals	5, 2–3mm, equal, spear-shaped, pointed
Petals	5, 4–6mm, equal, oval, edge rounded, separate
Stamens	5, bases joined
Stigmas	5, club-shaped
Ovary	1, 5-celled
	FRUIT
Type	1 globular, angled capsule, splits into 10 parts
Size	2–3mm
Seeds	10, *c*1mm, flattened

Herb-Robert *Geranium robertianum*

Common in shady places, it attains its full glory on walls or rocks where the sun turns stems and leaves brilliant crimson. Native *Geranium* species are of a genus different from the Geraniums *(Pelargonium)* of gardens, but they are related and even smell similar. *Status:* native or introduced; south-west of area, naturalized elsewhere. *Similar species:* other species have leaves with shallower, radiating lobes. Two with notched petals are Hedgerow Crane's-bill, which has upright, perennial stems, and low-growing, annual Dove's-foot Crane's-bill. Shining Crane's-bill is almost hairless, with glossy leaves and broad, angular sepals.

1 Hedgerow Crane's-bill *(G. pyrenaicum)*; **2** Dove's-foot Crane's-bill *(G. molle)*; **3** Shining Crane's-bill *(G. lucidum)*

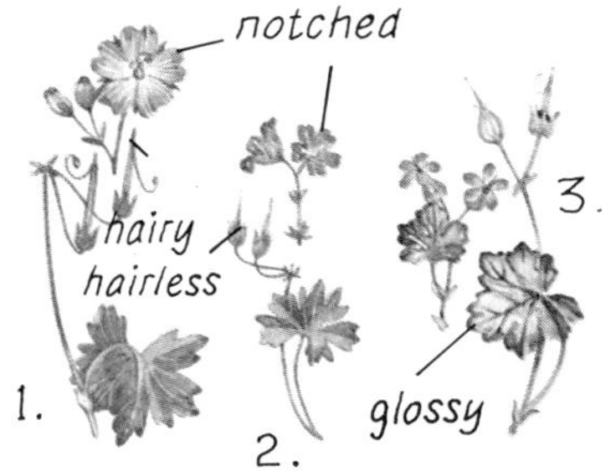

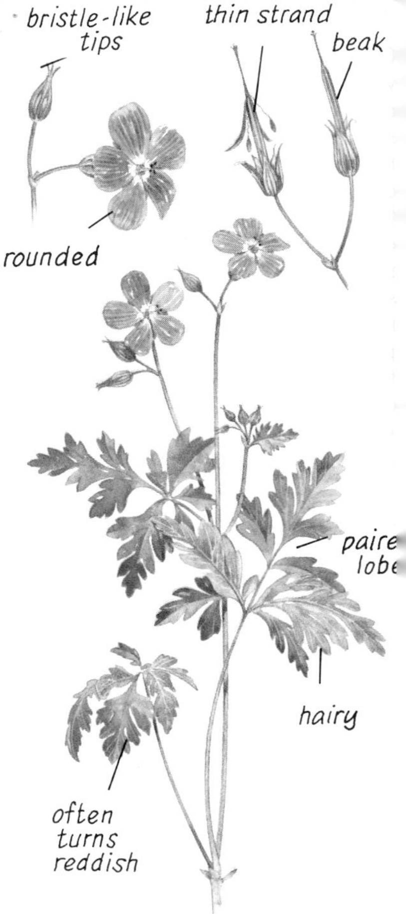

	HERB-ROBERT
Type	annual or biennial
Height	10–50cm
Habitat	woods, hedges, rocks, walls
Flowering	May–September
	STEMS AND LEAVES
Stem	angled upwards, branched from base, brittle
Root	slender tap-root
Hairs	dense below, sparse above
Stipules	small, oval
Leaves	basal or paired either side of stem, 15–65mm, deeply cut into 3–5 lobes, toothed, strong-smelling, often red-tinged
Leaf-stalk	lower long, upper short
	FLOWERS
Position	1–2, from leaf-base
Bracts	scale-like
Type	⚥
Size	16–20mm
Colour	purplish, pink, rarely white
Stalk	longer than flower
Sepals	5, 7–9mm, oval, bristle-like tip, upright
Petals	5, 9–13mm, equal, oval, rounded, base stalk-like
Stamens	10, orange or purple
Stigmas	5, slender
Ovary	1, 3–5-celled
	FRUIT
Type	1, long-beaked capsule, strip from beak coils up with each segment
Size	12–20mm
Seeds	1 per segment, *c*2mm, oblong, smooth

Geranium dissectum Cut-leaved Crane's-bill

One of the most common of roadside wild flowers, it is distinguished from most other sorts of Crane's-bill with small flowers by its notched petals and narrow-lobed leaves. Ripe fruits have one-seeded segments. Each splits at the base and a strip of the beak suddenly coils, hurling the seed away. *Status:* native; throughout area. *Similar species:* Long-stalked Crane's-bill has much longer flower-stalks, rounded petals and almost hairless fruits. Small-flowered Crane's-bill has less deeply divided leaves, with mostly wedge-shaped, three-lobed segments and tiny flowers.

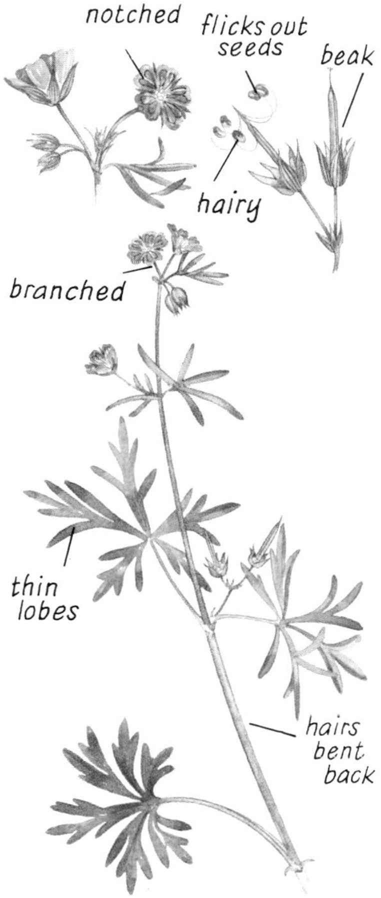

1 Long-stalked Crane's-bill *(G. columbinum)*; **2** Small-flowered Crane's-bill *(G. pusillum)*

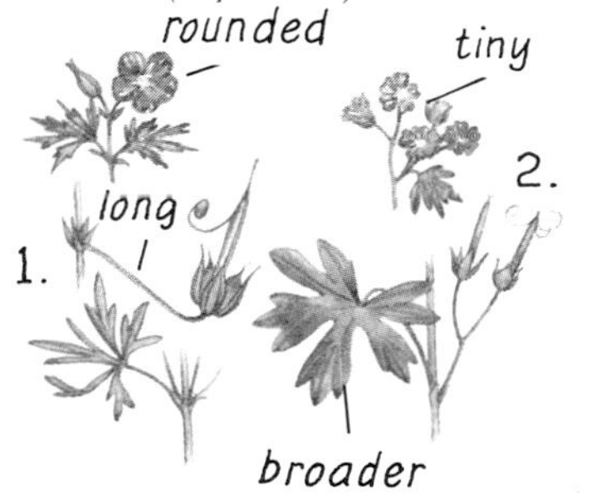

	CUT-LEAVED CRANE'S-BILL
Type	annual
Height	10–60cm
Habitat	cultivated or waste ground, grassland; dryish soil
Flowering	May–August
	STEMS AND LEAVES
Stem	straggling, usually branched
Root	slender tap-root
Hairs	dense, bent back
Stipules	small, triangular
Leaves	paired either side of stem, 20–70mm, almost circular, deeply cut into 5–7 narrow, main lobes; those of lower leaves further lobed or toothed
Leaf-stalk	long below, short above

	FLOWERS
Position	1–2, from leaf-base
Bracts	slender
Type	⚥
Size	8–10mm
Colour	reddish-pink
Stalk	5–15mm
Sepals	5, 5–6mm, oval, tip bristle-like, hairy
Petals	5, 4–5mm, equal, oval, notched
Stamens	10
Stigmas	5, slender
Ovary	1, usually 5-celled
	FRUIT
Type	1, lobed, long-beaked capsule, hairy
Size	7–12mm
Seeds	1 per segment, 2–2.5mm, minutely pitted

Meadow Crane's-bill *Geranium pratense*

A strikingly beautiful plant of summer meadows and grassy roadsides, it has bold, deeply lobed leaves and large, bluish-violet flowers. This is one of the few native plants that finds a permanent place in gardens, often as a double form. *Status:* native, naturalized in parts of north; most of area. *Similar species:* Wood Crane's-bill, in shadier places, has smaller flowers and more finely toothed leaves. Dusky Crane's-bill often escapes from gardens and has blackish-purple petals with pointed tips. Bloody Crane's-bill is a creeping plant with reddish-purple flowers that are carried singly.

1 Wood Crane's-bill *(G. sylvaticum)*;
2 Dusky Crane's-bill *(G. phaeum)*;
3 Bloody Crane's-bill *(G. sanguineum)*

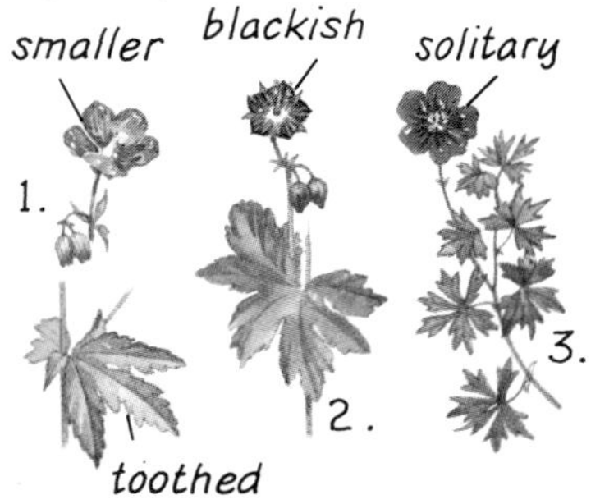

	MEADOW CRANE'S-BILL
Type	perennial
Height	30–80cm
Habitat	grassy, sunny places; mainly lime-rich soils
Flowering	June–September
	STEMS AND LEAVES
Stem	upright or angled upwards
Root	thick rhizome
Hairs	short, bent back below, long, dense above
Stipules	wide, papery, upper slender
Leaves	basal or on alternate sides of stem, 70–150mm, 3–7 deep, radiating lobes, each further toothed or lobed, tips pointed
Leaf-stalk	lower much longer than leaf, upper very short

	FLOWERS
Position	stalked pair from leaf-base
Bracts	narrowly triangular
Type	⚥, cup-shaped
Size	30–40mm
Colour	bright bluish violet
Stalk	shorter than flower
Sepals	5, 11–15mm, oval, thin tip
Petals	5, 15–20mm, equal, broadly oval, tip rounded
Stamens	10
Stigmas	5, slender
Ovary	1, usually 5-celled
	FRUIT
Type	capsule, lobed, long-beaked, strip from beak coils up with each lobe
Size	25–30mm
Seeds	1 per segment, 3–4mm

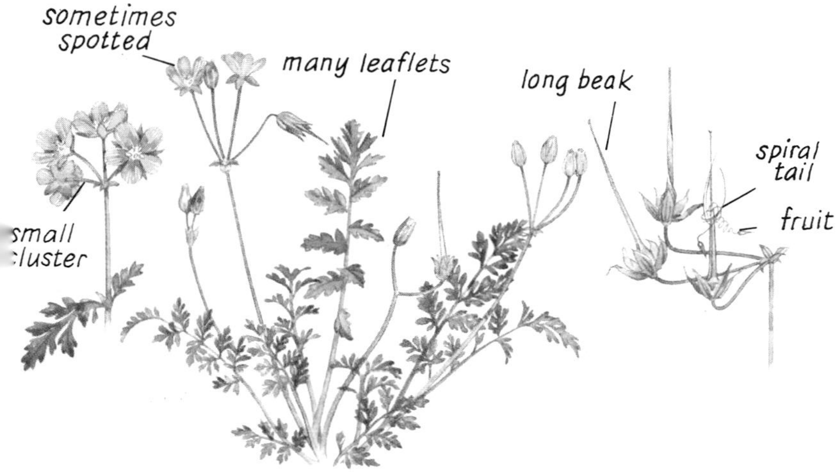

A variable, mainly coastal species. Stickily hairy plants with slender stems and unspotted flowers are often regarded as a different subspecies, the typical version having stout stems and two dark-spotted petals. The beaked fruit of Stork's-bill splits from the top, each strip twisting spirally and parting with a one-seeded segment. This corkscrew-like structure twists and buries the seed. *Status:* native, mostly near sea. *Similar species:* the musk-scented Musk Stork's-bill has blunt stipules, sticky leaves and larger flowers. Sea Stork's-bill has shallow-lobed leaves and tiny flowers.

1 Musk Stork's-bill *(E. moschatum)*; **2** Sea Stork's-bill *(E. maritimum)*

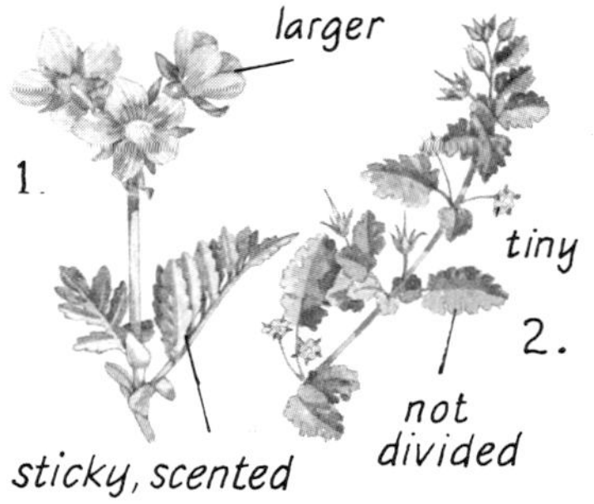

	COMMON STORK'S-BILL
Type	annual
Height	to 60cm, rarely 100cm
Habitat	dunes, cultivated or waste ground; dry, sandy soil
Flowering	June–September
	STEMS AND LEAVES
Stem	variable, slender to stout
Root	slender to stout tap-root
Hairs	sparse to dense
Stipules	oval, papery, whitish
Leaves	most paired either side of stem, 20–200mm, paired leaflets are deeply lobed
Leaf-stalk	lower long, upper short
	FLOWERS
Position	1–9, in long-stalked head, from leaf-base
Bracts	oval, papery, brownish
Type	⚥
Size	8–18mm
Colour	pinkish purple, often black spot at base of upper 2 petals
Stalk	longer than flower
Sepals	5, 3–7mm, oval, tip bristle-like
Petals	5, 4–11mm, often unequal
Stamens	5, orange
Stigmas	5, slender
Ovary	1, 5-celled
	FRUIT
Type	1, lobed, long-beaked capsule, beak splits, each strip twists spirally, parts with 1 segment
Size	15–40mm
Seeds	1 per segment, 3–4mm, elongated

Dog's Mercury *Mercurialis perennis*

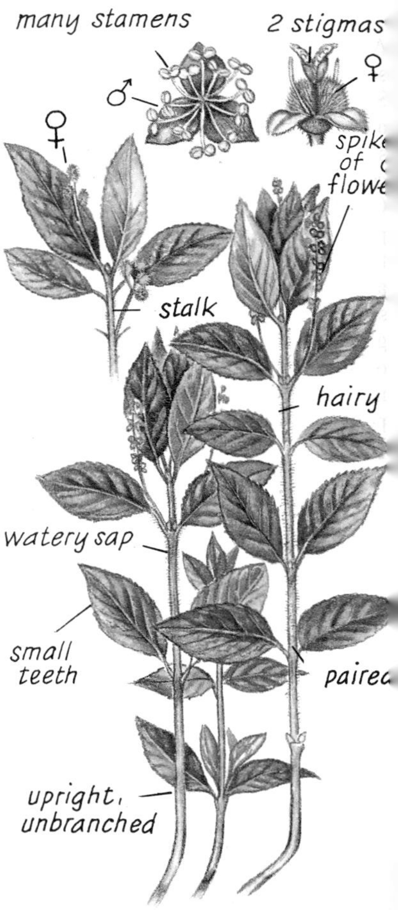

A poisonous plant mainly of Oak, Ash or Beech woodland, where it carpets the floor with sombre green. Plants are either male or female, but because Dog's Mercury spreads more effectively by the creeping underground stems than by seed, large areas are of the same gender. The common name implies that this was a worthless version of the Annual Mercury, which was used medicinally. *Status:* native or introduced in north and Ireland; most of area except extreme north. *Similar species:* Annual Mercury lacks underground stems and is more branched. Its leaves almost lack hairs and the female flowers their stalks.

Annual Mercury *(Mercurialis annua)*

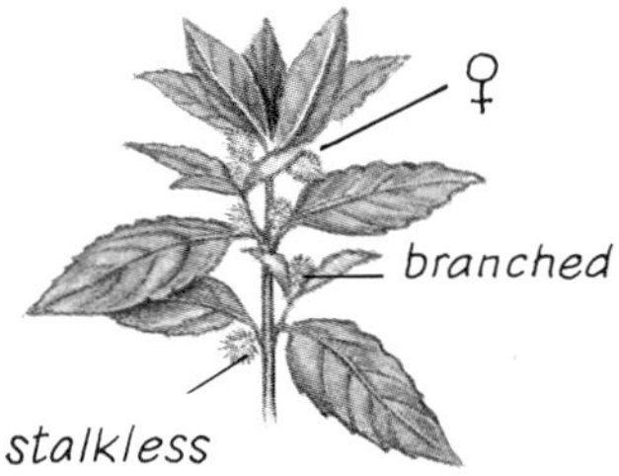

DOG'S MERCURY

Type perennial
Height 15–40cm
Habitat woods, hedges; fertile, often lime-rich soils
Flowering February–April

STEMS AND LEAVES

Stem upright, unbranched, watery sap
Root creeping underground stem
Hairs throughout plant
Stipules small
Leaves paired either side of stem, 30–80mm, more or less elliptical, pointed, edge with rounded teeth
Leaf-stalk 3–10mm, shorter than blade

FLOWERS

Position ♂ and ♀ flowers on different plants
Bracts absent
Type 1 many ♂ flowers in stalked spike from leaf-base
Type 2 1–3 ♀ flowers on stalk from leaf-base
Size 4–5mm
Colour green
Stalk more or less absent
Perianth 3-lobed
Stamens 8–15
Stigmas 2
Ovary 1, hairy, 2-celled

FRUIT

Type capsule, broad, hairy, opening by 2 vertical splits
Size 6–8mm
Seeds 2, 3–3.5mm, globular, rough

Sun Spurge

Although the curious flowers lack sepals or petals, the bracts of Sun Spurge are yellowish and function like a large flower. This is the same structure as in the related, brightly coloured Poinsettia, most popular at Christmas. The milky sap is acrid and poisonous, and was formerly used to treat warts. *Status:* native; throughout area. *Similar species:* three other spurges have horn-like ends to the glands of the flowers. Petty Spurge has oval, green leaves, and Dwarf Spurge narrow, bluish leaves. Wood Spurge is perennial, hairy, and has joined pairs of bracts below the flowers.

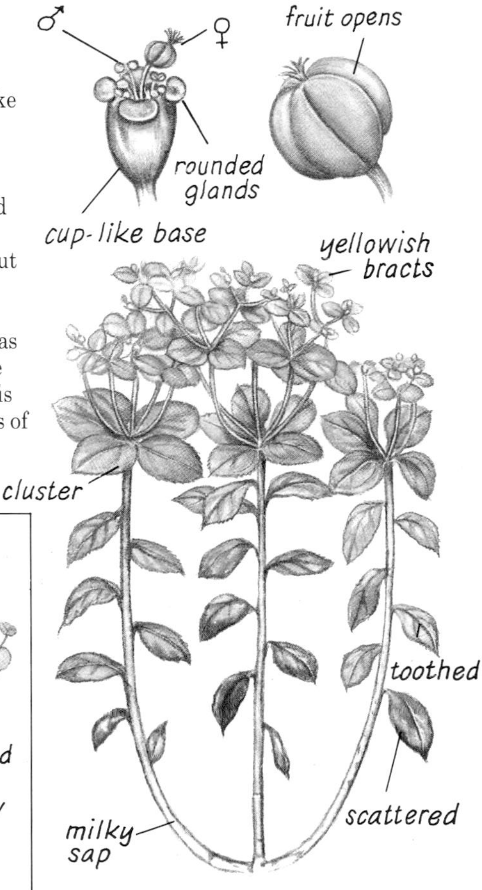

1 Petty Spurge *(E. peplus)*; **2** Dwarf Spurge *(E. exigua)*; **3** Wood Spurge *(E. amygdaloides)*

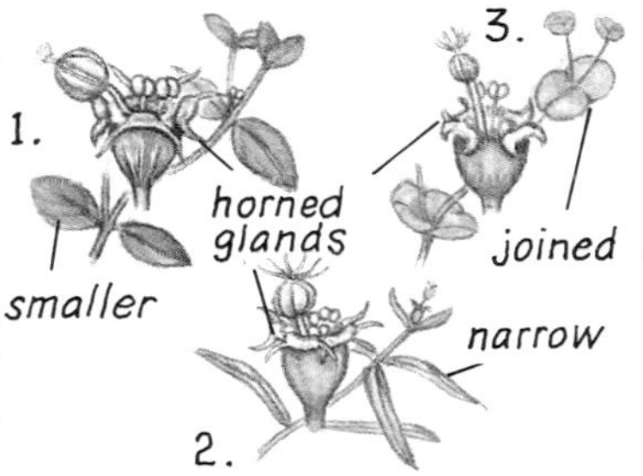

	SUN SPURGE
Type	annual
Height	10–50cm
Habitat	cultivated and waste ground; fertile soil
Flowering	May–October
	STEMS AND LEAVES
Stem	single, upright, with 5 branches above, sap milky
Root	vertical main root
Hairs	more or less hairless
Stipules	absent
Leaves	spirally arranged around stem, 15–30mm, oval, broad above, blunt, minutely toothed, base wedge-shaped
Leaf-stalk	absent

	FLOWERS
Position	♂ and ♀ flowers on same plant, each ♀ with several ♂ flowers and cup-like base with 4–5 oval, green glands around lip
Bracts	leaf-like, yellowish green
Type 1	♂ a stamen on jointed stalk
Type 2	♀ a stalked ovary
Size	1–2mm
Colour	green
Stalk	elongating in fruit
Sepals	absent
Petals	absent
Stigmas	3, often forked
Ovary	1, 3-celled
	FRUIT
Type	1, broad, 3-angled, smooth capsule, opens by 3 splits
Size	3–5mm
Seeds	3, *c*2mm, brown, rough

Common Milkwort *Polygala vulgaris*

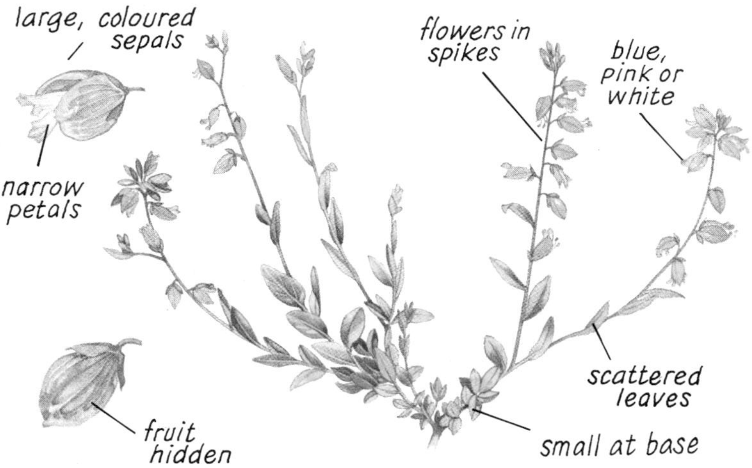

A bright jewel of a flower, brightening grassland with patches of sky-blue, mauve, pink or white. Its colour comes more from the two large sepals than it does from the relatively small and partly hidden petals. The plant was believed to increase the milk of nursing mothers, although this effect is unsubstantiated. *Status:* native; fairly common, throughout area. *Similar species:* Heath Milkwort, mainly in lime-free soils, has leaves paired either side of the stem. Chalk Milkwort, in lime-rich soils, has large lower leaves forming a rosette.

1 Heath Milkwort *(P. serpyllifolia)*; 2 Chalk Milkwort *(P. calcarea)*

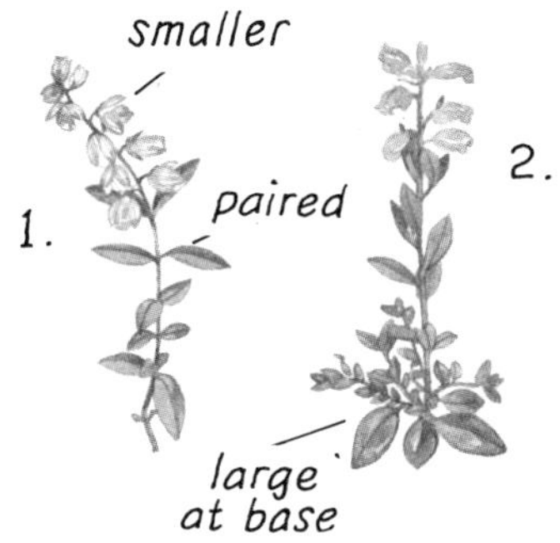

	COMMON MILKWORT
Type	perennial
Height	10–30cm
Habitat	grassland, heaths, dunes
Flowering	May–September
	STEMS AND LEAVES
Stem	upright or angled upwards
Root	woody stock
Hairs	absent or sparse
Stipules	absent
Leaves	on alternate sides of stem, 5–35mm, pointed, edge unbroken, lower oval or elliptical, small; upper spear-shaped
Leaf-stalk	absent
	FLOWERS
Position	10–40, in spike at stem-tip, often one-sided
Bracts	small, translucent
Type	⚥
Size	4–8mm
Colour	blue, purplish pink, or white
Stalk	shorter than flower
Sepals	5, 3 outer *c*3mm, 2 inner 4–7mm, oval, petal-like, coloured
Petals	3, 4–8mm, unequal, narrow, lower fringed, bases joined
Stamens	8, partly joined
Stigma	1, 2-lobed, style long
Ovary	1, usually 2-celled
	FRUIT
Type	1, 2-celled capsule, heart-shaped, flattened, splits at edge, hidden by sepals
Size	4–6mm
Seeds	2, 2.5–3mm, oblong, hairy

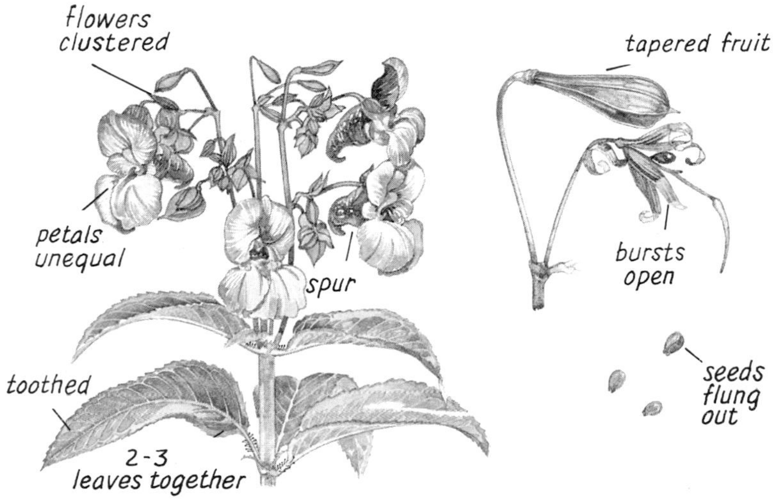

A spectacular plant that has hooded, pink flowers; stout, red-flushed stems; and purple, stalked glands at the leaf-bases. Walls of the ripe capsule are elastic and, at the slightest touch, rapidly roll back to fling out the seeds. *Status:* introduced from the Himalaya; often common, most of area. *Similar species:* the leaves of other Balsams are not paired. Orange Balsam, from North America, is fairly common in Britain and France. Touch-me-not Balsam, which has bright yellow flowers, is native. Small Balsam is Asiatic, and has much smaller, pale yellow flowers.

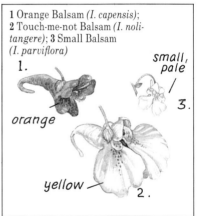

1 Orange Balsam *(I. capensis)*; **2** Touch-me-not Balsam *(I. noli-tangere)*; **3** Small Balsam *(I. parviflora)*

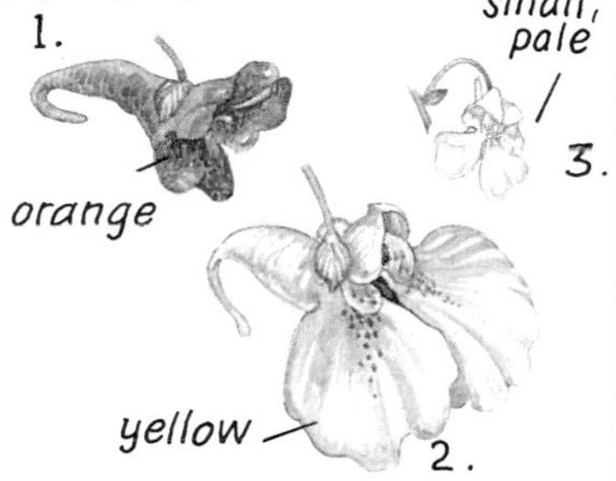

	INDIAN BALSAM
Type	annual
Height	100–200cm
Habitat	river banks, lakesides, waste ground; damp soil
Flowering	July–October
	STEMS AND LEAVES
Stem	stout, fleshy, upright, often reddish
Root	thick, vertical main root
Hairs	more or less absent
Stipules	absent
Leaves	paired or in threes, 60–150mm, spear-shaped or elliptical, pointed, sharp-toothed
Leaf-stalk	shorter than blade, often with purple, stalked glands
	FLOWERS
Position	5–10, spike from leaf-base
Bracts	oval, pointed
Type	⚥
Size	24–40mm
Colour	purplish pink, rarely white
Stalk	almost equalling flower
Sepals	3, 2 small, lower 12–27mm, hollow, tip spur-like
Petals	5, 2 joined each side, upper broad, 10–25mm
Stamens	5, mostly joined
Stigma	1, 5-toothed
Ovary	1, 5-celled
	FRUIT
Type	1, capsule, club-shaped, angled, walls elastic, sides coil back when ripe
Size	15–30mm
Seeds	few, 4–5mm, egg-shaped

Perforate St John's-wort *Hypericum perforatum*

A common plant of dry, grassy places, especially hedge-banks, its leaves are covered with translucent dots as if punctured, and are described in the common name. Stamens resembling a pin-cushion are gathered by their bases into three bundles. St John's-worts were long used to treat wounds and are still found in some medicines. *Status:* native; throughout area. *Similar species:* Slender St John's-wort has blunt sepals and mostly heart-shaped leaf-bases. Square-stalked St John's-wort has four-angled stems and smaller flowers. Marsh St John's-wort, in wet ground, has softly hairy stems and sepals fringed with reddish glands.

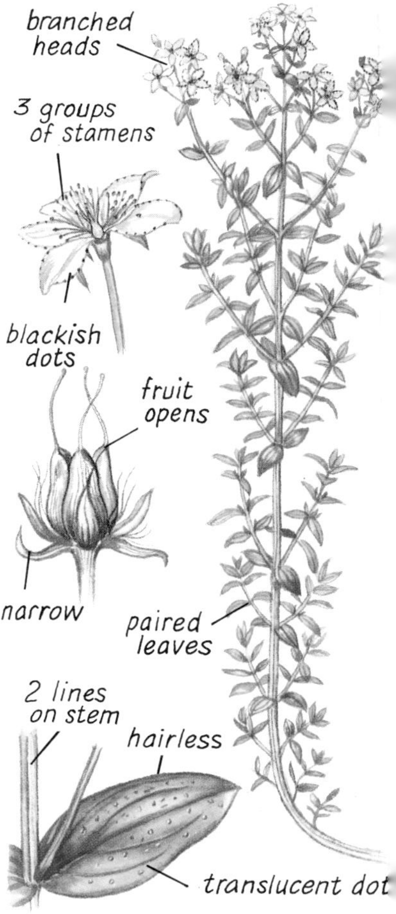

1 Slender St John's-wort *(H. pulchrum)*; **2** Square-stalked St John's-wort *(H. tetrapterum)*; **3** Marsh St John's-wort *(H. elodes)*

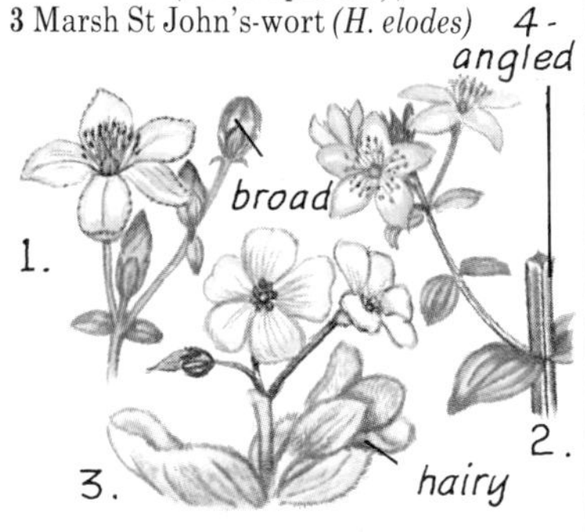

	PERFORATE ST JOHN'S-WORT
Type	perennial
Height	30–90cm
Habitat	grassland, hedges, woods; mainly lime-rich soils
Flowering	June–September
	STEMS AND LEAVES
Stem	upright, woody at base, with 2 raised lines
Root	creeping underground stem
Hairs	absent
Stipules	absent
Leaves	paired either side of stem, 10–20mm, elliptical to narrowly oblong, blunt, edge unbroken, base narrowed, many translucent dots
Leaf-stalk	absent

	FLOWERS
Position	many in wide-branched head
Bracts	present, lower leaf-like
Type	⚥
Size	17–25mm
Colour	yellow, petal-edge dotted with black
Stalk	shorter than flower
Sepals	5, 5–7mm, spear-shaped
Petals	5, 8–14mm, rather wedge-shaped with oblique end
Stamens	numerous
Stigmas	3, on long styles
Ovary	1, 3-celled
	FRUIT
Type	1, almost pear-shaped capsule, splits into 3
Size	*c*6mm
Seeds	many, *c*1mm, oblong, finely pitted

In the centre of each yellow flower of this shrub is a prominent tuft of long stamens. The berries turn to red, then purplish black. Corrupted from French, the common name means 'all wholesome' and the leaves were widely used to treat wounds. *Status:* native; rather scattered, mainly south-west of area. *Similar species:* Stinking Tutsan has a goat-like smell, stamens longer than the petals, and the ripe fruit is red but scarcely succulent. Rose-of-Sharon is low-growing and has much larger flowers. Commonly planted, it often escapes and spreads with creeping underground stems to cover large areas.

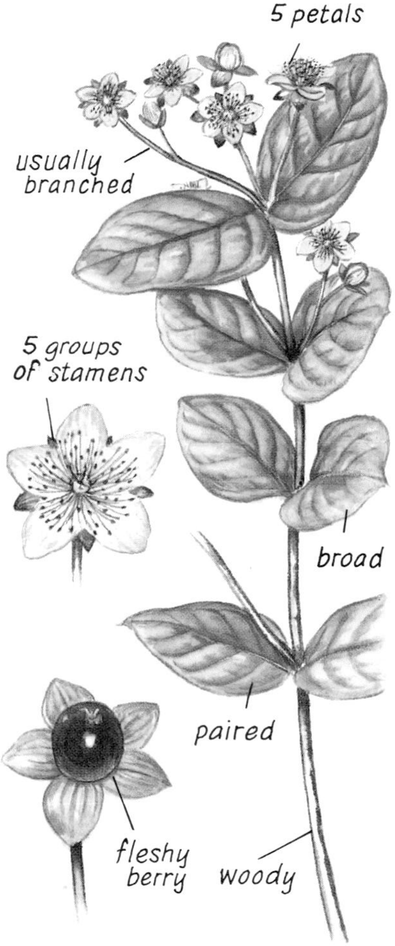

1 Stinking Tutsan *(H. hircinum)*;
2 Rose-of-Sharon *(H. calycinum)*

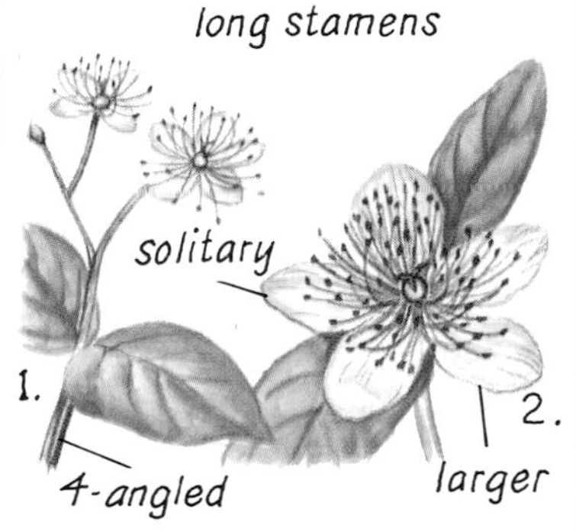

TUTSAN

Type	shrub
Height	40–100cm
Habitat	woods, hedges; damp soils
Flowering	June–August

STEMS AND LEAVES

Stem	woody, branched, with 2 raised lines
Root	woody stock
Hairs	absent
Stipules	absent
Leaves	paired either side of stem, 50–100mm, oval, blunt, edge unbroken, base heart-shaped, partly evergreen
Leaf-stalk	absent

FLOWERS

Position	few, in branched cluster from leaf-base
Bracts	present
Type	⚥
Size	12–23mm
Colour	yellow
Stalk	about equalling flower
Sepals	5, 8–15mm, oval, blunt, unequal, often reddish-tinged, remaining in fruit
Petals	5, 6–12mm, oval
Stamens	many, about equalling petals
Stigmas	3, on curved styles
Ovary	1, partly 3-celled

FRUIT

Type	1, ellipsoidal to globular berry, fleshy, turning red then purplish black
Size	7–12mm
Seeds	numerous, *c*1mm, oblong, narrowly winged

Common Dog-violet *Viola riviniana*

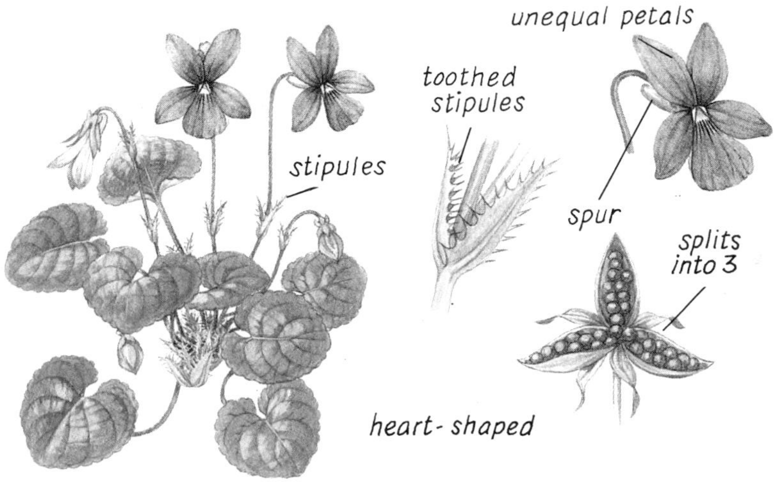

One of the most attractive wild flowers of shady hedge-banks or the edges of woodland. The reference to 'dog' in the name probably means that this was thought to be inferior to the scented violet. *Status:* native; throughout area. *Similar species:* Sweet Violet is the familiar, sweetly-scented Violet of gardens and has all its leaves at the base of the plant. Heath Dog-violet, which has clear blue flowers, has narrower leaves and smaller short-toothed stipules. Marsh Violet, of wet places, has kidney-shaped leaves from underground, creeping stems and lilac, dark-veined flowers.

1 Heath Dog-violet *(V. canina)*; **2** Sweet Violet *(V. odorata)*; **3** Marsh Violet *(V. palustris)*

	COMMON DOG-VIOLET
Type	perennial
Height	2–40cm
Habitat	woods, hedges, heaths, mountain rocks
Flowering	April–June
	STEMS AND LEAVES
Stem	main, non-flowering stem short, side-shoots longer
Root	slender, short, upright, some shoots from root-buds
Hairs	absent or sparse, short
Stipules	short, spear-shaped, fringed
Leaves	basal or on alternate sides of stem, 5–80mm, heart-shaped, blunt to sharpish, edge with rounded teeth
Leaf-stalk	often longer than leaf

	FLOWERS
Position	single, from leaf-base
Bracts	2, slender
Type	⚥, not scented
Size	14–22mm
Colour	blue-violet, spur whitish
Stalk	much longer than flower
Sepals	5, 7–12mm, spear-shaped, lobed at base
Petals	5, 8–18mm, spur 3–5mm, oval, overlapping, lowest with backward-pointing spur
Stamens	5, 2 lower with spur
Stigma	1, style hook-like at tip
Ovary	1, 1-celled
	FRUIT
Type	1, 3-angled, pointed capsule, splits into 3
Size	6–13mm
Seeds	many, 2–2.5mm, egg-shaped

ace-like markings on the flowers of /ild Pansy have long made it a ıvourite, the wild species of Pansy eing developed as the familiar garden lants. Pansies differ from Violets ıainly in the large, leaf-like stipules nd flatter flowers with side petals ngled upwards. *Status:* native; ıroughout area. *Similar species:* easide Pansy is a low-growing erennial found by the coast. Field ansy, usually a weed, has small petals bout equalling the sepals. Mountain 'ansy is a perennial of hilly areas, oreading by underground stems to form ırge clumps on fairly lime-rich soils.

1 Seaside Pansy *(V. tricolor* subsp. *curtisii)*; 2 Field Pansy *(V. arvensis)*; 3 Mountain Pansy *(V. lutea)*

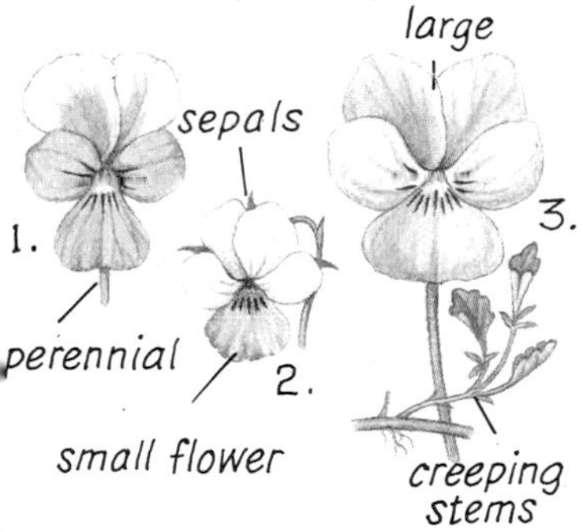

	WILD PANSY
Type	usually annual
Height	15–30cm, rarely 45cm
Habitat	cultivated and waste ground, grassland; mainly lime-free soils
Flowering	April–September
	STEMS AND LEAVES
Stem	usually many-branched
Root	fibrous, rarely with short underground stems
Hairs	absent or very short
Stipules	large, with paired lobes
Leaves	on alternate sides of stem, 10–50mm, oval, spear-shaped or elliptical, blunt, with rounded teeth
Leaf-stalk	lower long, upper short

	FLOWERS
Position	solitary, from leaf-base
Bracts	2, tiny
Type	⚥
Size	15–25mm, rarely 35mm
Colour	petals violet, yellow, pink or white with purplish marks
Stalk	long
Sepals	5, 5–14mm, spear-shaped
Petals	5, 7–17mm, unequal, oval, flattish, side petals turn upwards, lowest with spur
Stamens	5, 2 lower with spur
Stigma	1, club-shaped
Ovary	1, 1-celled
	FRUIT
Type	1, 3-angled capsule, splits into 3
Size	6–10mm
Seeds	many, 1.5–2mm, egg-shaped

Musk Mallow *Malva moschata*

These attractive, large, pink flowers resemble those of the related Hollyhock or Hibiscus, and have stamens joined into a club-shaped cluster. Mallows make copious mucilage, formerly used in cough-mixtures, poultices or to treat wasp-stings. *Status:* native or naturalized in north; widespread except for much of north. *Similar species:* other Mallows have leaves less divided. Common Mallow has purplish, dark-striped flowers. Dwarf Mallow is a low-growing annual with small pale flowers. Marsh-mallow, in marshy places near the sea, has soft, velvety leaves, pale pink flowers and more bracts beneath the sepals.

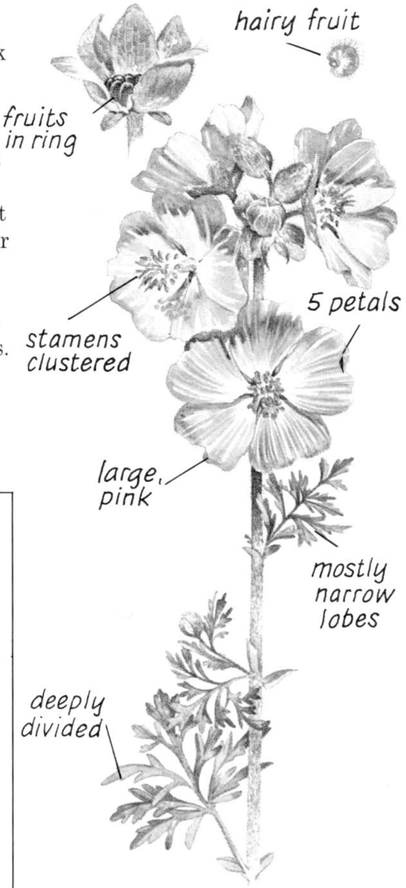

1 Common Mallow *(M. sylvestris)*;
2 Dwarf Mallow *(M. neglecta)*;
3 Marsh-mallow *(Althaea officinalis)*

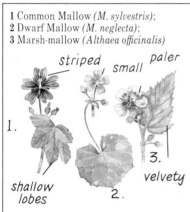

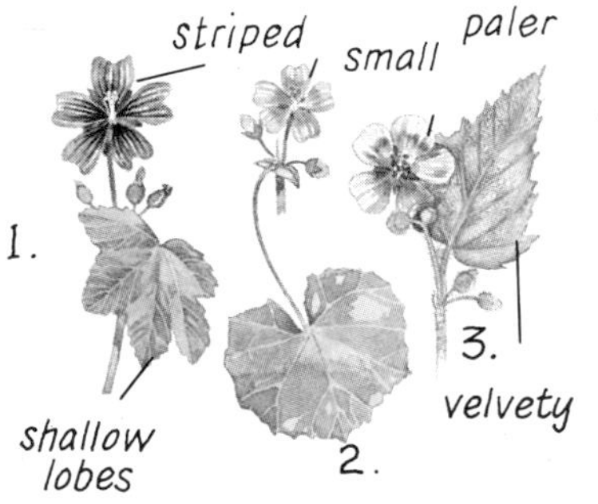

	MUSK MALLOW
Type	perennial
Height	30–80cm
Habitat	grassy places; mainly fertile soils
Flowering	July–August
	STEMS AND LEAVES
Stem	upright, rounded
Root	thick, branched stock
Hairs	sparse
Stipules	small, spear-shaped
Leaves	basal or on alternate sides of stem, variable, 50–80mm, 3–7 lobes, toothed, lower kidney-shaped, upper mostly cut into thin lobes
Leaf-stalk	lower long, upper short
	FLOWERS
Position	single from leaf-base or irregular head at stem-tip
Bracts	3 beneath base of sepals
Type	☿
Size	30–60mm
Colour	rose-pink, rarely white, veins crimson
Stalk	shorter than flower
Sepals	5, 6–12mm, oval, pointed
Petals	5, 14–25mm, twisted together in bud, equal, oval, squarish and notched
Stamens	many, in club-shaped head
Stigmas	numerous, slender
Ovary	1, usually many-celled
	FRUIT
Type	a ring of wedge-shaped, hairy, nut-like segments
Size	*c*2mm
Seeds	1 per segment, nearly circular, flattened

Helianthemum nummularium Common Rock-rose

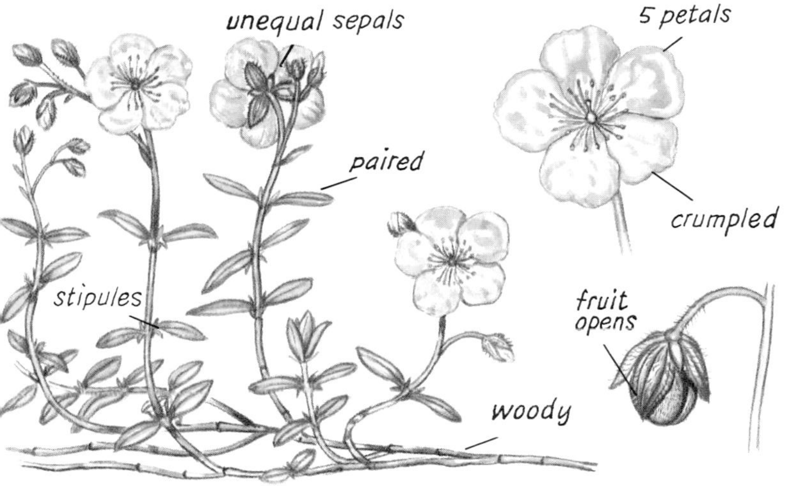

A wiry-stemmed plant, its yellow petals crumpled like tissue-paper, opening in sunny weather and falling within a few hours. The flowers open with a tuft of stamens in the centre, so the first insect visitor is dusted with pollen. Once touched, the stamens move apart so that the flower can receive pollen from the next visitor. *Status:* native; often common, absent from much of north, west and many islands. *Similar species:* White Rock-rose has narrow, greyish, woolly leaves and white flowers. Spotted Rock-rose is an annual with a rosette of leaves at the base and smaller petals, often with a red spot at the base.

1 White Rock-rose *(H. apenninum)*; 2 Spotted Rock-rose *(Tuberaria guttata)*

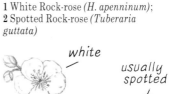

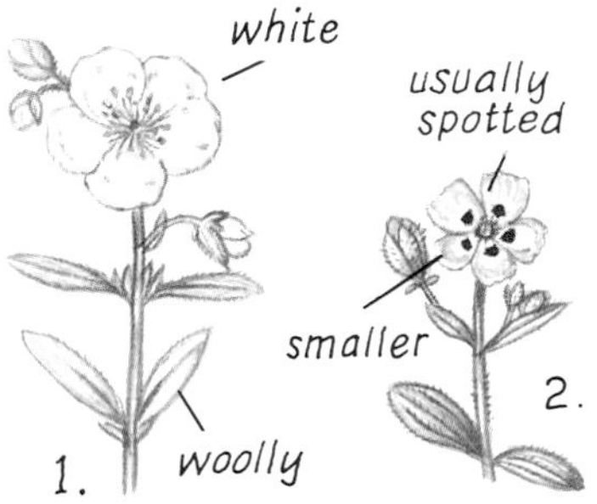

	COMMON ROCK-ROSE
Type	perennial
Height	5–30cm
Habitat	grassland, scrub; lime-rich soils
Flowering	June–September
	STEMS AND LEAVES
Stem	many, woody below, low-growing or angled upwards
Root	thick, woody stock, vertical tap-root
Hairs	sparse or short; dense, whitish beneath leaves
Stipules	narrowly spear-shaped
Leaves	paired either side of stem, 5–20mm, oblong or oval, blunt, edge unbroken
Leaf-stalk	much shorter than blade
	FLOWERS
Position	1–12, in 1-sided, spike-like head from stem-tip
Bracts	narrowly spear-shaped
Type	⚥
Size	14–25mm, rarely 30mm
Colour	usually bright yellow
Stalk	about equalling flower
Sepals	5, 2 slender, *c*2mm; 3 oval, *c*6mm
Petals	5, 6–12mm, equal, oval, crumpled, soon falling
Stamens	numerous, moving apart when touched
Stigma	1, 3-lobed on S-shaped style
Ovary	1, 1-celled
	FRUIT
Type	1, capsule, almost globular, splits into 3
Size	*c*6mm
Seeds	many, *c*2mm, egg-shaped

White Bryony *Bryonia cretica* subsp. *dioica*

Most noticeable in fruit, the stems bearing clusters of red berries hang like festoons in a leafless Autumn hedgerow. Although attractive, the berries are poisonous and can be fatal. White Bryony was cultivated for the massive rootstock; its uses included the treatment of rheumatic and arthritic pain. *Status:* native or naturalized in north; sometimes common, rare in north. *Similar species:* Black Bryony is unrelated, although in fruit and with withered leaves the two look similar. This plant has twining stems, glossy, heart-shaped leaves, and six-petalled flowers, the males in long spikes.

Black Bryony *(Tamus communis)*

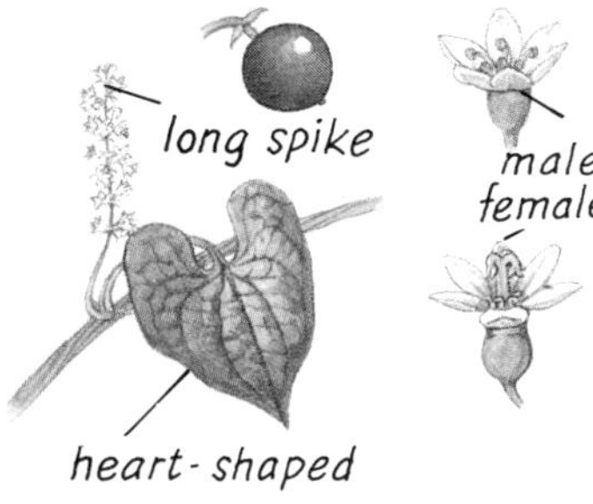

	WHITE BRYONY
Type	perennial
Height	up to 400cm
Habitat	hedgerows, scrub, woods; mainly well-drained soils
Flowering	May–September
	STEMS AND LEAVES
Stem	long, angled, bristly; climbs with coiled tendrils at base of leaf-stalks
Root	large, swollen, stock
Hairs	stiff, swollen-based
Stipules	absent
Leaves	spirally placed around stem, 50–100mm, most with 5 radiating lobes, wavy-toothed
Leaf-stalk	shorter than blade
	FLOWERS
Position	♂ and ♀ flowers on different plants
Bracts	absent
Type 1	♂, 3–8 in long-stalked head
Type 2	♀, 2–5 in stalkless cluster from leaf-base, 10–12mm
Size	12–18mm
Colour	greenish white
Stalk	present
Sepals	5, triangular, bases joined
Petals	5, oblong, hairy, bases joined
Stamens	5, 4 joined in pairs
Stigmas	3, 2-lobed, on thick style
Ovary	1, globular, beneath petals, 3-celled
	FRUIT
Type	1, berry, globular, smooth, red when ripe
Size	5–8mm
Seeds	3–6, 4–5mm, flattened, black and yellow mottled

n elegant plant with tall spikes of urple flowers. Each plant has one of ıree sorts of flowers. The style is either ıorter than, about equal to, or much ɔnger than the sepals, and the stamens re equally different in length. This nsures that a flower receives pollen ·om a different plant. *Status:* native; ıore or less throughout area, rare or bsent towards north. *Similar species:* wo related plants of wet places are maller annuals with each flower at a ·af-base. Grass-poly is upright with blong leaves; creeping Water-purslane as spoon-shaped leaves and tiny owers.

1 Grass-poly *(L. hyssopifolia)*;
2 Water-purslane *(L. portula)*

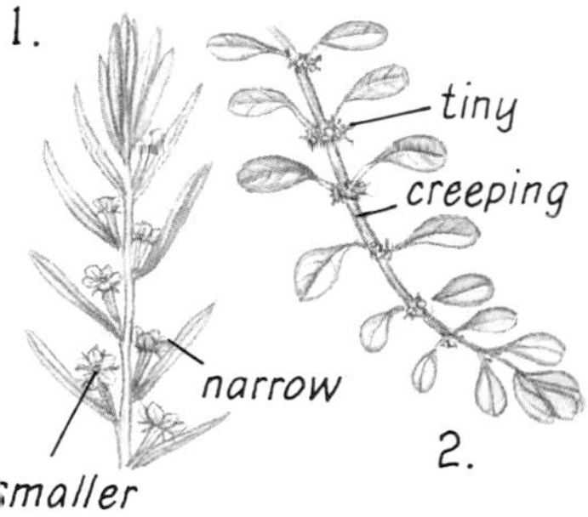

	PURPLE-LOOSESTRIFE
Type	perennial
Height	60–120cm
Habitat	edges of lakes or rivers, fens; wet ground
Flowering	June–August
	STEMS AND LEAVES
Stem	upright, 4-angled, usually unbranched
Root	thick stock
Hairs	short, often sparse
Stipules	absent
Leaves	most paired or in threes, 40–70mm, spear-shaped to oval, pointed, edge unbroken, base heart-shaped
Leaf-stalk	absent

	FLOWERS
Position	numerous, in rings towards stem-tip, in spike-like head
Bracts	slender, soon falling
Type	⚥
Size	10–15mm
Colour	reddish-purple
Stalk	shorter than flower
Sepals	6, *c*6mm, teeth 2–3mm, bases joined into ribbed, hairy tube
Petals	6, 8–10mm, nearly oval
Stamens	12, 2 different lengths
Stigma	1, club-shaped, style short, medium or long
Ovary	1, 2-celled
	FRUIT
Type	1, capsule, splits into 2, egg-shaped, in sepal-tube
Size	3–4mm
Seeds	numerous, *c*1mm, flattened

Large-flowered Evening-primrose *Oenothera erythrosepala*

A tall, rather bushy plant, originally only a garden plant. At dusk the flowers open so rapidly that the petals move visibly. Within minutes, sepals split and petals unfurl. A delicate scent, like orange-blossom, and almost luminous, pale petals attract night-flying moths. *Status:* introduced; often common, absent from north. *Similar species:* Fragrant Evening-primrose lacks red-based hairs and has more strongly scented flowers which turn red. Common Evening-primrose lacks red-based hairs and has smaller flowers with green sepals.

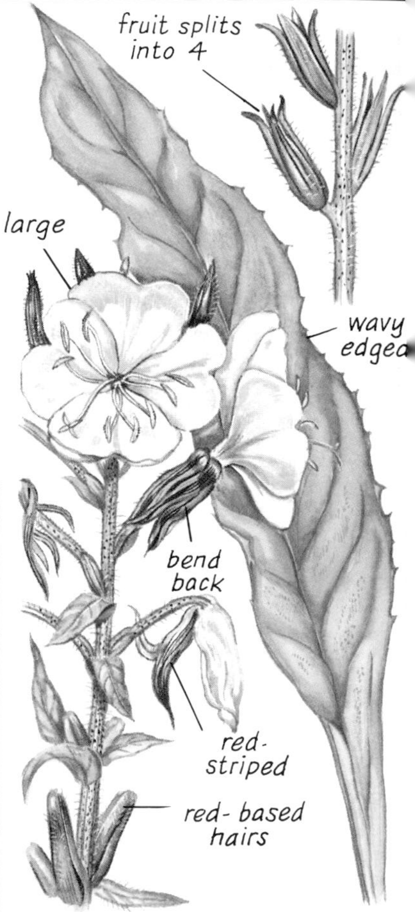

1 Common Evening-primrose *(O. biennis)*; **2** Fragrant Evening-primrose *(O. stricta)*

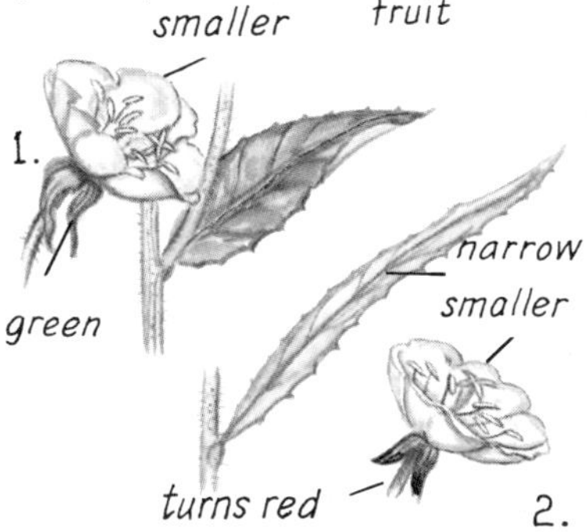

	LARGE-FLOWERED EVENING-PRIMROSE
Type	biennial
Height	50–100cm
Habitat	waste ground, banks of roads and railways, dunes
Flowering	June–September
	STEMS AND LEAVES
Stem	upright, stout, leafy
Root	thick, white tap-root
Hairs	mostly short, some long with swollen, red bases
Stipules	absent
Leaves	spirally arranged, 40–250mm, elliptical to spear-shaped, midrib white or pink, tip pointed, edge wavy, slightly toothed
Leaf-stalk	short or almost absent
	FLOWERS
Position	in loose spike at stem-tip
Bracts	leaf-like below
Type	⚥, scented
Size	80–100mm
Colour	pale yellow
Stalk	shorter than flower
Sepals	4, 35–50mm, bases joined, tubular, red-striped, bending back on opening
Petals	4, 40–50mm, twisted together in bud, broad, overlapping, notched
Stamens	8, bases curved
Stigma	1, 4-lobed, on long style
Ovary	1, below sepals, 4-celled
	FRUIT
Type	1, capsule, splits into 4, oblong, tapered, hairy
Size	25–40mm
Seeds	numerous, 1–2mm, oblong

An easily overlooked plant with small, two-petalled, white flowers, it is better known for its bur-like fruits, which become entangled in socks or pet's fur. This is the plant's method of dispersal, courtesy of passing animals. *Status:* native; throughout area except parts of north. *Similar species:* Upland Enchanter's-nightshade is a hybrid between the above and Alpine Enchanter's-nightshade. Like the latter, it has a tiny bract below each flower but its fruits never mature. Alpine Enchanter's-nightshade has heart-shaped leaf-bases, open flowers clustered at the tops of the stems and hairless sepals.

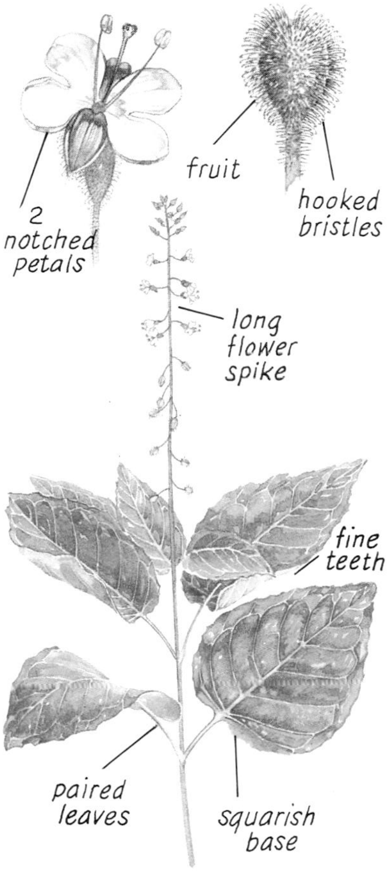

1 Upland Enchanter's-nightshade *(C. × intermedia)*; 2 Alpine Enchanter's-nightshade *(C. alpina)*

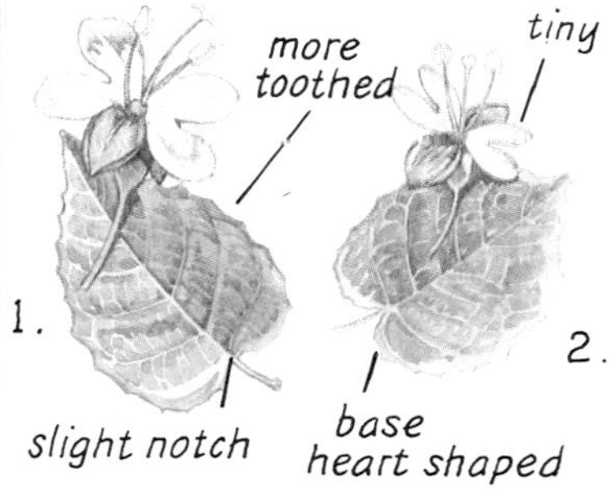

	ENCHANTER'S-NIGHTSHADE
Type	perennial
Height	20–70cm
Habitat	woods, hedges, scrub; damp, fertile soils
Flowering	June–August
	STEMS AND LEAVES
Stem	upright, or angled upwards, swollen at leaf-bases
Root	slender, creeping, underground stems
Hairs	sparse, short, gland-tipped
Stipules	absent
Leaves	paired either side of stem, 40–100mm, oval, pointed, edge minutely toothed, base usually rounded
Leaf-stalk	usually shorter than blade, furrowed above

	FLOWERS
Position	numerous, in loose spike at stem-tip
Bracts	few at base of spike
Type	⚥
Size	4–8mm
Colour	white or pinkish
Stalk	long, bent down in fruit
Sepals	2, 2–3.5mm, equal, bases joined into short tube, soon falling
Petals	2, 2–4mm, deeply notched
Stamens	2
Stigma	1, 2-lobed, on long style
Ovary	1, below sepals, 2-celled
	FRUIT
Type	1, capsule, ovoid, with dense, hooked bristles
Size	3–4mm
Seeds	1–2, 2–2.5mm, elongated

Rosebay Willowherb *Chamerion angustifolium*

Spreading underground to form vast clumps, this plant bears slender spikes of rose-purple flowers. In Autumn it has fluffy masses of plumed seeds. Formerly rarer, the species has spread with the creation of railway embankments and demolition sites. *Status:* native; throughout area, often common, rarer in Ireland and north. *Similar species:* other Willowherbs have mostly paired leaves and upright, equal-petalled flowers. Great Willowherb has hairy leaves which clasp the stem. Two species with smaller flowers are Hoary Willowherb, which has hairy leaves, and Broad-leaved Willowherb which has almost hairless leaves.

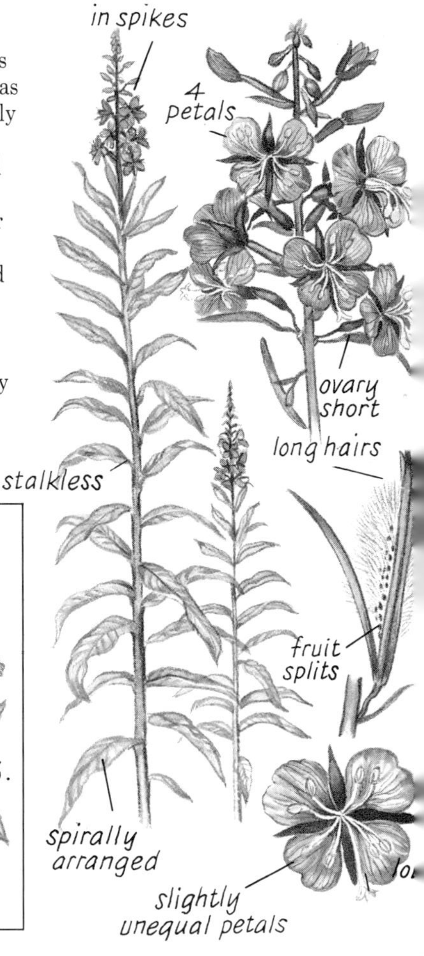

1 Great Willowherb *(Epilobium hirsutum)*; **2** Hoary Willowherb *(E. parviflorum)*; **3** Broad-leaved Willowherb *(E. montanum)*

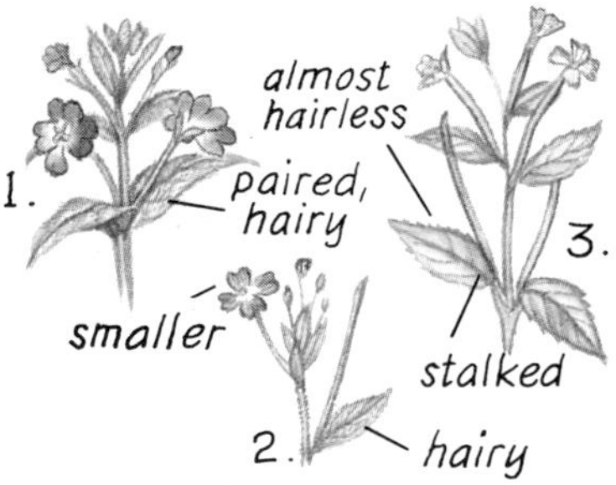

	ROSEBAY WILLOWHERB
Type	perennial
Height	30–120cm, rarely 250cm
Habitat	woodland clearings, scree, waste ground; mostly stony soils, often on burnt ground
Flowering	July–September
	STEMS AND LEAVES
Stem	upright, leafy
Root	woody, horizontal, creeping roots make new stems
Hairs	absent below, short above
Stipules	absent
Leaves	spirally arranged around stem, 50–150mm, narrowly spear-shaped or elliptical, pointed, edge unbroken or minutely toothed, wavy
Leaf-stalk	almost stalkless

	FLOWERS
Position	many, in spike at stem-tip
Bracts	leaf-like below
Type	⚥
Size	20–30mm
Colour	deep pinkish purple
Stalk	10–15mm
Sepals	4, 8–12mm, slender, purple
Petals	4, 10–16mm, oval, notched, upper 2 broader than lower 2
Stamens	8
Stigma	1, 4-lobed, on long style
Ovary	1, below sepals, 4-celled
	FRUIT
Type	1, capsule, 4-angled, slender, splits into 4
Size	25–80mm
Seeds	many, 1–2mm, egg-shaped, with plume of long bristles

One of the commonest Willowherbs but easily overlooked because it lacks showy flowers. In poorly-drained, cultivated ground it can be a troublesome weed as creeping stems root to make new plants. Willowherbs are larval food-plants for the Elephant Hawk-moth. *Status:* native; often common, most of area except parts of north and some islands. *Similar species:* two common species of similar wet places have rather smaller flowers. Pale Willowherb has stalked leaves and whitish, pink-streaked flowers. Marsh Willowherb has rounded stems without any raised lines. Its creeping stems end in bulb-like buds.

1 Pale Willowherb *(E. roseum)*;
2 Marsh Willowherb *(E. palustre)*

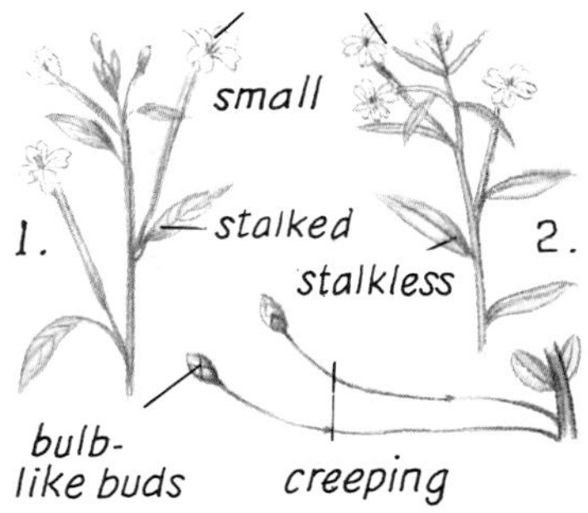

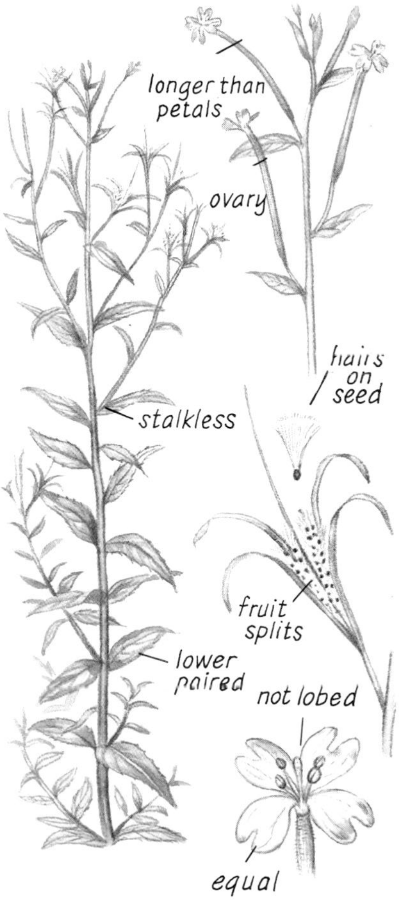

SHORT-FRUITED WILLOWHERB

Type	perennial
Height	30–60cm, rarely 80cm
Habitat	banks of streams, ditches, marshes; wet ground
Flowering	July–August

STEMS AND LEAVES

Stem	upright, 4 raised lines
Root	creeping, rooting stems at or below ground-level
Hairs	absent below, sparse above, pressed to surface
Stipules	absent
Leaves	lower paired, upper spirally arranged, 30–70mm, spear-shaped, edge with few, small teeth, base rounded, runs into lines on stem
Leaf-stalk	absent

FLOWERS

Position	many, in loose spike at stem-tip
Bracts	present, lowest leaf-like
Type	⚥
Size	7–9mm
Colour	pinkish purple
Stalk	shorter than flower
Sepals	4, 3–4mm, spear-shaped, bases joined into tube
Petals	4, 5–6mm, deeply notched
Stamens	8
Stigma	1, on short style
Ovary	1, 4-celled

FRUIT

Type	slender, 4-angled capsule, downy, splits into 4
Size	40–60mm
Seeds	many, base *c*1mm, rough, with long plume of hairs

Spiked Water-milfoil *Myriophyllum spicatum*

A submerged aquatic plant with feathery leaves mostly carried in fours. It is most noticeable in flower, when the slender, reddish flower-spikes appear above the water's surface. *Status:* native; most of area, absent from some islands. *Similar species:* Alternate-flowered Water-milfoil has leaf-like lower bracts and the upper flowers are not in rings. Whorled Water-milfoil has leaves in fives and toothed upper bracts. It overwinters in the form of club-shaped resting buds called 'turions'. Rigid Hornwort is unrelated and has rigid, repeatedly forked leaves. Each flower or spiny fruit is at the base of a leaf.

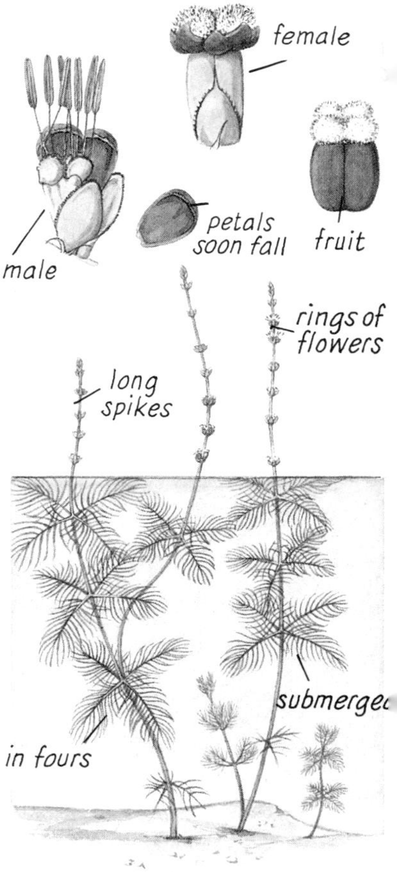

1 Whorled Water-milfoil *(M. verticillatum)*; **2** Alternate-flowered Water-milfoil *(M. alterniflorum)*; **3** Rigid Hornwort *(Ceratophyllum demersum)*

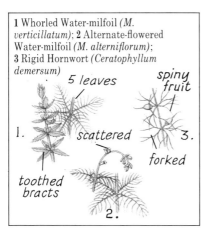

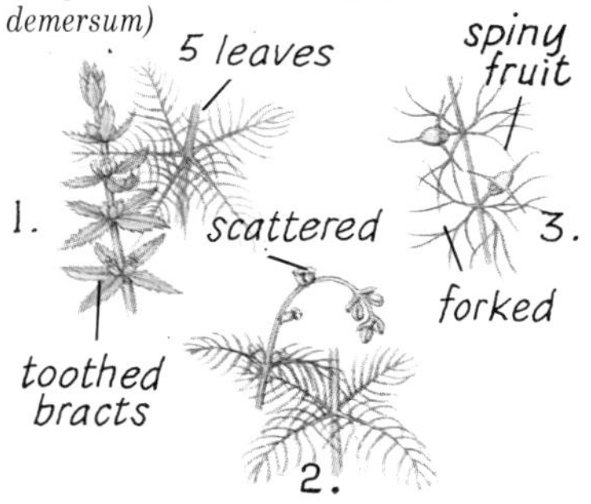

	SPIKED WATER-MILFOIL
Type	perennial
Height	50–250cm
Habitat	lakes, ponds, ditches; still water, especially in lime-rich areas
Flowering	June–July
	STEMS AND LEAVES
Stem	slender, branched, leafless towards base
Root	creeping underground stems
Hairs	absent
Stipules	absent
Leaves	usually rings of 4 around stem, 15–30mm, deeply cut either side into 15–35 thin segments
Leaf-stalk	absent
	FLOWERS
Position	mostly rings of 4, in spike towards stem-tip

Bracts	nearly all not toothed, shorter than flowers
Type	lowest ♀, next ⚥, upper ♂
Size	2–4mm
Colour	pinkish or dull red
Stalk	absent
Sepals	4, ♀ minute, ♂ *c*0.5mm
Petals	4, minute on ♀ flowers; ♂ *c*3mm, soon falling
Stamens	8
Stigmas	4, without a style
Ovary	1, below sepals, 4-celled
	FRUIT
Type	1, almost globular, splits into 4 nut-like parts
Size	2–3mm
Seeds	1 per segment, not released

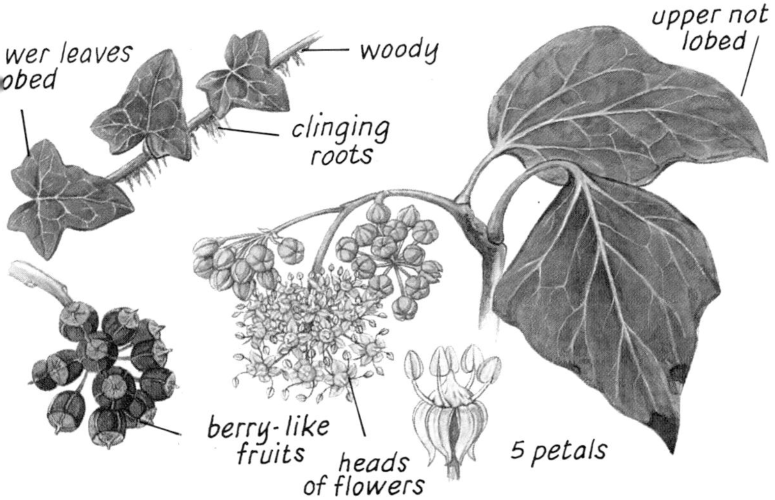

A woody climber with sombre, glossy leaves, Ivy is associated with death and decay because it needs a support to climb up on and there is none better than an old, crumbling wall or a dying tree. Ivy has gained a reputation for killing trees – an unfounded slander, for it has little effect other than to increase the weight on the branches and trunk or to shade some leaves. The yellowish flowers are rather insignificant, but produce copious nectar at a time when little else is in flower and so are visited by large numbers of insects, particularly wasps and hornets. The berries are eaten by birds, such as thrushes and blackbirds, and the plant makes a favoured nesting-site. Ivy is a food-plant for caterpillars of both butterflies and moths, including the Holly Blue and the Swallow-tailed Moth. Many horticultural forms of Ivy are grown, differing greatly in habit and in form and colour of the leaves. *Status:* native; common except in northernmost part of area. (There are no similar species.)

	IVY
Type	biennial
Height	up to 30cm
Habitat	woods, hedges, rocks, walls; most soils
Flowering	September–November
	STEMS AND LEAVES
Stem	woody, up to 25cm across, climbs with clinging roots
Root	woody stock; stem roots
Hairs	mostly hairless; young shoots with branched hairs
Stipules	paired either side of stem
Leaves	spirally arranged, 40–100mm, most with 3–5 triangular, radiating lobes, glossy, evergreen, base heart-shaped; oval or diamond-shaped on flowering stems, not lobed, base rounded or wedge-shaped

Leaf-stalk	shorter than blade
	FLOWERS
Position	many in compact, stalked heads towards stem-tip
Bracts	absent
Type	⚥
Size	5–8mm
Colour	yellowish green
Stalk	about equalling flower
Sepals	5 minute, triangular teeth
Petals	5, 3–4mm, equal, oval
Stamens	5
Stigma	1, slender
Ovary	1, below sepals, 5-celled
	FRUIT
Type	1, berry-like, leathery, almost globular, black
Size	6–8mm
Seeds	2–5, whitish, papery coat

Sanicle *Sanicula europaea*

An unusual species of the Carrot family with radiating lobes to the leaves and very few flowers in each head. Especially common in Beech and Oak woods, it carpets the ground in summer with glossy, dark green leaves. Like several other species of the woodland floor, it is animal-dispersed and has fruits with hooked bristles. *Status:* native; wooded parts of region, often common; absent from many of islands. *Similar species:* Marsh Pennywort also has few flowers in a head. Its leaves are nearly circular, the long stalk attached at the centre and arising from a creeping stem, often hidden among moss.

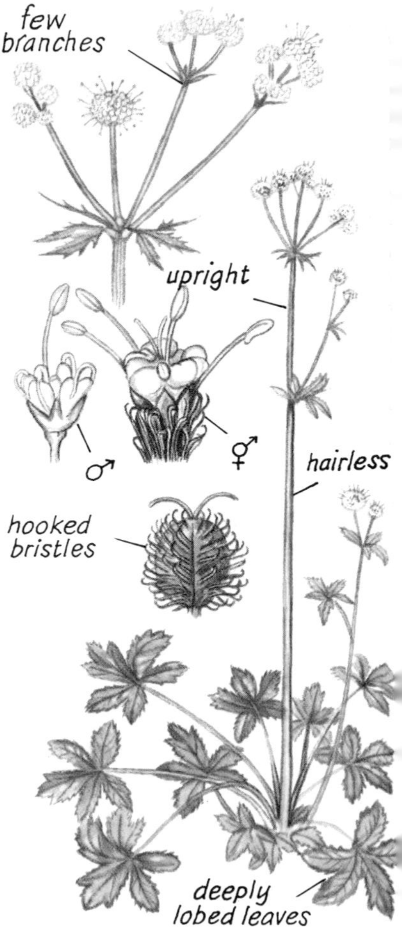

Marsh Pennywort *(Hydrocotyle vulgaris)*

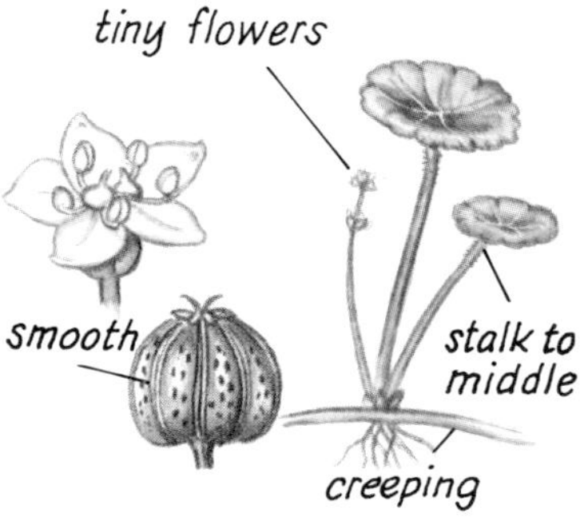

	SANICLE
Type	perennial
Height	20–60cm
Habitat	woods, hedges; rich soils
Flowering	May–September
	STEMS AND LEAVES
Stem	upright
Root	stout stock
Hairs	absent
Stipules	absent
Leaves	mostly basal, few on stem, 20–60mm, with 3–5 radiating lobes, each wedge-shaped, glossy, edge toothed
Leaf-stalk	lower 50–250mm, base broad, clasping stem; upper short
	FLOWERS
Position	few, in 3 or more long-stalked heads at stem-tip
Bracts	lower often lobed, toothed; upper narrow, edge unbroken
Type	♂ and ♀ in same flower-head, outer ♂
Size	2–3.5mm
Colour	pink or white
Stalk	shorter than flower
Sepals	5, 1–2mm, pointed, bases joined
Petals	5, 1.5–2mm, notched, curved inwards
Stamens	5
Stigmas	2, slender
Ovary	1, below sepals, 2-celled
	FRUIT
Type	1, splits into 2, egg-shaped, covered with hooked bristles, dry
Size	4–5mm
Seeds	1 per half, not released

A beautiful plant with a pale blue waxiness to both leaves and stems. Most unusually for a species of the Carrot family, the leaves have holly-like, spine-tipped teeth, and the flower-heads are compact and thistle-like. The thick, fleshy roots were peeled and boiled with sugar to make candied eryngoes. *Status:* nativc; coasts except for extreme north. *Similar species:* Field Eryngo, from southern parts, has more divided, greener leaves and narrow, often toothless bracts. Astrantia is often naturalized and has flattened flower-heads encircled by greenish-white or pink, petal-like bracts.

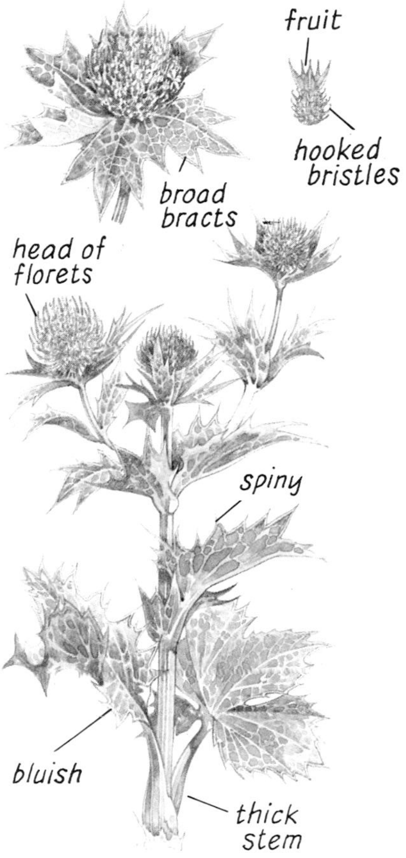

1 Field Eryngo *(E. campestre)*;
2 Astrantia *(Astrantia major)*

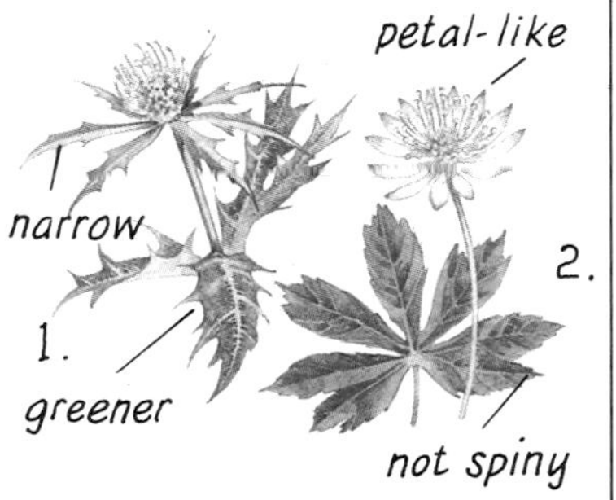

	SEA-HOLLY
Type	perennial
Height	15–60cm
Habitat	sand-dunes, shingle banks
Flowering	July–August
	STEMS AND LEAVES
Stem	more or less upright, thick, branched, hollow
Root	long, thick, fleshy
Hairs	absent
Stipules	absent
Leaves	basal or on alternate sides of stem, 40–120mm, with radiating lobes and spine-tipped teeth, pale bluish-green or purple-tinged, base heart-shaped, upper leaves clasp stem
Leaf-stalk	present or upper absent

	FLOWERS
Position	many in almost globular, stalked head, 15–30mm long
Bracts	leaf-like, spiny below head; 3-toothed below flowers
Type	⚥
Size	6–8mm
Colour	whitish or pale blue
Stalk	absent
Sepals	5, 4–5mm, thin, spine-tipped
Petals	5, 3–4mm, narrow, notched
Stamens	5, curved inwards
Stigmas	2, slender
Ovary	1, below sepals, 2-celled
	FRUIT
Type	1, dry, egg-shaped, corky-walled, covered with hooked spines, splits into 2
Size	5–6mm
Seeds	1 per half, not released

Cow Parsley *Anthriscus sylvestris*

Seemingly ubiquitous, this is the plant that forms the walls of white flanking many a country lane in the Spring. Fern-like foliage supports the broad, umbrella-shaped heads of tiny, five-petalled flowers. Although several species are rather similar, Cow Parsley is the earliest and most common, at least in the southern half of the area. *Status:* native; throughout area. *Similar species:* Bur Chervil is a related annual, which has egg-shaped fruits covered with hooked spines. Rough Chervil, with smooth fruits, has hairy, purple-spotted, solid stems and flowers later than Cow Parsley.

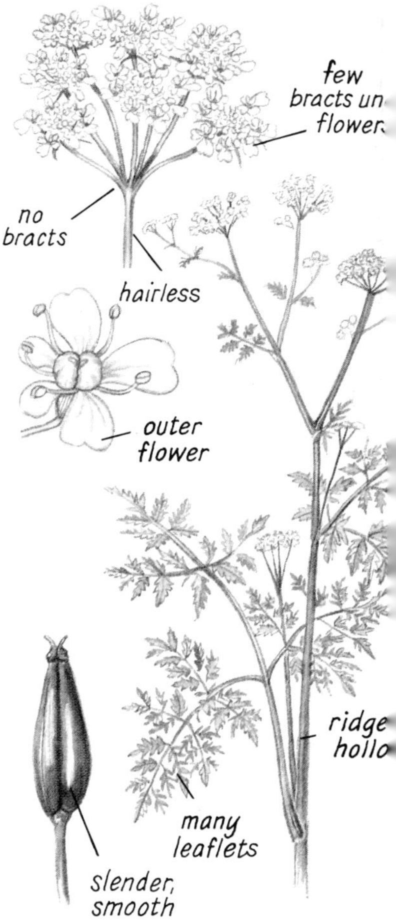

1 Bur Chervil *(A. caucalis)*; **2** Rough Chervil *(Chaerophyllum temulentum)*

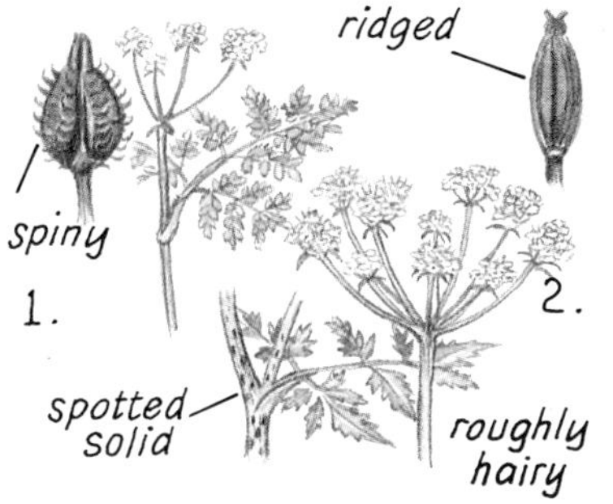

	COW PARSLEY
Type	biennial or perennial
Height	60–100cm
Habitat	hedges, woods, waste ground
Flowering	April–June
	STEMS AND LEAVES
Stem	upright, furrowed, hollow
Root	tap-root, often stout
Hairs	absent below, downy above
Stipules	absent
Leaves	basal or alternate sides of stem, up to 300mm, divided 2–3 times, lobes 15–25mm, oval, toothed
Leaf-stalk	long below, short above, base broad
	FLOWERS
Position	many in umbrella-shaped head 20–60mm wide, 8–16 branches, at stem-tip
Bracts	none below head; few below flower-stalks, 2–5mm, oval
Type	⚥
Size	3–5mm
Colour	white
Stalk	2–5mm
Sepals	5, minute
Petals	5, 1–2.5mm, equal except on outer flowers, notched
Stamens	5
Stigmas	2, slender
Ovary	1, below sepals, 2-celled
	FRUIT
Type	1, splits into 2, oblong, narrow above, dry, smooth, blackish brown, short, beak-like tip
Size	5–10mm
Seeds	1 per half, not released

On a hot summer's day this plant is usually smelled before seen, the air perfused with a cloying, aniseed-like smell. Sweet Cicely was widely cultivated because it is almost entirely edible. Surprisingly sweet, mildly aniseed-flavoured leaves are pleasant on their own or in mixed salads. Roots substitute for Parsnips, and the fruits are still used in liqueurs. *Status:* naturalized; mainly hilly or mountain districts in northern part of area. *Similar species:* Shepherd's-needle also has elongated fruits, but these are usually much longer and thinner. It is a more delicate, annual plant and often a weed.

Shepherd's-needle *(Scandix pecten-veneris)*

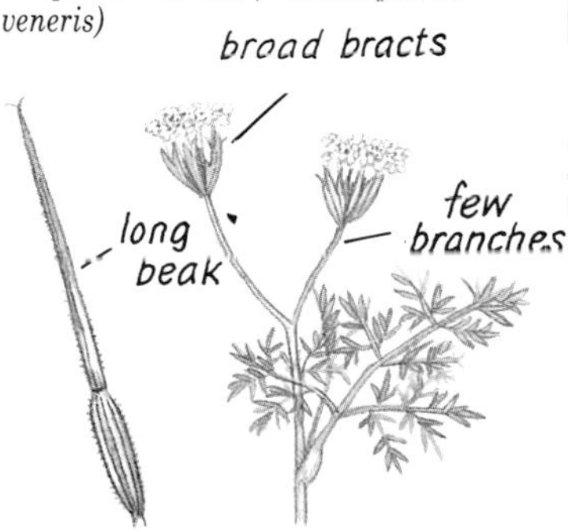

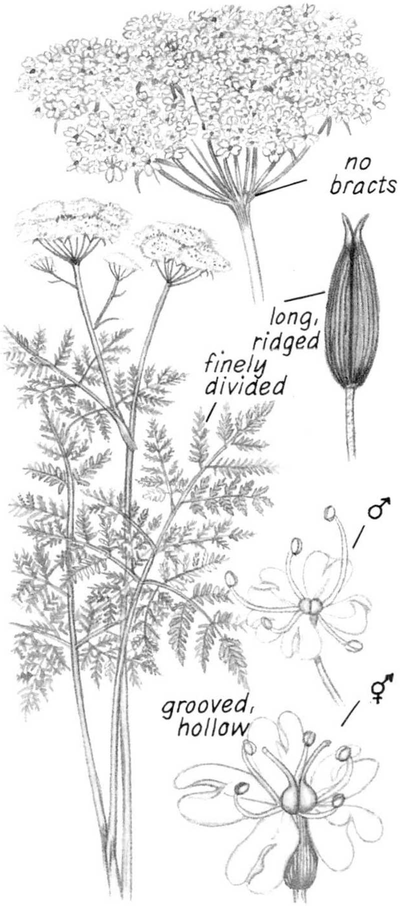

SWEET CICELY

Type perennial
Height 60–100cm
Habitat hedges, woods, grassy places
Flowering May–June

STEMS AND LEAVES

Stem upright, grooved, hollow
Root thick tap-root
Hairs short
Stipules absent
Leaves basal or on alternate sides of stem, to 300mm, divided 2–3 times, lobes oblong, toothed; strong-smelling
Leaf-stalk lower long, upper short, bases broad, sheathing

FLOWERS

Position many, heads 10–50mm across, umbrella-shaped at stem-tips; main branches 5–20
Bracts none below head; *c*5 below flower-stalks, spear-shaped
Type ♂ and ⚥ in same head
Size 2–5mm
Colour white
Stalk longest on ⚥ flowers
Sepals 5, minute
Petals 5, 1–3mm, equal except on outer flowers, oval, notched
Stamens 5
Stigmas 2, slender
Ovary 1, below sepals, 2-celled

FRUIT

Type 1, splits into 2, oblong, tapered, dry, sharply ridged, brown, tip beaked
Size 20–25mm
Seeds 1 per half, not released

Alexanders *Smyrnium olusatrum*

A robust plant of coastal districts, with glossy, dark green foliage, umbrella-shaped, greenish-yellow flower-heads and almost globular, blackish fruits. Probably brought by the Romans as a pot-herb, it was long used for the celery-like leaf-bases. *Status:* introduced, or native in extreme south; mostly near southern coasts. *Similar species:* Scots Lovage is native on northern coasts. A smaller plant, with fewer leaflets, whitish flowers and flattened fruits, it is also edible. Lovage, a garden herb that often escapes, has leaves with fewer, coarser teeth and smaller fruits.

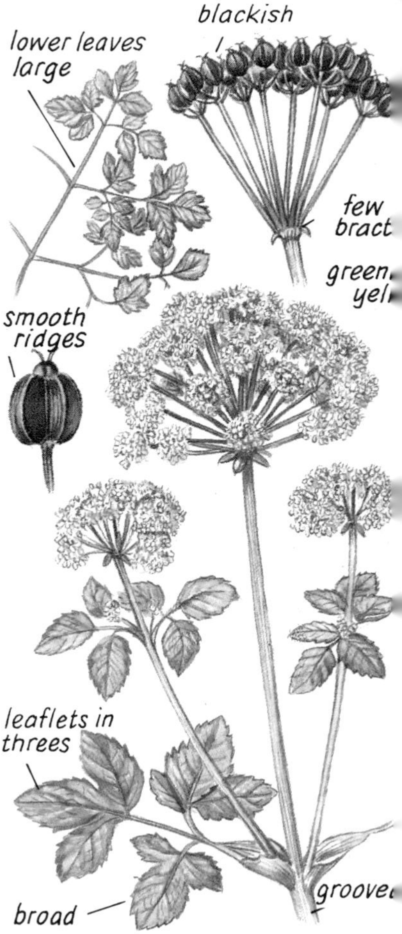

1 Scots Lovage *(Ligusticum scoticum)*; **2** Lovage *(Levisticum officinale)*

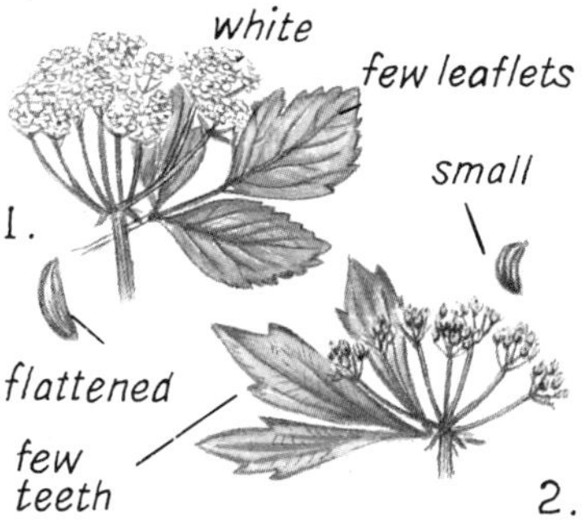

	ALEXANDERS
Type	biennial
Height	50–150cm
Habitat	grassy banks, hedges, cliffs
Flowering	April–June
	STEMS AND LEAVES
Stem	upright, stout, solid or oldest hollow, furrowed
Root	tap-root
Hairs	absent
Stipules	absent
Leaves	basal, scattered or upper paired, up to 300mm, divided 1–3 times, leaflets in 3s, oval, glossy dark green, toothed or lobed
Leaf-stalk	broad base sheaths stem, long or upper short

	FLOWERS
Position	many in umbrella-shaped head, 7–20 branches, at stem-tip
Bracts	few or absent
Type	⚥
Size	1.5–3.5mm
Colour	greenish yellow
Stalk	about equalling flower
Sepals	absent
Petals	5, 0.7–1.5mm, spear-shaped, tip curved in
Stamens	5
Stigmas	2, slender
Ovary	1, below petals, 2-celled
	FRUIT
Type	1, splits into 2, nearly globular, dry, smooth or 3-ridged, almost black
Size	7–8mm
Seeds	1 per half, not released

Crithmum maritimum Rock Samphire

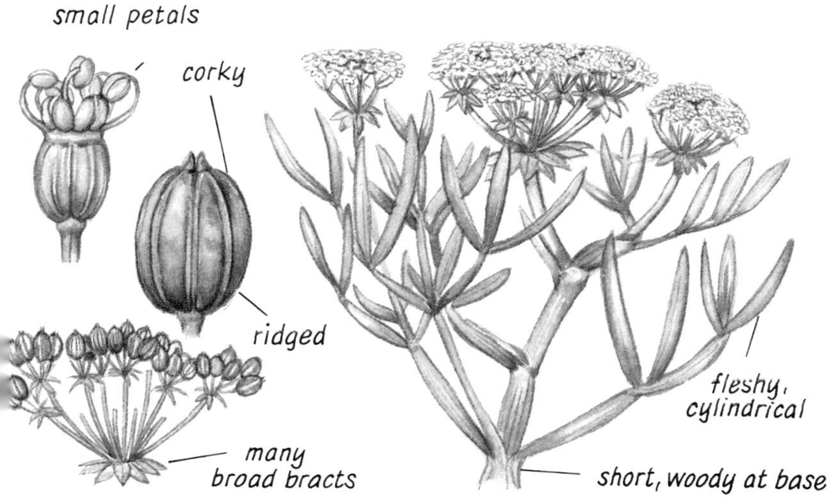

A curious member of the Carrot family, with the normal umbrella-shaped heads of flowers but swollen, succulent, aromatic leaves. These leaves can be made into a pickle or sauce, uses that were formerly commonplace but are now rarely tried. Rock Samphire commonly inhabits inaccessible ledges of sea-cliffs and its collection was an exceedingly hazardous and often lethal trade. Eating the plant was believed to aid digestion and have beneficial effects on the kidneys and bladder. Rock Samphire was sometimes grown as a vegetable on well-drained soils, especially in England and France. The succulent leaves, with a thick, translucent coat, are an adaptation to drought, for even though the plant may be drenched by spray from a rough sea, the salt in the water tends to dry out an unprotected leaf and makes it difficult for roots to take up usable water. *Status:* native; coastal, from Scotland southwards. (There are no similar species.)

	ROCK SAMPHIRE
Type	perennial
Height	15–30cm
Habitat	cliffs, rocks, shingle
Flowering	June–August
	STEMS AND LEAVES
Stem	angled upwards, solid, fleshy, woody at base
Root	woody stock
Hairs	absent
Stipules	absent
Leaves	on alternate sides of stem, divided 1–2 times into slender, smoothly rounded, fleshy, pointed segments, each 10–40mm, edge unbroken
Leaf-stalk	short with broad base sheathing stem
	FLOWERS
Position	many, in umbrella-shaped head 30–60mm across, 8–20 branches, at stem-tip
Bracts	many, spear-shaped, below head and flower-stalks
Type	⚥
Size	1.5–2.5mm
Colour	yellowish green
Stalk	about equalling flower
Sepals	5, minute
Petals	5, 0.6–1mm, heart-shaped
Stamens	5
Stigmas	2, slender
Ovary	1, below petals, 2-celled
	FRUIT
Type	1, splits into 2, corky, egg-shaped, angled, sometimes purplish
Size	5–6mm
Seeds	1 per half, not released

Burnet-saxifrage *Pimpinella saxifraga*

Like a curious mixture of other plants, this has umbrella-shaped flower-heads like Wild Carrot but lower leaves like Salad Burnet. Like true Saxifrages, it was used to treat kidney stones. The root has a goat-like smell. *Status:* native; most of area except extreme north and many islands. *Similar species:* Greater Burnet-saxifrage is larger, and has ridged, hollow stems, longer, pointed lower leaflets, and grows in shadier places. Two grassland species have lumpy edible tubers. Pignut has hollow stems, long styles and narrow-beaked fruits. Great Pignut has solid stems, short styles and fruits with a short, bent beak.

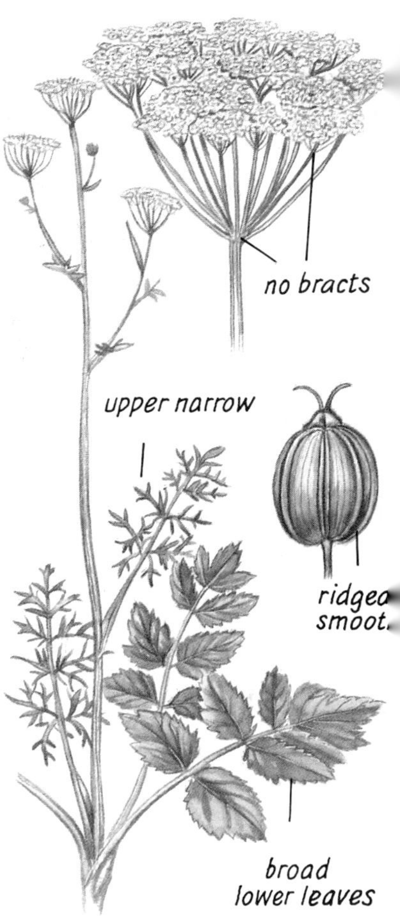

1 Greater Burnet-saxifrage *(P. major)*; 2 Pignut *(Conopodium majus)*; 3 Great Pignut *(Bunium bulbocastanum)*

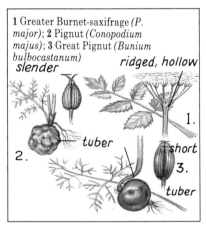

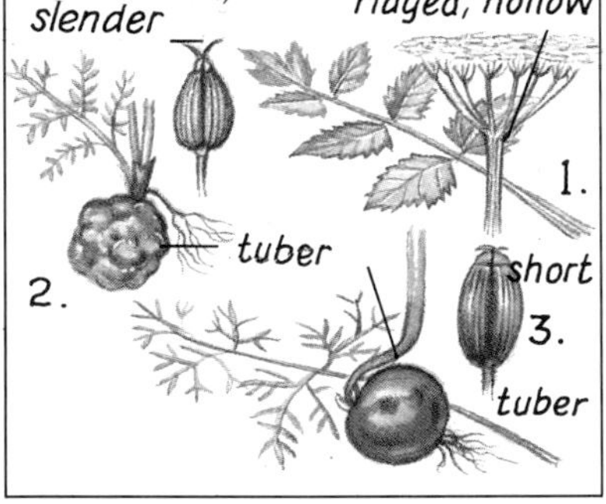

	BURNET-SAXIFRAGE
Type	perennial
Height	30–100cm
Habitat	grassy places; mostly dry, lime-rich soils
Flowering	July–August
	STEMS AND LEAVES
Stem	upright, mostly solid, slightly ridged
Root	slender stock, fibres from old leaves, strong-smelling
Hairs	short, often sparse
Stipules	absent
Leaves	basal with 6–14 leaflets, mostly paired, each 10–25mm, oval, toothed; stem-leaves scattered, cut 1–2 times into thin leaflets
Leaf-stalk	lower long, upper with base sheathing stem

	FLOWERS
Position	many, in umbrella-shaped heads 20–50mm wide, 10–20 branches, at stem-tip
Bracts	absent
Type	mostly ⚥
Size	2–3mm
Colour	white
Stalk	longer than flower
Sepals	5, minute
Petals	5, 0.8–1.5mm, tip curved in
Stamens	5
Stigmas	2, slender, short styles
Ovary	1, below sepals, 2-celled
	FRUIT
Type	1, splits into 2, dry, nearly globular, ridged
Size	2–3mm
Seeds	1 per half, not released

Aegopodium podagraria Ground-elder

Creeping, underground stems spring up, making a new plant at a distance from the original, and lead gardeners many a chase. Often a persistent weed, Ground-elder was formerly cultivated as a pot-herb and used to treat gout and arthritis. *Status:* native, introduced to Britain and Ireland; most of area. *Similar species:* also spreading by long, rooting stems but with mostly paired leaflets, are several species of damp soil or still water. Fool's Water-cress has short-stalked flower-heads. Lesser Marshwort has narrow-lobed lower leaves. Lesser Water-parsnip has leaf-like bracts.

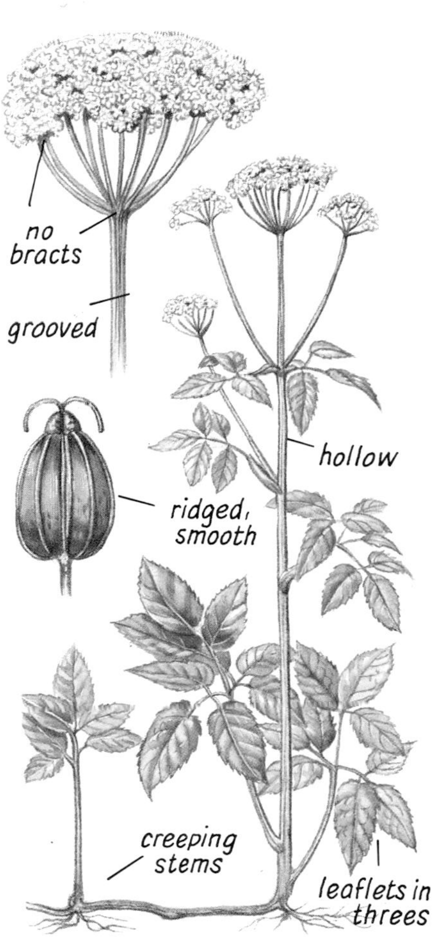

1 Fool's Water-cress *(Apium nodiflorum)*; **2** Lesser Marshwort *(A. inundatum)*; **3** Lesser Water-parsnip *(Berula erecta)*

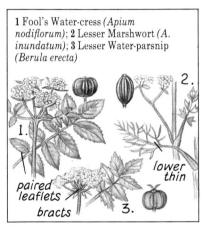

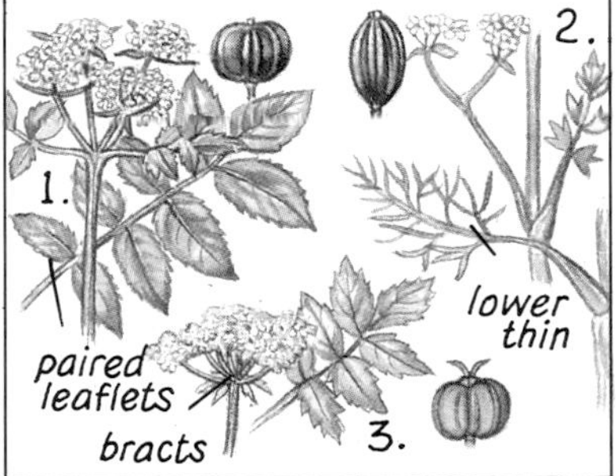

	GROUND-ELDER
Type	perennial
Height	40–100cm
Habitat	cultivated or waste ground, often a weed
Flowering	May–July
	STEMS AND LEAVES
Stem	upright, stout, grooved, hollow
Root	long, creeping, rooting, underground stems
Hairs	absent
Stipules	absent
Leaves	basal or scattered on stem, 100–200mm, divided 1–2 times, leaflets in 3s, 40–80mm, oval, pointed, toothed
Leaf-stalk	lower long, 3-angled, upper short, base sheathing stem

	FLOWERS
Position	many, in umbrella-shaped heads, 20–60mm wide, 15–20 branches, at stem-tip
Bracts	usually absent
Type	⚥
Size	1–3mm
Colour	white
Stalk	longer than flower
Sepals	absent
Petals	5, 0.5–1.5mm, slightly unequal, tip curved in
Stamens	5
Stigmas	2, slender
Ovary	1, below sepals, 2-celled
	FRUIT
Type	1, splits into 2, dry, egg-shaped, beak bent back
Size	3–4mm
Seeds	1 per half, not released

Hemlock Water-dropwort *Oenanthe crocata*

A robust plant of wet places, with large, much-divided lower leaves and umbrella-shaped flower-heads, it is extremely poisonous and often kills livestock. The tubers are attached to the base of the plant by thread-like roots, and this is the origin of the name 'dropwort'. *Status:* native; fairly common, south-west of region. *Similar species:* Fine-leaved Water-dropwort has tiny leaflets and no bracts. Parsley Water-dropwort has bracts but few, slender leaflets. Tubular Water-dropwort has curious, swollen stem-segments and flower-heads with few branches and no bracts.

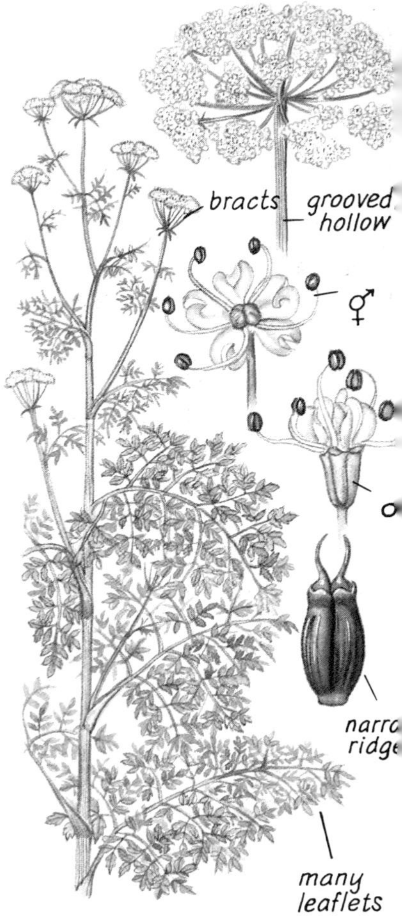

1 Fine-leaved Water-dropwort *(O. aquatica)*; **2** Parsley Water-dropwort *(O. lachenalii)*; **3** Tubular Water-dropwort *(O. fistulosa)*

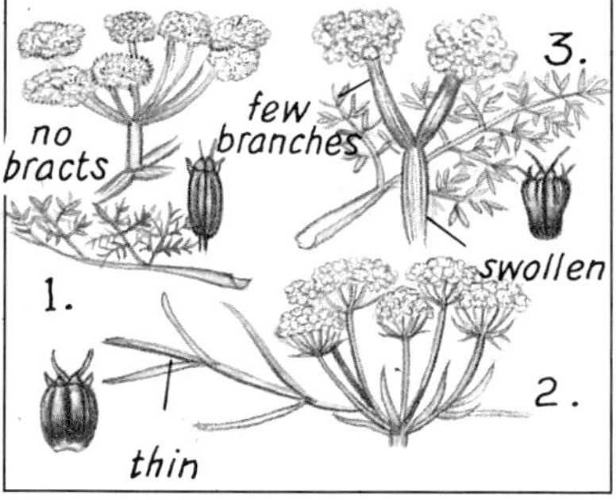

	HEMLOCK WATER-DROPWORT
Type	perennial
Height	50–150cm
Habitat	wet ditches, edge of water
Flowering	June–July
	STEMS AND LEAVES
Stem	upright, stout, grooved, hollow
Root	elongated tubers
Hairs	absent
Stipules	absent
Leaves	basal or scattered on stem, up to 400mm, divided 2–4 times; leaflets many, oval to narrowly spear-shaped, toothed or lobed
Leaf-stalk	base sheathing stem, lower long, upper short

	FLOWERS
Position	many, in umbrella-shaped heads 50–100mm wide, 12–40 branches, at stem-tip
Bracts	many, slender, below head and flower-stalks
Type	♂ and ⚥ in same head
Size	2–4mm
Colour	white
Stalk	longer than flower
Sepals	5, small, pointed
Petals	5, 1–2mm, notched, unequal on outer flowers
Stamens	5, anthers crimson
Stigmas	2, slender
Ovary	1, below sepals, 2-celled
	FRUIT
Type	1, splits into 2, dry, nearly cylindrical, ridged
Size	4–6mm
Seeds	1 per half, not released

A tall, rather elegant plant with fern-like foliage, purple-spotted stems and white, lacy flower-heads. Marring this image is a strong smell which hints at the extremely poisonous nature of the plant. Its powerful alkaloids can paralyse the respiratory system of animals or humans. In ancient times, preparations were made as a method of execution and, apparently, used by the Greeks to kill Socrates. Children should be warned of this plant: hollow stems cut for use as pea-shooters have proved fatal, although the toxicity of the plant varies greatly between different areas. Hemlock has been used as a drastic antidote to strychnine. In times long past it was used as an external treatment for herpes and breast tumours, and in controlled doses, equally misguidedly, to treat epilepsy and certain nervous afflictions; this practice has ceased because such usage can lead to paralysis or death. There are no plants quite like Hemlock, although several others, such as Rough Chervil, have purple-spotted stems. *Status:* native; throughout area, rarer in north. (There are no similar species.)

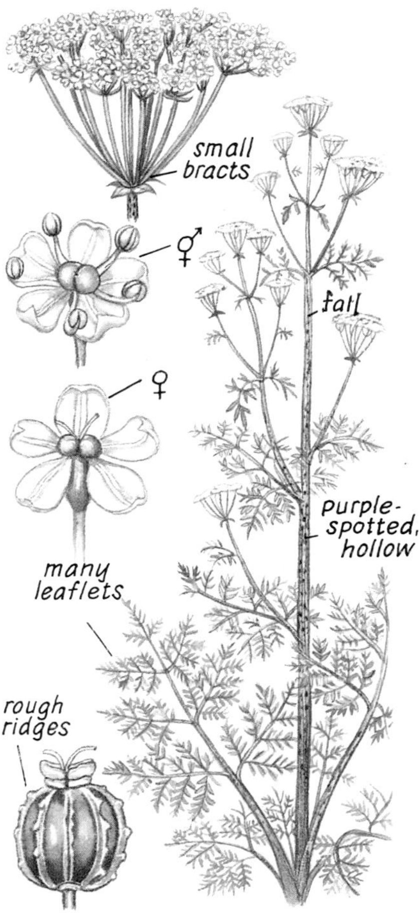

	HEMLOCK		**FLOWERS**
Type	perennial	**Position**	many in umbrella-shaped heads 20–50mm wide, 10–20 branches
Height	50–250cm	**Bracts**	few, bent back, below head and flower-stalks
Habitat	woodland edges, waste ground; mostly damp soils	**Type**	⚥ in head at stem-tip, ♂ in head from leaf-base
Flowering	June–July	**Size**	2–3mm
	STEMS AND LEAVES	**Colour**	white
Stem	upright, grooved, smooth, purple-spotted, hollow	**Stalk**	longer than flower
Root	stout tap-root	**Sepals**	absent
Hairs	absent	**Petals**	5, 1–1.5mm, oval, notched
Stipules	absent	**Stamens**	5
Leaves	basal or scattered on stem, up to 300mm, divided 2–3 times; leaflets 10–20mm, spear-shaped to triangular, coarsely toothed	**Stigmas**	2, on slender styles
		Ovary	1, below petals, 2-celled
			FRUIT
Leaf-stalk	lower long, upper very short, base broad	**Type**	1, splits into 2, nearly globular
		Size	3–4mm
		Seeds	1 per half, not released

Wild Parsnip *Pastinaca sativa*

Yellow, umbrella-shaped flower-heads and coarse, hairy foliage of Wild Parsnip are common by many roadsides in high Summer. The whole plant has a strong smell of Parsnips, for this is the same species as the cultivated plant. Wild roots are slender and often woody. *Status:* native, escaped from cultivation in north; often common, most of area. *Similar species:* two yellow-flowered species have finely divided, hairless leaves and oblong, wingless fruits. Fennel is more robust, the aniseed-scented foliage having almost hair-like segments. Pepper-saxifrage has spear-shaped segments and fruits with the beak curved back.

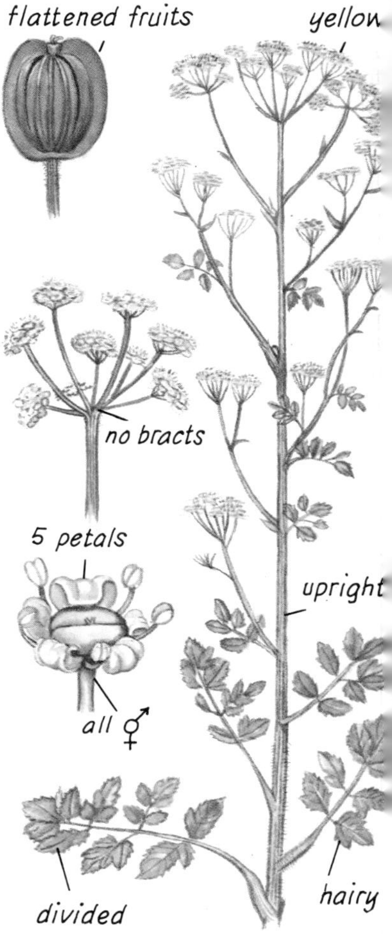

1 Fennel *(Foeniculum vulgare)*;
2 Pepper-saxifrage *(Silaum silaus)*

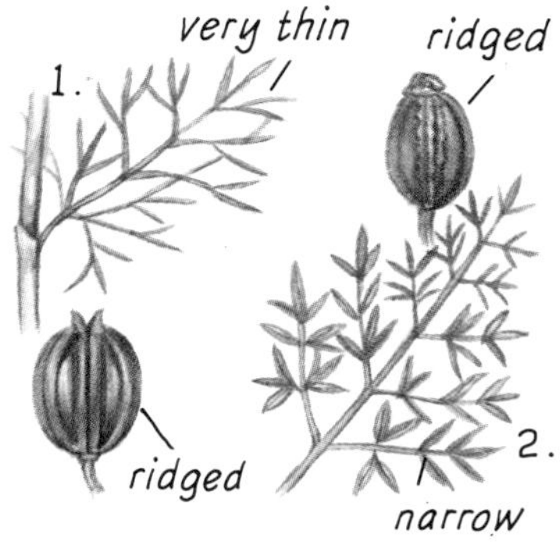

	WILD PARSNIP
Type	biennial
Height	30–150cm
Habitat	grassy and waste ground; mainly lime-rich soil
Flowering	July–August
	STEMS AND LEAVES
Stem	upright, ridged, hollow
Root	tap-root, strong-smelling
Hairs	straight, throughout plant
Stipules	absent
Leaves	basal or scattered on stem, up to 300mm, divided 1–2 times; leaflets oval, lobed, toothed
Leaf-stalk	mostly short, base sheathing stem

	FLOWERS
Position	many in umbrella-shaped heads 30–100mm wide, 5–15 unequal branches, at stem-tip
Bracts	absent or few, soon falling
Type	⚥
Size	1.5–2.5mm
Colour	yellow
Stalk	little longer than flower
Sepals	absent
Petals	5, oval, curved inwards
Stamens	5
Stigmas	2, styles short
Ovary	1, below petals, 2-celled
	FRUIT
Type	1, splits into 2, broad, flattened with encircling wing, ridged, dark-lined
Size	5–8mm
Seeds	1 per half, not released

A robust, bristly plant that has coarse foliage and almost flat-topped flower-heads with larger petals around the edges. These broad flower-heads attract many insects, especially the orange or brownish Soldier Beetle. Hollow stems are frequently used as pea-shooters by children, and the leaves are edible. *Status:* native; throughout area. *Similar species:* often naturalized in damp places, Giant Hogweed is distinguished by its great size, some stems growing over 5 metres tall and having flower-heads half a metre across. Wild Angelica has smoother, purplish stems and more divided, hairless leaves.

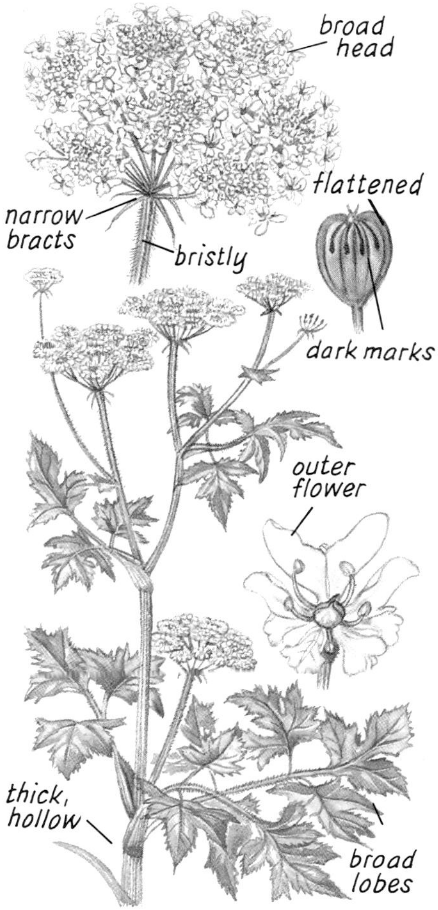

1 Giant Hogweed *(H. mantegazzianum)*; 2 Wild Angelica *(Angelica sylvestris)*

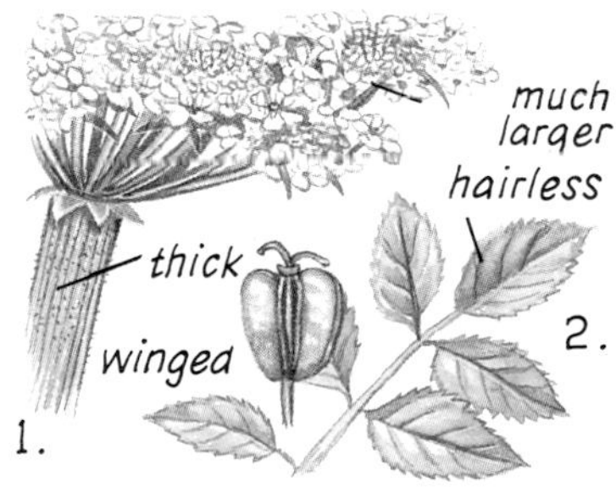

	HOGWEED
Type	biennial
Height	50–200cm
Habitat	grassland, hedges, woods
Flowering	June–September
	STEMS AND LEAVES
Stem	upright, stout, ridged, hollow
Root	stout tap-root
Hairs	stiff, over whole plant
Stipules	absent
Leaves	basal or scattered on stem, 150–600mm, divided; leaflets 50–150mm, broad, irregularly lobed, toothed, paired
Leaf-stalk	lower longest, bases broad, sheathing stem
	FLOWERS
Position	many, in umbrella-shaped heads at stem-tips, 50–150mm wide, 7–25 branches
Bracts	slender, usually below head and flower-stalks
Type	⚥
Size	5–10mm
Colour	white or pink
Stalk	longer than flower
Sepals	5, small, unequal
Petals	5, 2–7mm, notched, very unequal on outer flowers
Stamens	5
Stigmas	2, styles short
Ovary	1, below sepals, 2-celled
	FRUIT
Type	1, splits into 2, nearly circular, flattish, winged, ridged, dark-lined
Size	7–8mm
Seeds	1 per half, not released

Upright Hedge-parsley *Torilis japonica*

One of the later-flowering hedgerow species of the Carrot family, with lacy umbrella-shaped heads of pinkish flowers. Spiny fruits and many slender bracts distinguish it from most other native species of the family. *Status:* native; often very common, most of area except extreme north. *Similar species:* Knotted Hedge-parsley has almost stalkless flower-heads with few branches. Spreading Hedge-parsley has heads with fewer branches and usually one bract. Fool's Parsley has long, downward-pointing bracts below the flower-stalks, and smoothly ridged fruits.

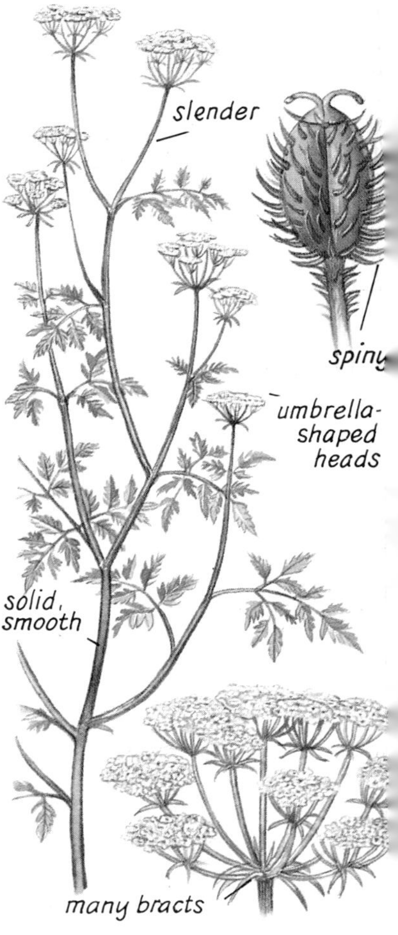

1 Knotted Hedge-parsley *(T. nodosa)*; **2** Spreading Hedge-parsley *(T. arvensis)*; **3** Fool's Parsley *(Aethusa cynapium)*

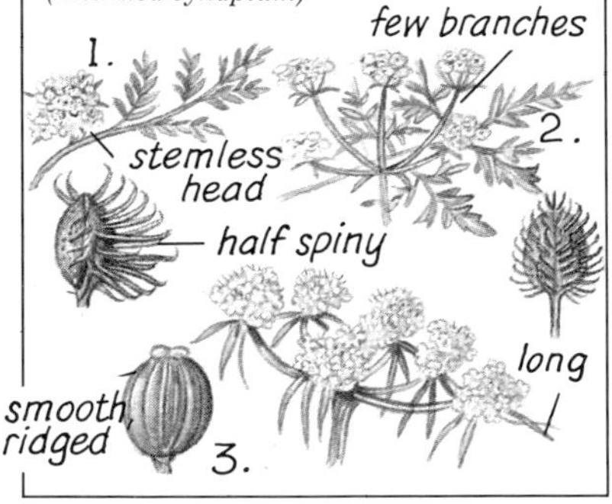

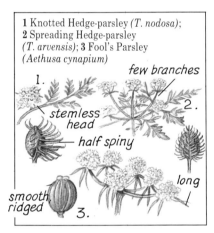

	UPRIGHT HEDGE-PARSLEY
Type	annual
Height	5–125cm
Habitat	hedges, grassy places
Flowering	July–August
	STEMS AND LEAVES
Stem	more or less upright, solid
Root	slender tap-root
Hairs	short, pressed to surface
Stipules	absent
Leaves	on alternate sides of stem, divided 1–3 times; leaflets 10–20mm, oval to spear-shaped, lobed or toothed
Leaf-stalk	lower longest
	FLOWERS
Position	many, in umbrella-shaped heads 15–40mm wide, 5–12 branches, most at stem-tip
Bracts	many, unequal, thin, below head and flower-stalks
Type	⚥
Size	2–3mm
Colour	white tinged pink or purple
Stalk	longer than flower
Sepals	5, small, triangular
Petals	5, 1–1.5mm, unequal, notched, tip curved in
Stamens	5
Stigmas	2, styles short
Ovary	1, below sepals, 2-celled
	FRUIT
Type	1, splits into 2, egg-shaped, ridged, covered with spines, beak-like tips curved back
Size	3–4mm
Seeds	1 per half, not released

Distinct among the many species of the family because of the conspicuous, divided bracts beneath the flower-heads. In the middle of the white flower-head there is usually a single purple flower. The fruiting head curls up like a ball and bristles with spiny fruits. Cultivated Carrot belongs to a different subspecies. *Status:* native or introduced in extreme north; throughout area. *Similar species:* Sea Carrot, from the Atlantic coasts of Britain and France, is often short-stemmed, with more triangular leaves having broader, fleshier segments, and the fruiting heads are flat or slightly domed.

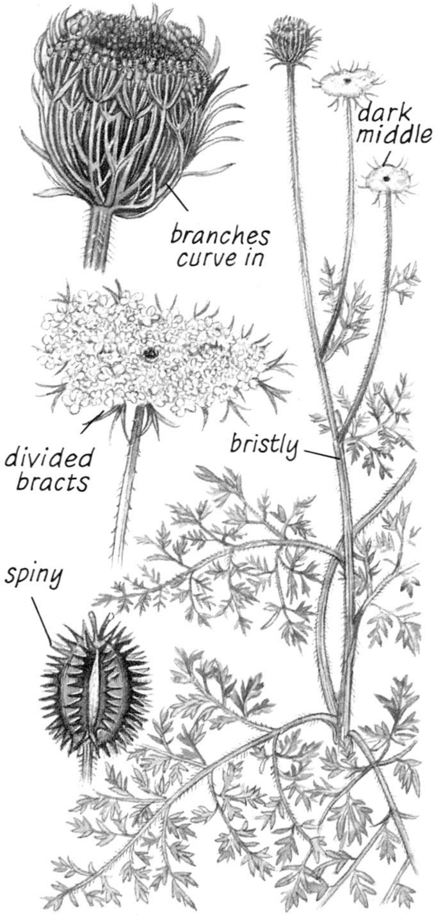

Sea Carrot *(D. carota* subsp. *gummifer)*

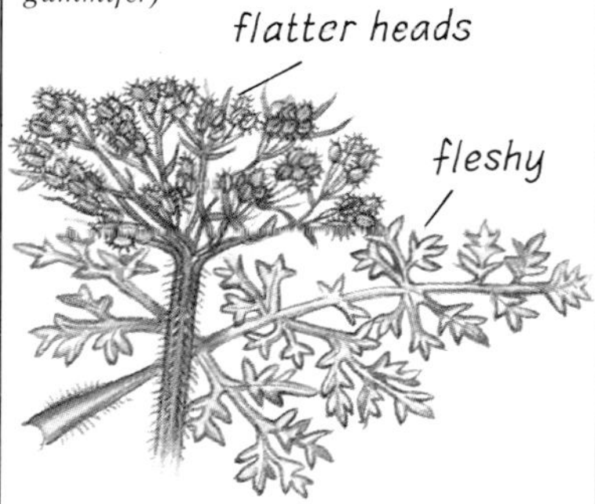

	WILD CARROT
Type	biennial
Height	30–100cm, rarely 150cm
Habitat	grassland, often lime-rich soils
Flowering	June–August
	STEMS AND LEAVES
Stem	upright, ridged, solid
Root	usually thin tap-root
Hairs	stems stiffly hairy
Stipules	absent
Leaves	on alternate sides of stem, divided 2–3 times; leaflets 4–7mm, slender, lobed
Leaf-stalk	lower longest, base sheathing stem
	FLOWERS
Position	many, in umbrella-shaped heads at stem-tips 30–70mm wide, many branches
Bracts	7–13 below head, deeply cut into thin lobes, undivided below flowers, edges papery
Type	⚥
Size	2–4mm
Colour	white, middle flower usually purple or red
Stalk	about equalling flower
Sepals	5, small
Petals	5, 1–2mm, notched, unequal on outer flowers
Stamens	5
Stigmas	2, styles short
Ovary	1, below sepals, 2-celled
	FRUIT
Type	1, splits into 2, nearly oblong, ridged, spiny
Size	2.5–4mm
Seeds	1 per half, not released

Thorow-wax *Bupleurum rotundifolium*

A most peculiar member of the Carrot family, its stems appear to pass straight through the bluish, undivided leaves, as referred to in the common name. Broad bracts and dull yellow flowers look rather like some sort of Spurge. Once a common cornfield weed, it became extinct in many areas with seed-cleaning and selective herbicides. *Status:* native or introduced; uncommon, south of area. *Similar species:* warty fruits are found on False Thorow-wax, with narrower leaves, and Slender Hare's-ear, with grass-like leaves. Sickle-leaved Hare's-ear is perennial, and has smooth fruits and narrow, often curved leaves.

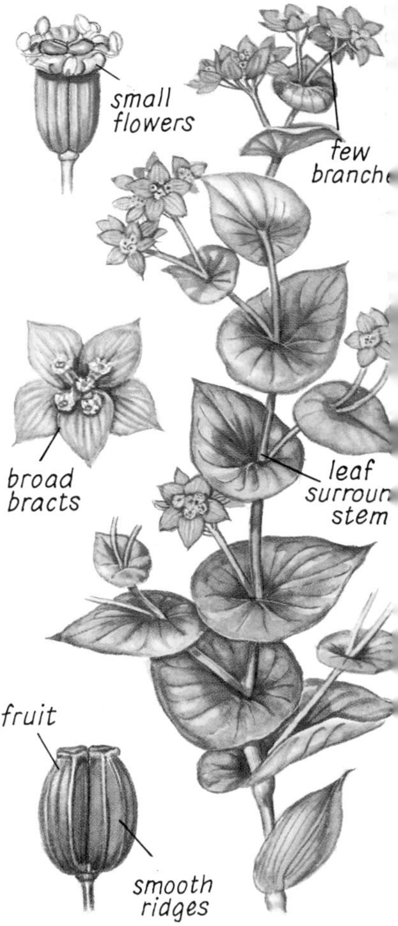

1 False Thorow-wax *(B. subovatum)*; **2** Slender Hare's-ear *(B. tenuissimum)*; **3** Sickle-leaved Hare's-ear *(B. falcatum)*

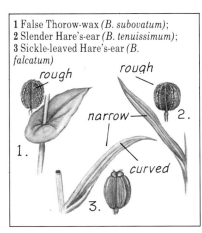

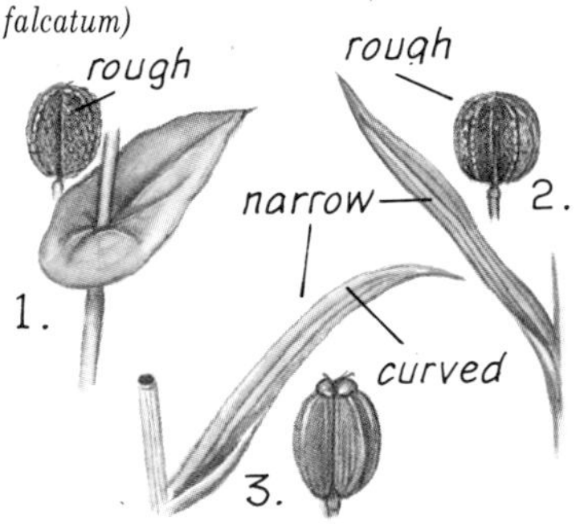

	THOROW-WAX
Type	annual
Height	15–30cm
Habitat	cornfields, waste ground; mostly dry soils
Flowering	June–July
	STEMS AND LEAVES
Stem	upright, smooth, hollow
Root	fibrous
Hairs	absent
Stipules	absent
Leaves	scattered around stem, 20–50mm, elliptical to almost circular, bluish green, edge unbroken, upper with stem passing through blade
Leaf-stalk	absent or short on lower

	FLOWERS
Position	few, umbrella-shaped heads 10–30mm wide, 3–8 branches, at stem-tip or leaf-base
Bracts	none below head, large below flower-stalks, oval, yellowish
Type	⚥
Size	1.5–2mm
Colour	yellow
Stalk	about equalling flower
Sepals	absent
Petals	5, 0.5–0.8mm, equal, oval
Stamens	5
Stigmas	2, styles slender
Ovary	1, below petals, 2-celled
	FRUIT
Type	1, splits into 2, egg-shaped, ridged, blackish
Size	2–3mm
Seeds	1 per half, not released

Pyrola minor Common Wintergreen

rom a cluster of broad, glossy leaves, ›ng, scaly stems arise bearing the odding, globular flowers. Wintergreen :aves were used to treat wounds and idney or bladder infections, because hey have both diuretic and disinfectant roperties. *Status:* native; scattered ver much of area, rarer in south, bsent from many islands. *Similar pecies:* other species have a projecting tyle with a thickened tip. Intermediate Vintergreen has a straight style. ꞉ound-leaved Wintergreen has more pen flowers, a curved style and longer eaf-stalks. Serrated Wintergreen has ›ne-sided flower-heads, a straight style ınd sharp-toothed leaves.

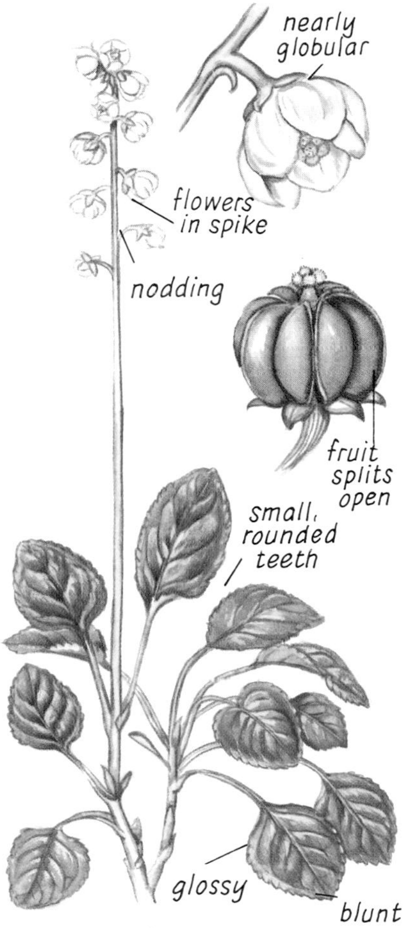

1 Intermediate Wintergreen *(P. media)*; **2** Round-leaved Wintergreen *(P. rotundifolia)*; **3** Serrated Wintergreen *(Orthilia secunda)*

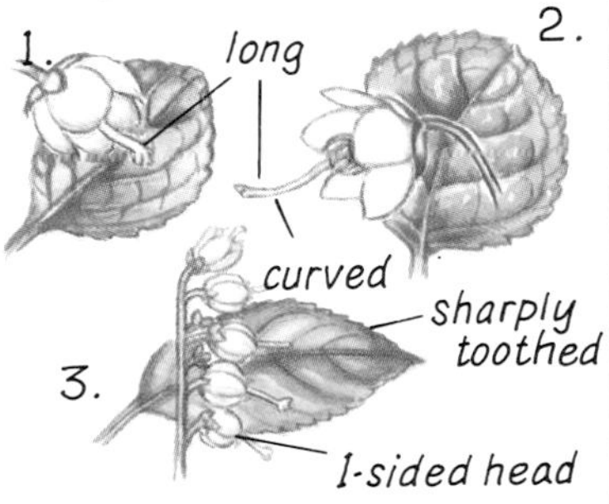

	COMMON WINTERGREEN
Type	perennial
Height	5–30cm
Habitat	woods, moors, rocks, dunes; mostly damp soils
Flowering	May–June
	STEMS AND LEAVES
Stem	short, leafy; flowering stems upright, scaly
Root	creeping underground stem
Hairs	absent
Stipules	absent
Leaves	basal or scattered on stem, often a rosette, 25–40mm, oval, mostly blunt with tiny, rounded teeth, base wedge-shaped or squarish
Leaf-stalk	shorter than blade

	FLOWERS
Position	5–17, in crowded spike-like head at stem-tip
Bracts	slender, pointed
Type	☿, globular, nodding
Size	5–6.5mm
Colour	whitish pink
Stalk	almost equalling flower
Sepals	5, 1.5–2mm, bases joined
Petals	5, 5–6.5mm, equal, not joined, overlapping
Stamens	10
Stigma	1, 5-lobed, style straight, shorter than petals
Ovary	1, 5-celled
	FRUIT
Type	1, capsule, globular, splits into 5
Size	4–5mm
Seeds	numerous, minute

Bell Heather *Erica cinerea*

A wiry, evergreen, dwarf shrub with needle-like leaves and nodding, bell-shaped flowers. Garden forms have varying flowering times and colours. Species of Heathers can be so prolific that they change the colour of vast tracts of land as flowering commences. *Status:* native; most of area, commoner in west. *Similar species:* Cross-leaved Heath has leaves in fours, edged with long, gland-tipped hairs. Cornish Heath is larger with long flower-stalks and projecting stamens. Heather, or Ling, has small, closely-packed leaves and the large, purple sepals are longer than the petals.

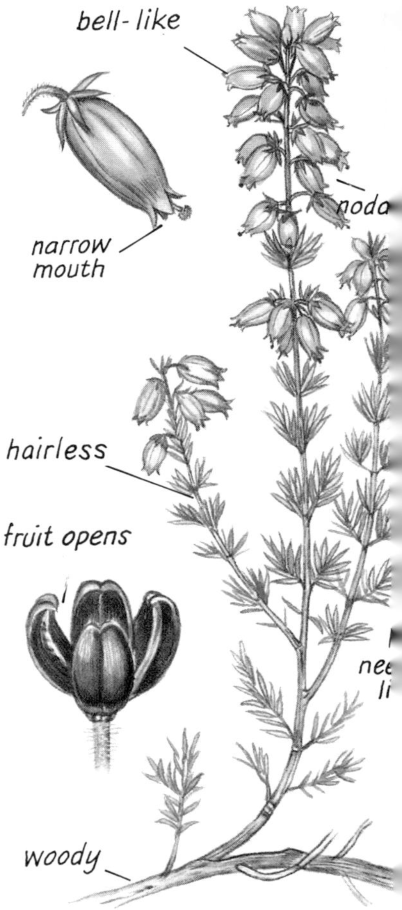

1 Cross-leaved Heath *(E. tetralix)*;
2 Cornish Heath *(E. vagans)*;
3 Heather *(Calluna vulgaris)*

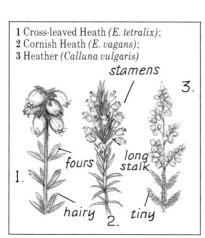

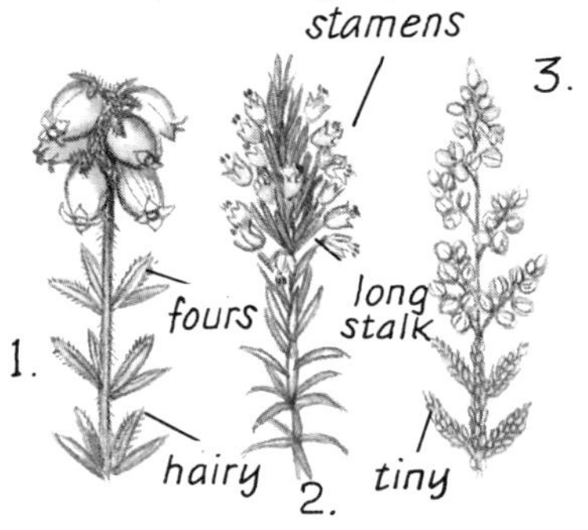

	BELL HEATHER
Type	dwarf, evergreen shrub
Height	15–75cm
Habitat	heaths, moors, woodland edges; dryish, acid soils
Flowering	July–September
	STEMS AND LEAVES
Stem	many, branched, woody, rooting, almost upright
Root	woody stock
Hairs	only on young shoots
Stipules	absent
Leaves	rings of 3, 5–7mm, slender, straight-sided, pointed, edges curved under
Leaf-stalk	very short
	FLOWERS
Position	many in head, 10–70mm, at stem-tip
Bracts	3 tiny bracts below sepals
Type	⚥, nodding
Size	4–7mm
Colour	reddish purple
Stalk	shorter than flower
Sepals	4, 2–3mm, pointed, bases joined
Petals	4, 4–7mm, joined except at tips, bell-shaped with narrow mouth
Stamens	8, not projecting
Stigma	1, club-shaped, on long style, projecting
Ovary	1, 4-celled
	FRUIT
Type	1, capsule, splits open, enclosed by dry petals
Size	1.5–2mm
Seeds	numerous, minute

A small deciduous shrub of moors and heaths, with globular pink flowers followed by globular black fruits. The berries have a bluish 'bloom', as on black grapes. Although small and rather watery, they are edible and often eaten in pies, tarts or with cream. *Status:* native; most of area, on mountains in south. *Similar species:* Cowberry is evergreen with glossy leaves, bell-shaped flowers and red fruits. Cranberry has long-stalked, red fruits, and petals bent sharply back revealing purple stamens. Although with blue-black fruits, Crowberry is unrelated, having heather-like leaves and six-petalled flowers.

1 Cowberry *(V. vitis-idaea)*;
2 Cranberry *(V. oxycoccos)*;
3 Crowberry *(Empetrum nigrum)*

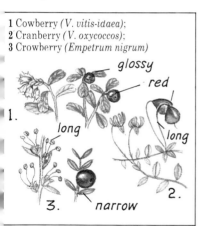

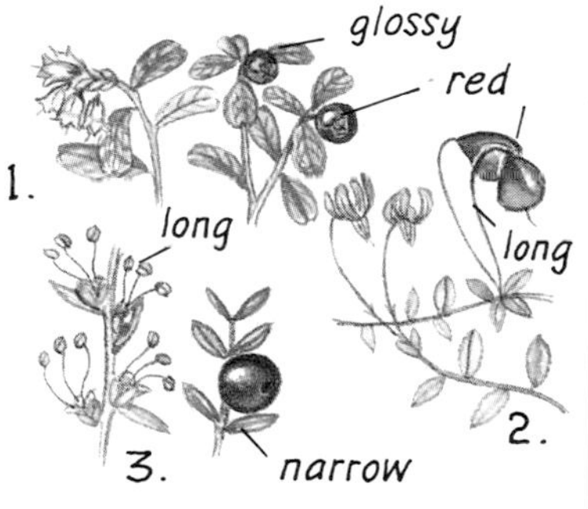

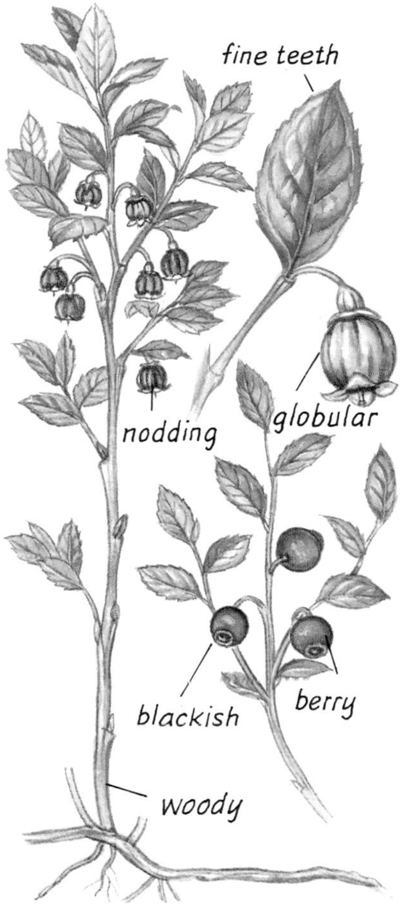

	BILBERRY
Type	deciduous shrub
Height	15–60cm
Habitat	moors, heaths, woods; acid soils
Flowering	July–September
	STEMS AND LEAVES
Stem	upright, many, young shoots 3-angled
Root	creeping underground stem
Hairs	absent
Stipules	absent
Leaves	on alternate sides of stem, 10–30mm, oval, pointed, finely toothed
Leaf-stalk	shorter than blade
	FLOWERS
Position	mostly single, at leaf-base
Bracts	2, scale-like
Type	⚥, nodding
Size	4–6mm
Colour	pink, sometimes greenish
Stalk	about equalling flower
Sepals	4–5, joined, forming scarcely lobed ring
Petals	4–5, 4–6mm, joined, globular, tips bent back
Stamens	8–10
Stigma	1, club-shaped, long style
Ovary	1, below sepals, 4–5-celled
	FRUIT
Type	1, berry, globular, black with bluish, waxy bloom, edible
Size	6–10mm
Seeds	many, small

Primrose *Primula vulgaris*

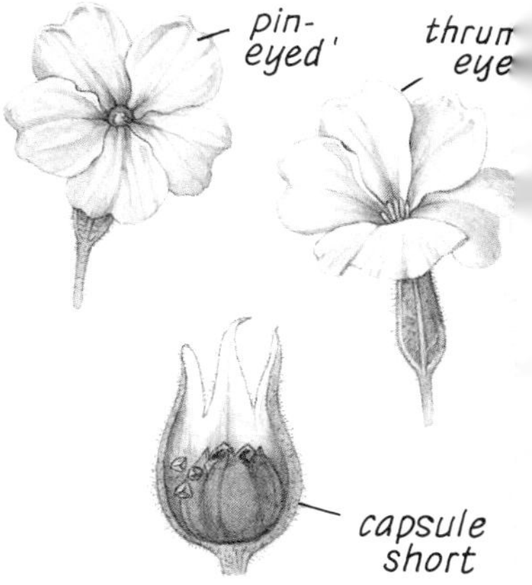

Few sights are more welcome after a bleak Winter, than a bank covered with the soft yellow flowers of Primroses. Two forms of flower differ by the look of the tube-mouth. One has five stamens ('thrum-eyed'), the other a stigma ('pin-eyed'), an arrangement enhancing the chances of cross-pollination. *Status:* native; most parts except extreme north. *Similar species:* other species have stalked flower-clusters. Cowslip has small, often darker petals; Oxlip has large, whitish-yellow petals and a long capsule. Bird's-eye Primrose has floury-looking leaves and lilac flowers.

1 Cowslip *(P. veris)*; **2** Oxlip *(P. elatior)*; **3** Bird's-eye Primrose *(P. farinosa)*

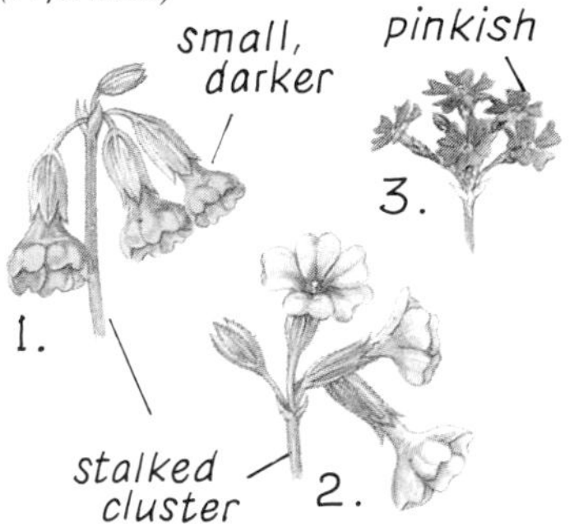

	PRIMROSE
Type	perennial
Height	10–20cm
Habitat	woods, hedgerows, grassy banks; damp soils
Flowering	December–May
	STEMS AND LEAVES
Stem	very short
Root	short underground stem; thick, white roots
Hairs	few below leaves, none above; long on flower-stalks and sepals
Stipules	absent
Leaves	rosette at base, 80–200mm, oval to spoon-shaped, widest above middle, blunt, irregularly toothed
Leaf-stalk	short or absent
	FLOWERS
Position	in cluster at base or on very short stem
Bracts	present
Type	⚥, facing upwards
Size	width 20–40mm
Colour	pale yellow, deeper marks around throat, rarely pink
Stalk	50–200mm, with long hairs
Sepals	5, joined into tube, 15–17mm, teeth 4–6mm
Petals	5, 20–40mm, base forms tube
Stamens	5, at tube-mouth or middle
Stigma	1, club-shaped, style long, at mouth of tube or middle
Ovary	1, 1-celled
	FRUIT
Type	1, capsule, nearly globular
Size	5–7mm
Seeds	numerous, *c*1mm, angular

A delightful little plant, the upswept petals of its nodding, pink flowers spotted purple at the base. Leaves arise singly from the underground stem and only as the flowers fade, and are often marked with silver above and tinged purple below. The young capsule's stalk spirals from the tip until it lies on the ground, looking like a coil-spring. Cyclamen multiplies readily by seed and becomes naturalized. *Status:* introduced from southern Europe; scattered, mainly southern. *Similar species:* one species is native in the south-eastern part of the area. It has scented flowers, rounded leaves, and purplish petals lacking basal lobes.

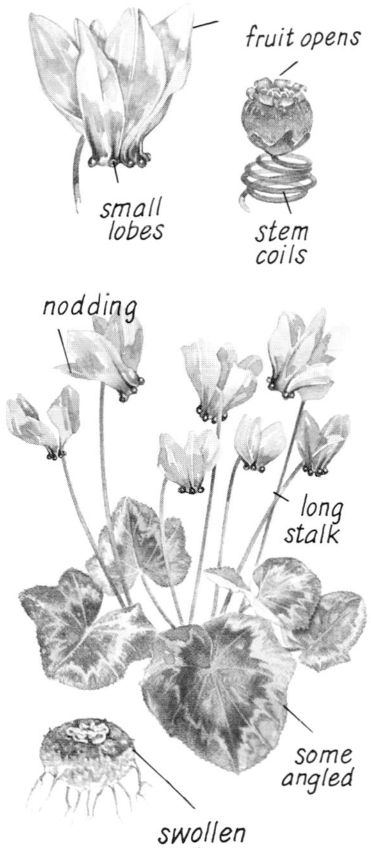

C. purpurascens

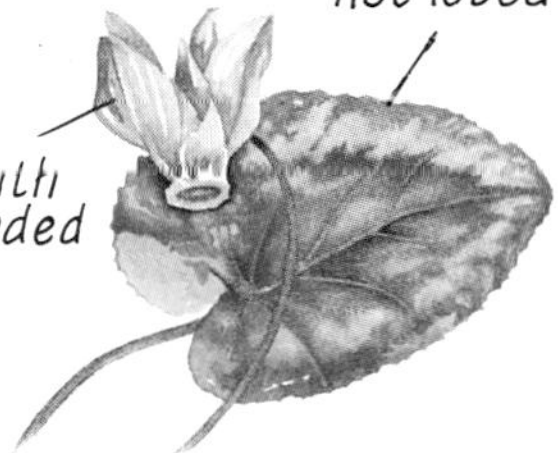

	CYCLAMEN
Type	perennial
Height	10–30cm
Habitat	woods, hedges, near gardens
Flowering	August–September
	STEMS AND LEAVES
Stem	very short
Root	underground, swollen stem to 100mm wide, globular or hollow upper face
Hairs	more or less absent
Stipules	absent
Leaves	at base, 30–140mm, oval to kidney-shaped, 5–9-angled, often pale marks above and purple below, blunt, finely toothed, appearing after flowers
Leaf-stalk	often longer than blade
	FLOWERS
Position	single, from base
Bracts	absent
Type	⚥, nodding
Size	15–25mm
Colour	pink with purple blotches at base, rarely white
Stalk	10–30mm, nearly upright
Sepals	5, 4–8mm, oval, bases joined
Petals	5, 15–25mm, equal, elliptical, bases joined into 5-angled tube, each petal bent back, 2 small lobes at base
Stamens	5, forming short cone
Stigma	1, scarcely projecting
Ovary	1, 1-celled
	FRUIT
Type	1, capsule, globular, splits from middle, purple-flecked, centre sticky; stalk coiled
Size	10–18mm
Seeds	many, 2–4mm, angular

Yellow Pimpernel *Lysimachia nemorum*

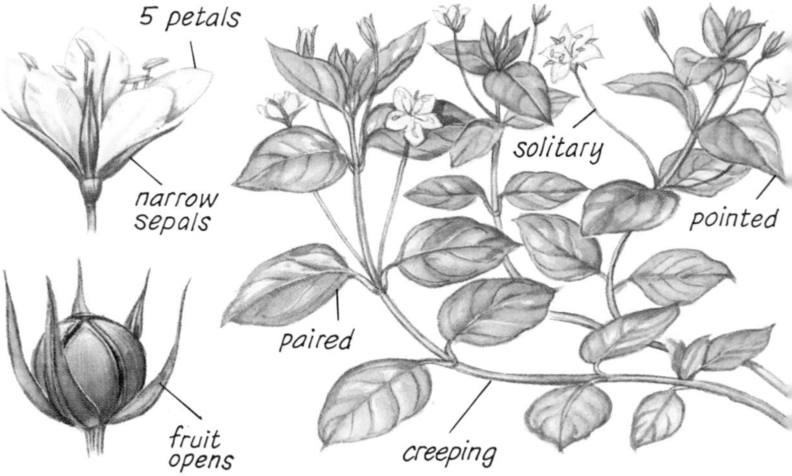

Rather a delicate, trailing plant with starry, yellow flowers dotted over a shady woodland floor. Paired oval leaves and long-stalked flowers look rather like those of the Scarlet Pimpernel. *Status:* native; most of area except extreme north. *Similar species:* often escaping from cultivation, Creeping-Jenny has rounded leaves and larger flowers with much broader sepals. Two related species with upright stems are Yellow Loosestrife, with clusters of flowers towards the stem-tips, and Tufted Loosestrife with spikes of narrow-petalled flowers from the upper leaf-bases.

1 Creeping-Jenny *(L. nummularia)*; **2** Yellow Loosestrife *(L. vulgaris)*; **3** Tufted Loosestrife *(L. thyrsiflora)*

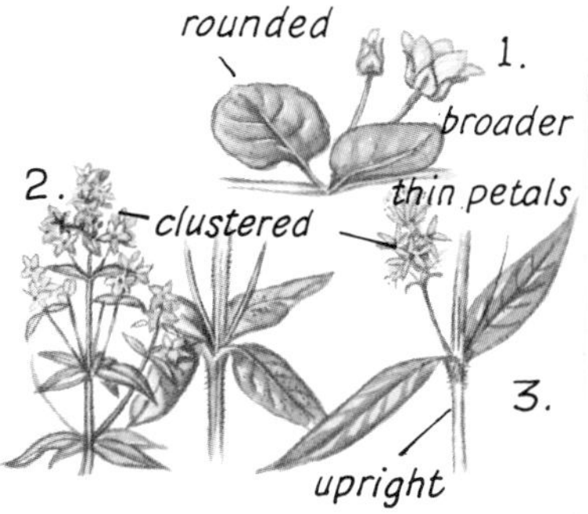

	YELLOW PIMPERNEL
Type	perennial
Height	10–45cm
Habitat	woods, hedges; mostly damp soils
Flowering	May–September
	STEMS AND LEAVES
Stem	slender, low-growing
Root	fibrous
Hairs	absent
Stipules	absent
Leaves	paired either side of stem, 20–40mm, oval, evergreen, pointed, edge unbroken, base rounded
Leaf-stalk	shorter than blade
	FLOWERS
Position	solitary, at leaf-base
Bracts	absent
Type	⚥
Size	6–8.5mm
Colour	yellow
Stalk	much longer than flower, hair-like
Sepals	5, 3.5–6mm, very slender, pointed
Petals	5, 6–8.5mm, equal, bases joined, wide-spreading
Stamens	5
Stigma	1, slender, style long
Ovary	1, 1-celled
	FRUIT
Type	1, capsule, globular, splits into 5
Size	3–4mm
Seeds	many, 1.5–2mm, circular, flattened

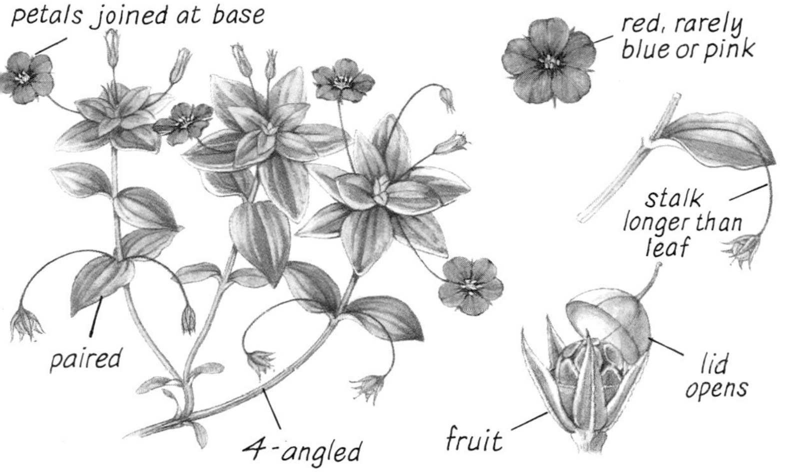

Although commonly a weed, Scarlet Pimpernel has jewel-like flowers of scarlet, sometimes deep blue, or rarely other, colours. Petals close in the afternoon, or when overcast, and soon drop, falling as a joined ring. *Status:* native; almost throughout area, rarer in north. *Similar species:* Blue Pimpernel usually has shorter-stalked, blue flowers, lacking hairs on the petal-edges. Bog Pimpernel, in marshy places, has narrow-petalled, pink flowers. Sea-milkwort also has pink flowers, although short-stalked, and has succulent leaves like many other plants from the upper fringe of sea-shores.

1 Blue Pimpernel *(A. foemina)*; **2** Bog Pimpernel *(A. tenella)*; **3** Sea-milkwort *(Glaux maritima)*

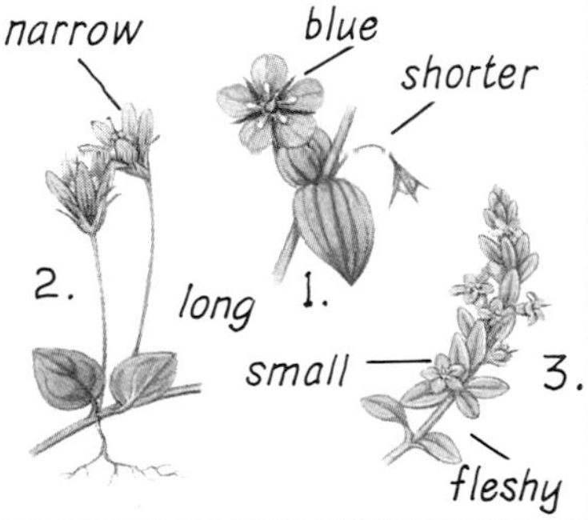

	SCARLET PIMPERNEL
Type	annual
Height	6–30cm, rarely 90cm
Habitat	cultivated and waste ground, dunes; most soils
Flowering	June–August
	STEMS AND LEAVES
Stem	low-growing, 4-angled
Root	fibrous
Hairs	absent
Stipules	absent
Leaves	paired either side of stem, 15–18mm, oval or spear-shaped, black-dotted below, edge unbroken
Leaf-stalk	absent
	FLOWERS
Position	solitary, at leaf-base
Bracts	absent
Type	⚥
Size	5–14mm
Colour	red, sometimes blue, rarely paler colours
Stalk	3–35mm, slender, curved back in fruit
Sepals	5, 3.5–5mm, narrow, pointed
Petals	5, 2–6mm, oval, equal, bases joined, edges usually with many small hairs
Stamens	5, stalks hairy
Stigma	1, slender, style long
Ovary	1, 1-celled
	FRUIT
Type	1, capsule, globular, top splits off
Size	2.5–4mm
Seeds	12–45, 1–1.5mm, nearly circular, slightly flattened

Water Violet *Hottonia palustris*

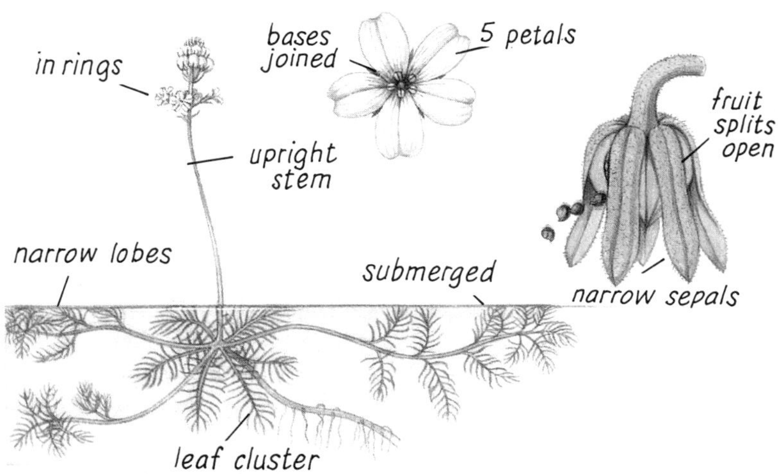

A most attractive plant that has rings of lilac, yellow-eyed flowers quite like those of some garden Primulas, but with very different foliage. This water-plant has feathery leaves on submerged stems which turn up at the tip and emerge from the water before flowering. *Status:* native, introduced to Ireland and elsewhere; scattered through much of area except parts of north. *Similar species:* no species is quite like Water Violet but Bogbean is also aquatic and has stalked spikes of pale flowers, although pink, with fringed petals. The leaves have three broad leaflets and are carried above the water.

Bogbean *(Menyanthes trifoliata)*

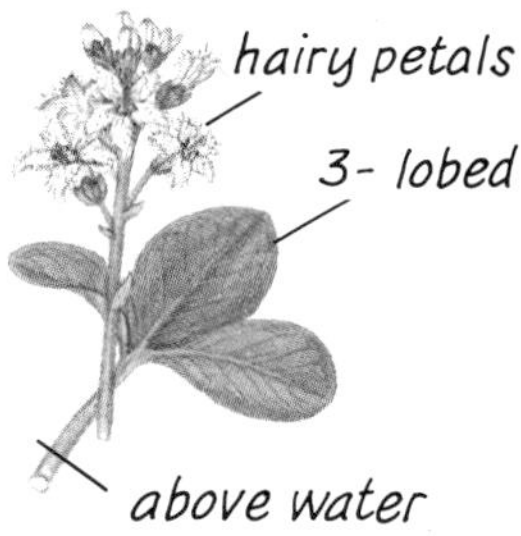

	WATER VIOLET
Type	perennial
Height	30–90cm
Habitat	ponds, ditches; shallow, still, fresh water
Flowering	May–June
	STEMS AND LEAVES
Stem	submerged or floating, turns upright to flower above water
Root	fibrous; stems root
Hairs	absent except for flowers
Stipules	absent
Leaves	in rings or scattered around stem, 20–130mm, cut 1–2 times into very slender lobes, some float
Leaf-stalk	shorter than blade

	FLOWERS
Position	3–8 in a ring, 3–9 rings around stem
Bracts	5–10mm, thin, pointed
Type	⚥
Size	20–25mm
Colour	lilac with yellow centre
Stalk	about equalling flower
Sepals	5, 5–10mm, narrowly oblong
Petals	5, 12–17mm, bases joined into slender tube
Stamens	5, attached to petals
Stigma	1, club-shaped, style short or long
Ovary	1, 1-celled
	FRUIT
Type	1, capsule, globular, splits into 5 except at tip
Size	3–6mm
Seeds	numerous, *c*1mm, angular

A plant mostly of mountain and moorland, Chickweed Wintergreen has white flowers rather like Anemones, above a ring of broad leaves. Slender stems spring up singly from a creeping underground stem. The plant was formerly applied to wounds and has been used to counteract blood-poisoning. *Status:* native; common in north, mostly in mountains in south or often absent. *Similar species:* although no species looks quite alike, Brookweed has flowers of similar construction although much smaller, with five petals, and in spike-like heads. It also occurs in damp places, often in coastal areas.

Brookweed *(Samolus valerandi)*

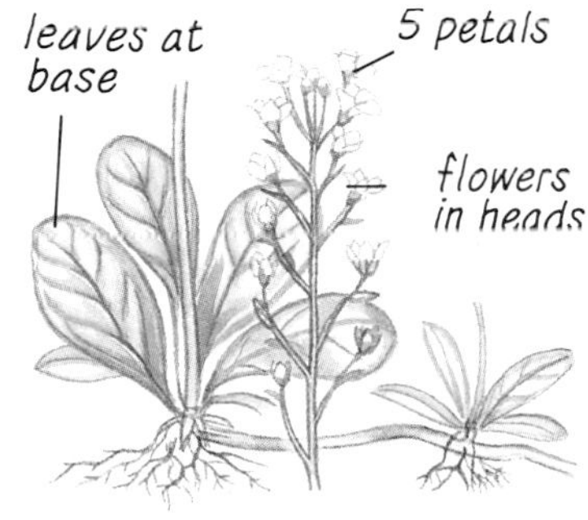

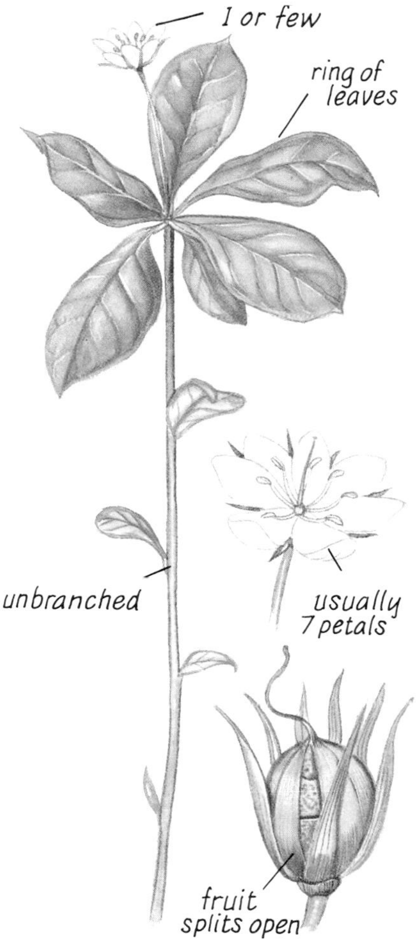

	CHICKWEED WINTERGREEN
Type	perennial
Height	5–30cm
Habitat	among grass or moss, often in pine-woods; damp places
Flowering	June–July
	STEMS AND LEAVES
Stem	single, unbranched, upright
Root	creeping, underground stems
Hairs	absent
Stipules	absent
Leaves	few small, scattered below, ring of 5–6 leaves above, 10–90mm, oval or spear-shaped, broadest above, glossy, edge unbroken or finely toothed above
Leaf-stalk	short or absent

	FLOWERS
Position	1–few, from upper leaf-base
Bracts	absent
Type	⚥
Size	11–19mm
Colour	white
Stalk	10–70mm, thin, upright
Sepals	usually 7, 4–7mm, very narrow, pointed
Petals	usually 7, 11–19mm, oval, joined at extreme base
Stamens	7
Stigma	1, club-shaped; style long
Ovary	1, 1-celled
	FRUIT
Type	1, capsule, globular, usually splits into 5
Size	4–6mm
Seeds	7–11, 1.5–2mm, circular, flattened, black

Thrift *Armeria maritima*

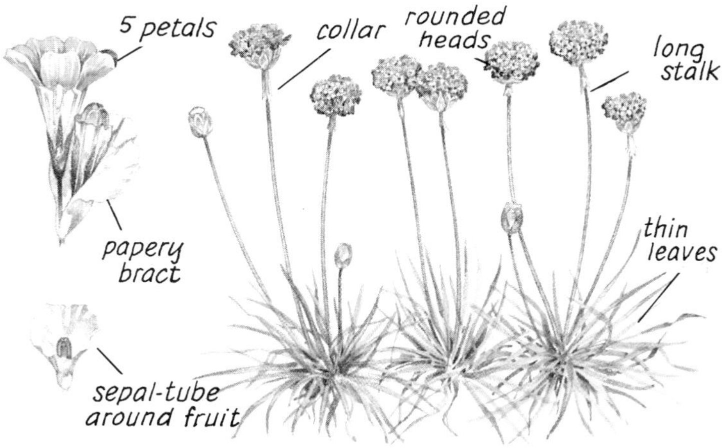

A distinctive plant of coastal areas. On exposed cliff-tops, the leaves disappear among grassy tufts so that the pink heads, held aloft above the short turf, provide the first indication of the plant's presence. The only common *Armeria* in the area. *Status:* native; common in coastal areas, sometimes on inland mountains. *Similar species:* although at first sight rather different, Sea-lavenders grow in similar places, have much the same growth-habit and similar flowers. Common Sea-lavender prefers muddy salt-marshes and has bluish-purple flowers in widely-branched heads.

Common Sea-lavender *(Limonium vulgare)*

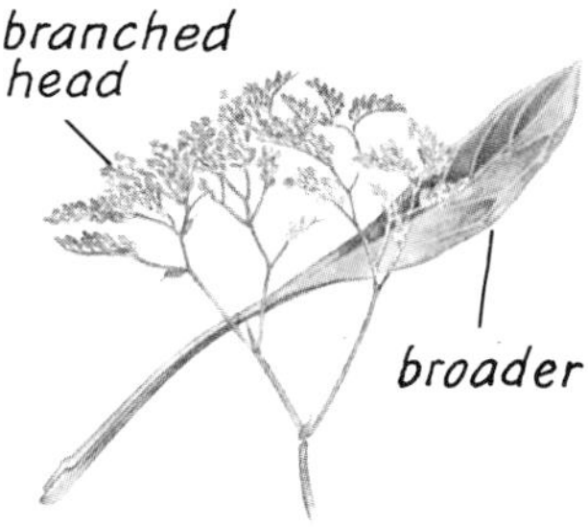

	THRIFT
Type	perennial
Height	5–30cm
Habitat	coastal cliffs, rocks, salt-marshes
Flowering	April–October
	STEMS AND LEAVES
Stem	leafy part very short; stalk of flower-head upright, unbranched
Root	woody, branched stock
Hairs	short or absent
Stipules	absent
Leaves	basal, forming rosette, 20–150mm, grass-like, rather thick, edge unbroken
Leaf-stalk	absent
	FLOWERS
Position	small clusters grouped into rounded head at stalk-tip
Bracts	lowest form tubular sheath up to 20mm long, around stalk-tip; innermost papery
Type	⚥, slightly scented
Size	7–10mm; heads 15–25mm
Colour	pink, rarely red or white
Stalk	shorter than flower
Sepals	5, 5–10mm, joined, papery, funnel-shaped, 5 hairy ribs
Petals	5, equal, oval, bases joined
Stamens	5
Stigmas	5, slender; long styles
Ovary	1, 1-celled
	FRUIT
Type	1, oblong capsule, opening irregularly, surrounded by sepals and withered petals
Size	2.5–3mm
Seeds	1, 2–2.5mm, egg-shaped

A delicate plant with slender stems, glossy leaves and pink petals. It is very variable in height, branching, and the size and number of the flowers. Common Centaury is a bitter-tasting herb, formerly taken to stimulate appetite and to treat digestive disorders. It was also used to combat fevers and treat anaemia. *Status:* native; absent from much of north. *Similar species:* Lesser Centaury has distinctly stalked flowers in less crowded heads; Seaside Centaury has narrower, oblong leaves. Yellow-wort is more distantly related, has the upper leaves joined, and flowers with six to eight yellow petals.

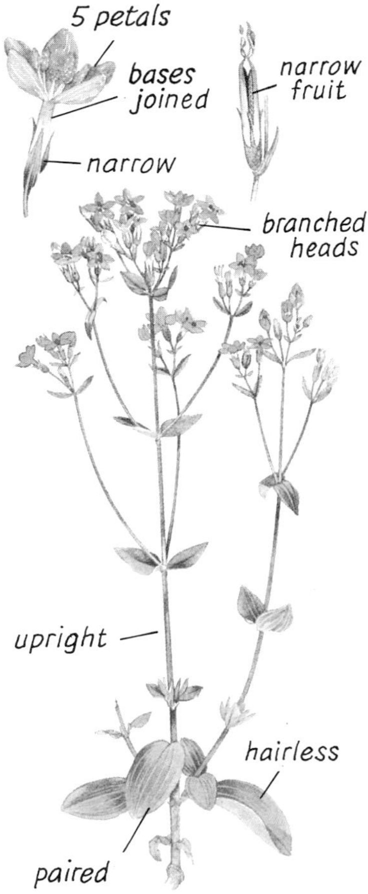

1 Lesser Centaury *(C. pulchellum)*; **2** Seaside Centaury *(C. littorale)*; **3** Yellow-wort *(Blackstonia perfoliata)*

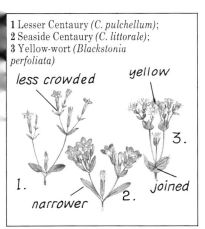

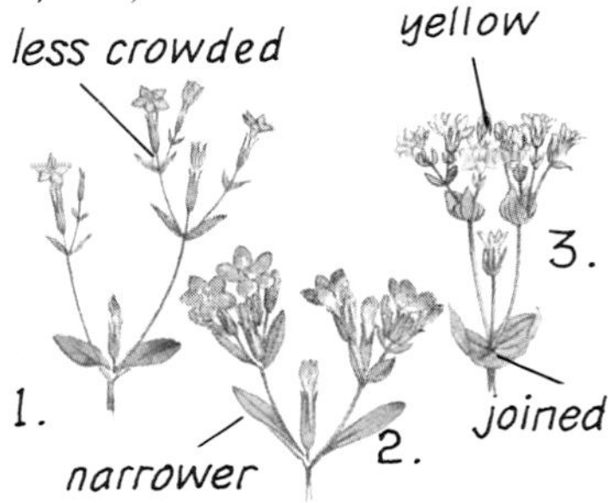

	COMMON CENTAURY
Type	annual or biennial
Height	2–50cm
Habitat	mostly grassy places or dunes; dry soils
Flowering	June–October
	STEMS AND LEAVES
Stem	1–few, upright, often branched
Root	small tap-root
Hairs	absent
Stipules	absent
Leaves	basal forming rosette or paired either side of stem, 10–50mm, oval or elliptical 3–7 main veins, blunt or sharpish, edge unbroken; upper smaller
Leaf-stalk	absent

	FLOWERS
Position	many in branched, crowded, flattish-topped heads
Bracts	present
Type	⚥, facing upwards
Size	10–14mm
Colour	pink, rarely white
Stalk	short or absent
Sepals	5, 5–8mm, narrow, pointed, bases joined
Petals	5, lobes 5–6mm, equal, bases joined into tube
Stamens	5, at top of petal-tube
Stigmas	2; style forked
Ovary	1, 1-celled
	FRUIT
Type	1, slender capsule, pointed
Size	8–12mm
Seeds	many, 0.8–1mm, rounded

Field Gentian *Gentianella campestris*

A small-flowered relative of the garden Gentians, with clusters of purplish, tubular flowers. Field Gentian is bitter-tasting and one of several plants used to flavour ales before the introduction of Hops. Native species were sometimes made into a tonic used medicinally and to stimulate appetite. *Status:* native; common, especially in north. *Similar species:* Autumn Gentian has narrower, equal, non-overlapping sepals. True Gentians have non-fringed petal-lobes separated by small lobes. Of these, Marsh Gentian has a broad, green-striped petal-tube, and Spring Gentian has a slender, deep-blue petal-tube.

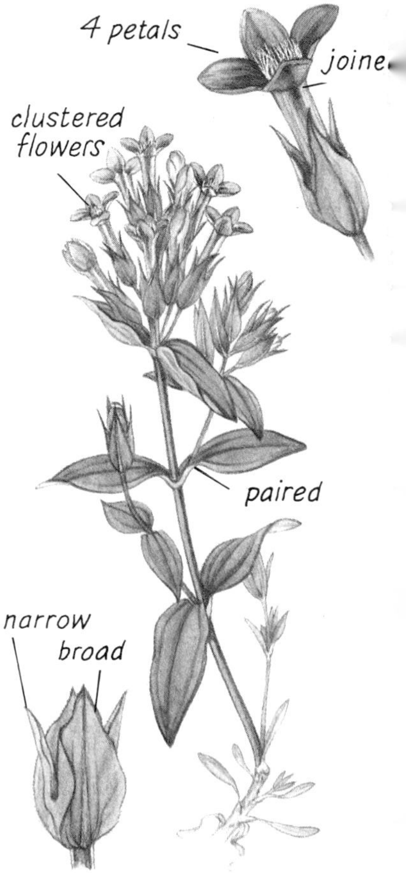

1 Autumn Gentian *(G. amarella)*; **2** Marsh Gentian *(Gentiana pneumonanthe)*; **3** Spring Gentian *(G. verna)*

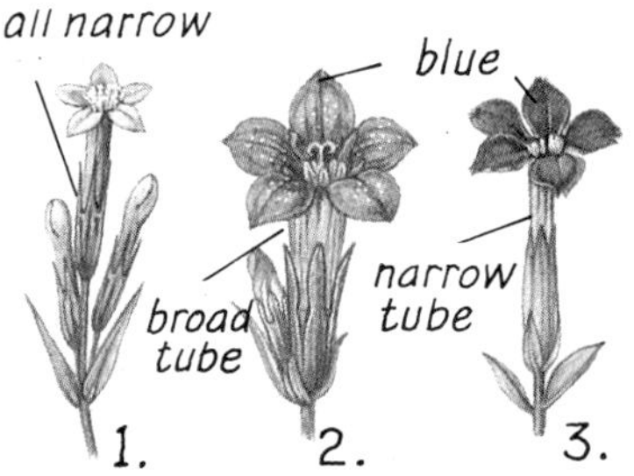

FIELD GENTIAN

Type	annual or biennial
Height	10–30cm
Habitat	grassy places, dunes; mostly lime-free soils
Flowering	July–October

STEMS AND LEAVES

Stem	upright, branched above
Root	fibrous
Hairs	absent
Stipules	absent
Leaves	basal or paired either side of stem, 10–30mm, oval to oblong, blunt or pointed, edge unbroken
Leaf-stalk	absent

FLOWERS

Position	many, in branched heads
Bracts	present
Type	⚥
Size	15–30mm
Colour	bluish lilac, rarely white
Stalk	shorter than flower
Sepals	4, 10–18mm, very unequal, bases joined, 2 outer oval, widest below middle, pointed, 2 inner narrow
Petals	4, 15–30mm, equal, joined into long tube, the oblong lobes fringed at base
Stamens	4
Stigmas	2, somewhat flattened
Ovary	1, 1-celled

FRUIT

Type	1, elongated capsule, splits lengthwise
Size	20–25mm
Seeds	many, 0.8–1mm, globular

An evergreen, carpeting shady banksides with glossy leaves and a sprinkling of bluish-purple, white-eyed blooms. Cultivated for many centuries, it has often escaped. Species of Periwinkle have had many medicinal uses, including staunching bleeding and reducing blood-pressure; other members of the family provide anti-cancer drugs. *Status:* native, introduced in northwest; scattered through area except extreme north. *Similar species:* Greater Periwinkle is more robust, with larger leaves and flowers. The stems arch over and root at the tips, springing up again as a new plant.

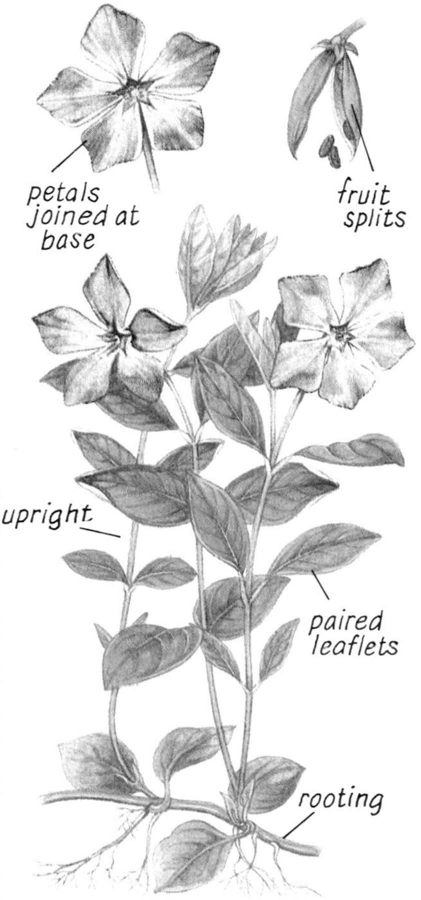

Greater Periwinkle *(V. major)*

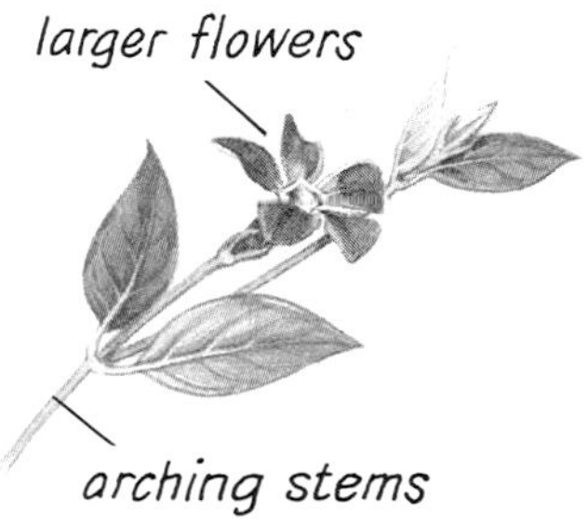

	LESSER PERIWINKLE
Type	evergreen perennial
Height	300–600cm
Habitat	woods, hedges; often dry, lime-rich soils
Flowering	March–May
	STEMS AND LEAVES
Stem	trailing with short, upright flowering stems
Root	woody stock; stems root
Hairs	absent
Stipules	absent
Leaves	paired either side of stem, 25–40mm, oval to elliptical, pointed or blunt, edge unbroken
Leaf-stalk	shorter than blade
	FLOWERS
Position	1, rarely 2, at leaf-base
Bracts	absent
Type	⚥
Size	25–32mm
Colour	bluish purple, rarely white or pink
Stalk	about equalling flower
Sepals	5, 4–5mm, spear-shaped
Petals	5, 12–16mm, equal, bases joined into tube, lobes broad, twisted together in bud, spreading widely, tip asymmetrical
Stamens	5, joined to petal-tube
Stigmas	forming broad head; styles joined
Ovaries	2, 1-celled
	FRUIT
Type	2, dry, pointed, spreading apart, splitting lengthwise
Size	20–25mm
Seeds	1–4, 5–6mm, oblong, grooved

Cleavers *Galium aparine*

A plant known better for its foliage than for its tiny flowers, Cleavers (or Goosegrass) has stiff, backward-curving hairs on stems and leaves with which it clings tenaciously to the least support. The fruits are covered with hooked hairs and are dispersed by animals. *Status:* native; very common, throughout area. *Similar species:* Woodruff is smaller, upright and glossy-leaved, with larger, sweetly-scented flowers. Two species with larger flower-heads and smooth fruits are Heath Bedstraw, which has smooth stems, and Common Marsh-bedstraw, which has roughish stem-angles and blunt leaves.

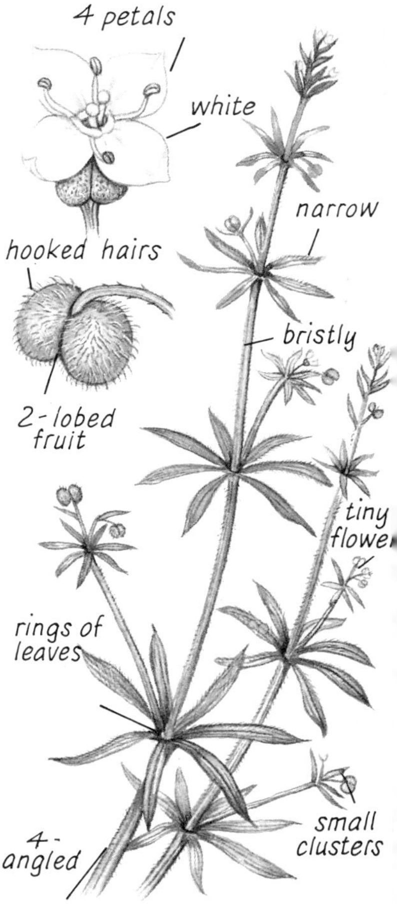

1 Woodruff *(G. odoratum)*; **2** Heath Bedstraw *(G. saxatile)*; **3** Common Marsh-bedstraw *(G. palustre)*

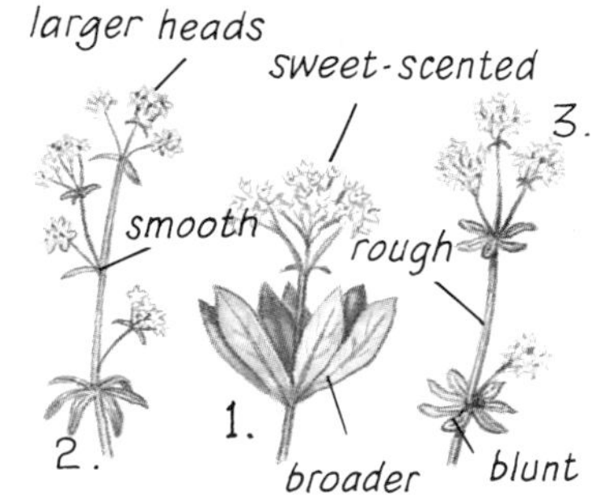

	CLEAVERS
Type	annual
Height	15–120cm
Habitat	hedges, waste ground, rocks and shingle
Flowering	June–August
	STEMS AND LEAVES
Stem	trailing or climbing by means of stiff, hook-like hairs, 4-angled
Root	fibrous
Hairs	stiff, curved, mostly backward-pointing
Stipules	like the leaves
Leaves	rings of 6–8 leaves and stipules on stem, 12–50mm, narrowly spear-shaped or elliptical, with slender point, edge unbroken
Leaf-stalk	absent

	FLOWERS
Position	2–5 in cluster at leaf-base
Bracts	leaf-like
Type	⚥
Size	1.5–2mm
Colour	white
Stalk	about equalling flower
Sepals	4, minute, forming ridge
Petals	4, 0.6–1mm, oval, wide-spreading, bases joined
Stamens	4, projecting
Stigmas	2, club-shaped
Ovary	1, below petals, 2-celled
	FRUIT
Type	1, dry, 2-lobed, splits in half, with hooked bristles
Size	4–6mm
Seeds	1 per half, not released

Rather a delicate plant, with slender stems bearing rings of needle-like leaves and golden heads of tiny, four-petalled flowers. The plant has a pleasant smell of new-mown hay when dried and was formerly used for making bedding. Bedstraws are food-plants for caterpillars of the Broad-bordered Bee Hawk-moth, a remarkable bee-mimic with transparent wings. *Status:* native; common, most of area. *Similar species:* Crosswort has hairy leaves in fours and flowers clustered at the leaf-bases. Wild Madder is much larger, with greenish-yellow five-petalled flowers and hooked teeth around the broad leaves.

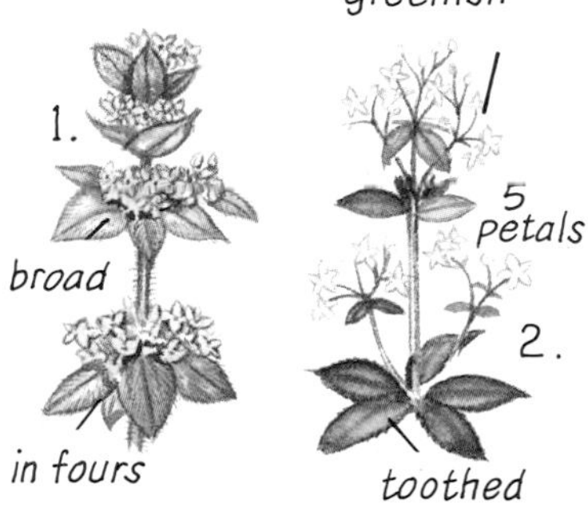

1 Crosswort *(G. cruciata)*; **2** Wild Madder *(Rubia peregrina)*

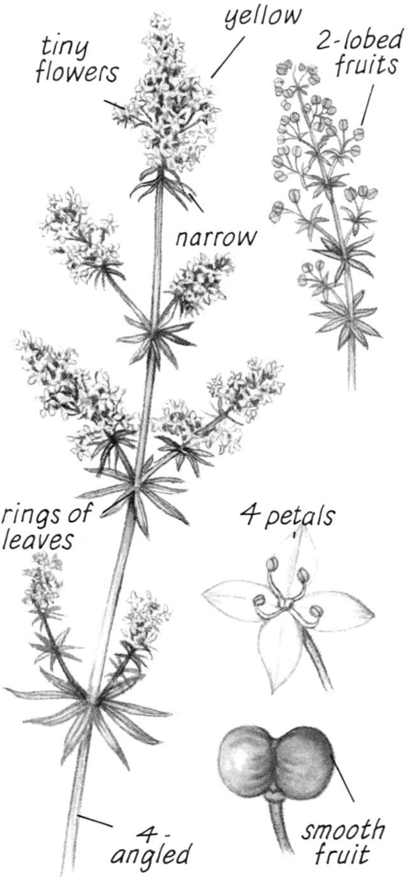

	LADY'S BEDSTRAW
Type	perennial
Height	15–100cm
Habitat	grassy places, dunes; all but poorest soils
Flowering	July–August
	STEMS AND LEAVES
Stem	upright or angled upwards, 4-angled, much-branched
Root	fibrous; creeping underground stems
Hairs	absent or sparse
Stipules	resembling leaves
Leaves	8–12 leaves and stipules in ring, 6–25mm, narrow, straight-sided, rough, with thin point, edge unbroken
Leaf-stalk	absent

	FLOWERS
Position	many, in branched cluster at tip of stem or branch
Bracts	present
Type	⚥
Size	2–4mm
Colour	bright yellow
Stalk	about equalling flower
Sepals	4, minute, forming ridge
Petals	4, 1–2mm, oval, wide-spreading, bases joined
Stamens	4, projecting
Stigmas	2, club-shaped
Ovary	1, below petals, 2-celled
	FRUIT
Type	1, 2-lobed, smooth, dry, becomes black, splits in half
Size	2.5–3mm
Seeds	1 per half, not released

Field Madder *Sherardia arvensis*

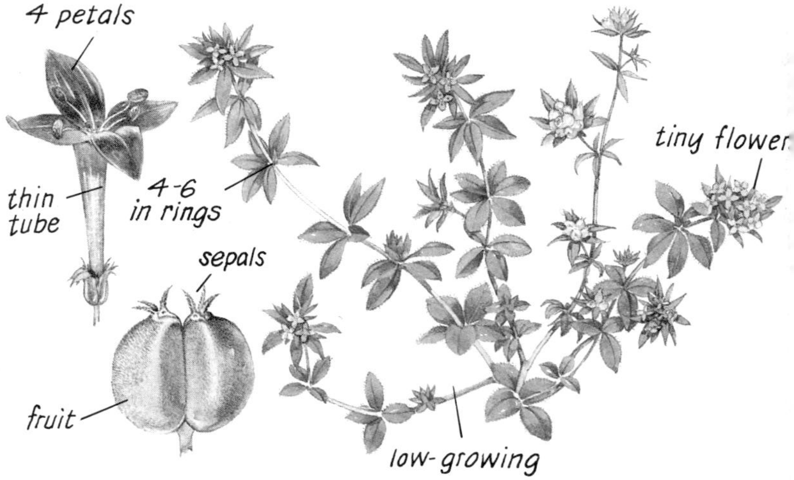

A dimunitive annual species with leaves in rings and small heads of tubular, lilac flowers, Field Madder often turns up in gardens as a weed, in flowerbeds and lawns. *Status:* native; common throughout region. *Similar species:* Squinancywort, mainly on chalk grassland, is a more slender, hairless plant with branched heads of pink flowers. Dune Squinancywort is similar but has orange underground stems, smaller, slightly fleshy leaves and stalkless flowers. Pink Woodruff is a larger, broad-leaved plant with heads of whitish-pink flowers and is sometimes naturalized.

1 Squinancywort *(Asperula cynanchica)*; 2 Dune Squinancywort *(A. occidentalis)*; 3 Pink Woodruff *(A. taurina)*

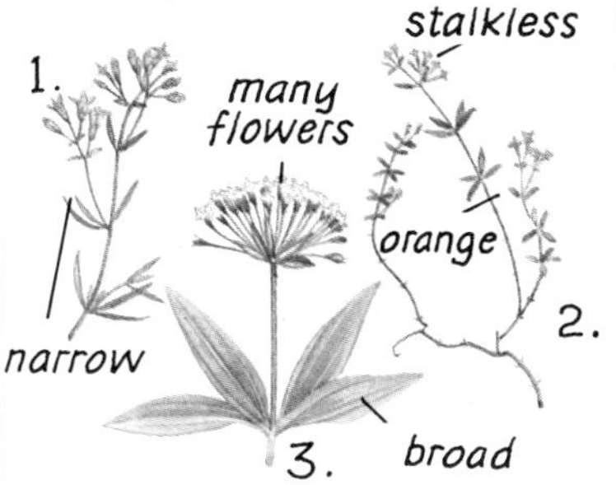

	FIELD MADDER	**Bracts**	8–10 in ring beneath head
Type	annual	**Type**	☿
Height	5–40cm	**Size**	4–5mm
Habitat	cultivated and waste ground	**Colour**	pale, pinkish purple
Flowering	May–October	**Stalk**	shorter than flower
	STEMS AND LEAVES	**Sepals**	4–6, 0.7–1.5mm, spear-shaped, fringed with hairs
Stem	many, low-growing, 4-angled	**Petals**	4, 4–5mm, equal, bases form thin tube, lobes oval
Root	slender, reddish	**Stamens**	4, protruding
Hairs	sparse, pointing backwards on stem-angles, forwards on leaves	**Stigmas**	2; style long, forked
Stipules	resembling leaves	**Ovary**	1, below sepals, 2-celled
Leaves	rings of 4–6 leaves and stipules on stem, 5–18mm, oval or elliptical, pointed, edge unbroken		**FRUIT**
Leaf-stalk	absent	**Type**	1, 2-lobed, splits in half, bristly, sepals at tip
	FLOWERS	**Size**	2–7mm
Position	4–8, in head at tip of stem or branch	**Seeds**	1 per half, not released

Polemonium caeruleum **Jacob's-ladder**

handsome plant with long heads of azy-blue showy flowers and finely ivided foliage. When ripe, each anther ursts, releasing a mass of bright range pollen, contrasting vividly with ne blue of the petals. Creeping nderground stems propagate the plant o that, given time, it forms extensive lumps. The common name derives from he ladder-like pattern made by the umerous parallel, narrow leaflets. A istant relative of the garden Phlox, acob's-ladder is widely cultivated for rnament, although many plants are the arer white form or an introduced ariant with larger flowers. Until the ast century in some parts of Europe, he species was thought to be effective n the treatment of syphilis and rabies. t was used in more ancient times gainst dysentery and toothache. *Status:* native or often introduced; cattered, mostly north and east of area. There are no similar species.)

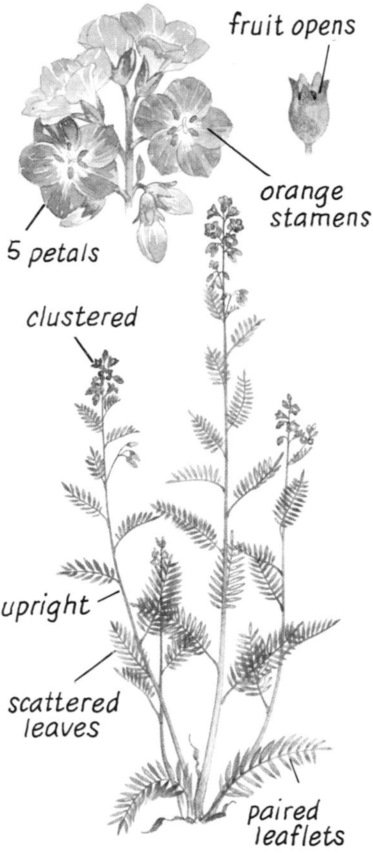

	JACOB'S-LADDER
Type	perennial
Height	30–90cm
Habitat	grassy places, rocks and scree; mostly lime-rich, often damp soils
Flowering	June–July
	STEMS AND LEAVES
Stem	1–few, upright, unbranched
Root	creeping underground stem
Hairs	gland-tipped in flower-head
Stipules	absent
Leaves	spirally placed on stem, 100–400mm, 3–25 mostly paired leaflets, each 20–40mm, oval to oblong, pointed, edge unbroken
Leaf-stalk	lower long, upper short

	FLOWERS
Position	many, in branched clusters at leaf-base or stem-tip
Bracts	few
Type	⚥ or rarely some ♀
Size	20–30mm
Colour	blue, rarely white
Stalk	shorter than flower
Sepals	5, 5–9mm, bases joined
Petals	5, 8–15mm, broadly oval, bases form short tube, lobes widely spreading
Stamens	5, protruding; pollen orange
Stigmas	3, slender, on long style
Ovary	1, 3-celled
	FRUIT
Type	1, capsule, splits into 3, globular, hidden by sepals
Size	5–7mm
Seeds	12–18, 2.5–3mm, angular

Hedge Bindweed *Calystegia sepium*

A spectacular climber with funnel-shaped flowers of pure white, just as large as those of many treasured garden plants. Gardeners shun Hedge Bindweed because it has long, creeping underground stems which sprout up all around, and its vigorous growth swamps all but the most robust plants. This rampant vine is beneficial in that it covers abandoned ruins, refuse tips, even a scrapped car or telegraph pole. *Status:* native; throughout area except for extreme north. *Similar species:* Large Bindweed has larger flowers and larger, balloon-like bracts. Hairy Bindweed has pink flowers and short hairs on young stems, stalks and bracts.

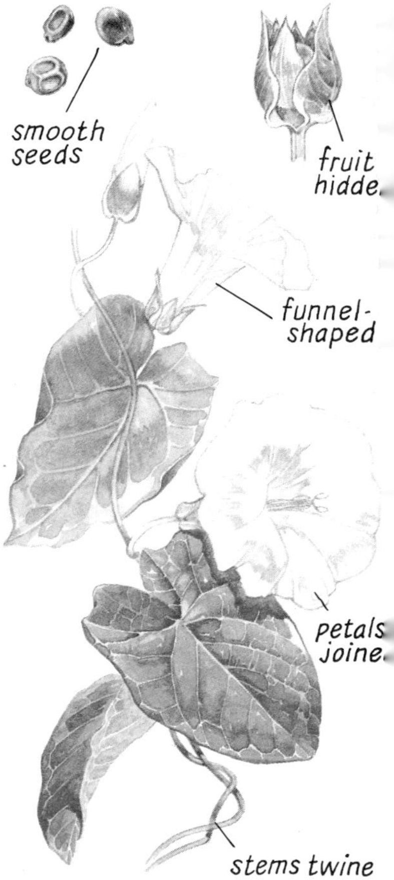

1 Large Bindweed *(C. silvatica)*;
2 Hairy Bindweed *(C. pulchra)*

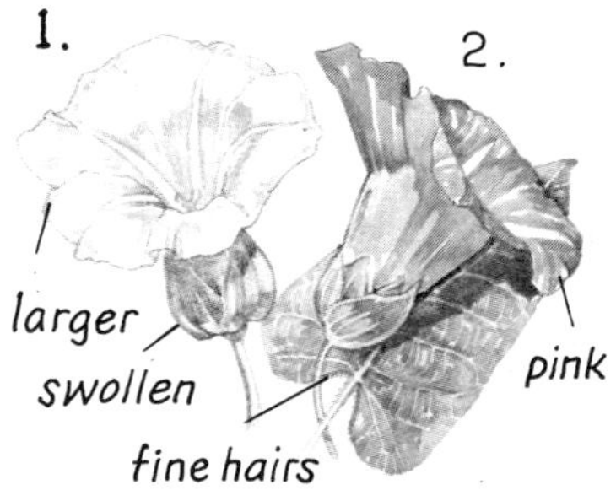

HEDGE BINDWEED

Type	perennial
Height	100–300cm
Habitat	hedges, woods, waste and cultivated ground
Flowering	April–July

STEMS AND LEAVES

Stem	climbs by twining anticlockwise, some creeping
Root	long, white, rooting, underground stems
Hairs	absent
Stipules	absent
Leaves	spirally placed on stem, to 150mm, heart- or arrow-shaped, blunt or with small point, edge unbroken
Leaf-stalk	mostly shorter than blade

FLOWERS

Position	solitary, at leaf-base
Bracts	2 below sepals, 10–30mm, broad, nearly flat
Type	⚥
Size	30–55mm
Colour	white
Stalk	shorter than flower
Sepals	5, 9–12mm, oval, bases joined, enclosed by bracts
Petals	5, 30–50mm, equal, almost completely joined into tube
Stamens	5, at base of petal-tube
Stigmas	2, broad; style forked
Ovary	1, 1-celled

FRUIT

Type	1, capsule, globular, hidden by sepals
Size	7–12mm
Seeds	4, 4–7mm, angular brown

A climber with delightful pink and white, candy-striped flowers; its funnel-shaped petal-tube is pleated and opens fan-like by day, attracting many sorts of insect. On bare ground, such as railway ballast, long, radiating stems of Field Bindweed spread in a circle and sometimes twist together, using each other for support. This species is unwelcome in gardens because it has extremely invasive underground stems. *Status:* native; throughout area, rarer in north. *Similar species:* Sea Bindweed is a trailing plant from sand-dunes and shingle, with kidney-shaped leaves and larger flowers.

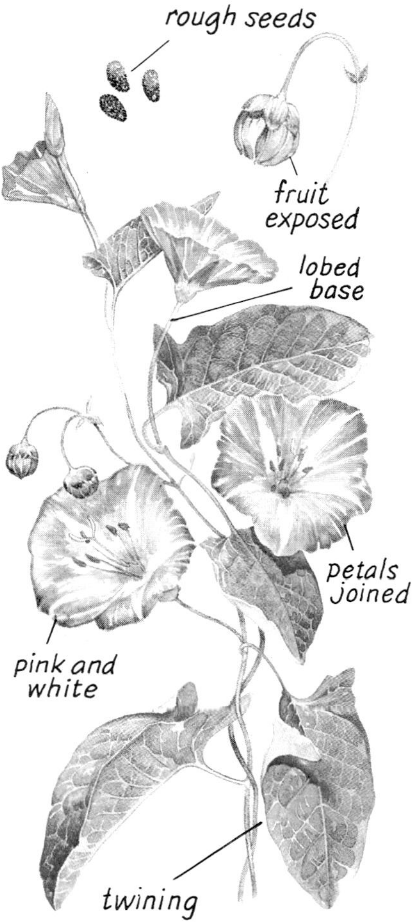

Sea Bindweed *(Calystegia soldanella)*

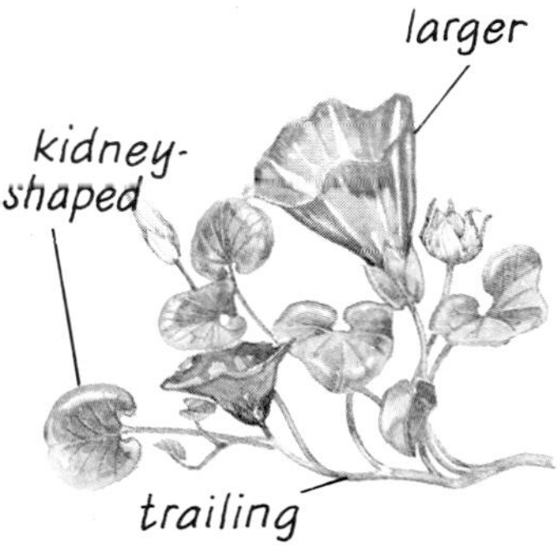

	FIELD BINDWEED
Type	perennial
Height	20–100cm, rarely to 200cm
Habitat	cultivated and waste ground, often near sea
Flowering	June–September
	STEMS AND LEAVES
Stem	trailing or climbing by twisting anticlockwise
Root	long, creeping, underground stems
Hairs	absent or on young shoots
Stipules	absent
Leaves	on alternate sides of stem, 20–50mm, oblong, oval or arrow-shaped, blunt, edge more or less unbroken
Leaf-stalk	shorter than blade
	FLOWERS
Position	1–3, in stalked cluster at leaf-base
Bracts	2, small, below flower-stalks
Type	⚥, scented
Size	10–30mm
Colour	pink and white
Stalk	shorter than flower
Sepals	5, 4–6mm, bases joined
Petals	5, 9–25mm, almost completely joined, funnel-shaped
Stamens	5, at base of petal-tube
Stigmas	2, slender; style forked
Ovary	1, 2-celled
	FRUIT
Type	1, capsule, almost globular
Size	3–5mm
Seeds	2–4, 2.5–4mm, angular, rough

Dodder *Cuscuta epithymum*

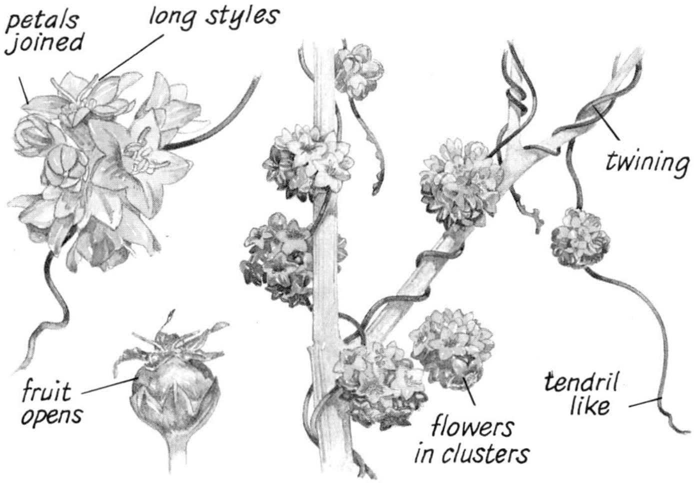

A most curious plant, with leafless, tendril-like stems. Individually scarcely noticeable, these stems can swamp a clump of Heather or Dwarf Gorse with a tangled mass of lurid pink and yellow threads. Dodder lacks green pigment because it is a parasite, drawing nourishment through sucker-like, modified roots which are firmly attached to the stem of another plant. It is rooted in the ground only as a seedling. *Status:* native; common in many localities, scattered through area except extreme north. *Similar species:* Greater Dodder usually attacks nettles or hops and has larger petals.

Greater Dodder *(C. europaea)*

	DODDER
Type	annual, parasite
Height	15–120cm
Habitat	mainly on species of Heather, Gorse and Clover
Flowering	July–September
	STEMS AND LEAVES
Stem	thread-like, white or yellow tinged with red or purple, twining, branched
Root	sucker-like, on stem, attached to other plants
Hairs	absent
Stipules	absent
Leaves	on alternate sides of stem, 0.5–2mm, scale-like, pointed, edge unbroken
Leaf-stalk	absent

	FLOWERS
Position	8–17, crowded in rounded heads 5–10mm wide
Bracts	minute, below each flower
Type	⚥
Size	2.5–5mm
Colour	white tinged pink or red
Stalk	absent
Sepals	5, 1–2mm, joined below
Petals	5, 2.5–4mm, joined, lobes pointed, spreading, with scales at base closing mouth of tube
Stamens	5, between petal-lobes
Stigmas	2, slender
Ovary	1, 2-celled
	FRUIT
Type	1, capsule, globular, splits near base, hidden by withered petals
Size	1.5–2mm
Seeds	2–4, 1–1.5mm, angled

\ plant usually noticed as fresh green ·osettes of small leaves, floating on the ›urface of a pond or stream. It is very ·ariable, the shape of the leaves :hanging with the depth and speed of he water and the flowering or fruiting ›tate. Plants growing on mud look very lifferent. Closely related species are dentified only with difficulty, and if ·ipe fruit is present. *Status:* native; :ommon, most of area. *Similar species:* ›ther aquatic plants include Canadian Naterweed, with leaves in threes and ong-stalked flowers, and Nuttall's Waterweed with narrower, pointed eaves. Mare's-tail has leaves in rings of ›ix to twelve.

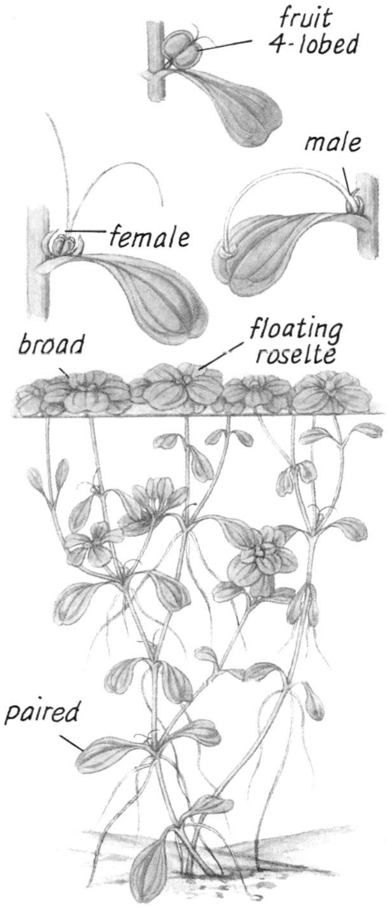

1 Canadian Waterweed *(Elodea canadensis)*; **2** Nuttall's Waterweed *(E. nuttallii)*; **3** Mare's-tail *(Hippuris vulgaris)*

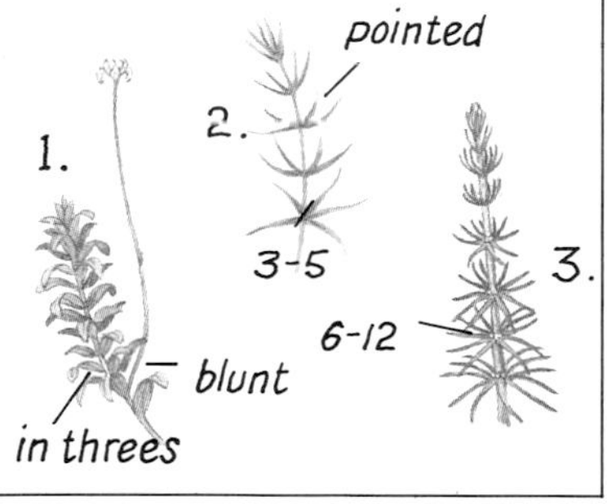

COMMON WATER-STARWORT

Type annual or perennial
Height 10–60cm
Habitat ponds, streams; shallow fresh water or wet mud
Flowering May–September

STEMS AND LEAVES

Stem submerged or low-growing
Root fibrous; stems root
Hairs absent
Stipules absent
Leaves paired or in rosette at stem-tip, 10–20mm, rounded or notched, edge unbroken; lower usually submerged, elliptical or spoon-shaped; upper usually floating, broader, forming rosette
Leaf-stalk shorter than blade

FLOWERS

Position solitary, at base of upper leaf, separate ♂ and ♀
Bracts 2, curved
Type 1 ♂, with stamen
Type 2 ♀, with ovary
Size 1.5–2mm
Colour white or green
Stalk shorter than flower
Sepals absent
Petals absent
Stamen 1, *c*2mm
Stigmas 2; styles curved, 2–3mm
Ovary 1, 4-celled

FRUIT

Type 1, splits into 4, nearly circular, 4-ridged
Size 1.6–2mm
Seeds 4, 1.4–1.8mm, winged

Field Gromwell *Lithospermum arvense*

A stiffly upright plant with narrow, bristly leaves and white flowers, rather like those of Forget-me-not. Predominantly a cornfield weed, this plant has become much rarer in recent years with the increased use of selective weed-killers and more effective methods of cleaning the seeds of crops. *Status:* native or introduced; scattered through area, most common in south. *Similar species:* Common Gromwell is a perennial with a thick stock bearing many stems. It differs in the broader leaves with distinct side-veins, and shiny, smooth, white fruits.

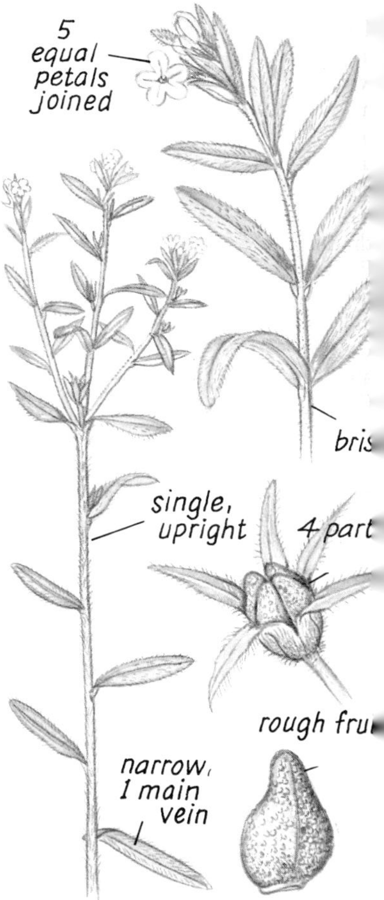

Common Gromwell *(L. officinale)*

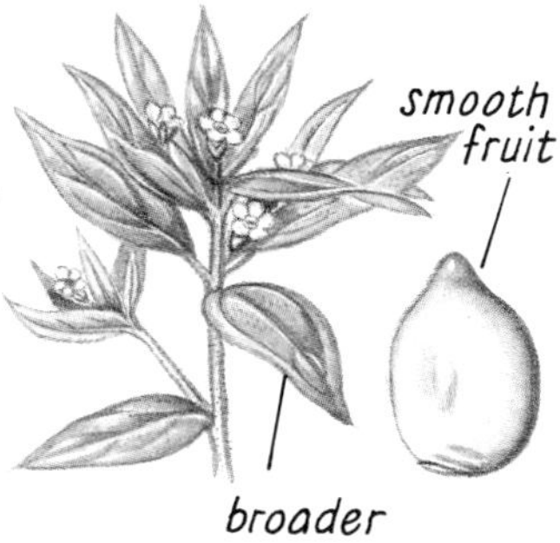

FIELD GROMWELL

Type	annual
Height	10–50cm, rarely to 90cm
Habitat	cultivated and waste ground; mostly dry places
Flowering	May–July

STEMS AND LEAVES

Stem	single, upright, sometimes branched, rough
Root	fibrous
Hairs	bristly, close to surface
Stipules	absent
Leaves	on alternate sides of stem, 30–50mm, oval to narrowly spear-shaped, blunt to sharp, edge unbroken
Leaf-stalk	only on lower leaves

FLOWERS

Position	head at stem-tip, curved in bud, lengthening in fruit
Bracts	lower leaf-like
Type	⚥
Size	6–9mm
Colour	white, rarely tinged blue
Stalk	shorter than flower
Sepals	5, 4.5–8mm, narrow, pointed, bases joined
Petals	5, 6–9mm, equal, joined into narrrow tube; lobes oblong, spreading widely
Stamens	5, at base of petal-tube
Stigma	1, club-shaped
Ovary	1, 2-celled, each half 2-lobed

FRUIT

Type	splits into 4, each nut-like, 3-angled, rough, greyish brown
Size	3–4mm
Seeds	1 per segment, not released

This bristly plant has blades of the upper leaves running down the stem as wings. Curved heads of tubular, nodding flowers are variously cream, pink, red or purple. Leaves were once used to dress cuts or bruises and roots made into cough-medicine. *Status:* native, or naturalized in north; throughout region. *Similar species:* Russian Comfrey, a hybrid with the next species, has almost wingless stems and usually blue flowers. Tuberous Comfrey has thick, underground stems and cream-coloured flowers. White Comfrey has soft, hairy leaves and white flowers with short, blunt sepals.

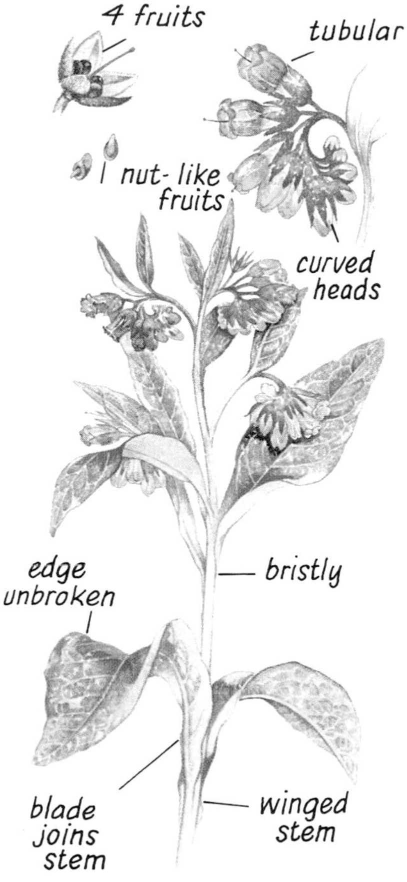

1 Russian Comfrey *(S. × uplandicum)*; **2** Tuberous Comfrey *(S. tuberosum)*; **3** White Comfrey *(S. orientale)*

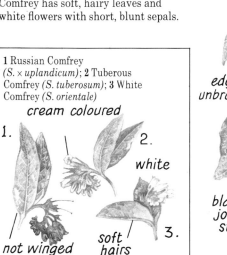

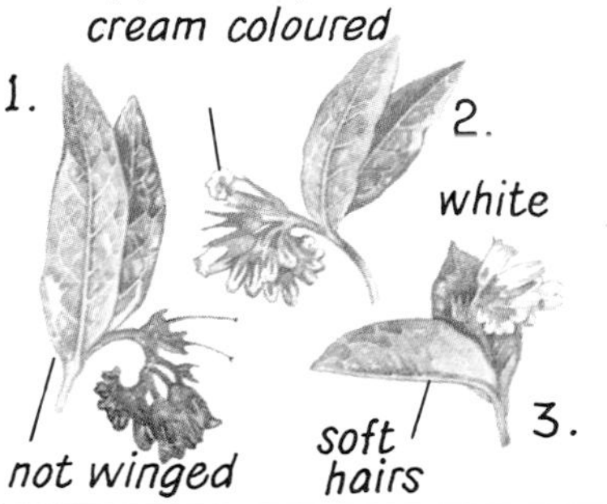

	COMMON COMFREY
Type	perennial
Height	30–120cm
Habitat	grassland, river-banks; damp soil
Flowering	May–June
	STEMS AND LEAVES
Stem	upright, branched, winged
Root	thick stock; roots fleshy
Hairs	stiff, dense, throughout
Stipules	absent
Leaves	on alternate sides of stem, 40–250mm, oval or upper spear-shaped, the blade joining wings on stem, pointed, edge unbroken
Leaf-stalk	lower long, absent above
	FLOWERS
Position	many, in curved heads
Bracts	absent
Type	⚥, nodding
Size	15–18mm
Colour	yellowish white, variably tinged red, purple or pink
Stalk	shorter than flower
Sepals	5, 7–8mm, narrow, pointed, bases joined
Petals	5, 15–18mm, equal, joined into tube; lobes short
Stamens	5, inside tube
Stigma	1; style long
Ovary	1, 2-celled, each 2-lobed
	FRUIT
Type	splits into 4, each part nut-like, almost egg-shaped, smooth, shiny, black
Size	5–6mm
Seeds	1 per segment, not released

Green Alkanet *Pentaglottis sempervirens*

Widely grown for its bright blue, white-eyed flowers, bristly-leaved Green Alkanet often escapes from gardens. It is native to the extreme south-west of Europe, but is naturalized further north. The roots yield a reddish dye that may have been an early reason for cultivation. *Status:* introduced; south-western part of area. *Similar species:* Bugloss is annual, with narrower leaves and a curved petal-tube. Borage has blackish stamens, projecting as a spike beyond the petal-tube. Viper's-bugloss has many curved flower-heads towards the stem-tip and some stamens project beyond the unequal petal-lobes.

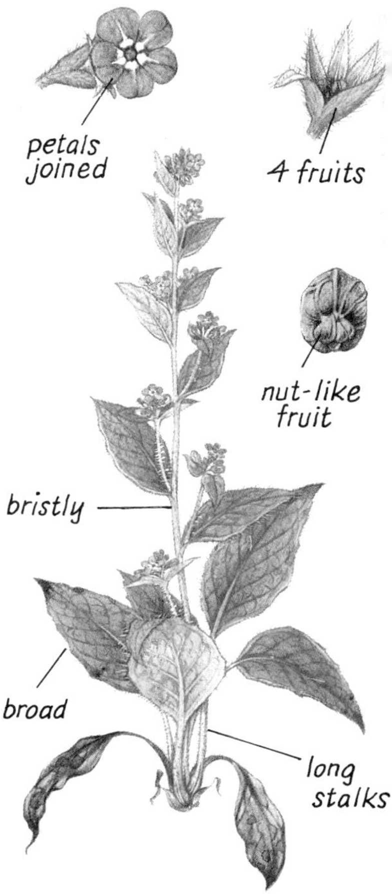

1 Bugloss *(Anchusa arvensis)*;
2 Borage *(Borago officinalis)*;
3 Viper's-bugloss *(Echium vulgare)*

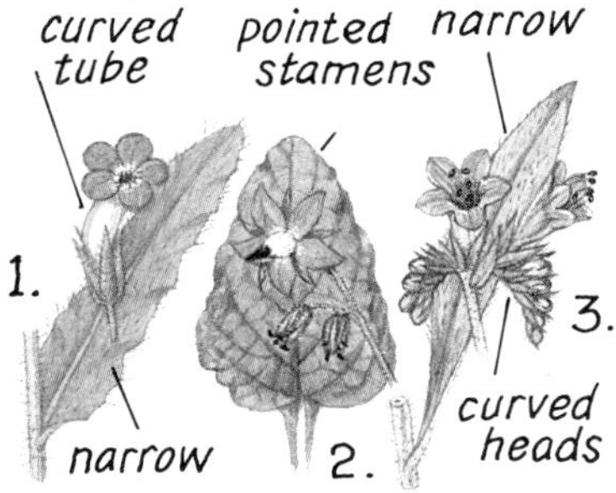

	GREEN ALKANET
Type	perennial
Height	30–100cm
Habitat	woods, hedges, mainly near houses; damp soils
Flowering	May–June
	STEMS AND LEAVES
Stem	angled upwards or upright
Root	underground creeping stem
Hairs	bristly throughout
Stipules	absent
Leaves	basal or on alternate sides of stem, 30–400mm, oval, tip pointed, edge unbroken or slightly wavy
Leaf-stalk	lower stalked
	FLOWERS
Position	5–15, in head at leaf-base
Bracts	leaf-like, below head
Type	⚥
Size	8–10mm
Colour	bright blue
Stalk	almost absent
Sepals	5, 2.5–8mm, narrowly spear-shaped
Petals	5, 6–8mm, equal, joined into tube at base, lobes broad, spreading widely
Stamens	5, not protruding
Stigma	1, club-shaped
Ovary	1, deeply 4-lobed
	FRUIT
Type	splits into 4 nut-like parts, egg-shaped with ring-like base, rough
Size	1.5–2mm
Seeds	1 per segment, not released

This greyish, softly hairy plant with dull red flowers has a strong smell rather like places where mice have been. Rabbits find it distasteful, so the plants are among the few untouched in the close-grazed turf surrounding their burrows. *Status:* native; rather scattered through area, mainly near coasts. *Similar species:* Green Hound's-tongue has greener leaves, nearly hairless above, and the fruit lacks a thickened edge. Other species do not have spiny fruits. Lungwort has white-spotted leaves and flowers opening pink, turning blue or purple. Oysterplant, mainly from northern seashores, is hairless with rough dots.

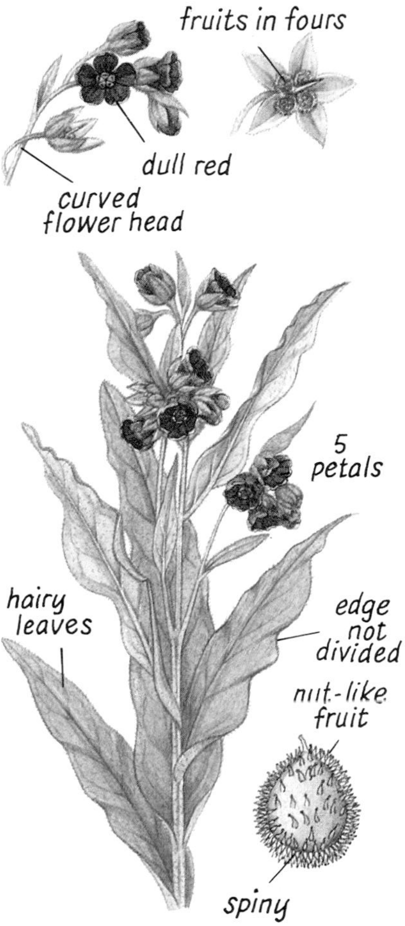

1 Green Hound's-tongue *(C. germanicum)*; 2 Lungwort *(Pulmonaria officinalis)*; 3 Oysterplant *(Mertensia maritima)*

	HOUND'S-TONGUE
Type	biennial
Height	30–90cm
Habitat	grassy places or wood edges; mostly dry soils
Flowering	June–August
	STEMS AND LEAVES
Stem	upright
Root	tap-root
Hairs	long, soft, grey
Stipules	absent
Leaves	basal or scattered around stem, 30–300mm, spear-shaped to oval, usually pointed, edge unbroken
Leaf-stalk	lower long, upper stalkless
	FLOWERS
Position	long heads at stem-tips
Bracts	few, lower leaf-like

Type	⚥
Size	6–10mm
Colour	purplish red, rarely white
Stalk	about equalling flower
Sepals	5, bases joined, 4–8mm, oblong or oval, bluntish
Petals	5, 7–11mm, equal, bases form tube, lobes with scales closing tube-mouth
Stamens	5, not protruding
Stigma	1; style thick
Ovary	1, deeply 4-lobed
	FRUIT
Type	splits into 4 nut-like parts, flattened, oval, covered with barbed spines, edge thickened
Size	5–6mm
Seeds	1 per segment, not released

Field Forget-me-not *Myosotis arvensis*

A Spring-flowering plant with pink buds opening into pale blue, yellow-eyed flowers. Young flower-heads are coiled, but straighten and lengthen as the fruits develop. Forget-me-nots are popular garden plants, in varying shades of blue or pink. *Status:* native; common throughout area. *Similar species:* Wood Forget-me-not has larger flowers with flat petal-lobes; those of the Field Forget-me-not are slightly hollow. Two small-flowered, annual species are Changing Forget-me-not, which has tiny flowers turning from yellow to blue, and Early Forget-me-not, which has short flower-stalks.

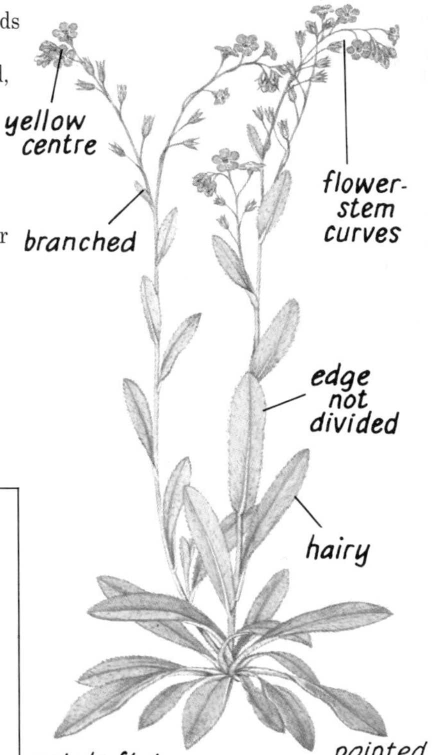

1 Wood Forget-me-not *(M. sylvatica)*; **2** Changing Forget-me-not *(M. discolor)*; **3** Early Forget-me-not *(M. ramosissima)*

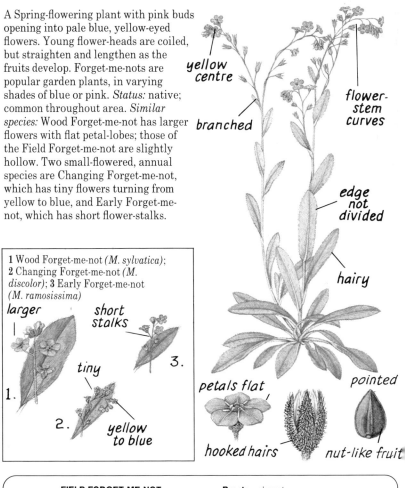

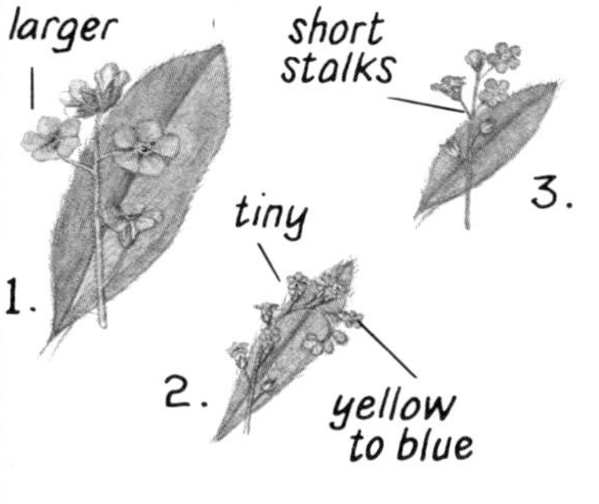

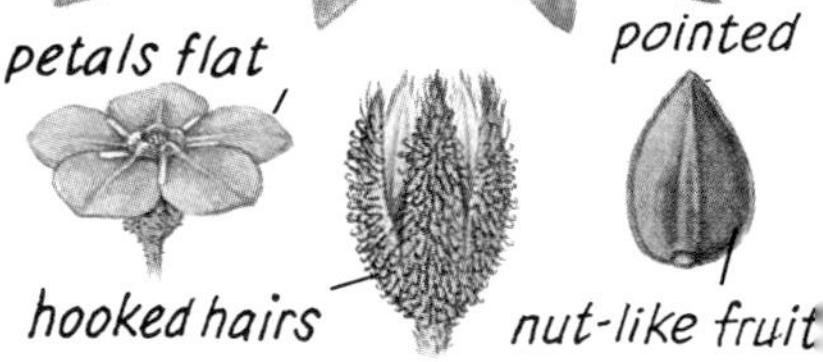

	FIELD FORGET-ME-NOT
Type	biennial
Height	15–30cm, rarely 60cm
Habitat	woods, hedges, cultivated ground, dunes; dryish soils
Flowering	April–September
	STEMS AND LEAVES
Stem	upright, branched
Root	fibrous
Hairs	short, throughout plant
Stipules	absent
Leaves	basal or scattered around stem, 6–80mm, oblong to spear-shaped, mostly blunt, edge unbroken
Leaf-stalk	only on lower leaves
	FLOWERS
Position	many in heads at stem-tips, coiled in bud, lengthening
Bracts	absent
Type	⚥
Size	3–5mm
Colour	blue with yellow centre, buds pinkish
Stalk	about equalling flower, longer in fruit
Sepals	5, 2.5–7mm, bases joined, covered with hooked hairs
Petals	5, 1.5–3mm, equal, bases form tube, lobes spreading
Stamens	5, inside tube
Stigma	1, tip swollen
Ovary	1, deeply 4-lobed
	FRUIT
Type	splits into 4 nut-like parts, angled, brown
Size	*c*1.5mm
Seeds	1 per segment, not released

Myosotis laxa subsp. *caespitosa* **Tufted Forget-me-not**

This species has coiled heads of small, sky-blue, yellow-eyed flowers like other Forget-me-nots, but grows in damp or wet places. The Forget-me-nots of wet places have straight hairs on the sepals, whereas those of dry places have distinctly hooked hairs. *Status:* native; common, throughout area. *Similar species:* two other species of damp or wet places are perennials with creeping stems. Water Forget-me-not has broad sepals joined for at least two-thirds of their length. Creeping Forget-me-not has narrower sepals joined to the middle, and long, projecting hairs near the base of the stems.

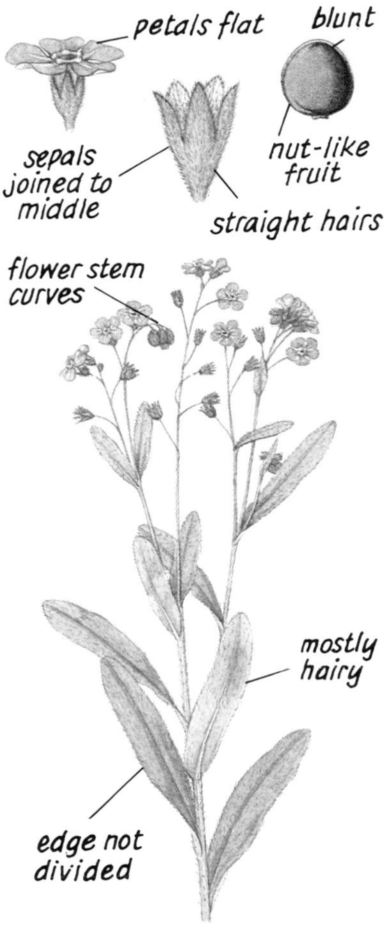

1 Water Forget-me-not *(M. scorpioides)*; 2 Creeping Forget-me-not *(M. secunda)*

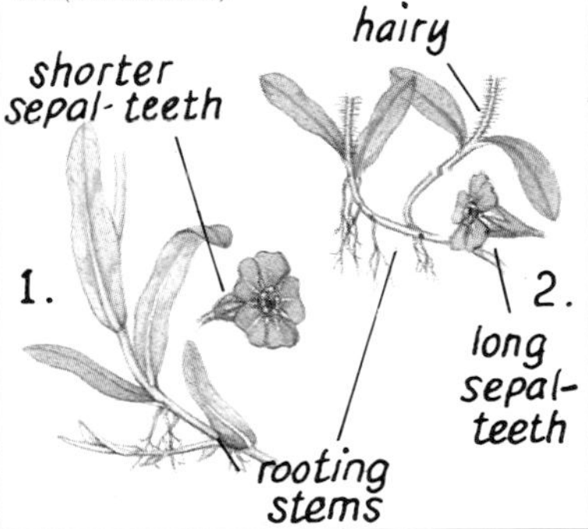

	TUFTED FORGET-ME-NOT
Type	annual or biennial
Height	20–40cm
Habitat	streams, ponds, marshes; damp soil
Flowering	May–August
	STEMS AND LEAVES
Stem	sometimes branched, upright
Root	fibrous
Hairs	on most of plant, pointing towards stem- or leaf-tip
Stipules	absent
Leaves	on alternate sides of stem, 10–80mm, oblong or spear-shaped, blunt, edge unbroken, base narrowed
Leaf-stalk	absent
	FLOWERS
Position	many in heads at stem-tips, coiled, becoming straight
Bracts	absent or few at base
Type	⚥
Size	2–4mm
Colour	light blue with yellow centre; buds pink
Stalk	about equalling flower, longer in fruit
Sepals	5, 2.5–4mm, up to 8mm in fruit, joined to middle
Petals	5, 2–4mm, forming tube at base, lobes rounded
Stamens	5, inside petal-tube
Stigma	1, tip swollen
Ovary	1, deeply 4-lobed
	FRUIT
Type	splits into 4 nut-like parts, oval, glossy brown
Size	1.3–1.8mm
Seeds	1 per segment, not released

Vervain *Verbena officinalis*

A tall plant with stiffly upright, tough stems and slender spikes of tiny lilac and pink flowers. It belongs to a family which includes the Verbenas of gardens, yet it is similar in many respects to species of the Mint family. Vervain had many herbal uses and was attributed magical properties. *Status:* native, introduced in north; rather scattered through region except for extreme north. *Similar species:* Gypsywort is a species of the Mint family and is found in wet places, often partly submerged. It has clusters of small flowers at the base of the upper leaves.

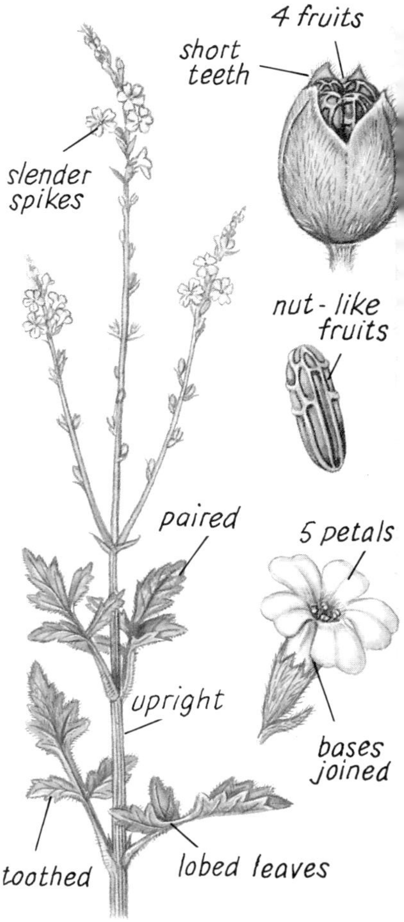

Gypsywort *(Lycopus europaeus)*

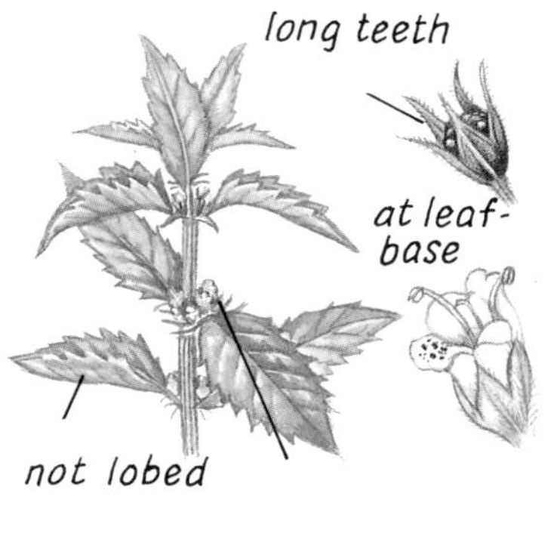

	VERVAIN
Type	perennial
Height	30–60cm
Habitat	waste ground or roadsides; mostly dry soils
Flowering	July–September
	STEMS AND LEAVES
Stem	usually several, upright, branched, 4-angled
Root	woody stock
Hairs	stiff, on leaves
Stipules	absent
Leaves	paired on stem, 20–75mm, deeply lobed, the lobes mostly paired, dull green, sharp or blunt, toothed
Leaf-stalk	stalked or upper stalkless

	FLOWERS
Position	many in long, spike-like heads at stem-tips
Bracts	small, pointed
Type	⚥
Size	4–6mm
Colour	lilac, tube pink
Stalk	almost absent
Sepals	5, 2–3mm, joined forming 5-ribbed tube, teeth short
Petals	5, 4–6mm, bases form tube, lower lobes longest
Stamens	4, rarely 2, inside tube
Stigma	1, tip swollen, slightly 2-lobed
Ovary	1, 4-celled
	FRUIT
Type	splits into 4 nut-like parts, oblong, ridged, reddish-brown
Size	1.5–2mm
Seeds	1 per segment, not released

A soft-leaved, lilac-flowered relative of Garden Mint, with broad leaves having a similar aroma. Water Mint makes a refreshing herbal tea. *Status:* native; suitable places throughout area. *Similar species:* Peppermint has almost hairless leaves and oblong heads of flower-clusters. A hybrid with the following species, it does not produce fruit. Many variants are known, differing in leaf-shape, hairiness and scent. Spear Mint has stalkless leaves and flower-clusters in a slender spike. Corn Mint is found in drier places and has small, widely spaced clusters of flowers at the base of the upper leaves.

1 Peppermint *(M. × piperita)*; 2 Corn Mint *(M. arvensis)*; 3 Spear Mint *(M. spicata)*

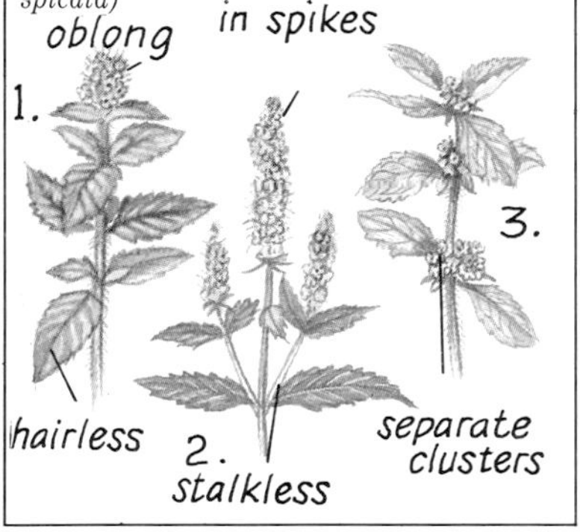

	WATER MINT
Type	perennial, strongly scented
Height	15–90cm
Habitat	marshes, rivers, wet woods
Flowering	July–October
	STEMS AND LEAVES
Stem	upright, some branched, 4-angled, often red-tinged
Root	creeping underground stems
Hairs	over most of plant, soft
Stipules	absent
Leaves	paired, 20–90mm, most oval, blunt or pointed, toothed, base slightly heart-shaped
Leaf-stalk	shorter than blade
	FLOWERS
Position	many in 2–6 rounded clusters towards stem-tip
Bracts	lowest leaf-like; small bracts beneath each flower
Type	⚥ or some ♀
Size	5–8mm
Colour	pinkish lilac
Stalk	shorter than flower
Sepals	5, 2.5–4mm, forming tube with 10–13 veins, teeth pointed, almost equal
Petals	5, 5–8mm, bases form tube, upper 2 lobes nearly joined, lower 3 lobes separate
Stamens	4, protruding
Stigmas	2 on forked style
Ovary	1, deeply 4-lobed
	FRUIT
Type	splits into 4 nut-like parts, egg-shaped, brown
Size	1–1.5mm
Seeds	1 per segment, not released

Wood Sage *Teucrium scorodonia*

A mint relative with vaguely sage-like, crinkly leaves and one-sided spikes of greenish-yellow flowers. In spite of its name, this is more a plant of sunny, grassy places than woodland, where it grows on the margins or in clearings. The flowers have very short upper petal-lobes. *Status:* native; most of area except parts of north. *Similar species:* the related Wall Germander has purple flowers of a similar form. Native in the south-east of the area, it is naturalized in Britain. Yellow Archangel is a yellow-flowered mint relative with nettle-like leaves and long upper lobes to the petal-tube.

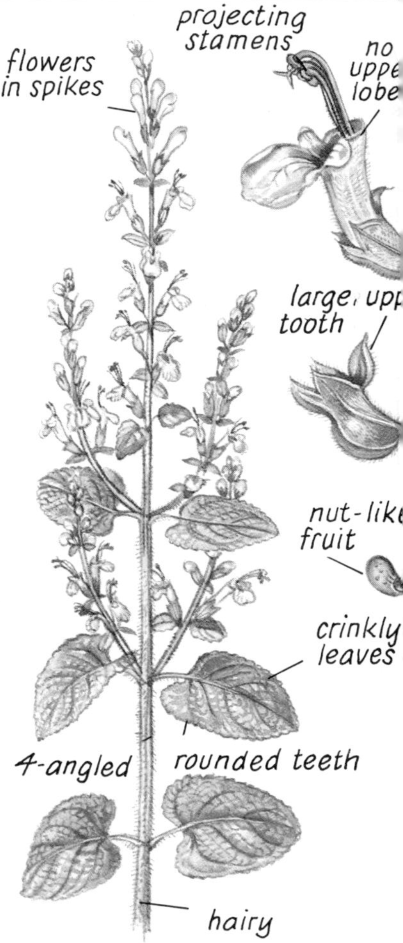

1 Wall Germander *(T. chamaedrys)*;
2 Yellow Archangel *(Lamiastrum galeobdolon)*

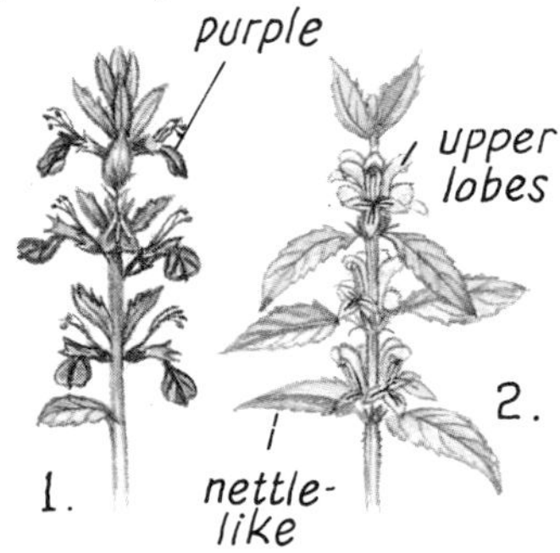

	WOOD SAGE
Type	perennial
Height	15–50cm
Habitat	grassland, heaths, dunes, woods; mostly dry soils
Flowering	July–September
	STEMS AND LEAVES
Stem	upright, branched, woody at base
Root	creeping underground stem
Hairs	short, over most of plant
Stipules	absent
Leaves	paired on stem, 30–70mm, oval, rough, blunt to sharpish, with rounded teeth, base heart-shaped
Leaf-stalk	shorter than blade

	FLOWERS
Position	many, in spikes at stem-tips
Bracts	oval, shorter than flowers
Type	⚥
Size	9–12mm
Colour	greenish yellow
Stalk	shorter than flower
Sepals	5, 4–6mm, joined, with pointed teeth, upper often largest
Petals	5, 9–12mm, bases joined into narrow tube, lower lobe largest, upper 2 very short
Stamens	4, protruding
Stigmas	2 on long, forked style
Ovary	1, deeply 4-lobed
	FRUIT
Type	splits into 4 nut-like parts, egg-shaped, smooth
Size	1.5–2mm
Seeds	1 per segment, not released

A bristly plant with nettle-like leaves and purple, mint-like flowers with spiny sepal-teeth. The brittle stems usually have distinct swellings below the attachment of each leaf-pair, and a tuft of reddish, gland-tipped hairs. The lower three petals have two cone-shaped projections at the base, which are not found in related genera. *Status:* native; common, throughout area. *Similar species:* Red Hemp-nettle is softly hairy, without swellings on the stems, and with narrower leaves. Its pinkish-purple flowers have yellow markings. Large-flowered Hemp-nettle has larger, pale yellow, purple-spotted flowers.

1 Red Hemp-nettle *(G. angustifolia)*; **2** Large-flowered Hemp-nettle *(G. speciosa)*

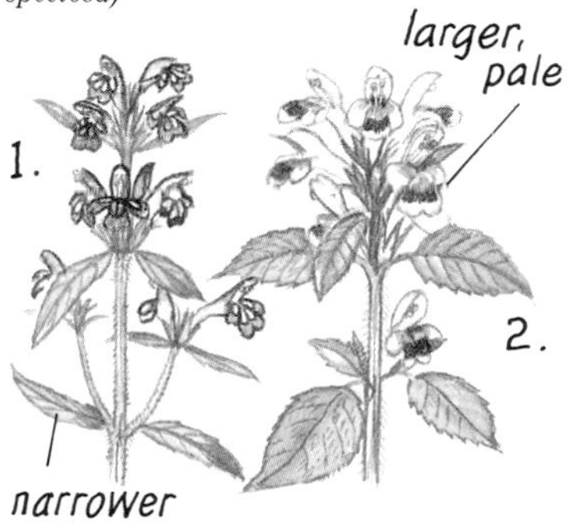

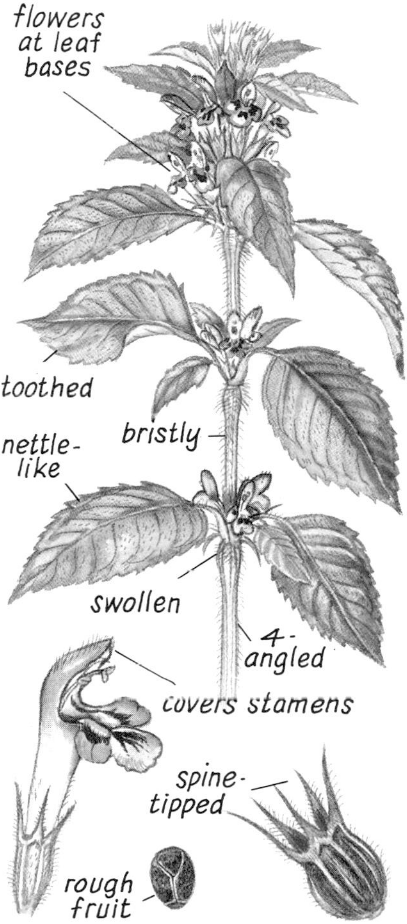

	COMMON HEMP-NETTLE
Type	annual
Height	10–100cm
Habitat	cultivated ground, hedges, woods
Flowering	July–September
	STEMS AND LEAVES
Stem	angled upwards, 4-angled, swollen below leaf-pairs
Root	fibrous
Hairs	stiff, over most of plant
Stipules	absent
Leaves	paired on stems, 25–100mm, oval, pointed, toothed, base wedge-shaped
Leaf-stalk	shorter than blade
	FLOWERS
Position	clusters at leaf-bases and near stem-tip
Bracts	leaf-like but most smaller
Type	⚥
Size	15–20mm, rarely to 28mm
Colour	purple or pink marked with purple, rarely white
Stalk	much shorter than flower
Sepals	5, 12–14mm, joined into tube, teeth spine-tipped
Petals	5, 15–28mm, bases form tube, upper 2 lobes joined, hood-like, lower 3 bent back, with 2 swellings
Stamens	4, under upper petal-lobes
Stigmas	2 on long, forked style
Ovary	1, deeply 4-lobed
	FRUIT
Type	splits into 4 nut-like parts, rounded, 3-angled
Size	3–4mm
Seeds	1 per segment, not released

White Dead-nettle *Lamium album*

Nettle-like foliage but with softer, stingless hairs and clusters of white, two-lipped flowers identify the White Dead-nettle. Long-tongued insects, such as bees, pollinate the flowers. The faintly aromatic leaves were once used in the north to make herbal teas. *Status:* mostly native, introduced to Ireland; common in most of area except parts of north. *Similar species:* Cat-mint has grey-green foliage with a mint-like scent. This is closely related to the garden Cat-mint, with low-growing stems and blue flowers, that cats find irresistible. White Horehound has rounded, white-haired leaves and ten hooked sepal-teeth.

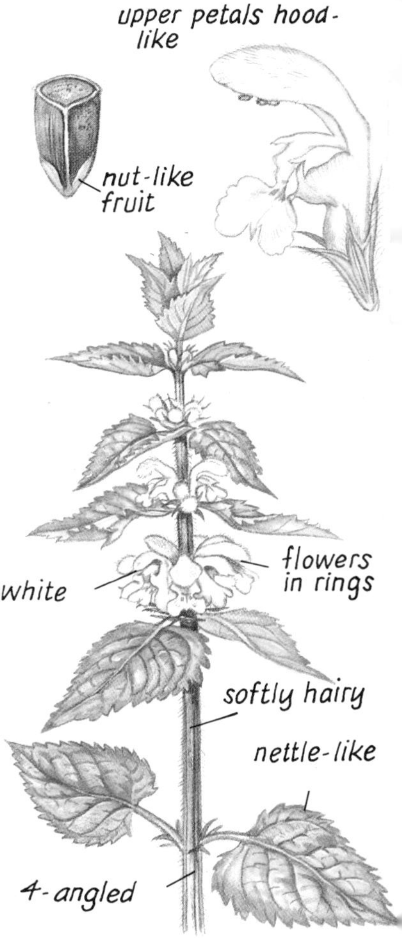

1 Cat-mint *(Nepeta cataria)*; **2** White Horehound *(Marrubium vulgare)*

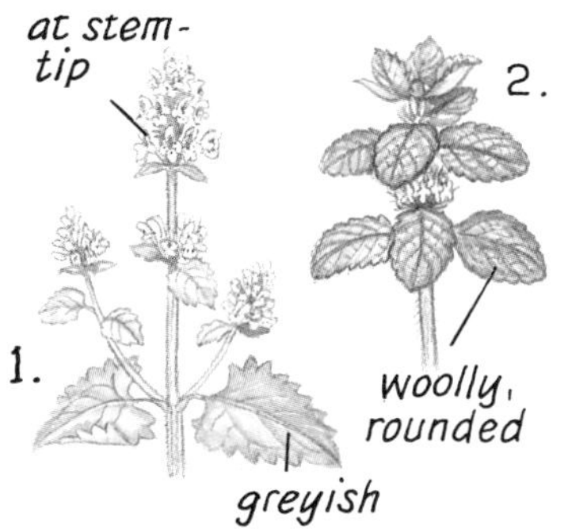

	WHITE DEAD-NETTLE
Type	perennial
Height	20–80cm
Habitat	roadsides, hedges, waste ground
Flowering	May–December
	STEMS AND LEAVES
Stem	upright
Root	creeping underground stems
Hairs	long, fairly soft
Stipules	absent
Leaves	paired, 25–120mm, oval, with slender point, coarsely toothed, base heart-shaped
Leaf-stalk	shorter than blade
	FLOWERS
Position	many, in clusters at upper leaf-bases
Bracts	present
Type	⚥
Size	20–25mm
Colour	white
Stalk	much shorter than flower
Sepals	5, 9–13mm, forming tube, teeth long, slender
Petals	5, 20–25mm, bases form tube; upper 2 lobes joined, hood-like, lowest lobe large, bent back, side lobes small, toothed
Stamens	4, under upper petal-lobes
Stigmas	2 on long, forked style
Ovary	1, deeply 4-lobed
	FRUIT
Type	splits into 4 nut-like parts, 3-angled, tip squarish
Size	2.5–3mm
Seeds	1 per segment, not released

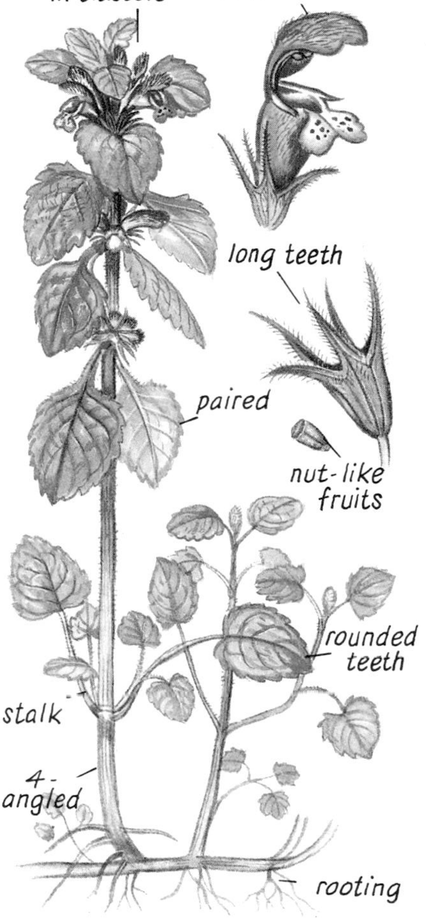

. vaguely nettle-like plant but with :ingless hairs on the leaves and four-ngled stems, with flowers and clusters f four nut-like fruits typical of the 1int family. The creeping, rooting, asal parts of the plant were formerly sed as pig-feed. In complete contrast, he flowers were crystallized in sugar .nd eaten as sweets. *Status:* native; very ommon, throughout area. *Similar pecies:* Henbit Dead-nettle has stalkless .pper leaves. Cut-leaved Dead-nettle ıas deeply lobed leaves with few teeth. 3lack Horehound is a more robust erennial, with short, broad sepal-teeth.

1 Henbit Dead-nettle *(L. amplexicaule)*; **2** Cut-leaved Dead-nettle *(L. hybridum)*; **3** Black Horehound *(Ballota nigra)*

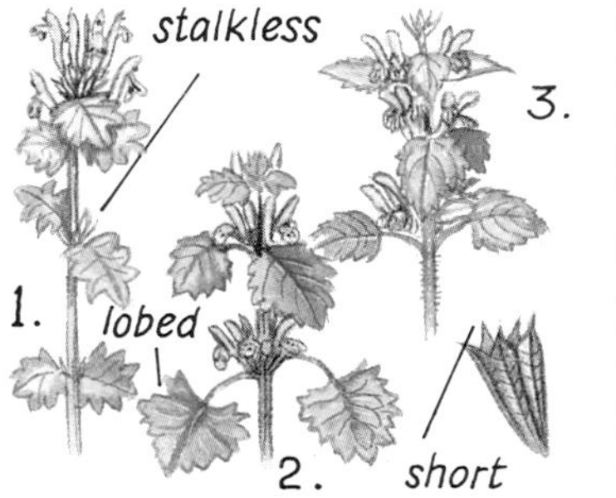

	RED DEAD-NETTLE
Type	annual
Height	10–45cm
Habitat	cultivated and waste ground
Flowering	March–October
	STEMS AND LEAVES
Stem	base branched, often rooting, upper parts upright, 4-angled, purplish
Root	fibrous
Hairs	short, over most of plant
Stipules	absent
Leaves	paired on stem, 10–50mm, oval, blunt, with rounded teeth, base heart-shaped
Leaf-stalk	lowest long, upper short
	FLOWERS
Position	few, in clusters towards stem-tip
Bracts	similar to leaves
Type	⚥
Size	10–18mm
Colour	pinkish purple
Stalk	very short
Sepals	5, 5–7mm, bases joined, teeth long, pointed
Petals	5, 10–18mm, bases form tube, upper 2 lobes joined, hood-like, lowest large, 2-lobed, side 2 short, toothed
Stamens	4, under upper petal-lobes
Stigmas	2 on long, forked style
Ovary	1, deeply 4-lobed
	FRUIT
Type	splits into 4 nut-like parts, 3-angled, tip square
Size	2–2.5mm
Seeds	1 per segment, not released

Betony *Stachys officinalis*

Almost leafless stems of Betony arise from a basal tuft of long-stalked leaves, and each bears a fairly compact, cylindrical head of reddish-purple flowers at the tip. To Betony was attributed many properties, both medicinal and magical, and it was used in herbal tea and herbal tobacco. *Status:* native; common in south, absent from parts of north. *Similar species:* related species lack leaves at the base but have many on the stems. Stem-leaves of Hedge Woundwort are long-stalked, whereas those of Marsh Woundwort are stalkless. Field Woundwort is a small-flowered annual with broad stem-leaves.

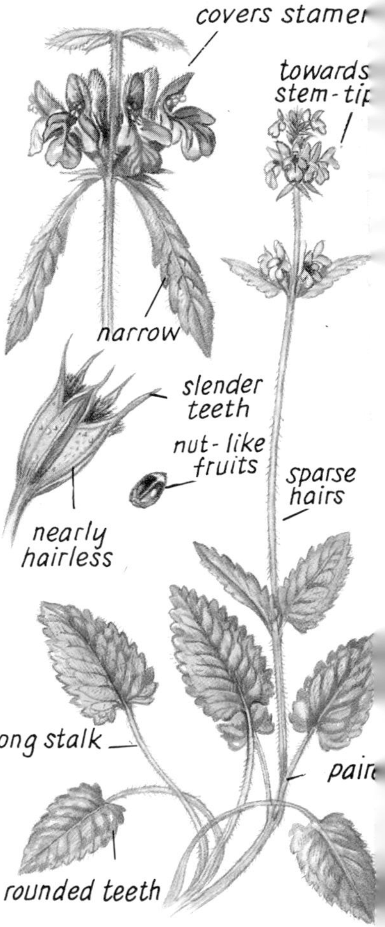

1 Hedge Woundwort *(S. sylvatica)*;
2 Marsh Woundwort *(S. palustris)*;
3 Field Woundwort *(S. arvensis)*

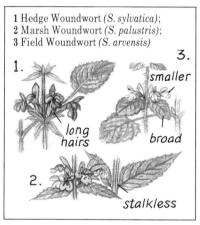

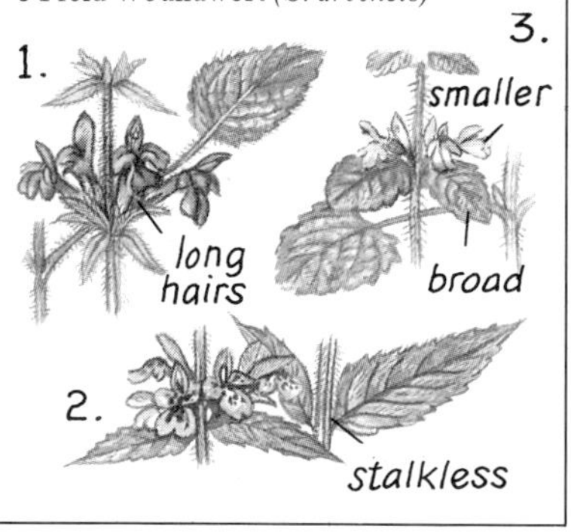

BETONY

Type perennial
Height 15–60cm
Habitat woods, hedges, grassy places; light soils
Flowering June–September

STEMS AND LEAVES

Stem upright, mostly unbranched
Root woody underground stem
Hairs sparse
Stipules absent
Leaves most basal, 2–4 pairs on stem, 30–70mm, oval to oblong, blunt, with rounded teeth, base heart-shaped
Leaf-stalk lowest twice as long as blade, uppermost stalkless

FLOWERS

Position many, in clusters around stem, towards stem-tip
Bracts lowest leaf-like
Type ⚥
Size 12–18mm
Colour bright reddish purple
Stalk much shorter than flower
Sepals 5, 5–9mm, bases form tube, teeth sharply pointed
Petals 5, 12–18mm, bases form tube, upper 2 lobes joined, hood-like, other lobes bent back
Stamens 4, under upper lobes
Stigmas 2 on long, forked style
Ovary 1, deeply 4-lobed

FRUIT

Type splits into 4 nut-like parts, 3-angled, tip rounded
Size 2.5–3mm
Seeds 1 per segment, not released

very variable plant, usually with pikes of violet, 2-lipped flowers and airs of rough, lobed leaves. Some pecimens produce flowers which never pen fully, being pollinated in bud and etting a full crop of nut-like fruits. Ieight, lobing of the leaves and size of he flowers vary considerably. The ruits swell and become sticky when vet. *Status:* native; scattered localities, nainly in south-west of area, north to Scotland. *Similar species:* Meadow Clary has larger flowers with long, curved, hood-like upper petal-lobes, and acks white hairs on the sepal-tube.

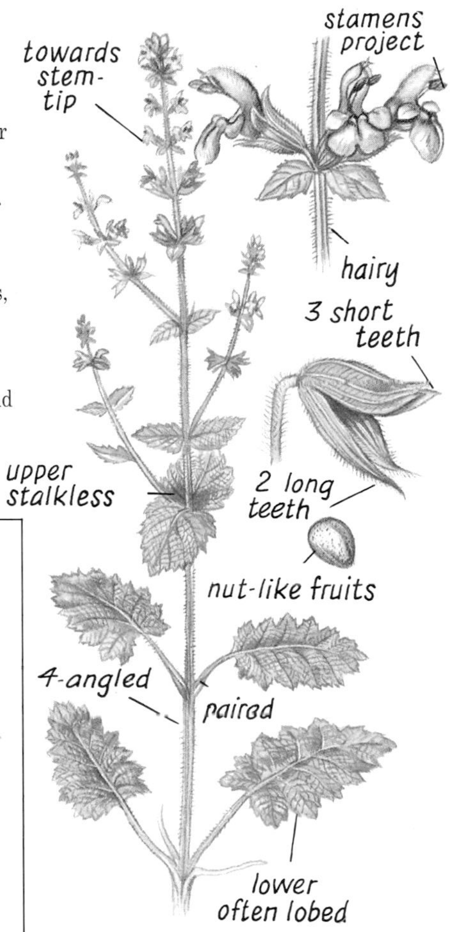

Meadow Clary *(S. pratensis)*

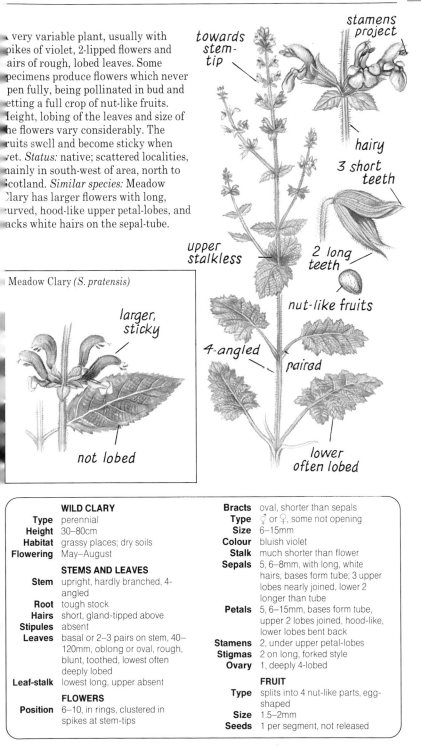

	WILD CLARY
Type	perennial
Height	30–80cm
Habitat	grassy places; dry soils
Flowering	May–August
	STEMS AND LEAVES
Stem	upright, hardly branched, 4-angled
Root	tough stock
Hairs	short, gland-tipped above
Stipules	absent
Leaves	basal or 2–3 pairs on stem, 40–120mm, oblong or oval, rough, blunt, toothed, lowest often deeply lobed
Leaf-stalk	lowest long, upper absent
	FLOWERS
Position	6–10, in rings, clustered in spikes at stem-tips
Bracts	oval, shorter than sepals
Type	⚥ or ♀, some not opening
Size	6–15mm
Colour	bluish violet
Stalk	much shorter than flower
Sepals	5, 6–8mm, with long, white hairs, bases form tube; 3 upper lobes nearly joined, lower 2 longer than tube
Petals	5, 6–15mm, bases form tube, upper 2 lobes joined, hood-like, lower lobes bent back
Stamens	2, under upper petal-lobes
Stigmas	2 on long, forked style
Ovary	1, deeply 4-lobed
	FRUIT
Type	splits into 4 nut-like parts, egg-shaped
Size	1.5–2mm
Seeds	1 per segment, not released

Ground-ivy *Glechoma hederacea*

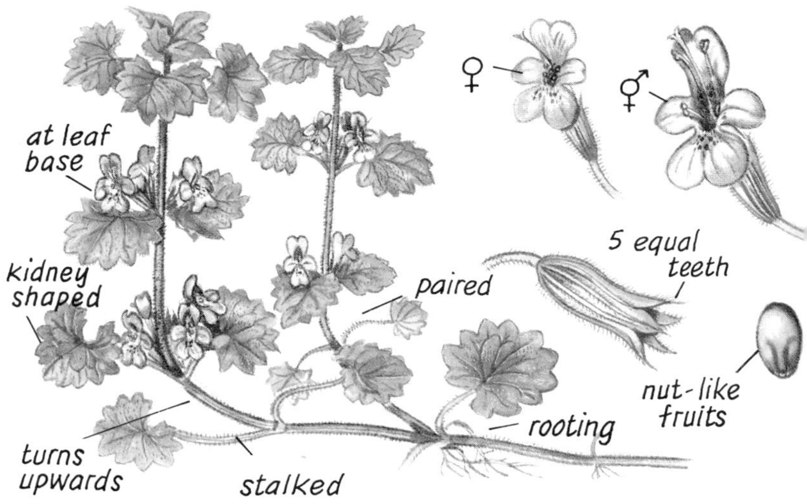

A charming plant with violet-coloured, two-lipped flowers, creeping beneath hedgerows and over woodland floors. It is sometimes grown in gardens, often as a variegated form used to trail over hanging baskets. Ground-ivy was formerly known best as a bitter herb used for flavouring ale, although it also had medicinal uses. *Status:* native; common, most of area. *Similar species:* Skullcap also has violet, two-lipped flowers. It has elongated leaves, a swelling on the upper side of the sepal-tube, and grows in wet, sunny places. Lesser Skullcap has smaller, pinkish flowers and sparsely toothed leaves.

1 Skullcap *(Scutellaria galericulata)*; 2 Lesser Skullcap *(S. minor)*

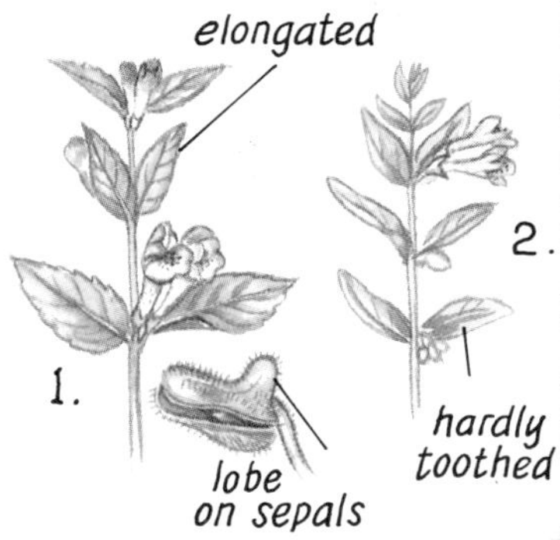

	GROUND-IVY
Type	perennial
Height	10–50cm
Habitat	hedges, woods, grassy places; usually damp soil
Flowering	March–May
	STEMS AND LEAVES
Stem	creeping, rooting, angled upwards to flower
Root	fibrous, stems root
Hairs	soft, fairly long
Stipules	absent
Leaves	paired on stem, 5–35mm, kidney-shaped to nearly oval, blunt, coarsely-toothed, base heart-shaped
Leaf-stalk	most longer than blade
	FLOWERS
Position	clusters of 2–4 towards stem-tips
Bracts	resembling leaves
Type	⚥ or sometimes ♀
Size	15–22mm
Colour	bluish violet, spotted reddish purple
Stalk	much shorter than flower
Sepals	5, 5–6.5mm, bases joined, teeth nearly equal, pointed
Petals	5, 15–22mm, bases joined; upper 2 lobes nearly joined, hood-like, lower 3 larger
Stamens	4, under upper petal-lobes
Stigmas	2 on long, forked style
Ovary	1, deeply 4-lobed
	FRUIT
Type	splits into 4 nut-like parts, egg-shaped, smooth
Size	2–3mm
Seeds	1 per segment, not released

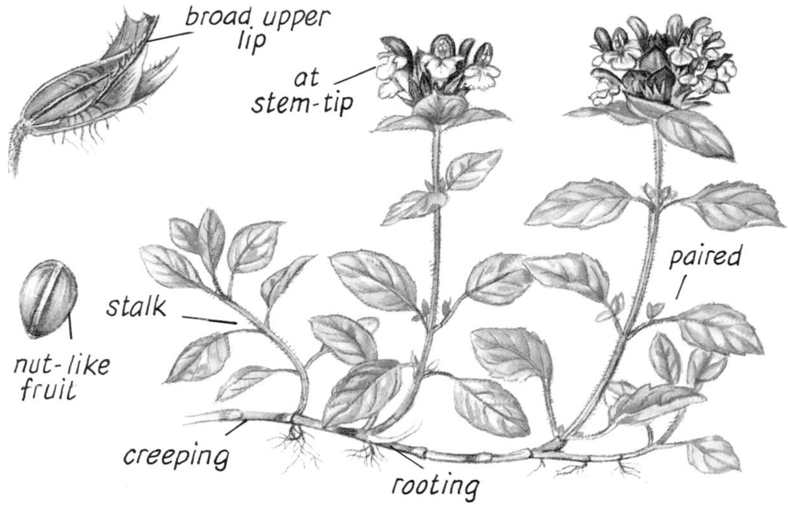

A grassland plant, often thriving in close-grazed or mown turf, from which it raises its compact, cylindrical heads of deep violet-coloured flowers. It was much prized as a herb for treating wounds and also taken for sore throats. *Status:* native; very common, throughout area. *Similar species:* Cut-leaved Selfheal has divided upper leaves and cream-coloured flowers. It is native only in the south of the area but is naturalized in Britain. Bugle has more widely spaced clusters of flowers with larger bracts, often tinged with blackish violet and contrasting vividly with the bluish flowers.

1 Cut-leaved Selfheal *(P. laciniata)*; 2 Bugle *(Ajuga reptans)*

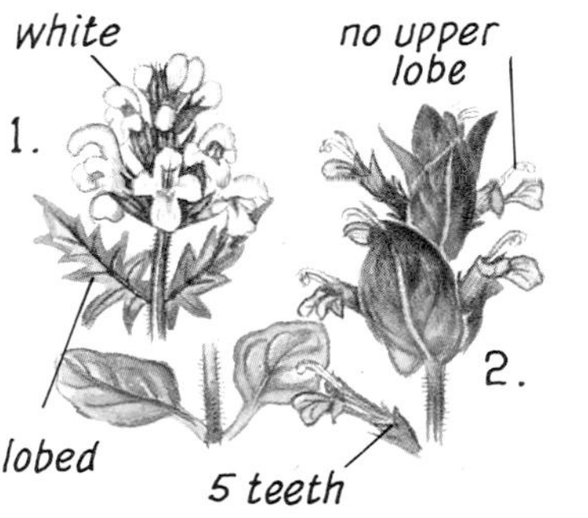

	SELFHEAL
Type	perennial
Height	5–50cm
Habitat	grassland, woodland clearings; most soils
Flowering	June–September
	STEMS AND LEAVES
Stem	angled upwards or upright
Root	short underground stem
Hairs	sparse, short
Stipules	absent
Leaves	paired on stem, 20–50mm, oval or diamond-shaped, edge toothed or unbroken
Leaf-stalk	shorter than blade
	FLOWERS
Position	rings of 6, in compact, oblong head at stem-tip
Bracts	circular, stalkless, often purple-tinged
Type	⚥
Size	10–15mm
Colour	violet, rarely pink or white
Stalk	much shorter than flower
Sepals	5, 8–9mm, bases joined, upper 3 teeth almost joined, lower 2 longer
Petals	5, 10–15mm, bases form tube, upper 2 lobes joined, hood-like, lower 3 bent back
Stamens	4, under upper petal-lobes
Stigmas	2 on long, forked style
Ovary	1, deeply 4-lobed
	FRUIT
Type	splits into 4 nut-like parts, oblong, smooth
Size	2–2.5mm
Seeds	1 per segment, not released

Marjoram *Origanum vulgare*

Usually found among tall grasses, this rather bushy plant has branched heads of pink flowers and contrasting purple bracts. It is sometimes used as a pot-herb and is related to Oregano, which derives from Mediterranean plants. Native plants were widely used to treat coughs and headaches. *Status:* native; most of area, most common in south. *Similar species:* two other species have longer, less crowded heads of larger flowers and unequal, hairier sepal-teeth. Wild Basil has almost stalkless flower-clusters and a curved sepal-tube, whereas Common Calamint has stalked clusters of flowers.

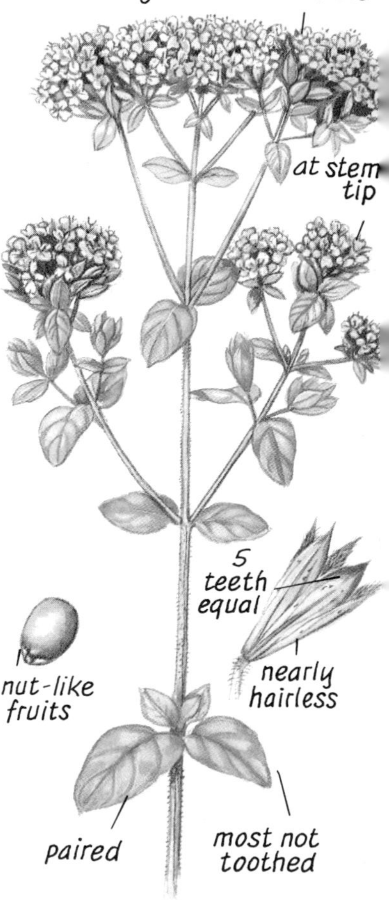

1 Wild Basil *(Clinopodium vulgare)*; **2** Common Calamint *(Calamintha sylvatica* subsp. *ascendens)*

	MARJORAM
Type	perennial
Height	30–90cm
Habitat	grassy places, scrub; dry, often lime-rich soils
Flowering	July–September
	STEMS AND LEAVES
Stem	upright, usually branched
Root	woody, creeping underground stem
Hairs	usually scattered
Stipules	absent
Leaves	paired on stem, 10–45mm, oval, strongly scented, blunt or sharp, edge unbroken or hardly toothed
Leaf-stalk	shorter than blade

	FLOWERS
Position	many, in widely branched clusters of short spikes
Bracts	oval, smaller than leaves, usually purple
Type	⚥ or sometimes ♀
Size	4–8mm
Colour	pinkish purple or white
Stalk	much shorter than flower
Sepals	5, 2–4mm, bases joined, teeth nearly equal
Petals	5, 4–8mm, bases joined, lower 3 lobes longer than upper 2
Stamens	4, usually protruding
Stigmas	2 on long, forked style
Ovary	1, deeply 4-lobed
	FRUIT
Type	splits into 4 nut-like parts
Size	1.5–2mm
Seeds	1 per segment, not released

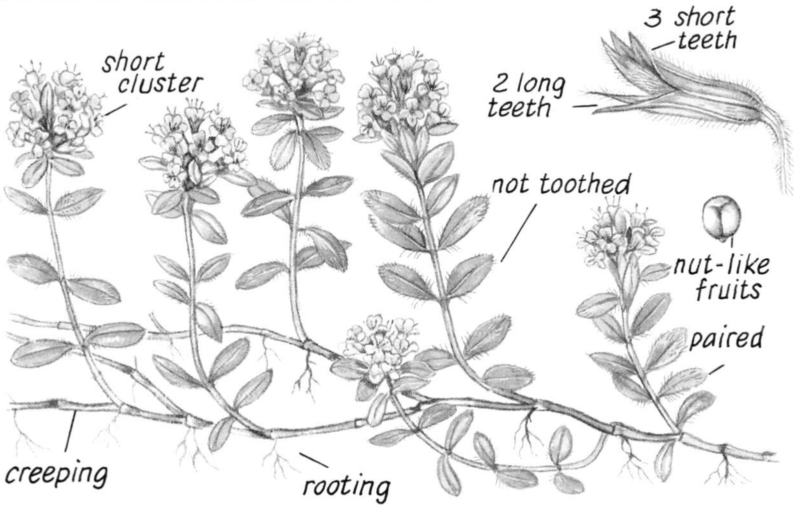

A mat-forming plant of dry places, that has short flowering stems bearing compact heads of purple flowers. The leaves have a faint but distinctive aroma of Thyme as used in the kitchen. Species of Thyme formerly had medicinal as well as culinary uses. *Status:* native; common in south, absent from much of north. *Similar species:* Large Thyme usually has much taller stems, with cylindrical heads of larger flowers. The stems are more upright, sharply four-angled, and the whole plant is more strongly scented. Basil Thyme is a much hairier plant, with toothed leaves and larger flowers.

1 Large Thyme *(T. pulegioides)*;
2 Basil Thyme *(Acinos arvensis)*

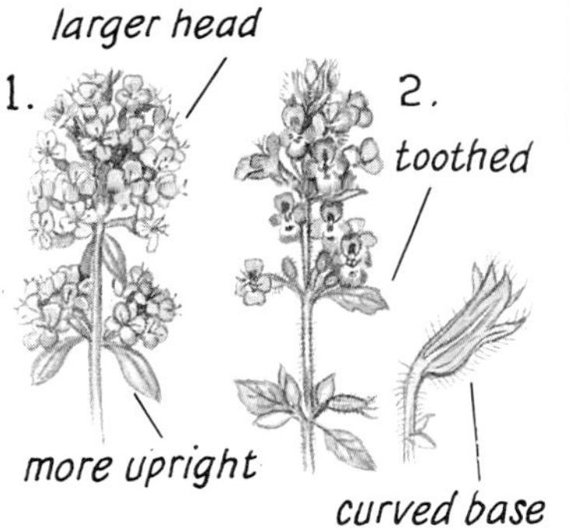

	WILD THYME
Type	perennial, aromatic
Height	1–8cm
Habitat	grasslands, heaths, dunes, rocks; dry soils
Flowering	May–August
	STEMS AND LEAVES
Stem	long, creeping, forming mats, branches angled upwards to flower
Root	woody stock; stems root
Hairs	on 2 sides of stem, long on leaf-edges
Stipules	absent
Leaves	paired on stem, 4–8mm, elliptical or oval, blunt, edge unbroken
Leaf-stalk	very short

	FLOWERS
Position	short heads at stem-tips
Bracts	lowest leaf-like
Type	⚥ or ♀
Size	4–7mm
Colour	pinkish purple
Stalk	much shorter than flower
Sepals	5, 3–4mm, bases form tube, upper 3 teeth short, lower 2 long
Petals	5, 4–7mm, bases joined, upper 2 lobes nearly joined
Stamens	4, protruding on ♀ flowers
Stigmas	2 on long, forked style
Ovary	1, deeply 4-lobed
	FRUIT
Type	splits into 4 nut-like parts, egg-shaped, smooth
Size	0.7–1mm
Seeds	1 per segment, not released

Deadly Nightshade *Atropa belladonna*

A powerful narcotic plant; even a few berries can prove fatal. It has bushy stems, rather dull purple flowers, and black, cherry-like fruits. Although toxic, Deadly Nightshade has long been cultivated for medicinal purposes. An alkaloid extract from the plant is used in hospitals to dilate the pupil of the eye. *Status:* native in south, naturalized in north and Ireland; scattered, absent from most of north. *Similar species:* Henbane is stickily hairy; the yellow flowers, veined purple are clustered in long heads and each capsule is hidden within its sepal-tube. It is also poisonous but used medicinally.

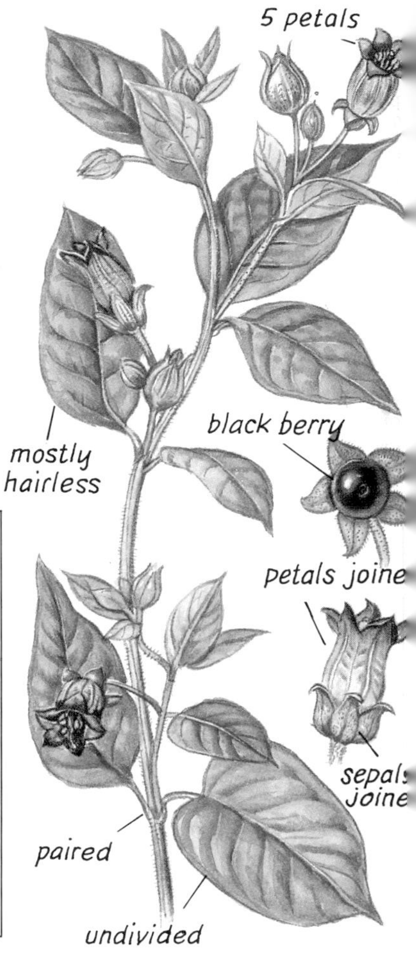

Henbane *(Hyoscyamus niger)*

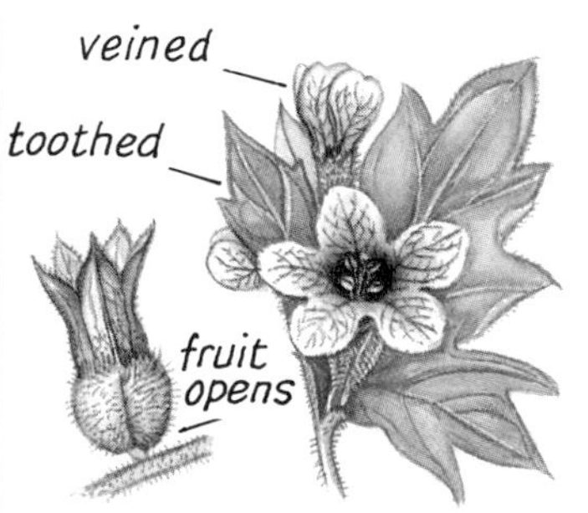

	DEADLY NIGHTSHADE
Type	perennial
Height	50–150cm, rarely 200cm
Habitat	woods, scrub, hedges; lime-rich soils
Flowering	June–August
	STEMS AND LEAVES
Stem	upright, many-branched
Root	fibrous
Hairs	absent or short, gland-tipped
Stipules	absent
Leaves	mostly on alternate sides of stem, 25–200mm, oval, pointed, edge unbroken, base wedge-shaped
Leaf-stalk	shorter than blade

	FLOWERS
Position	solitary, from leaf-base
Bracts	absent
Type	⚥
Size	25–30mm
Colour	violet or greenish
Stalk	shorter than flower, drooping
Sepals	5, 10–15mm, joined, bell-shaped, spreading in fruit
Petals	5, 25–30mm, equal, joined into broad tube
Stamens	5, shorter than petals
Stigma	1, tip swollen, style long
Ovary	1, 2-celled
	FRUIT
Type	1, globular berry, glossy, black
Size	15–20mm
Seeds	many, 1.5–2mm, egg-shaped

This woody plant threads its way through hedgerows or clambers over plants and rocks. Related to both Tomato and Potato, the flowers similarly have five petals curved back, but of purple with contrasting yellow stamens. The red berries are far less poisonous than those of Deadly Nightshade. *Status:* native; common, most of area. *Similar species:* related species are annual, with white flowers and almost globular fruits. Black Nightshade has black or green fruits; those of Hairy Nightshade are yellow, orange or red; Green Nightshade has green or rarely black fruits, partly hidden by the enlarged sepals.

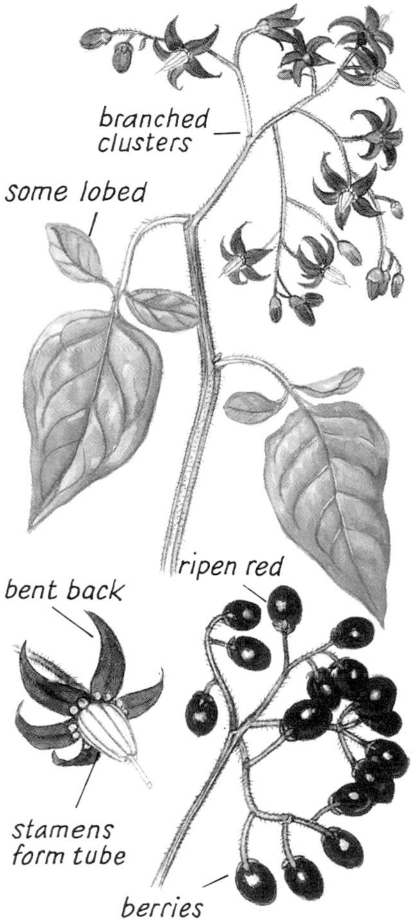

1 Black Nightshade *(S. nigrum)*; **2** Green Nightshade *(S. sarrachoides)*; **3** Hairy Nightshade *(S. luteum)*

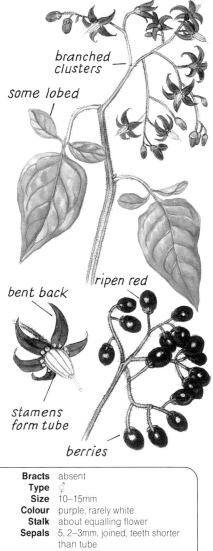

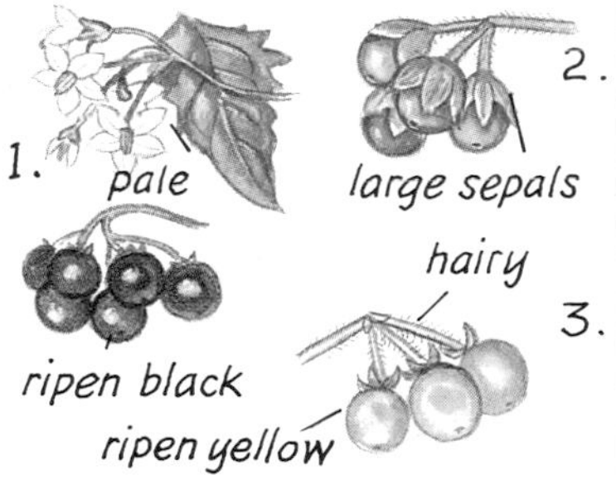

	BITTERSWEET
Type	perennial
Height	30–200cm
Habitat	hedges, woods, rocks, shingle, waste ground
Flowering	June–September
	STEMS AND LEAVES
Stem	trailing or clambering, woody below
Root	woody stock
Hairs	absent or sometimes dense
Stipules	absent
Leaves	most on alternate sides of stem, 30–90mm, oval, often 1–4 lobes at base, pointed, edge unbroken
Leaf-stalk	shorter than blade
	FLOWERS
Position	10–25 in stalked, branched cluster opposite leaf-base
Bracts	absent
Type	⚥
Size	10–15mm
Colour	purple, rarely white
Stalk	about equalling flower
Sepals	5, 2–3mm, joined, teeth shorter than tube
Petals	5, 4–7mm, equal, bases joined, lobes spear-shaped, curved back
Stamens	5, protruding, yellow
Stigma	1, style long
Ovary	1, 2-celled
	FRUIT
Type	1, berry, egg-shaped, glossy, red
Size	10–15mm
Seeds	many, 1.7–2mm, rounded

Great Mullein *Verbascum thapsus*

A stiffly upright plant that has slender, crowded spikes of yellow flowers and is clothed with whitish wool. Innumerable branched hairs give the leaves a softness and warmth. Dried tops of plants were used to make tapers for burning; leaves provided shoe-liners; and flowers a cough medicine. *Status:* native; most of area except north. *Similar species:* White Mullein has wide-spaced, whitish, smaller flowers, and all stamens are hairy. Two species have stamens with purple hairs: Dark Mullein has dark green, rather hairy leaves; Moth Mullein has almost hairless leaves and long-stalked, widely-spaced flowers.

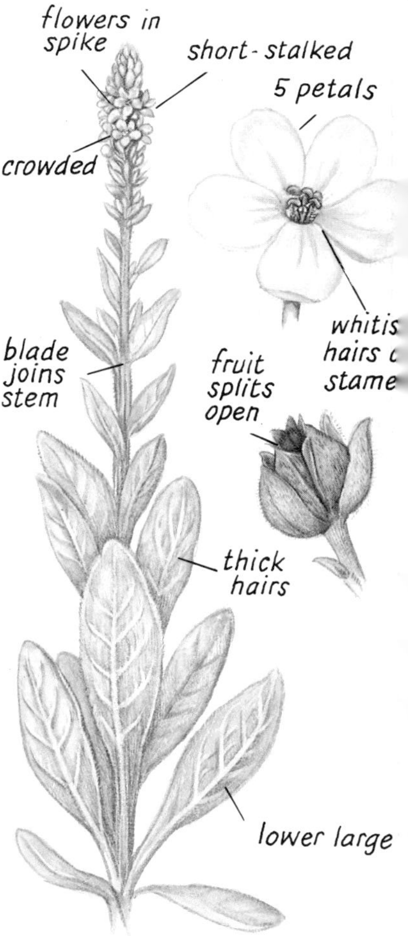

1 White Mullein *(V. lychnitis)*; **2** Dark Mullein *(V. nigrum)*; **3** Moth Mullein *(V. blattaria)*

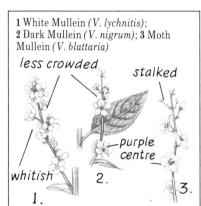

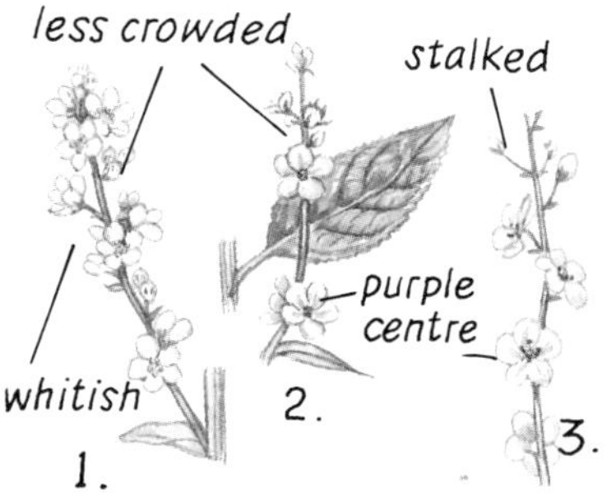

	GREAT MULLEIN
Type	biennial
Height	30–200cm
Habitat	grassy banks, waste ground; dry, often sandy soil
Flowering	June–August
	STEMS AND LEAVES
Stem	upright, usually unbranched
Root	tap-root
Hairs	dense, woolly, whitish
Stipules	absent
Leaves	basal rosette or spirally placed on stem, 40–500mm, oval to oblong, most pointed, edge unbroken or fine-toothed, upper blades run down stem as wings
Leaf-stalk	lowest short, upper absent
	FLOWERS
Position	in dense spike at stem-tip
Bracts	narrowly triangular, pointed
Type	⚥
Size	12–30mm
Colour	yellow
Stalk	much shorter than flowers
Sepals	5, 8–12mm, bases joined, lobes equal, oval, pointed
Petals	5, 6–14mm, almost equal, bases joined, lobes rounded, spreading widely
Stamens	5, upper 3 with long, white hairs, lower 2 hairless
Stigma	1, tip swollen
Ovary	1, 2-celled
	FRUIT
Type	1, egg-shaped capsule, splits lengthwise
Size	7–10mm
Seeds	many, 0.8–1mm, oblong, pitted

A tall, perhaps sombre plant, with broad, dark leaves and dull, brownish-purple flowers. Small flowers, rather unpleasantly scented, are pollinated mainly by wasps. Leaves of Figwort were used as poultices for skin complaints. *Status:* native; common, almost throughout area. *Similar species:* two Figworts have wing-like angles to the stems and broader papery edges to the sepals. Water Figwort has blunt leaves with rounded teeth and often two lobes at the base. Green Figwort has more pointed leaves with pointed teeth and lacks lobes. Yellow Figwort is softly hairy, and has pointed sepals and yellow flowers.

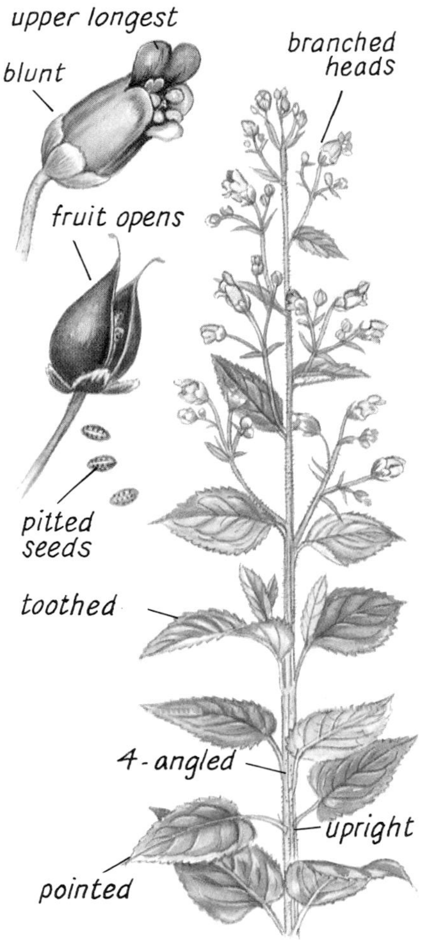

1 Water Figwort (*S. auriculata*);
2 Green Figwort (*S. umbrosa*);
3 Yellow Figwort (*S. vernalis*)

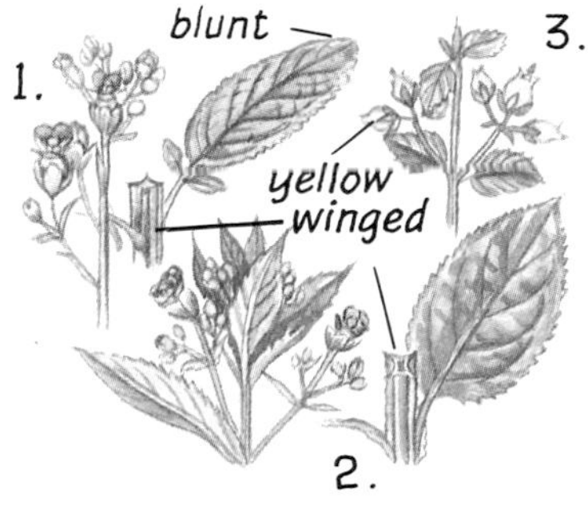

	COMMON FIGWORT
Type	perennial
Height	30–80cm
Habitat	woods, hedges; damp soils
Flowering	June–September
	STEMS AND LEAVES
Stem	upright, 4-angled
Root	short, irregularly swollen, underground stem
Hairs	absent below, gland-tipped in flower-head
Stipules	absent
Leaves	paired on stem, 60–130mm, oval, pointed, with uneven teeth, base squarish
Leaf-stalk	shorter than blade
	FLOWERS
Position	5–7 in branched heads, clustered towards stem-tip
Bracts	small or lowest leaf-like
Type	⚥
Size	7–10mm
Colour	green below, reddish brown on upper petal-lobes
Stalk	2–3 times length of flower
Sepals	5, 2–3.5mm, joined, lobes oval, blunt, edge papery
Petals	5, 7–10mm, bases joined, nearly globular, upper 2 lobes rounded, lower shorter
Stamens	4 normal, 1 broad, sterile
Stigma	1, tip swollen, style short
Ovary	1, 2-celled
	FRUIT
Type	1, capsule, egg-shaped, pointed, splits lengthwise
Size	5–10mm
Seeds	many, *c*1mm, oblong, pitted

Ivy-leaved Toadflax *Cymbalaria muralis*

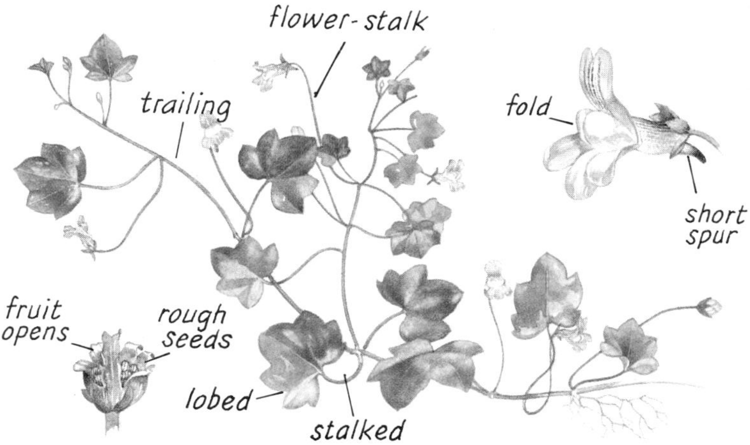

Lilac, Snapdragon-like flowers, backed by broad, lobed, glossy leaves make this a charming plant. In full sun, stems, stalks and the base of the flowers have a purple tinge which is lacking in shady places. Long stalks hold flowers clear of the foliage but, in fruit, curve round to bury the seeds in crevices. *Status:* introduced, from southern Europe; most common in south. *Similar species:* Fluellens, of cornfields or waste ground, have capsules with circular lids and pitted seeds. Sharp-leaved Fluellen has arrow-shaped leaves, with backward-pointing lobes; Round-leaved Fluellen lacks the lobes and has sepals that enlarge in fruit.

1 Sharp-leaved Fluellen *(Kickxia elatine)*; **2** Round-leaved Fluellen *(K. spuria)*

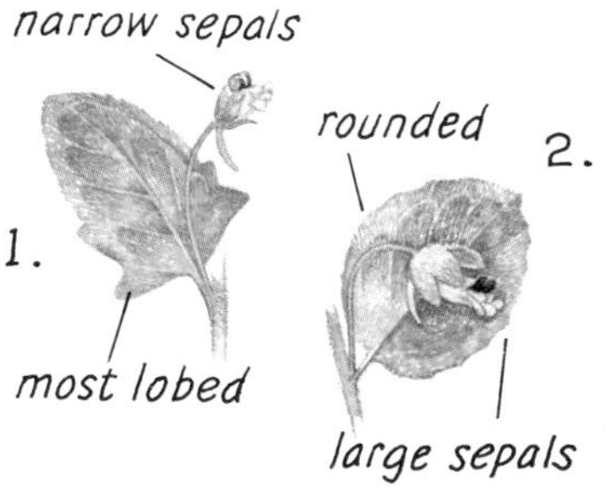

	IVY-LEAVED TOADFLAX
Type	perennial
Height	5–15cm
Habitat	walls, rocks, shingle, railway ballast; dry places
Flowering	May–September
	STEMS AND LEAVES
Stem	trailing, hanging, to 80cm long, often tinged purple
Root	fibrous, stems root
Hairs	absent
Stipules	absent
Leaves	most on alternate sides of stem, lowest paired, 7–25mm, kidney-shaped, 5–9 rounded or triangular lobes
Leaf-stalk	longer than blade
	FLOWERS
Position	single from base of leaf
Bracts	absent
Type	⚥
Size	9–15mm
Colour	lilac, yellow on fold of lower petals, violet veins
Stalk	much longer than flower, bends down in fruit
Sepals	5, 2–2.5mm, spear-shaped, pointed, bases joined
Petals	5, 9–15mm, bases form tube, spur at base, lower 3 lobes with fold closing tube
Stamens	4, inside petal-tube
Stigma	1, tip swollen
Ovary	1, 2-celled
	FRUIT
Type	capsule, sides split open
Size	2.5–4mm
Seeds	many, 0.8–1mm, globular, irregularly ridged, black

A popular garden plant that has often escaped, known to generations of children for the mouth-like flower which snaps open when the sides are pressed. Snapdragon originated in the western Mediterranean region, but the exact location has been obscured by many centuries of cultivation outside its original range. *Status:* introduced; mainly south of area, often near coasts. *Similar species:* Lesser Snapdragon is a native annual that has small flowers, long sepals and seeds with one face smooth, the other encircled by a ridge. Asarina is sometimes naturalized and has large, yellow flowers, trailing stems and kidney-shaped, lobed leaves.

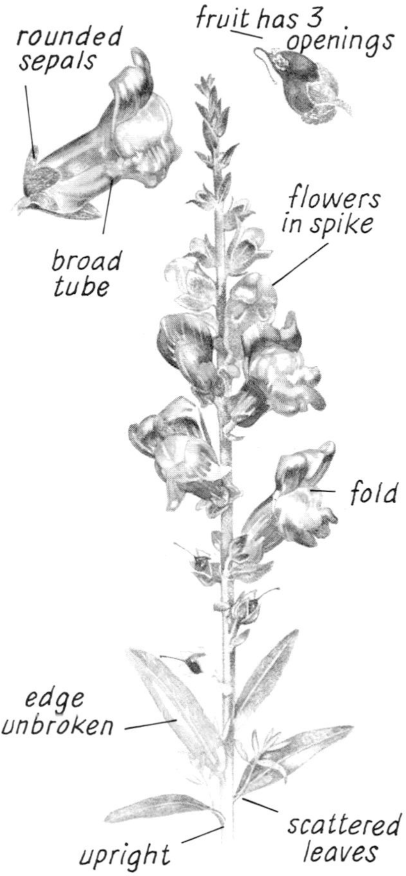

1 Lesser Snapdragon *(Misopates orontium)*; **2** Asarina *(Asarina procumbens)*

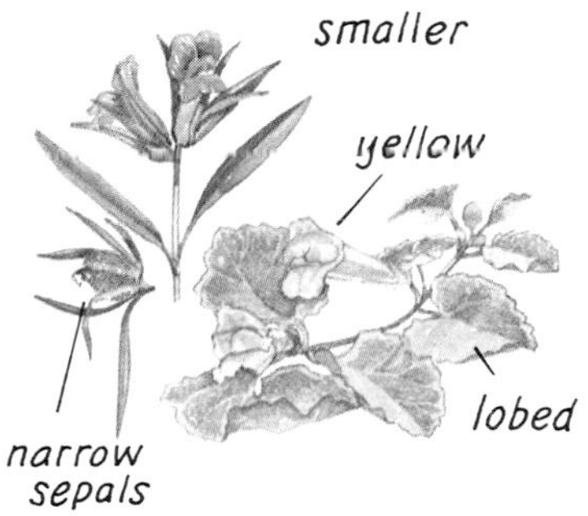

	SNAPDRAGON
Type	perennial
Height	30–80cm
Habitat	walls, cliffs; dry soils
Flowering	July–September
	STEMS AND LEAVES
Stem	upright, base woody
Root	fibrous
Hairs	absent below, sticky, gland-tipped in flower-head
Stipules	absent
Leaves	spirally placed on stem or lowest paired, 30–50mm, spear-shaped or oblong, edge unbroken, base tapered
Leaf-stalk	absent
	FLOWERS
Position	many, in spike at stem-tip
Bracts	oval, smaller than leaves
Type	⚥
Size	30–40mm
Colour	reddish purple with yellow mark, some pink or white
Stalk	much shorter than flower
Sepals	5, 6–8mm, slightly unequal, bases joined, lobed oval
Petals	5, bases form broad tube, lower 3 lips with fold closing mouth of tube
Stamens	4, inside petal-tube
Stigma	1, tip swollen
Ovary	1, 2-celled
	FRUIT
Type	1, egg-shaped capsule, sides unequal, 3 pores at tip
Size	10–14mm
Seeds	many, 1–1.2mm, egg-shaped, with net-like ridges

Small Toadflax *Chaenorhinum minus*

A delicate annual, Small Toadflax has tiny flowers like those of Snapdragon but with a small spur at the base. Mainly a weed of arable fields, it thrives on railway ballast although recent use of weedkillers has led to a decline. *Status:* native or introduced; mainly south of region. *Similar species:* other small-flowered Toadflaxes from the south of the area have spikes of flowers, capsules with equal halves and seeds with an encircling wing. Sand Toadflax, on sand-dunes, is stickily hairy, with yellow flowers. Field Toadflax, an almost hairless weed of cultivation, has blue flowers with a slender, curved spur.

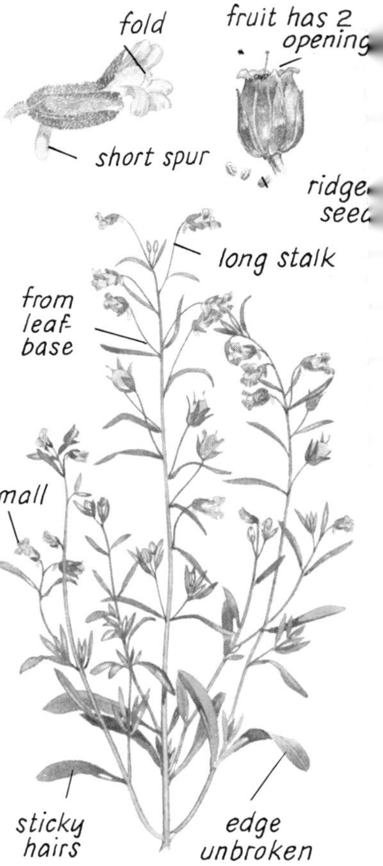

1 Sand Toadflax *(Linaria arenaria)*;
2 Field Toadflax *(L. arvensis)*

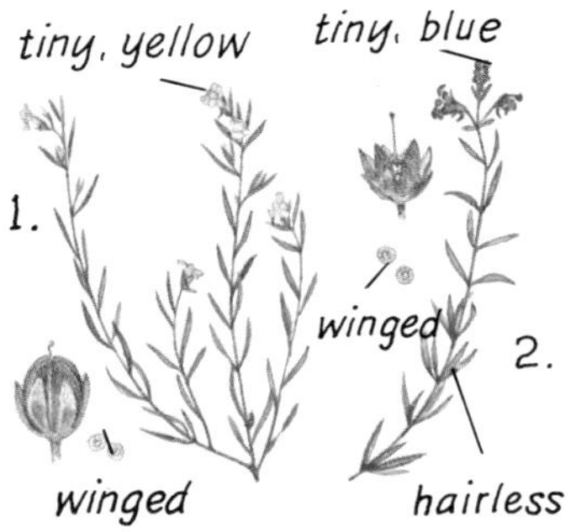

	SMALL TOADFLAX
Type	annual
Height	8–25cm
Habitat	cultivated and waste ground, railway ballast
Flowering	May–October
	STEMS AND LEAVES
Stem	upright, branched
Root	fibrous
Hairs	short, gland-tipped
Stipules	absent
Leaves	lower paired, upper on alternate sides of stem, 5–25mm, narrow, spear-shaped to oblong, blunt, edge unbroken, tapered
Leaf-stalk	short
	FLOWERS
Position	each at base of upper leaf
Bracts	absent
Type	⚥
Size	6–9mm
Colour	whitish, lobes and veins purple
Stalk	mostly longer than flower
Sepals	5, 2–5mm, unequal, narrow, blunt, bases joined
Petals	5, 6–9mm, bases form tube, with spur, fold of lower 3 lobes closes tube-mouth
Stamens	4, inside petal-tube
Stigma	1, tip swollen
Ovary	1, 2-celled
	FRUIT
Type	1, egg-shaped capsule, sides unequal, 2 pores at tip
Size	3–6mm
Seeds	many, 0.5–0.8mm, egg-shaped, ridged lengthwise

'lowering in late Summer, commonly n grassy banks, many stems arise from reeping roots. Pollination is almost olely by bees, which have enough veight and strength to open the flower, nd a long tongue to reach the nectar at he base. *Status:* native; common, most f area. *Similar species:* two species ave purplish flowers and wingless eeds. Purple Toadflax has long spikes f flowers each with a slender, curved pur. Pale Toadflax has fewer flowers vith a short, straight spur; it sometimes orms hybrids with Common Toadflax. 'rostrate Toadflax is low-growing, its ale yellow flowers with longer petal-obes than those of Common Toadflax.

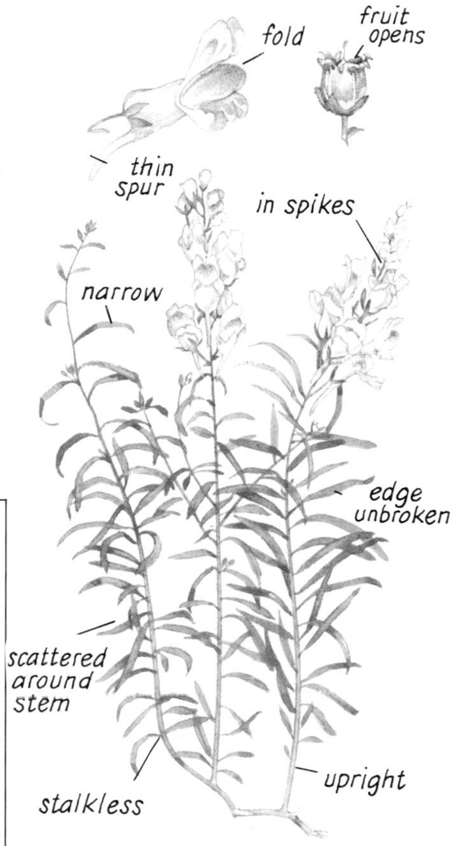

1 Purple Toadflax *(L. purpurea)*;
2 Pale Toadflax *(L. repens)*;
3 Prostrate Toadflax *(L. supina)*

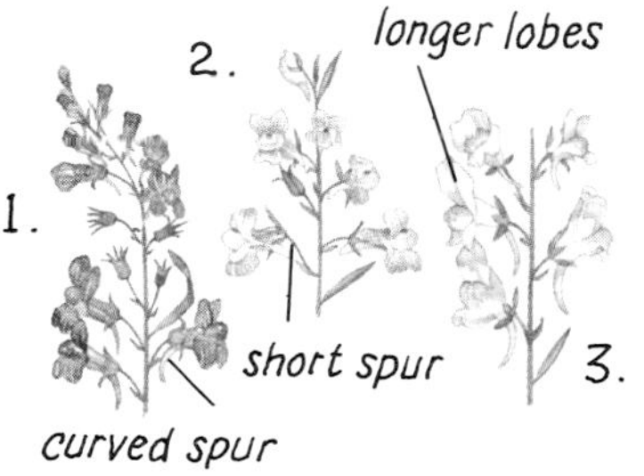

	COMMON TOADFLAX
Type	perennial
Height	30–80cm
Habitat	grassy and waste places, railway embankments
Flowering	July–October
	STEMS AND LEAVES
Stem	many, upright, branched
Root	fibrous, long, creeping roots produce new stems
Hairs	absent or sticky hairs above
Stipules	absent
Leaves	spirally around stem, lowest in ring or paired, 20–60mm, narrow, straight-sided or spear-shaped, pointed, edge unbroken
Leaf-stalk	absent

	FLOWERS
Position	5–30, in crowded spike
Bracts	small, oval, pointed
Type	⚥
Size	20–33mm
Colour	yellow, darker fold at base of lower petal-lobes
Stalk	shorter than flower
Sepals	5, 3–6mm, oval, pointed
Petals	5, 20–33mm, forming tube, spur at base, fold of lower 3 lobes closes tube-mouth
Stamens	4, paired
Stigma	1, style slender
Ovary	1, 2-celled
	FRUIT
Type	1, oblong capsule, 2 pores at tip
Size	5–11mm
Seeds	many, 2–3mm, flattened, encircling wing, black

Monkeyflower *Mimulus guttatus*

Large, bright yellow flowers of Monkeyflower brighten many a stream and look so well established that they appear native. But this is an introduced plant that has often escaped from cultivation and spread widely along water-courses. Other species and hybrids are often cultivated in gardens. *Status:* introduced from North America; common, much of area. *Similar species:* Blood-drop-emlets has large, red blotches on the flowers and is almost hairless. The hybrid with Monkeyflower is often more common than either species. Musk has smaller, unspotted flowers and stickily hairy foliage.

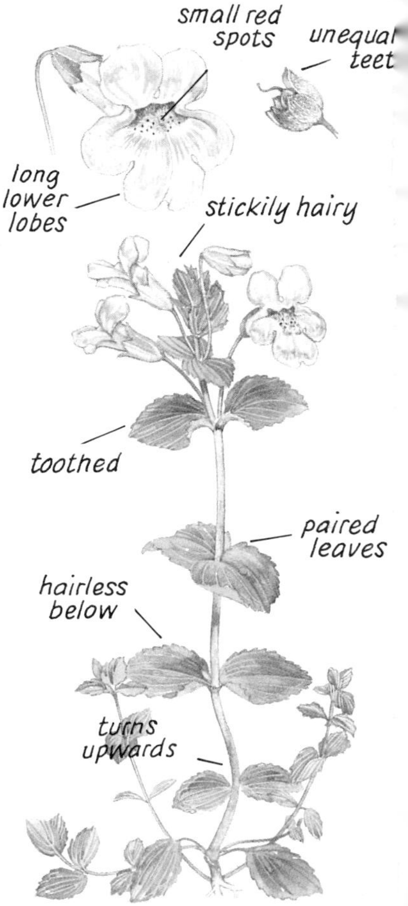

1 Blood-drop-emlets *(M. luteus)*;
2 Musk *(M. moschatus)*

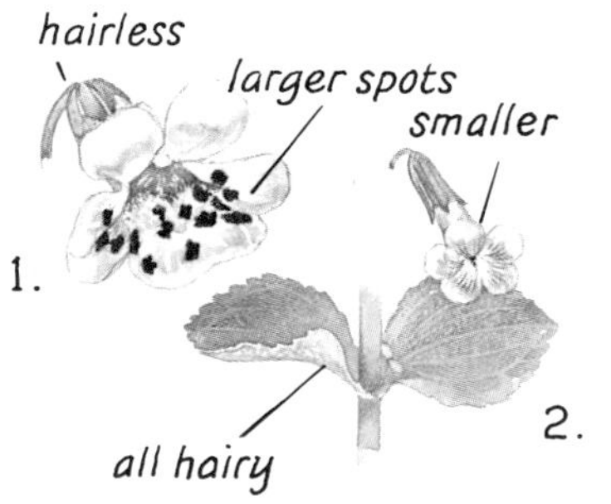

	MONKEYFLOWER	**Bracts**	leaf-like or upper smaller
Type	perennial	**Type**	⚥
Height	5–50cm	**Size**	25–45mm
Habitat	streams, slow rivers; wet ground or shallow water	**Colour**	yellow, red-spotted in tube
Flowering	July–September	**Stalk**	nearly equalling flower
	STEMS AND LEAVES	**Sepals**	5, 15–20mm, bases form 5-angled tube, inflated in fruit, teeth unequal
Stem	low-growing, angled upwards, hollow	**Petals**	5, 25–45mm, bases form tube, lower 3 lobes longer, folds nearly close tube-mouth
Root	fibrous; stems root	**Stamens**	4, paired, inside tube
Hairs	absent below, stickily hairy in flower-head	**Stigma**	1, 2 flat lobes; style long
Stipules	absent	**Ovary**	1, 2-celled
Leaves	paired on stem, 10–70mm, oval to circular, blunt to pointed, irregularly toothed		**FRUIT**
Leaf-stalk	lower short, upper absent	**Type**	1, oblong capsule, splits lengthwise
	FLOWERS	**Size**	8–12mm
Position	few to many, in heads towards stem-tips	**Seeds**	many, 0.7–0.9mm, oblong

A tall, majestic plant, with long spikes of purple, tubular flowers, it is widely grown for ornament, in varying shades of purple, pink or white, and with more flowers all around the stem. Species of Foxglove yield the drug digitalis, which speeds and strengthens the heart-beat. *Status:* native, sometimes introduced; common, most of area. *Similar species:* two Foxgloves with yellowish flowers and almost hairless leaves, are native in the south-east of the area. Large Yellow-foxglove has a broad petal-tube; Small Yellow-foxglove has a narrow tube with almost equal petal-lobes.

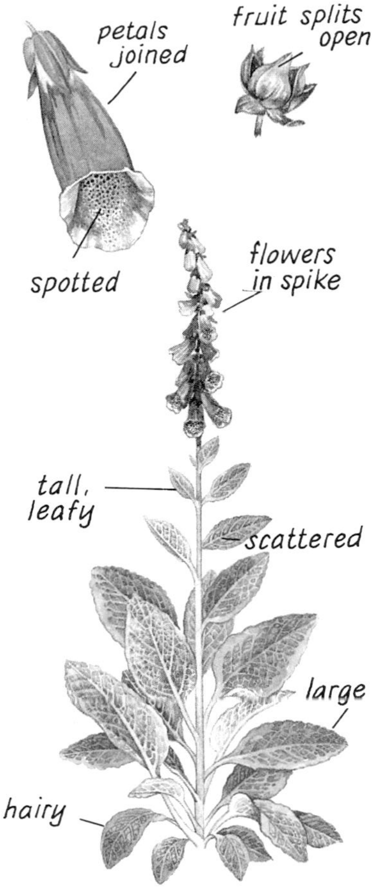

1 Large Yellow-foxglove *(D. grandiflora)*; **2** Small Yellow-foxglove *(D. lutea)*

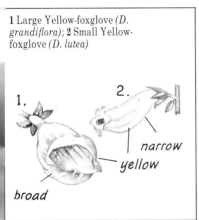

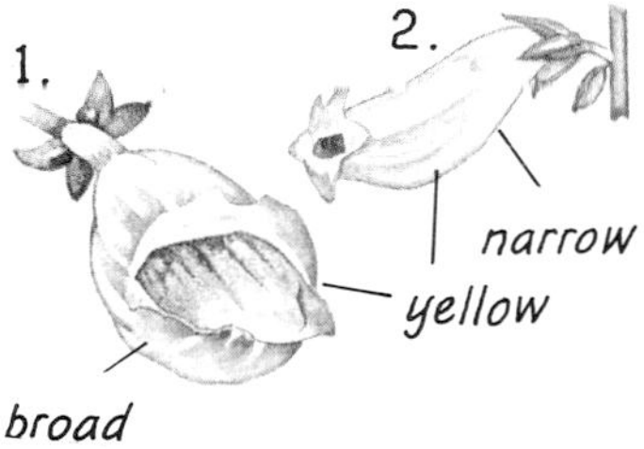

	FOXGLOVE
Type	biennial, rarely perennial
Height	50–150cm
Habitat	wood clearings, heaths, among rocks; lime-free soils
Flowering	June–September
	STEMS AND LEAVES
Stem	upright, stout, unbranched
Root	rather woody tap-root
Hairs	long, greyish
Stipules	absent
Leaves	basal rosette or spirally placed on stem, 150–300mm, oval to spear-shaped, blunt or pointed, with rounded teeth
Leaf-stalk	shorter than blade
	FLOWERS
Position	20–80, in one-sided spike
Bracts	spear-shaped, not toothed
Type	⚥
Size	40–50mm
Colour	pinkish purple, usually purple spots inside tube
Stalk	much shorter than flower
Sepals	5, 10–13mm, oval, upper spear-shaped, bases joined
Petals	5, 40–50mm, forming broad tube; lower lobe largest
Stamens	4, inside tube, paired
Stigma	1, 2 flat lobes; style long
Ovary	1, 2-celled
	FRUIT
Type	1, egg-shaped capsule, splits lengthwise
Size	14–18mm
Seeds	many, 0.8–1mm, oblong, net-like pattern

Germander Speedwell *Veronica chamaedrys*

Brilliant blue, white-eyed flowers of Speedwells gleam on grassy banks and lawns in Spring and early Summer. The four petals are joined in a ring at the base and soon fall together. Speedwells are related to the shrubby species of *Hebe*, much grown in gardens and often escaping. *Status:* native; very common, most of area. *Similar species:* two species have a capsule longer than the sepals. Wood Speedwell has stems hairy all round and longer leaf-stalks. Heath Speedwell has crowded heads of short-stalked flowers. Spiked Speedwell has upright stems ending in a crowded spike of deep blue flowers.

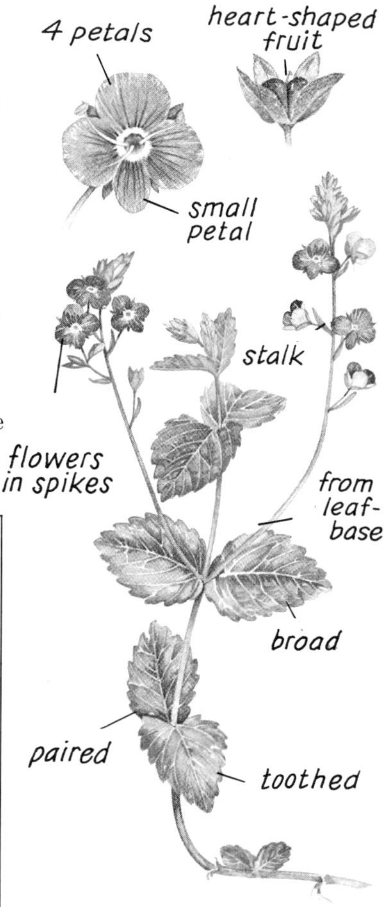

1 Wood Speedwell *(V. montana)*;
2 Heath Speedwell *(V. officinalis)*;
3 Spiked Speedwell *(V. spicata)*

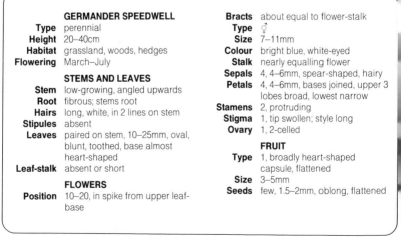

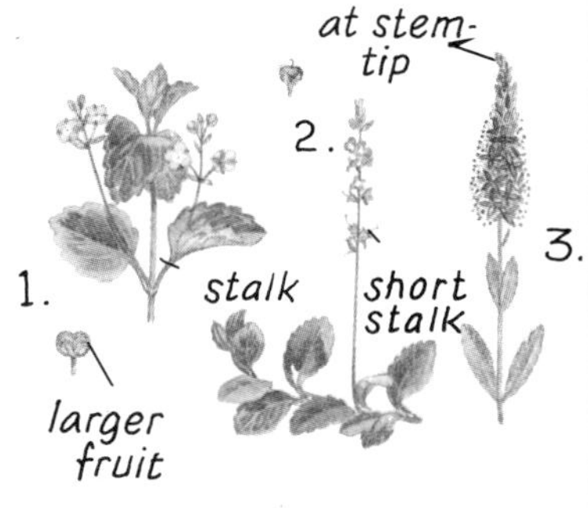

GERMANDER SPEEDWELL

Type	perennial
Height	20–40cm
Habitat	grassland, woods, hedges
Flowering	March–July

STEMS AND LEAVES

Stem	low-growing, angled upwards
Root	fibrous; stems root
Hairs	long, white, in 2 lines on stem
Stipules	absent
Leaves	paired on stem, 10–25mm, oval, blunt, toothed, base almost heart-shaped
Leaf-stalk	absent or short

FLOWERS

Position	10–20, in spike from upper leaf-base
Bracts	about equal to flower-stalk
Type	⚥
Size	7–11mm
Colour	bright blue, white-eyed
Stalk	nearly equalling flower
Sepals	4, 4–6mm, spear-shaped, hairy
Petals	4, 4–6mm, bases joined, upper 3 lobes broad, lowest narrow
Stamens	2, protruding
Stigma	1, tip swollen; style long
Ovary	1, 2-celled

FRUIT

Type	1, broadly heart-shaped capsule, flattened
Size	3–5mm
Seeds	few, 1.5–2mm, oblong, flattened

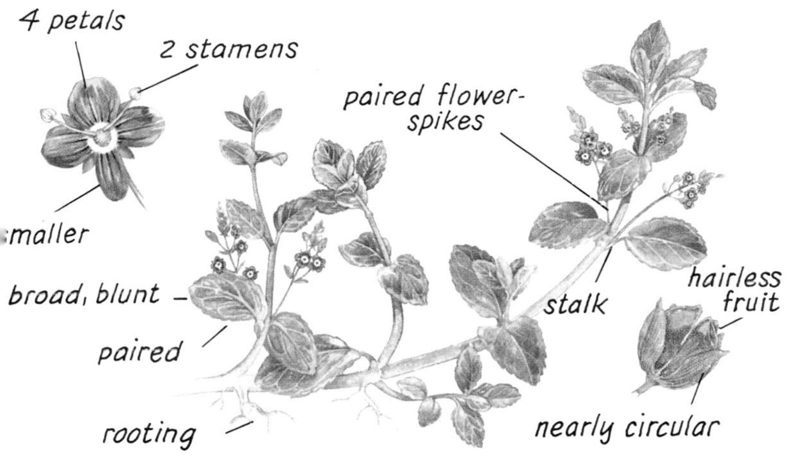

Spikes of deep blue flowers, set against glossy dark foliage, make this an attractive plant often cultivated in ornamental ponds. It is one of the Speedwells, of which species in wet places are more robust than their counterparts of dry grassland, and are mostly hairless. *Status:* native; common, throughout area. *Similar species:* three species have elongated, stalkless leaves. Blue Water-speedwell has long heads of flowers from both leaves of a pair. Pink Water-speedwell is similar but with smaller, pink flowers on widely spreading stalks. Marsh Speedwell has sparsely-flowered heads from only one leaf of a pair.

1 Blue Water-speedwell *(V. anagallis-aquatica)*; **2** Pink Water-speedwell *(V. catenata)*; **3** Marsh Speedwell *(V. scutellata)*

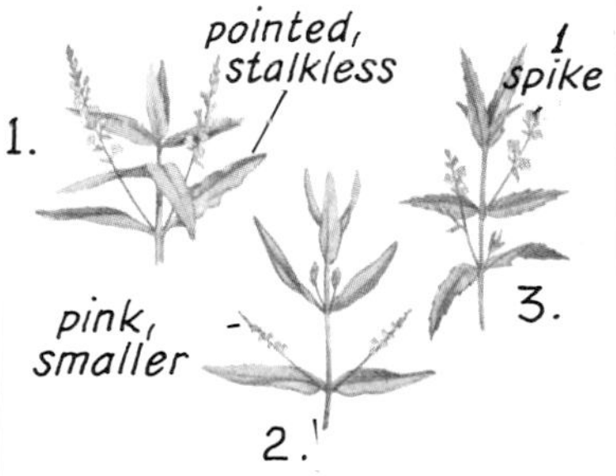

	BROOKLIME
Type	perennial
Height	20–60cm
Habitat	streams, ponds, wet meadows; wet places
Flowering	May–September
	STEMS AND LEAVES
Stem	creeping, angled upwards, fleshy
Root	fibrous; stems root
Hairs	absent
Stipules	absent
Leaves	paired on stem, 30–60mm, oval or oblong, thick, tip blunt, edge shallow-toothed, base rounded
Leaf-stalk	shorter than blade
	FLOWERS
Position	10–30, in spike at base of both leaves of pair
Bracts	small, narrow, pointed
Type	⚥
Size	5–8mm
Colour	usually deep blue
Stalk	nearly equal to flower
Sepals	4, 2–4mm, unequal, oval, pointed
Petals	4, 2.5–4mm, bases joined, lobes flat, upper largest
Stamens	2, protruding
Stigma	1, tip swollen; style long
Ovary	1, 2-celled
	FRUIT
Type	1, nearly circular capsule, flattened, notched
Size	2–4mm
Seeds	few, 0.8–1mm, oblong, flattened

Common Field-speedwell *Veronica persica*

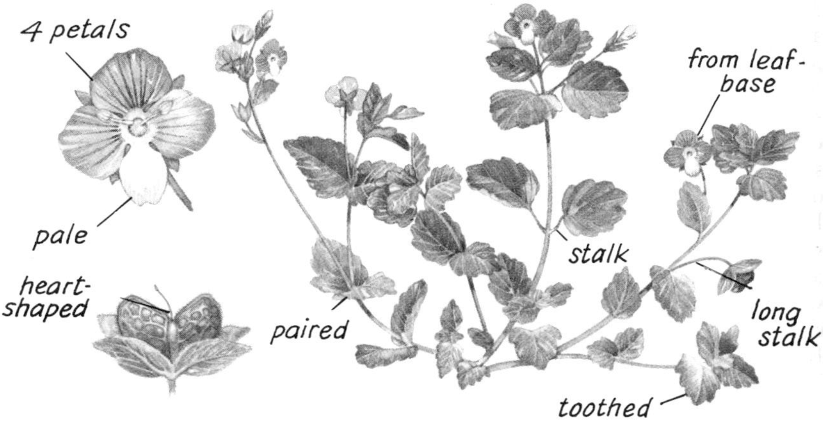

Sky-blue flowers with the lowest petal white make this an attractive weed for the short time that the flowers endure. Seeds germinate and flowers open in almost any month of the year. Introduced from Asia nearly two centuries ago, in many parts of Europe this is now the most common of all Speedwells. *Status:* introduced; common weed, throughout area. *Similar species:* Wall Speedwell has short-stalked flowers clustered in a rather lax spike at the stem-tip. Green Field-speedwell has small, pale flowers with shorter stalks. Ivy-leaved Speedwell has leaves with few, large lobes and broad-based sepals.

1 Wall Speedwell *(V. arvensis)*;
2 Green Field-speedwell *(V. agrestis)*;
3 Ivy-leaved Speedwell *(V. hederifolia)*

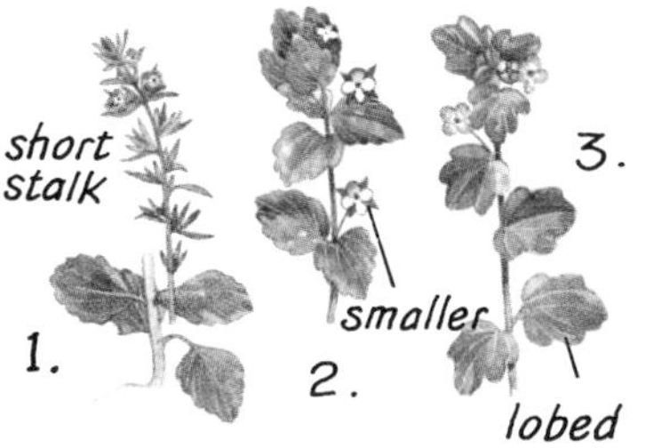

	COMMON FIELD-SPEEDWELL
Type	annual
Height	10–40cm
Habitat	arable fields, gardens
Flowering	January–December
	STEMS AND LEAVES
Stem	low-growing, branches angled upwards
Root	fibrous
Hairs	almost throughout plant
Stipules	absent
Leaves	on alternate sides of stem or lower paired, 10–30mm, oval, blunt, coarsely toothed, base squarish
Leaf-stalk	shorter than blade
	FLOWERS
Position	solitary, from leaf-base
Bracts	absent
Type	⚥
Size	8–12mm
Colour	bright blue, lower petal paler or white
Stalk	longer than leaf at base, bent down in fruit
Sepals	4, 5–7mm, unequal, oval, enlarging in fruit
Petals	4, 4–6mm, bases joined, upper broadest
Stamens	2, protruding
Stigma	1, tip swollen; style long
Ovary	1, 2-celled
	FRUIT
Type	2-lobed, flattened capsule, lobes spread apart
Size	5–10mm
Seeds	few, 1.5–1.8mm, oblong, one face hollow

An attractive grassland plant, the white flowers are blotched with deep yellow and veined with purple. Eyebrights are partly parasitic, their roots latching on to those of other plants and drawing sustenance. They also make food by using green pigment in their leaves and sunlight. *Status:* native; common, most of area. *Similar species:* the many Eyebrights are mostly identified only with difficulty. One of the most distinctive species is Irish Eyebright, which has narrow leaves with few, slender teeth and hairless capsules. Red Bartsia has reddish-purple flowers with longer, hood-like upper petal-lobes.

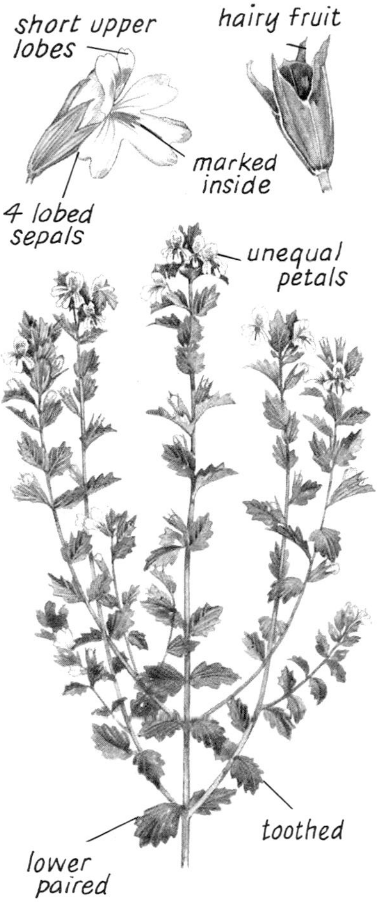

1 Irish Eyebright *(E. salisburgensis)*;
2 Red Bartsia *(Odontites verna)*

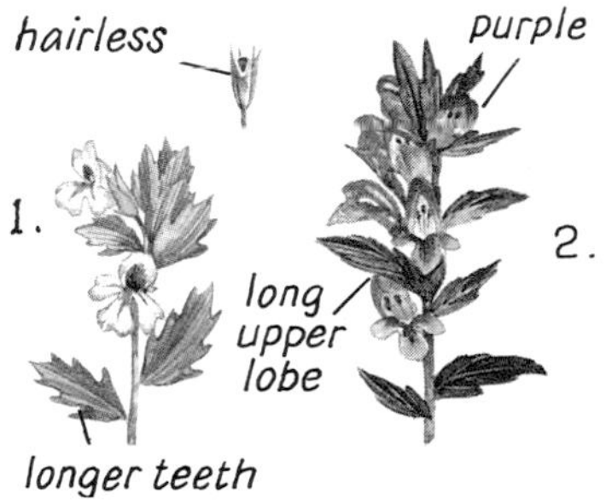

	COMMON EYEBRIGHT
Type	annual, partly parasitic
Height	10–35cm
Habitat	grassland, woods, heaths
Flowering	July–September
	STEMS AND LEAVES
Stem	upright, branched
Root	fibrous, attached to roots of other plants
Hairs	short, usually sparse
Stipules	absent
Leaves	paired or upper spirally placed on stem, 6–12mm, oblong or oval, blunt or upper pointed, edge with few pointed teeth
Leaf-stalk	absent
	FLOWERS
Position	in loose spike towards stem-tip
Bracts	leaf-like but smaller
Type	⚥
Size	5–8mm
Colour	white or purple-tinged, deep yellow blotch, veins purple
Stalk	much shorter than flower
Sepals	4, 3–6mm, bases form tube, teeth pointed
Petals	5, bases form tube, lobes notched, 3 lower longer
Stamens	4, inside tube
Stigma	1, tip swollen; style long
Ovary	1, 2-celled
	FRUIT
Type	1, oblong capsule, hairy at tip, splits lengthwise
Size	4–6mm
Seeds	numerous, 1.5–2mm, grooved, ends narrowed

Marsh Lousewort *Pedicularis palustris*

A striking plant, especially in water-meadows, where its purplish, finely-divided foliage and pink flowers stand out. The species is partly parasitic, attaching itself to roots of grasses and deriving nourishment from them. Grazing animals were thought to catch liver-fluke from Louseworts but it is now known that both fluke and plant just flourish in the same places. *Status:* native; fairly common, most of area. *Similar species:* the perennial Lousewort, of moors and heaths, is generally smaller with hairless sepals. Leafy Lousewort, from mountains in the south-east of the area, has leafy spikes of pale yellow flowers.

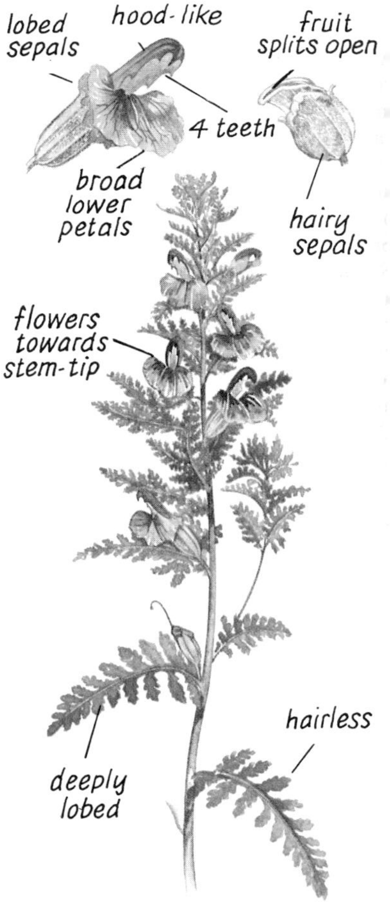

1 Lousewort *(P. sylvatica)*; **2** Leafy Lousewort *(P. foliosa)*

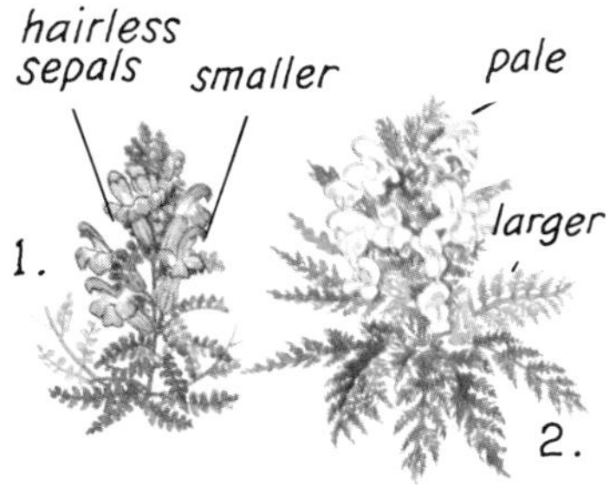

	MARSH LOUSEWORT
Type	biennial or annual, partly parasitic
Height	8–60cm
Habitat	meadows, heaths; wet places
Flowering	May–September
	STEMS AND LEAVES
Stem	single, branched below
Root	fibrous, attached to roots of other plants
Hairs	almost absent
Stipules	absent
Leaves	on alternate sides of stem, 20–40mm, deeply divided into paired, toothed lobes, often tinged purple
Leaf-stalk	shorter than blade
	FLOWERS
Position	many in spike at stem-tip
Bracts	leaf-like but smaller
Type	☿
Size	20–25mm
Colour	purplish pink
Stalk	much shorter than flower
Sepals	5, joined, hairy, lobes unequal, toothed, tube swollen in fruit
Petals	5, 18–25mm, upper 2 lobes joined, hood-like, 2 teeth each side
Stamens	4, under upper petal-lobes
Stigma	1, tip swollen; style long
Ovary	1, 2-celled
	FRUIT
Type	1, capsule, curved, flattened, pointed
Size	10–12mm
Seeds	few, 2–3mm, oblong, with net-like pattern

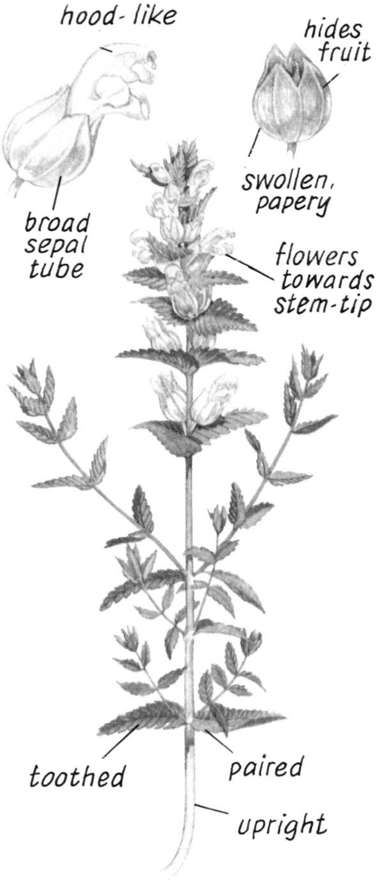

ι plant of sunny, grassy places, with 'ellow, hooded flowers, but best known n fruit when the seeds rattle inside the apsule and papery sepal-tube. This is ınother partial parasite, some of its ıourishment coming from grasses and ıther herbs through joined roots. *Status:* native; common, most of area. *Similar species:* Greater Yellow-rattle is ı larger plant of arable fields, and has 'ellowish, long-toothed bracts and a :urved petal-tube with longer upper obes. Yellow Bartsia is stickily hairy ınd the sepal-tube is not swollen. Common Cow-wheat, a woodland plant, ılso has a slender sepal-tube but the eaves are not toothed.

1 Greater Yellow-rattle *(R. angustifolius)*; **2** Yellow Bartsia *(Parentucellia viscosa)*; **3** Common Cow-wheat *(Melampyrum pratense)*

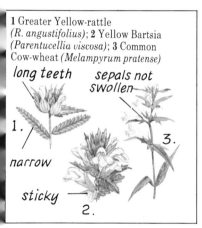

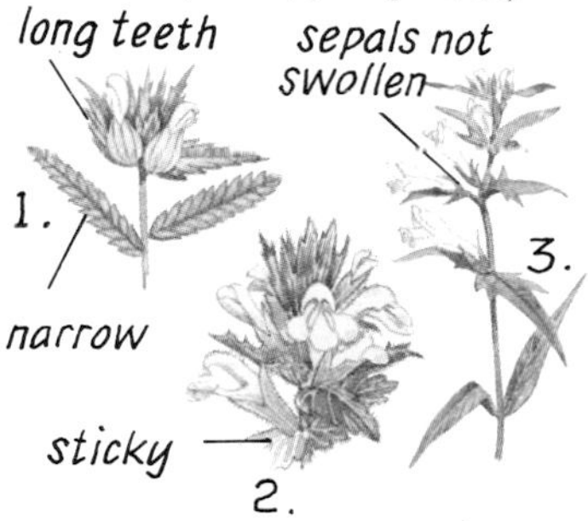

	YELLOW-RATTLE
Type	annual, partly parasitic
Height	12–50cm
Habitat	grassland, marshes, mountains
Flowering	May–August
	STEMS AND LEAVES
Stem	upright, usually black-spotted, sometimes branched
Root	fibrous, attached to those of other plants
Hairs	short, rough
Stipules	absent
Leaves	paired on stem, 10–50mm, oblong, toothed
Leaf-stalk	absent
	FLOWERS
Position	in spike at stem-tip
Bracts	triangular, leaf-like
Type	⚥
Size	12–15mm
Colour	yellow or purple-tinged
Stalk	much shorter than flower
Sepals	4, 12–18mm, bases joined, flattened, enlarged in fruit, almost hairless
Petals	5, 12–15mm, bases form tube, upper 2 lobes joined, hood-like
Stamens	4, under upper petal-lobes
Stigma	1, tip swollen; style long
Ovary	1, 2-celled
	FRUIT
Type	1, rounded, flattened capsule, splits lengthwise
Size	10–12mm
Seeds	few, 4–5mm, flattened, with encircling wing

Greater Broomrape *Orobanche rapum-genistae*

This curious plant is a parasite, deriving all sustenance from its host, usually a shrub of Broom or Gorse. It has no need of green pigment, so stems and scale-like leaves are a lurid yellow or purple, and give an impression of unhealthiness. *Status:* native; fairly common, from south to southern Scotland. *Similar species:* Common Broomrape, mainly on Clovers, is usually smaller, with fewer flowers and purple stigmas. Toothwort, mainly on Hazel or Elm, has one-sided heads of pinkish flowers, broad bracts and equal sepal-teeth. Yellow Bird's-nest has yellow, nodding flowers and grows on decaying leaves in woodland.

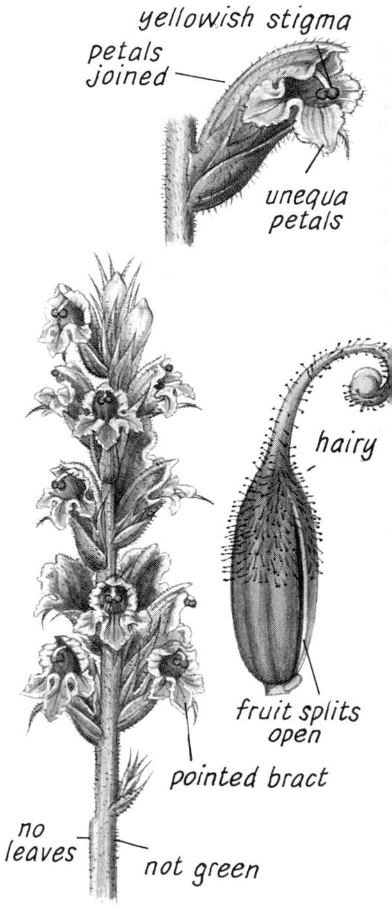

1 Common Broomrape *(O. minor)*;
2 Toothwort *(Lathraea squamaria)*;
3 Yellow Bird's-nest *(Monotropa hypopitys)*

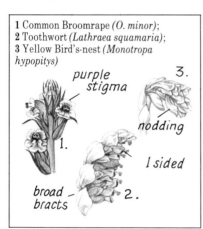

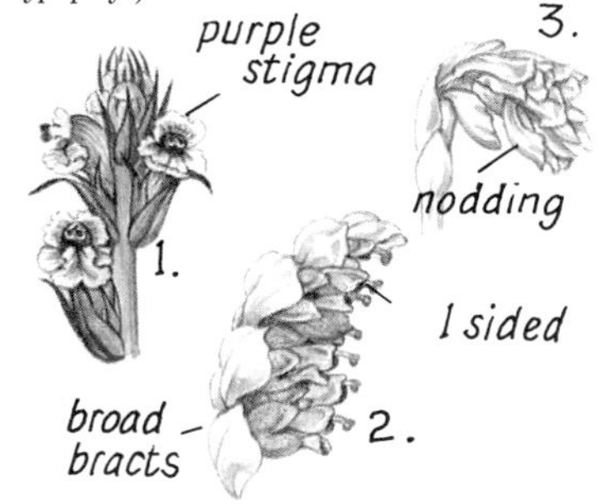

	GREATER BROOMRAPE
Type	perennial, parasite
Height	20–80cm
Habitat	heaths, woodland clearings; mainly on Gorse or Broom
Flowering	May–July
	STEMS AND LEAVES
Stem	single, unbranched, stout, yellowish or purple-tinged
Root	swollen, scaly; fibrous roots attach to other plants
Hairs	sticky, gland-tipped
Stipules	absent
Leaves	spirally around stem, 15–25mm, scale-like, spear-shaped, yellowish, pointed, edge unbroken
Leaf-stalk	absent

	FLOWERS
Position	many in long, crowded spike at stem-tip
Bracts	long, slender, pointed
Type	⚥
Size	20–25mm
Colour	pale yellow, tinged purple
Stalk	almost absent
Sepals	4, 8–15mm, bases joined, teeth unequal, slender
Petals	5, 20–25mm, bases form curved tube, lower 3 lobes bent downwards, upper short
Stamens	4, inside petal-tube
Stigma	1, 2-lobed, pale yellow
Ovary	1, 1-celled
	FRUIT
Type	capsule, splits lengthwise
Size	10–14mm
Seeds	many, 0.3–0.4mm, dust-like

Beautiful violet flowers arising from a cluster of glistening, yellowish leaves characterize the Common Butterwort. This plant of peat-bogs is carnivorous. Sticky leaves capture unwary insects that alight, then slowly roll up while digestive enzymes are secreted to dissolve the tissues. In this way the plant makes up for mineral deficiencies in the soil. *Status:* native; fairly common, most of area. *Similar species:* two species occur in the south-west of the area. Large-flowered Butterwort has flowers almost twice as large with overlapping petal-lobes. Pale Butterwort is much smaller, with grey-green leaves and lilac flowers.

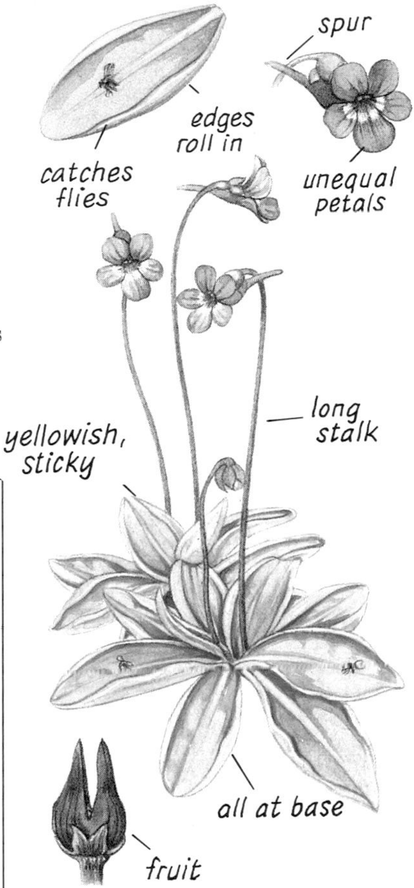

1 Large-flowered Butterwort *(P. grandiflora)*; 2 Pale Butterwort *(P. lusitanica)*

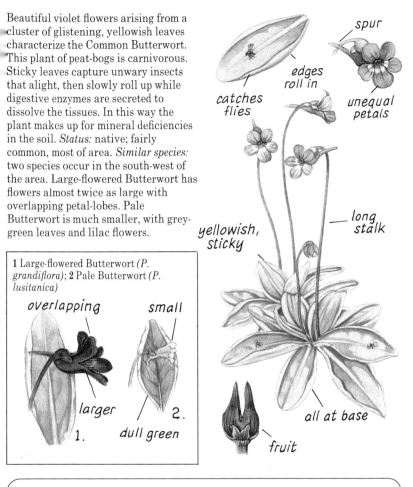

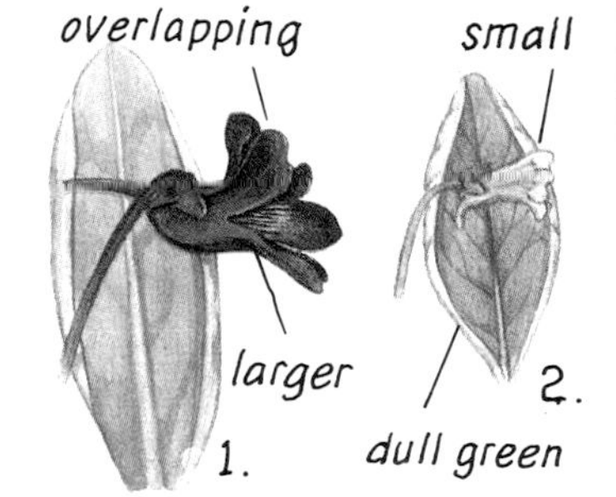

	COMMON BUTTERWORT
Type	perennial
Height	5–20cm
Habitat	bogs, wet rocks or heath; wet places
Flowering	May–July
	STEMS AND LEAVES
Stem	almost absent, 1–6 long flower-stalks
Root	fibrous
Hairs	leaves with sticky hairs
Stipules	absent
Leaves	rosette at base, 20–80mm, oblong, yellowish-green, blunt, edge unbroken, folds inwards
Leaf-stalk	absent
	FLOWERS
Position	solitary, from base
Bracts	absent
Type	⚥
Size	15–22mm
Colour	violet, paler in petal-tube
Stalk	50–200mm, much longer than flower
Sepals	5, 3–4mm, unequal, oval, bases joined
Petals	5, 15–22mm, bases form tube, slender spur at base, lower 3 lobes longer
Stamens	2, inside petal-tube
Stigma	1 broad lobe, 1 narrow; style very short
Ovary	1, 1-celled
	FRUIT
Type	1, egg-shaped capsule, splits lengthwise into 2
Size	5–9mm
Seeds	numerous, 0.8–1mm, oblong

Greater Bladderwort *Utricularia vulgaris*

Spikes of rich yellow flowers mark where this aquatic plant floats near the surface of the water. Finely-cut leaves bear small bladders, each a trap sprung when a tiny water-animal touches a bristle. A trap-door springs open and shut, sucking in the prey which is gradually digested. *Status:* native; scattered, most of area. *Similar species:* flowering is sporadic, making identification difficult. Bladderwort has flowers with a long upper lip and flatter lower lip. Other species have two sorts of leaf. Lesser Bladderwort lacks leaf-bristles and has a broad spur. Intermediate Bladderwort has bristle-edged leaves and a slender spur.

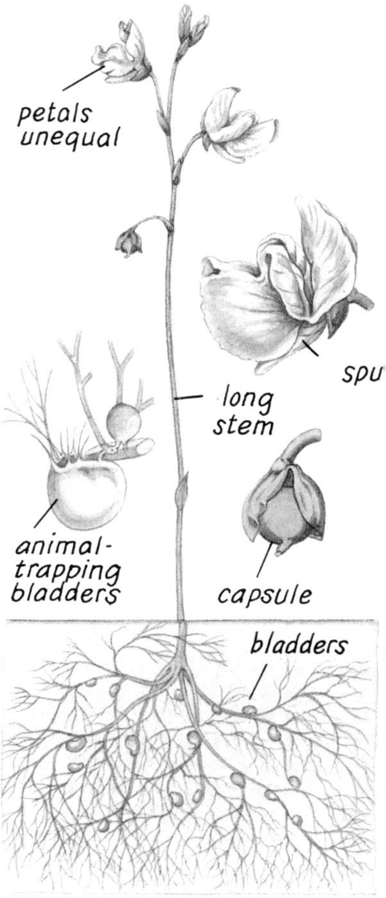

1 Bladderwort *(U. australis)*; **2** Lesser Bladderwort *(U. minor)*;
3 Intermediate Bladderwort *(U. intermedia)*

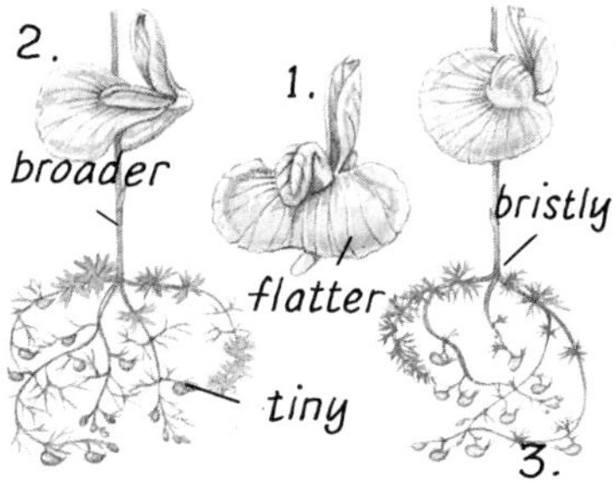

	GREATER BLADDERWORT
Type	perennial
Height	15–100cm
Habitat	ponds, lakes, ditches; still, often deep water
Flowering	July–August
	STEMS AND LEAVES
Stem	long, leafy, submerged, floats near surface
Root	absent
Hairs	absent
Stipules	absent
Leaves	spirally placed on stem, 20–25mm, finely cut, edges slightly toothed, bristly, some with tiny bladders
Leaf-stalk	shorter than blade

	FLOWERS
Position	2–8 in spike-like head above water, stalk 100–200mm
Bracts	shorter than flower-stalks
Type	⚥
Size	12–18mm
Colour	deep yellow
Stalk	shorter than flower
Sepals	2, oval, slightly toothed
Petals	bases joined, with conical spur, lobes form 2 lips, fold of lower lip about equalling upper lip
Stamens	2, inside petal-tube
Stigma	flattened lobe and much smaller lobe; style short
Ovary	1, 1-celled
	FRUIT
Type	1, capsule, globular
Size	3–5mm
Seeds	many, 0.5–0.7mm, angular

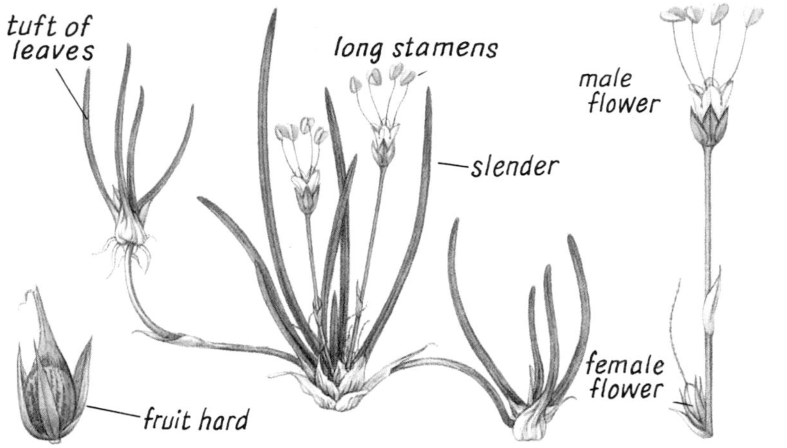

A number of superficially similar plants form a turf-like sward around the edges of northern lakes, sometimes submerged to a depth of several metres as the water-level fluctuates. Wind-pollinated flowers of Shoreweed, a relative of the Plantains, only appear on exposed plants. *Status:* native; most of area, more common in north. *Similar species:* Mudwort has five petals and short stamens. Awlwort, a relative of the Cabbage, has spike-like heads of four-petalled flowers and pod-like fruits. The most attractive of these plants is Water Lobelia, the long-stalked heads of white or lilac flowers with unequal petals.

1 Mudwort *(Limosella aquatica)*;
2 Awlwort *(Subularia aquatica)*;
3 Water Lobelia *(Lobelia dortmanna)*

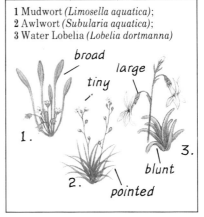

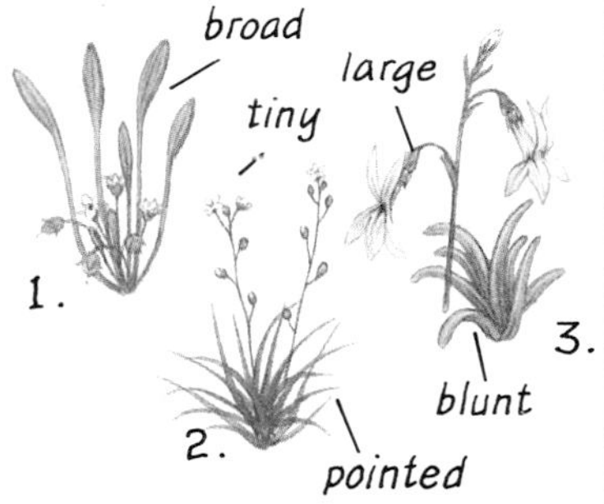

	SHOREWEED
Type	perennial
Height	15–100mm, rarely 250mm
Habitat	lakes, ponds; in or by lime-free water
Flowering	June–August
	STEMS AND LEAVES
Stem	creeping, producing upright tufts of leaves
Root	rather thick
Hairs	absent
Stipules	absent
Leaves	in rosette, 15–100mm, rarely 250mm, slender, almost cylindrical, edge unbroken, base broad, sheaths stem
Leaf-stalk	absent
	FLOWERS
Position	single ♂, sometimes several ♀ near base of stalked head
Bracts	oval, papery
Type 1	♂ with stamens
Type 2	♀ stalkless, with ovary
Size	5–6mm
Colour	whitish, translucent
Stalk	longer than flower
Sepals	3–4, edges papery, 3–5mm, oval or slender
Petals	3–4, 4–6mm, bases joined
Stamens	4, protruding, 10–20mm
Stigma	1; style long
Ovary	1, 1-celled
	FRUIT
Type	1, dry, hard, oblong, enclosed by petal-tube
Size	1.5–2mm
Seeds	1, not released

Greater Plantain *Plantago major*

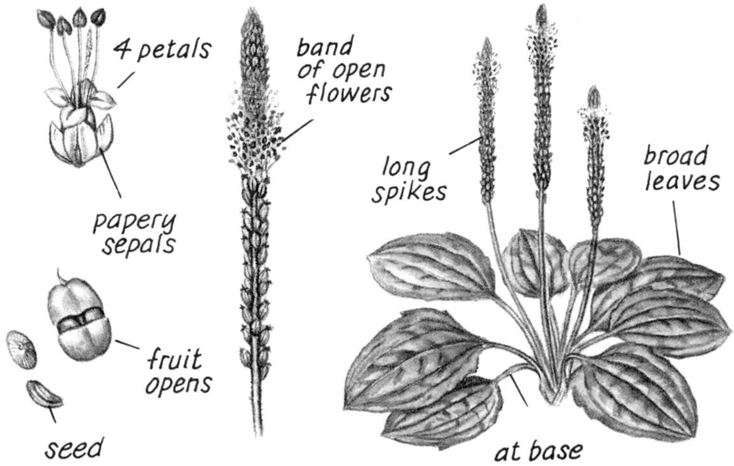

A rosette of broad, tough leaves and long spikes of insignificant flowers are characteristic of the Greater Plantain. It is often a weed of lawns. The flowers are pollinated by the wind: anthers dangle from the flowers to shed pollen, and a long, roughened stigma catches airborne pollen. Sparrows and Finches eagerly seek the seeds in the long fruiting-heads. *Status:* native; common, throughout area. *Similar species:* Hoary Plantain, a more attractive plant, has leaves of similar shape but with soft, whitish hairs and shorter, creamy-white flower-heads with lilac stamens.

Hoary Plantain *(P. media)*

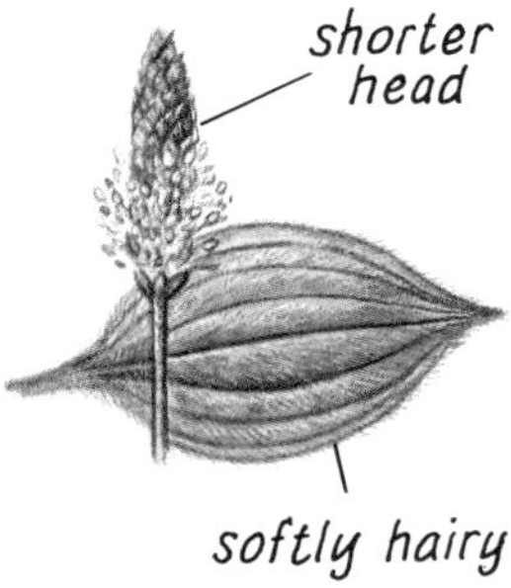

	GREATER PLANTAIN
Type	perennial
Height	10–15cm, rarely to 50cm
Habitat	cultivated and waste ground, grassy places
Flowering	May–September
	STEMS AND LEAVES
Stem	very short, stout; flower-stalks long
Root	thick, whitish
Hairs	absent or short
Stipules	absent
Leaves	rosette at base, 100–300mm, oval or elliptical, blunt, edge unbroken or slightly toothed, base squarish
Leaf-stalk	about equalling blade
	FLOWERS
Position	numerous, in long, slender, stalked, often curved spike
Bracts	shorter than flower, brown
Type	⚥
Size	2–3mm
Colour	yellowish-white
Stalk	absent
Sepals	4, 1.5–2.5mm, oval, almost equal, edges papery
Petals	4, 2–3mm, bases form tube, lobes oval
Stamens	4, protruding
Stigma	1, slender
Ovary	1, 2-celled
	FRUIT
Type	1, capsule, oblong, top splits away
Size	2–4mm
Seeds	6–13, 1–1.5mm, elliptical, flattened

A very common plant, distinctive in its long leaves with several almost parallel veins, and compact, blackish-brown flower-heads borne on very long stalks. It is familiar to children , for many games are played with the tough-stalked flower-heads and passed on or re-invented by successive generations. *Status:* native; common, throughout area. *Similar species:* several narrow-leaved Plantains grow by the coast or in sandy and rocky places inland. Leaves of Buck's-horn Plantain have paired lobes. Those of Sea Plantain are almost parallel-sided. Branched Plantain has long, branched, leafy stems and many flower-heads.

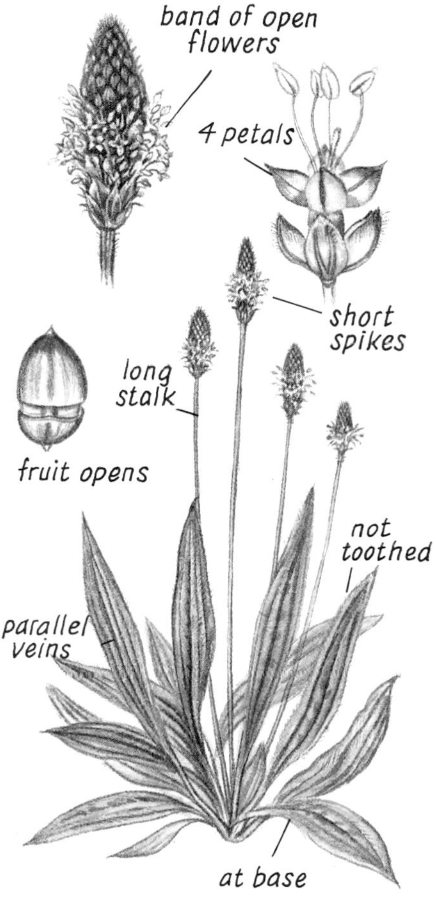

1 Buck's-horn Plantain *(P. coronopus)*; **2** Sea Plantain *(P. maritima)*; **3** Branched Plantain *(P. arenaria)*

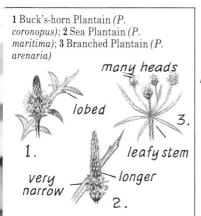

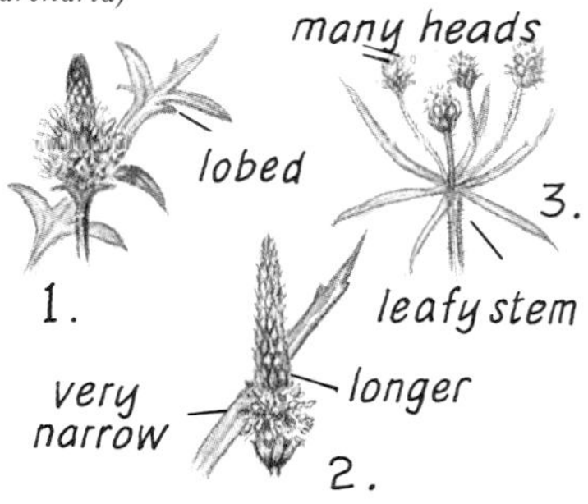

	RIBWORT
Type	perennial
Height	10–45cm
Habitat	grassland; all but most acid soils
Flowering	April–August
	STEMS AND LEAVES
Stem	short, sometimes branched; flower-stalks long
Root	fibrous
Hairs	sparse, pressed to surface
Stipules	absent
Leaves	rosette at base, 100–300mm, narrowly to broadly spear-shaped, 3–5 main veins, pointed, edge unbroken or slightly toothed, base tapered
Leaf-stalk	about half length of blade

	FLOWERS
Position	many, in crowded spike on long, grooved stalk
Bracts	oval, long-pointed
Type	⚥
Size	3–4mm; head 10–20mm, rarely to 50mm
Colour	pale brown
Stalk	absent
Sepals	4, 2.5–3mm, partly joined
Petals	4, 3–4mm, bases form tube, lobes oval
Stamens	4, 3–5mm, protruding
Stigma	1, slender
Ovary	1, 2-celled
	FRUIT
Type	1, capsule, oblong
Size	3–5mm
Seeds	2, 2–3mm, elliptical, flattened

Honeysuckle *Lonicera periclymenum*

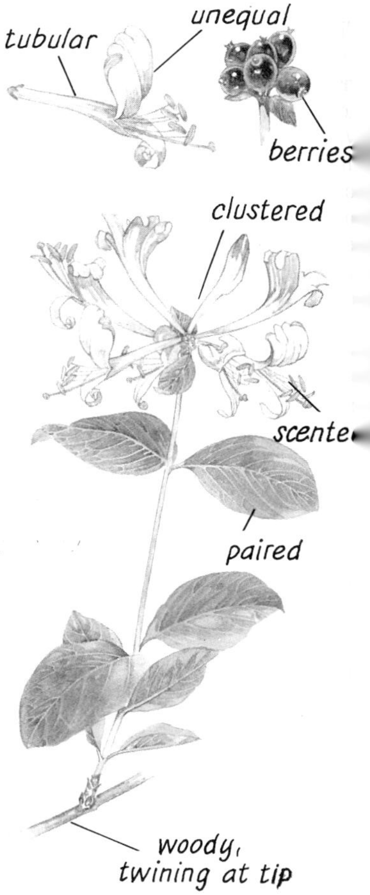

Sweet-scented Honeysuckle is a favourite hedgerow plant, its compact heads of creamy, trumpet-shaped flowers often flushed with red or purple. In Autumn it is also conspicuous, with its clusters of crimson berries. Night-flying moths are attracted by the scent, which is strongest at dusk, and pollinate the flowers as they seek nectar. *Status:* native; common, most of area except extreme north. *Similar species:* Perfoliate Honeysuckle, a garden plant that has often escaped, differs in its joined pairs of upper leaves and stalkless flower-heads. Fly Honeysuckle is a native, upright shrub with much shorter flowers.

1 Perfoliate Honeysuckle *(L. caprifolium)*; **2** Fly Honeysuckle *(L. xylosteum)*

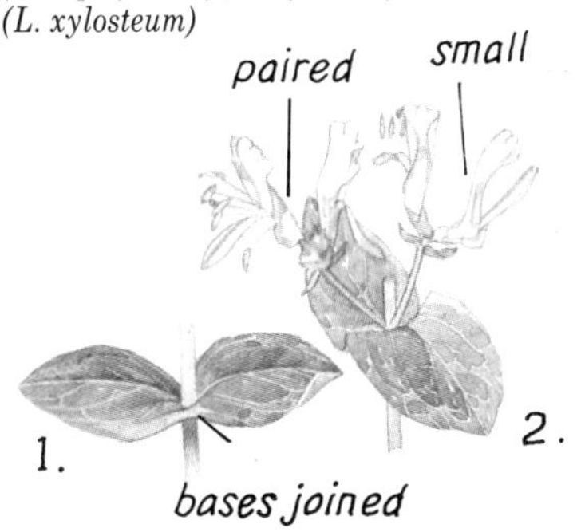

	HONEYSUCKLE
Type	climber
Height	up to 600cm
Habitat	woods, hedges, rocks
Flowering	June–September
	STEMS AND LEAVES
Stem	long, twining clockwise or trailing, woody below
Root	woody stock
Hairs	absent or sparse
Stipules	absent
Leaves	paired on stem, 30–70mm, oval to oblong, bluish green beneath, usually pointed, edge unbroken
Leaf-stalk	shorter than blade or absent
	FLOWERS
Position	4–30, in short, stalked head
Bracts	shorter than flowers
Type	⚥
Size	40–50mm
Colour	creamy white or yellowish, often tinged red or purple
Stalk	much shorter than flower
Sepals	5, 2–5mm, bases joined
Petals	5, 40–50mm, bases form long tube, upper 4 lobes joined into broad lip, lower lobe curved back
Stamens	5, protruding
Stigma	tip swollen; style long
Ovary	1, 2-celled
	FRUIT
Type	1, cluster of red, globular berries
Size	7–10mm
Seeds	2–8, 4–5mm, oblong

'his curious species often lurks ınnoticed at the base of a hedgerow, its reenish-yellow flowers lost against the elicate, rather Fern-like foliage. It is vorth searching out the plant because he flower-heads have a unique ırrangement: four flowers face utwards and a single flower faces ıpwards. Such an unusual arrangement ıas earned this species the picturesque lternative common name of 'Townhall Clock'. The top flower has four petals ut the side flowers have five. The lowers have a musk-like scent, articularly in the evening. No native lant resembles Moschatel at all losely, so its relationship to other pecies is obscure. Some place it with he Fumitories because of a vague imilarity in the foliage, but the form of he flowers is closer to that of Ioneysuckle. *Status:* native; rather cattered, most of area except many slands, mainly in mountains in south. There are no similar species.)

MOSCHATEL
Type perennial
Height 5–10cm
Habitat woods, hedges, rocks
Flowering April–May

STEMS AND LEAVES
Stem upright, unbranched
Root creeping, scaly, underground stem
Hairs absent
Stipules absent
Leaves basal with 2–3 on stem, 8–30mm, divided into threes, leaflets often 3-lobed, pale green, blunt
Leaf-stalk basal long, upper short

FLOWERS
Position 5, head 6–9mm, long-stalked, at stem-tip
Bracts absent
Type ⚥, slightly scented
Size 6–8mm
Colour yellowish green
Stalk absent
Sepals 2–3, 1.5–2mm, oval
Petals 4–5, 2–3.5mm, bases joined, lobes oval, spreading widely
Stamens 4–5, divided and appearing as 8 or 10
Stigmas 4–5; styles short
Ovary 1, partly below sepals, 3–5-celled

FRUIT
Type 1, globular, berry-like, green, rarely produced
Size 3–5mm
Seeds 1, 2–3mm, oval, flattened

Common Cornsalad *Valerianella locusta*

An easily overlooked, rather weedy plant that has compact heads of tiny flowers. The plant was formerly used and sometimes cultivated as a salad plant, especially in France. *Status:* native; scattered through most of area, rarer in north. *Similar species:* other sorts of Cornsalad are rather difficult to tell apart but differ in the shape of the fruit. Keeled-fruited Cornsalad has an oblong, grooved fruit. Broad-fruited Cornsalad has an egg-shaped fruit with distinct sepals at the tip. Narrow-fruited Cornsalad has a similar-shaped fruit but the sepals are very unequal, with one long tooth.

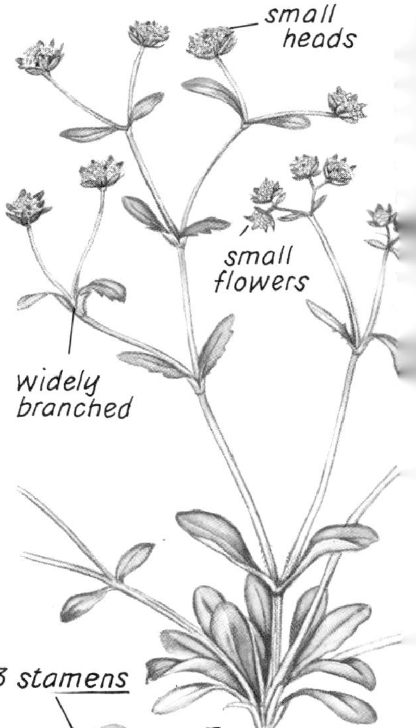

1 Narrow-fruited Cornsalad *(V. dentata)*; **2** Broad-fruited Cornsalad *(V. rimosa)*; **3** Keeled-fruited Cornsalad *(V. carinata)*

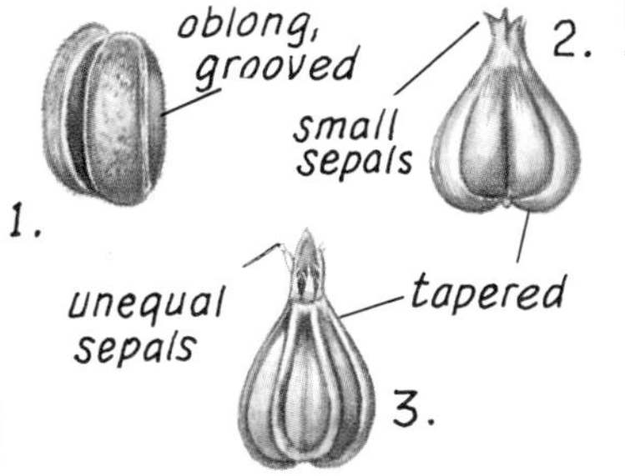

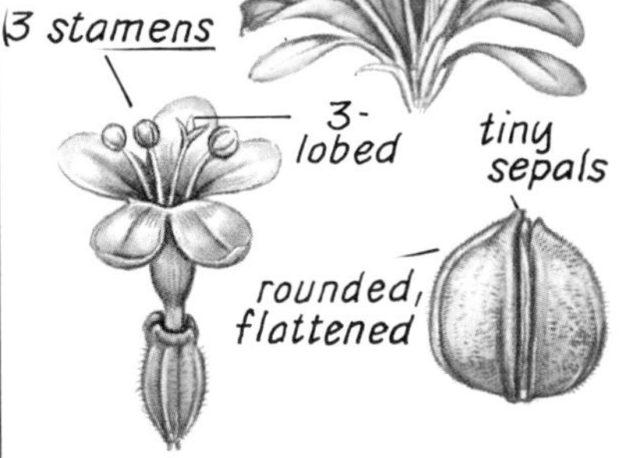

COMMON CORNSALAD	
Type	annual
Height	7–40cm
Habitat	cultivated or waste ground, rocks, dunes; dry soils
Flowering	April–June
STEMS AND LEAVES	
Stem	upright, slender, brittle, angular, widely branched
Root	fibrous
Hairs	stem minutely bristly
Stipules	absent
Leaves	basal or paired on stem, 20–70mm, oblong to spoon-shaped, mostly blunt, edge unbroken or some toothed
Leaf-stalk	shorter than blade

FLOWERS	
Position	compact heads at stem-tips, sometimes single flowers in forks of branches
Bracts	smaller than leaves
Type	⚥
Size	2–3mm
Colour	pale lilac
Stalk	absent
Sepals	5, 0.1–0.3mm, indistinct
Petals	5, 2–3mm, bases joined, funnel-shaped, lobes spreading widely
Stamens	3, protruding
Stigma	3-lobed; style long
Ovary	1, below petals, 3-celled
FRUIT	
Type	1, dry, nearly circular, flattened, smooth
Size	2–2.5mm
Seeds	1, not released

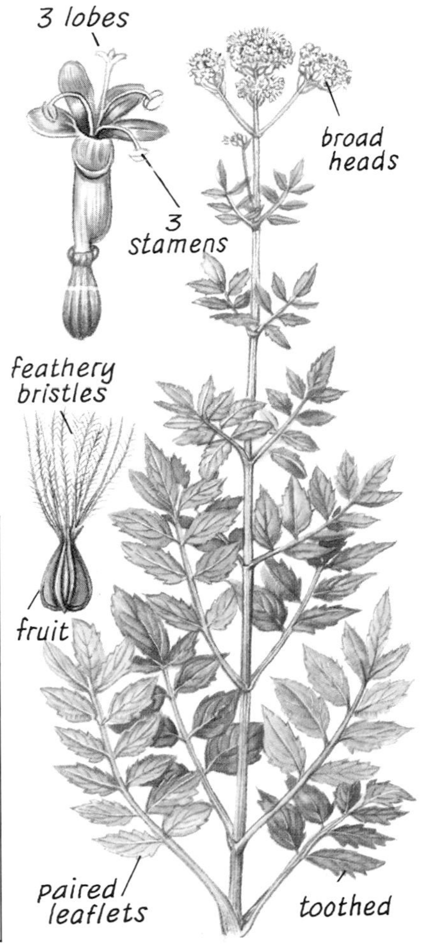

. tall, conspicuous plant of river banks nd damp ditches, its leaves cut into arrow leaflets and broad heads of lilac owers. This plant still has several ıedicinal uses. Extracts from the roots ave a sedative effect and were used for pilepsy, headaches and insomnia, lthough the drug can be addictive. *'tatus:* native; throughout area. *Similar pecies:* Marsh Valerian has rounded ɔwer leaves on the separate male and ɜmale plants. Red Valerian is an ntroduced plant which is very common n cliffs and walls in the west of the .rea. It has broad, bluish leaves and purred flowers with one stamen.

1 Marsh Valerian *(V. dioica)*; **2** Red Valerian *(Centranthus ruber)*

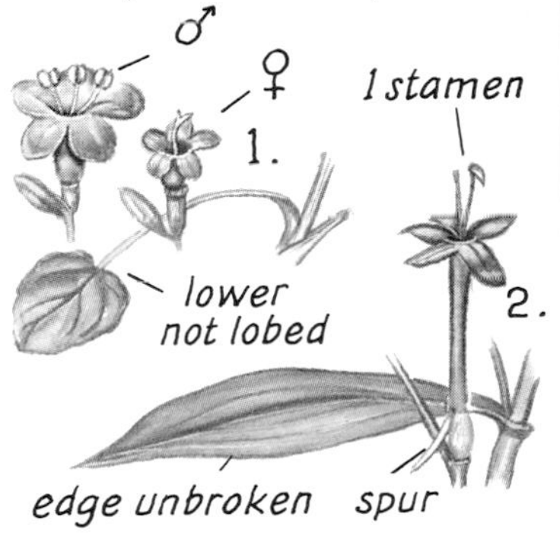

	COMMON VALERIAN
Type	perennial
Height	20–150cm, rarely 240cm
Habitat	grassy places, scrub; mostly damp soils
Flowering	June–August
	STEMS AND LEAVES
Stem	upright, rarely short, creeping stems at base
Root	short underground stem
Hairs	mostly below, absent above
Stipules	absent
Leaves	paired on stem, 25–200mm, paired, spear-shaped, toothed leaflets, leaflet at tip
Leaf-stalk	shorter than blade, upper almost absent
	FLOWERS
Position	many, in compact, branched, rounded heads at stem-tips
Bracts	shorter than flowers
Type	⚥
Size	4–5mm
Colour	pinkish lilac
Stalk	more or less absent
Sepals	15 lobes, up to 6mm, rolled inwards, enlarging, becoming feathery in fruit
Petals	5, 4–5mm, bases form tube, side swollen, lobes oblong
Stamens	3, protruding, white
Stigma	1, 3-lobed; style long
Ovary	1, apparently 1-celled
	FRUIT
Type	nut-like, oval, flattish, with feathery parachute
Size	2.5–4mm
Seeds	1, not released

Teasel *Dipsacus fullonum*

A striking plant, with large, spiny heads that bear rings of rosy-purple flowers. Bases of the stem-leaves are joined and fill with water, often drowning small insects. It has been speculated that the Teasel could benefit from these animals and might be carnivorous, although tropical plants use similar water-traps to protect flowers from insect attack. Spiny heads of Teasels have long been used to raise the nap on fabric. *Status:* native; often common, most of area except parts of north. *Similar species:* Small Teasel has stalked leaves and rounded flower-heads bearing white flowers.

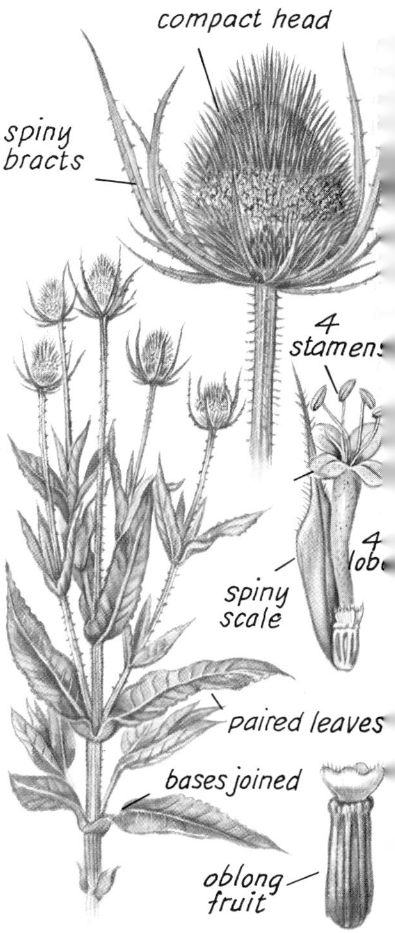

Small Teasel *(D. pilosus)*

	TEASEL
Type	biennial
Height	up to 200cm
Habitat	grassy places, river banks; often on clay soils
Flowering	July–August
	STEMS AND LEAVES
Stem	short in first year, then upright, with prickly angles, branched above
Root	stout, yellowish tap-root
Hairs	only scattered prickles
Stipules	absent
Leaves	rosette at base or paired on stem, oblong to spear-shaped, edge unbroken or toothed, bases of upper stem-leaves joined
Leaf-stalk	only on basal leaves

	FLOWERS
Position	numerous in conical, blunt, upright, long-stalked heads
Bracts	long, spiny under head; spine-tipped under flower
Type	⚥
Size	8–12mm; heads 30–80mm
Colour	rosy purple, rarely white
Stalk	absent
Sepals	1–1.5mm, joined, fringed
Petals	4, 8–12mm, bases form long tube; lobes unequal
Stamens	4, protruding
Stigma	1; style long
Ovary	1, under petals, 1-celled
	FRUIT
Type	1, nut-like, oblong, 4-angled, with sepals at tip
Size	4–5mm
Seeds	1, not released

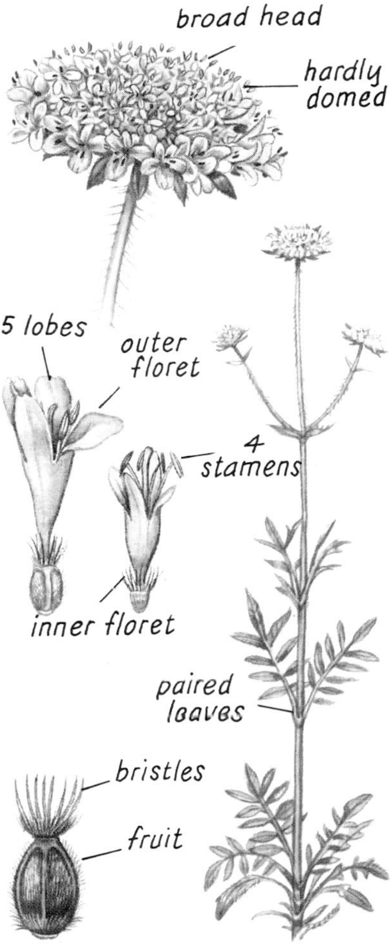

An attractive Summer-flowering meadow plant, its broad, bluish flower-heads are visible from a distance. Species of Scabious were used to treat scabies, hence the common name, and many other afflictions of the skin including sores caused by bubonic plague. *Status:* native; most of area except many northern islands, most common in south. *Similar species:* other species have more elongated heads with tiny bracts between the flowers and only five sepal-teeth. Small Scabious has five-lobed flowers and divided leaves; Devil's-bit Scabious has four-lobed flowers, all of the same size, and most leaves with unbroken edges.

1 Small Scabious *(Scabiosa columbaria)*; **2** Devil's-bit Scabious *(Succisa pratensis)*

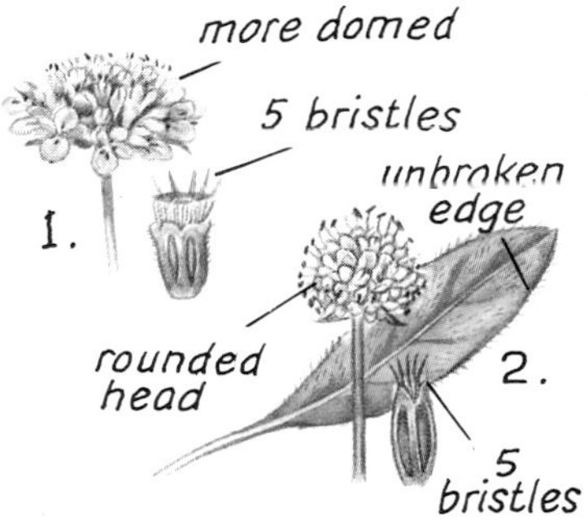

	FIELD SCABIOUS
Type	perennial
Height	25–100cm
Habitat	grassy places; dry soils
Flowering	July–September
	STEMS AND LEAVES
Stem	upright, branched
Root	tap-root
Hairs	long, stiffish, throughout, angled downwards on stem
Stipules	absent
Leaves	basal rosette or paired on stem, lowest to 300mm long, spear-shaped, upper smaller, with paired lobes, pointed, edge unbroken or toothed
Leaf-stalk	shorter than blade

	FLOWERS
Position	numerous, in rounded, flattish, long-stalked heads
Bracts	oval, only under head, shorter than flowers
Type	⚥ or ♀, outer larger
Size	8–14, heads 30–40mm
Colour	bluish lilac
Stalk	absent beneath flowers, long under heads
Sepals	2–4mm, 8 slender teeth
Petals	4, 7–14mm, bases form tube, lobes unequal
Stamens	4, protruding, pink
Stigma	1, notched; style long
Ovary	1, below petals, 1-celled
	FRUIT
Type	1, nut-like, cylindrical, hairy
Size	5–6mm
Seeds	1, not released

Nettle-leaved Bellflower *Campanula trachelium*

A tall plant of hedgerows and woodland margins, with toothed, nettle-like leaves and a spike of bluish, bell-shaped flowers. It was widely used for treating throat infections. *Status:* native; scattered throughout most of area, except many islands. *Similar species:* Clustered Bellflower is an attractive plant of lime-rich grassland, and has stalkless flowers more or less clustered in heads. Giant Bellflower has the largest flowers of these species, bluntly angled stems and the lower leaves tapered or rounded at the base. Creeping Bellflower has nodding flowers with widely spreading sepal-teeth.

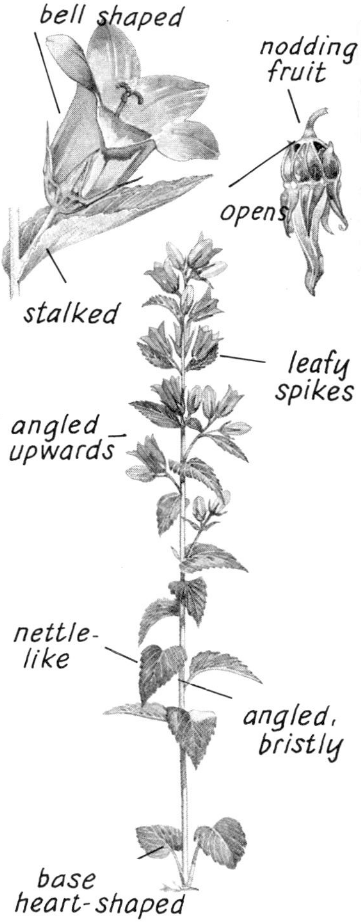

1 Clustered Bellflower *(C. glomerata)*; **2** Giant Bellflower *(C. latifolia)*; **3** Creeping Bellflower *(C. rapunculoides)*

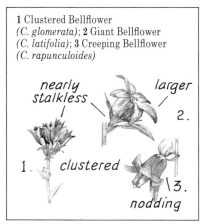

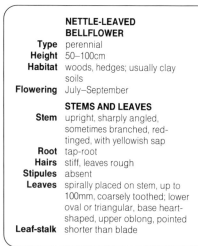

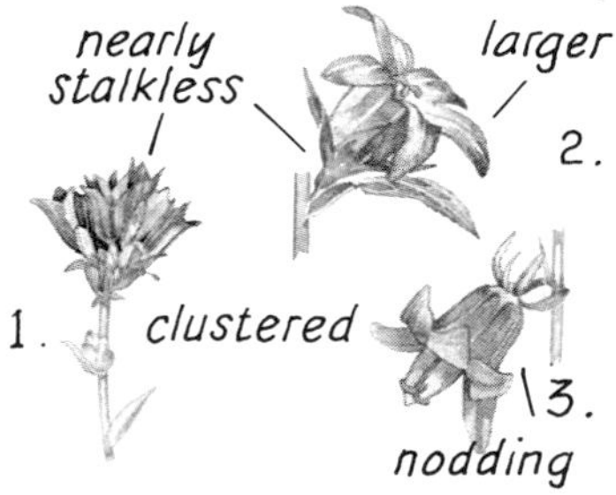

	NETTLE-LEAVED BELLFLOWER
Type	perennial
Height	50–100cm
Habitat	woods, hedges; usually clay soils
Flowering	July–September
	STEMS AND LEAVES
Stem	upright, sharply angled, sometimes branched, red-tinged, with yellowish sap
Root	tap-root
Hairs	stiff, leaves rough
Stipules	absent
Leaves	spirally placed on stem, up to 100mm, coarsely toothed; lower oval or triangular, base heart-shaped, upper oblong, pointed
Leaf-stalk	shorter than blade

	FLOWERS
Position	long head, 1–4 on branches
Bracts	narrow
Type	⚥, angled upwards
Size	25–50mm
Colour	purplish blue
Stalk	shorter than flower
Sepals	5, 13–15mm, bases joined, teeth triangular, pointed
Petals	5, 25–50mm, equal, joined, bell-shaped, lobes pointed
Stamens	5, long, soon withering
Stigmas	3; style long
Ovary	1, below sepals, 3-celled
	FRUIT
Type	nodding capsule, half spherical, pores at base
Size	6–8mm
Seeds	numerous, 0.6–0.8mm, oblong

Dainty, nodding, pale blue bells of the Harebell are a common sight on dry, grassy banks in Summer. In Scotland the plant is called 'Bluebell', although a different species bears the name in England. Upper and lower leaves of this plant are so different that they appear to belong to different species. *Status:* native; usually common, most of area. *Similar species:* the smaller relatives of the Bellflowers include Venus's-looking-glass, a cornfield annual with upright, purplish flowers and long, cylindrical capsules. Ivy-leaved Bellflower is a creeping plant of boggy places, with small, Ivy-shaped leaves and nodding, pale blue flowers.

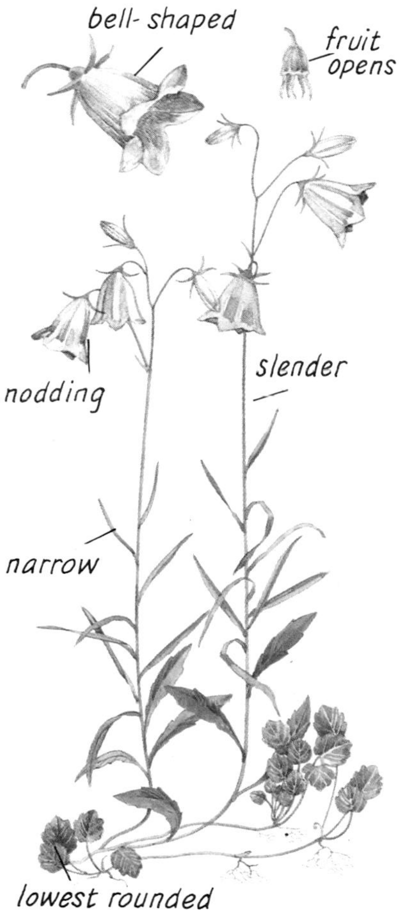

1 Venus's-looking-glass *(Legousia hybrida)*; **2** Ivy-leaved Bellflower *(Wahlenbergia hederacea)*

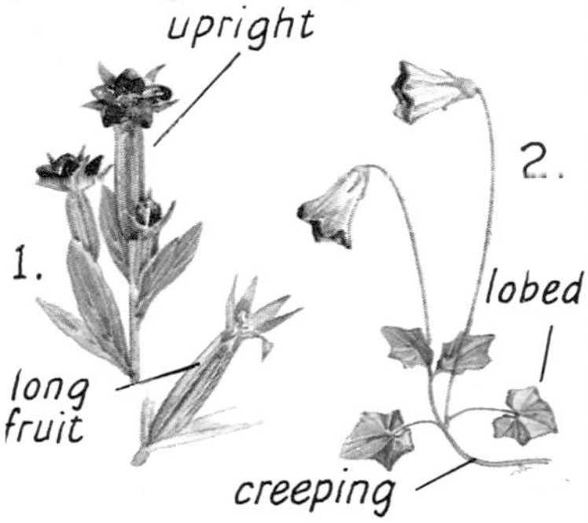

	HAREBELL
Type	perennial
Height	15–40cm, rarely 70cm
Habitat	grassy places, dunes; mostly dry soils
Flowering	July–September
	STEMS AND LEAVES
Stem	low-growing, turning upright to flower
Root	creeping underground stems
Hairs	absent above, short below
Stipules	absent
Leaves	on alternate sides of stem; lower 5–15mm, oval to nearly circular, toothed, base heart-shaped; upper narrow, straight-sided
Leaf-stalk	lower much longer than blade; upper absent

	FLOWERS
Position	solitary at stem-tip or few in widely branched head
Bracts	small, straight-sided
Type	⚥
Size	10–20mm
Colour	blue, rarely white
Stalk	long, slender, nodding
Sepals	5, 5–8mm, slender, spreading apart
Petals	5, 10–20mm, joined, bell-shaped, lobes broadly oval
Stamens	5, inside tube
Stigmas	3; style long
Ovary	1, below sepals, 3-celled
	FRUIT
Type	capsule, cone-shaped, nodding, pores at base
Size	4–6mm
Seeds	numerous, 0.6–0.8mm, oblong

Sheep's-bit *Jasione montana*

On dry, grassy banks and heathland, Sheep's-bit bears its rounded heads of pale blue flowers at the end of almost leafless stems. Although the flower-heads resemble those of Scabious species, this is a relative of the Bellflowers, and has joined stamens and capsules that release seeds. *Status:* native; scattered throughout area, often common. *Similar species:* Rampions have similar flower-heads but with curved buds and almost hairless stems and leaves. Round-headed Rampion has short heads of violet flowers and occurs in the south of the area. Spiked Rampion is more widespread and has longer heads of yellowish flowers.

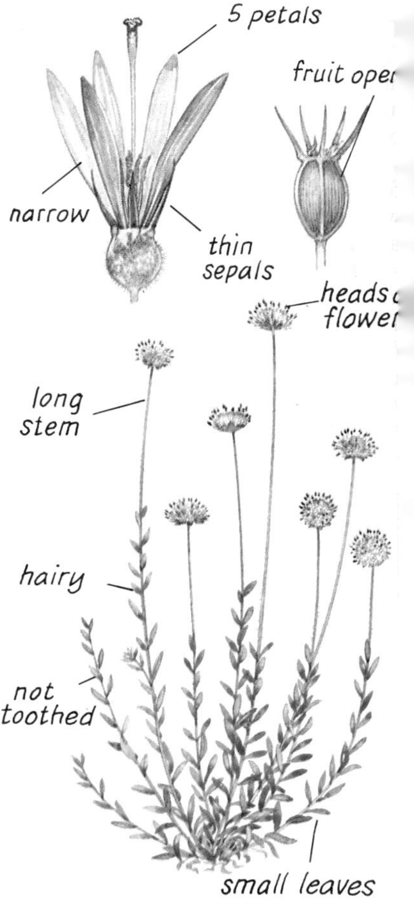

1 Round-headed Rampion *(Phyteuma orbiculare)*; **2** Spiked Rampion *(P. spicatum)*

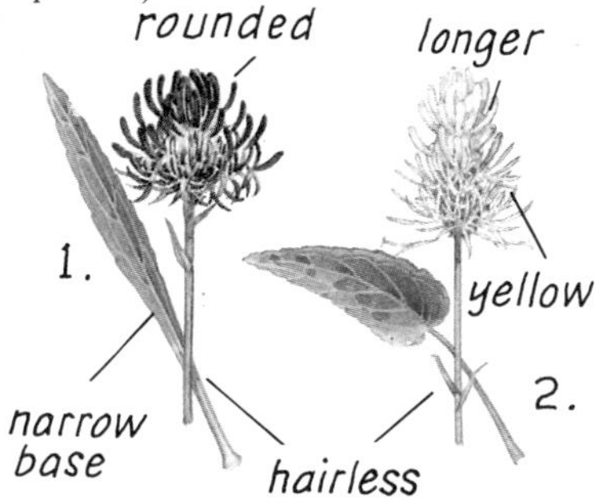

	SHEEP'S-BIT
Type	biennial, sometimes annual
Height	5–50cm
Habitat	grassy places, heaths, cliffs; lime-free soils
Flowering	May–August
	STEMS AND LEAVES
Stem	low-growing, turns upright to flower, some branched
Root	fibrous
Hairs	more or less throughout
Stipules	absent
Leaves	spirally placed on lower part of stem, to 50mm, narrowly oblong or spear-shaped, mostly blunt, edge straight or wavy
Leaf-stalk	lower short, upper absent
	FLOWERS
Position	up to 200 in almost globular head at stem-tip

Bracts	many, oval below head
Type	⚥
Size	4–6mm; head 5–35mm
Colour	blue, rarely white
Stalk	absent; head long-stalked
Sepals	5, 1.5–2.5mm, bases joined, teeth thin
Petals	5, 4–6mm, bases joined, narrow lobes spread apart
Stamens	5, elongated, joined
Stigmas	2; style long, protruding
Ovary	1, below petals, 2-celled
	FRUIT
Type	1, capsule, egg-shaped, sepals attached, opens by 2 short teeth
Size	3–4mm
Seeds	numerous, *c*0.5mm, glossy

This handsome, purple and yellow Daisy is commonly encountered in salt-marshes, where it covers extensive areas. Most plants have strap-shaped outer florets, but some only have the yellow inner florets. Sea Aster was formerly cultivated and used as a wound-herb. *Status:* native; common around coasts of region. *Similar species:* several species of Michaelmas-daisy are grown in gardens and commonly escape. Perhaps the most common is *Aster novi-belgii*, with broad-based leaves and mostly bluish outer florets. *A. lanceolatus* has narrower leaves with tapered bases and thin, white or bluish outer florets.

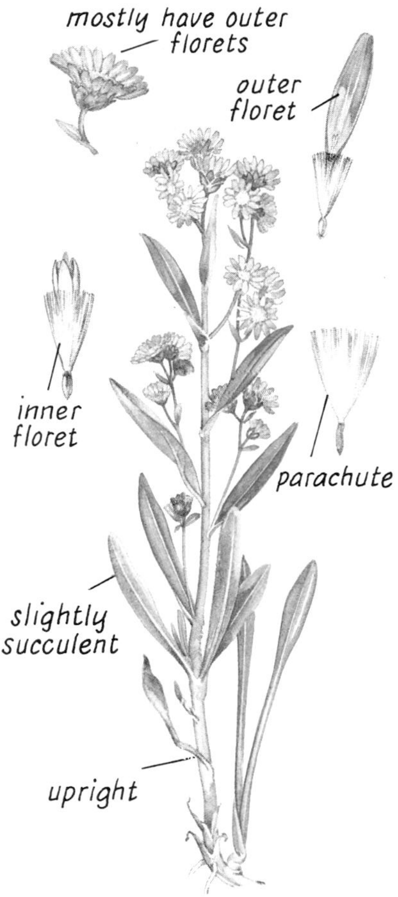

1 Michaelmas-daisy *(A. novi-belgii)*;
2 Michaelmas-daisy *(A. lanceolatus)*

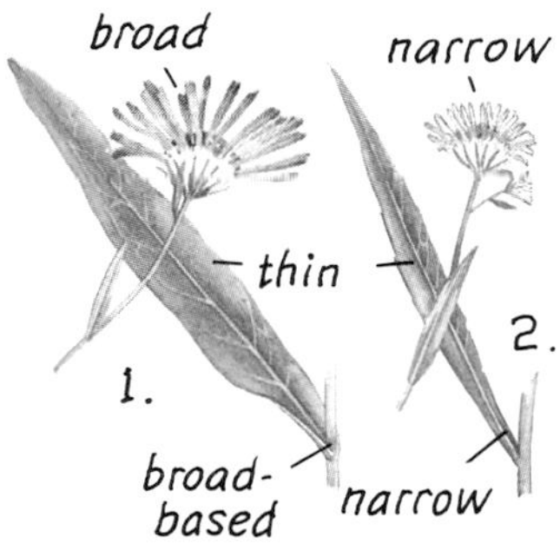

	SEA ASTER
Type	perennial
Height	15–100cm
Habitat	salt-marsh, sea-cliffs, rocks; salty soils
Flowering	July–October
	STEMS AND LEAVES
Stem	upright, stout, branched
Root	short underground stem
Hairs	mostly absent
Stipules	absent
Leaves	spirally placed on stem, 70–120mm, fleshy, edge unbroken or hardly toothed, lower spear-shaped, tapered upper oblong, broad-based
Leaf-stalk	long below, absent above
	FLOWERS
Position	daisy-like heads of florets surrounded by bracts
Bracts	papery-edged around head; none between florets
Type 1	inner ⚥, 7–8mm, tubular
Type 2	outer florets ♀ usually 10–30, 9–12mm, strap-shaped
Size	heads 8–20mm
Colour	yellow and purplish blue
Stalk	absent; short under heads
Sepals	a ring of hairs
Petals	5, 8–12mm, joined, tubular, lobes equal or very unequal
Stamens	5, joined into tube
Stigma	1, 2-lobed; style long
Ovary	1, below petals, 1-celled
	FRUIT
Type	nut-like, flattened, hairy, with parachute of hairs
Size	5–6mm
Seeds	1, not released

Hemp-agrimony *Eupatorium cannabinum*

A tall plant of riverbanks, with broad, fluffy heads of reddish or pink flowers. Hemp-agrimony has its small flower-heads clustered together and in sunny weather the whole top of the plant becomes alive with butterflies. *Status:* native; common, most of area except far north. *Similar species:* several species with small flower-heads have spirally-arranged undivided leaves and tiny, elongated florets around the heads. Canadian Fleabane has loose clusters of yellowish heads. Blue Fleabane has few, larger heads with purplish outer florets. Ploughman's-spikenard has toothed lower leaves and purplish bracts around the flower-heads.

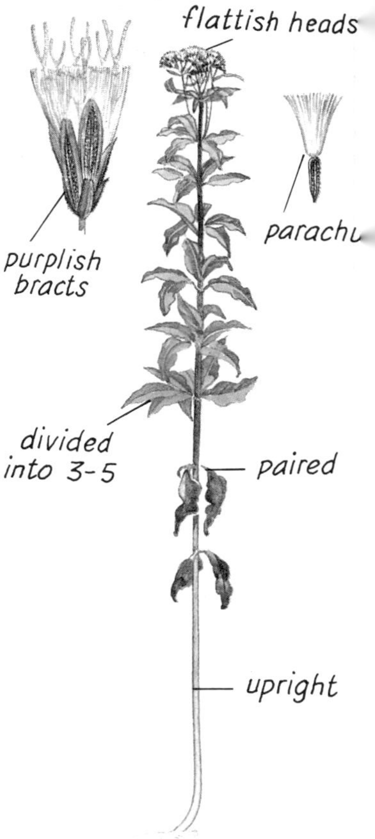

1 Canadian Fleabane *(Erigeron canadensis)*; **2** Blue Fleabane *(E. acer)*; **3** Ploughman's-spikenard *(Inula conyza)*

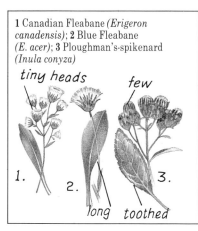

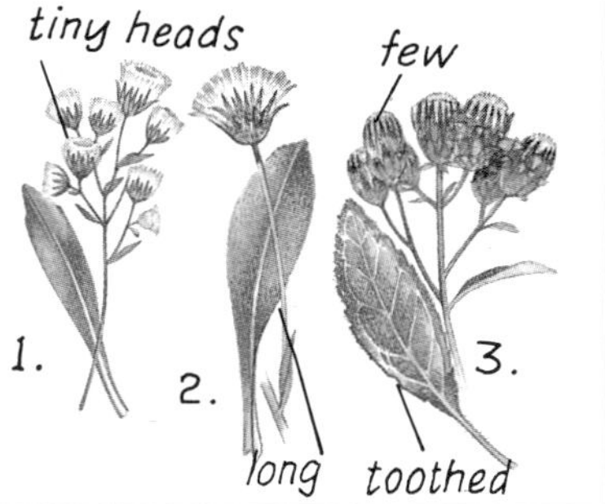

	HEMP-AGRIMONY
Type	perennial
Height	30–120cm, rarely 175cm
Habitat	banks of rivers, streams, marshes, woods; damp places
Flowering	July–September
	STEMS AND LEAVES
Stem	upright, few branches
Root	woody stock
Hairs	short, almost throughout
Stipules	absent
Leaves	paired on stem, to 100mm, divided into 3, rarely 5, elliptical parts, pointed, toothed; lowest undivided
Leaf-stalk	much shorter than blade

	FLOWERS
Position	heads of 5–6 tiny flowers (florets) surrounded by bracts, in broad, flattish clusters
Bracts	purplish around head; none between florets
Type	florets ⚥, 4.5–7mm, tubular
Size	heads 5–8mm
Colour	pale reddish purple or pink
Stalk	absent; short under heads
Sepals	a ring of hairs
Petals	5, joined, tubular, lobes equal
Stamens	5, joined into tube
Stigma	1, 2-lobed; style long
Ovary	1, below petals, 1-celled
	FRUIT
Type	1, dry, nut-like, 5-angled, with parachute of hairs
Size	2.5–3mm
Seeds	1, not released

This late-flowering plant is common in hilly places on dry grassland, cliffs and among rocks, but is rarely seen in lowland areas of the south. Long clusters of golden-yellow flower-heads contrast with the dark foliage and often blackish stems. Goldenrod was widely used as a wound-herb and was formerly in great demand. *Status:* native; almost throughout area, sometimes common. *Similar species:* Canadian Goldenrod has many more, smaller flower-heads, arranged on almost horizontal branches. This garden plant has often escaped and can be abundant around towns on railway embankments and disused sidings.

Canadian Goldenrod *(S. canadensis)*

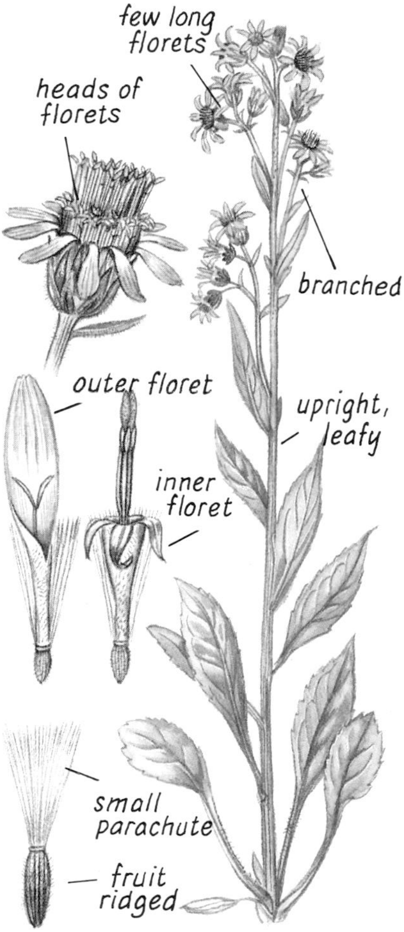

GOLDENROD	
Type	perennial
Height	5–75cm, rarely 100cm
Habitat	grassy places, cliffs, rocks, woods; dry soils
Flowering	July–September

STEMS AND LEAVES	
Stem	upright, branched above
Root	stout stock
Hairs	absent or short
Stipules	absent
Leaves	spirally placed on stem, 20–100mm, rarely 300mm, oval to elliptical, pointed, toothed
Leaf-stalk	short or absent

FLOWERS	
Position	daisy-like heads of tiny flowers (florets) surrounded by bracts, in long clusters
Bracts	4.5–8mm, narrow, yellowish green around head; none between florets
Type 1	inner florets ⚥, 10–30, 4–6mm, tubular
Type 2	outer florets ♀, 6–12, 6–9mm, strap-shaped
Size	heads 8–20mm
Colour	yellow
Stalk	absent; short under heads
Sepals	a ring of hairs
Petals	5, joined, tubular, lobes equal or very unequal
Stamens	5, joined into tube
Stigma	1, 2-lobed; style long
Ovary	1, below petals, 1-celled

FRUIT	
Type	1, dry, nut-like, ribbed, with parachute of hairs
Size	3–4mm
Seeds	1, not released

Daisy *Bellis perennis*

Familiar to children as a favourite flower for picking, and the raw material for daisy-chains, this plant is also known to gardeners as a pernicious weed that is almost impossible to eradicate from lawns. The flower-heads, carried singly above a rosette of leaves, close at night or in dull weather and provide the origin of the common name ('day's-eye'). *Status:* native; very common, throughout area. *Similar species:* Mexican Fleabane has flower-heads similar to the Daisy, but longer, branched stems with small leaves. Often escaping from cultivation, this plant forms small, bushy mounds on old walls.

Mexican Fleabane *(Erigeron mucronatus)*

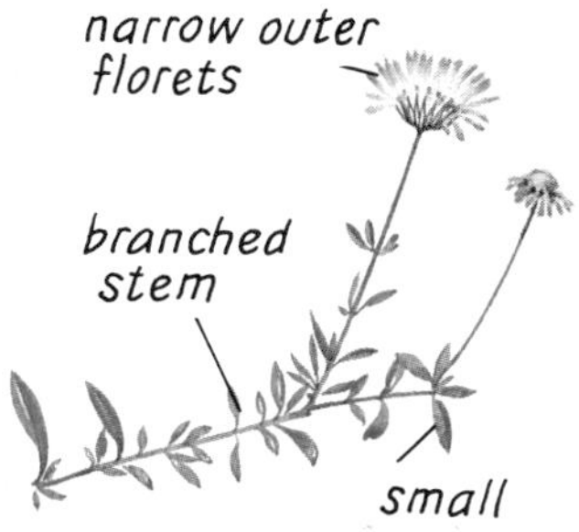

	DAISY
Type	perennial
Height	3–20cm
Habitat	short grassland
Flowering	March–October
	STEMS AND LEAVES
Stem	short; flower-heads stalked
Root	stout, fibrous; short stock
Hairs	rather sparse
Stipules	absent
Leaves	rosette at base, 20–40mm, rarely 80mm, oval to spoon-shaped, rounded, toothed
Leaf-stalk	shorter than blade
	FLOWERS
Position	solitary heads of tiny flowers (florets) surrounded by bracts
Bracts	3–5mm, oblong, blunt around head; none between florets
Type 1	inner florets ⚥, 2–3mm, tubular
Type 2	outer florets ♀, 4–8mm, strap-shaped
Size	heads 16–25mm
Colour	inner florets yellow, outer white, often tinged red
Stalk	absent; 3–20mm under heads
Sepals	a ring of hairs
Petals	5, joined, tubular, lobes equal or very unequal
Stamens	5, joined into tube
Stigma	1, 2-lobed; style long
Ovary	1, below petals, 1-celled
	FRUIT
Type	dry, nut-like, flattened, hairy, without parachute
Size	1.5–2mm
Seeds	1, not released

Tiny white and yellow flower-heads of Gallant Soldier resemble miniature Daisies. This weed of gardens, arable fields and waste ground is so widespread that it appears native, although it was introduced from South America to botanic gardens in Europe during the latter part of the eighteenth century. The common name is merely a corruption of the botanical name. *Status:* introduced, naturalized; common weed, much of area. *Similar species:* Shaggy Soldier has a similar history and appearance, but can be distinguished by the hairy stems and spear-shaped scales between the florets.

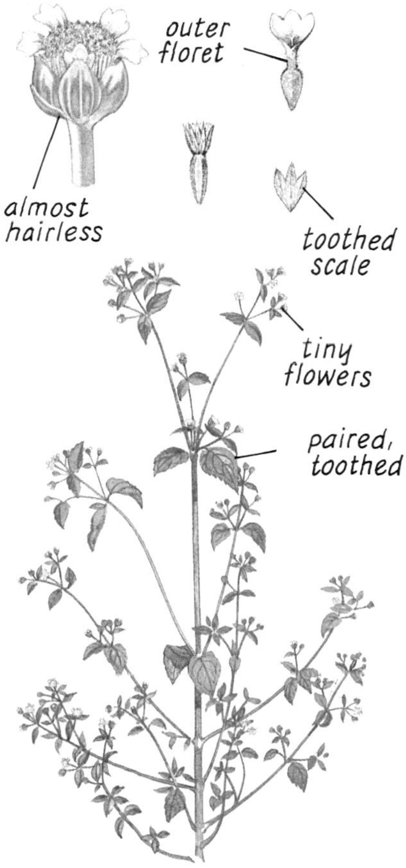

Shaggy Soldier *(Galinsoga ciliata)*

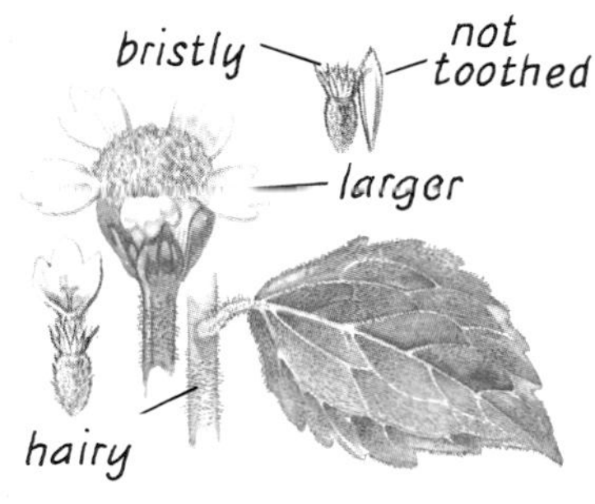

	GALLANT SOLDIER
Type	annual
Height	10–75cm
Habitat	cultivated and waste ground
Flowering	May–October
	STEMS AND LEAVES
Stem	upright, many-branched
Root	fibrous
Hairs	almost absent
Stipules	absent
Leaves	paired on stem, 50–90mm, oval, pointed, toothed
Leaf-stalk	shorter than blade
	FLOWERS
Position	few, daisy-like heads of tiny flowers (florets) surrounded by bracts
Bracts	2.5–4mm, oval, under head; 3-lobed scales between florets
Type 1	inner florets ⚥, few, 2–3mm, tubular
Type 2	outer florets ♀, 4–8, 3–4.5mm, broad, 3-toothed
Size	heads 3–5mm
Colour	inner florets yellow, outer white
Stalk	absent; short under heads
Sepals	8–20, narrow, scale-like
Petals	5, joined, tubular, lobes equal or very unequal
Stamens	5, joined into tube
Stigma	1, 2-lobed; style long
Ovary	1, below petals, 1-celled
	FRUIT
Type	1, dry, nut-like, egg-shaped, with silvery, scale-like sepals at tip
Size	1–1.5mm
Seeds	1, not released

Common Cudweed *Filago vulgaris*

A curious member of the Daisy family, it has woolly stems and clusters of tiny yellowish flower-heads. On robust plants, the stem branches immediately below a flower-cluster and the branch turns upright to bear a second cluster of heads. The common name derives from the practice of feeding the plant to cattle. *Status:* native; fairly common, most of area except extreme north. *Similar species:* Small Cudweed has narrower leaves and few flower-heads in a cluster. Two species have larger, spreading leaves. Marsh Cudweed has several leaves surrounding each cluster of heads; and Heath Cudweed is a perennial with spikes of heads.

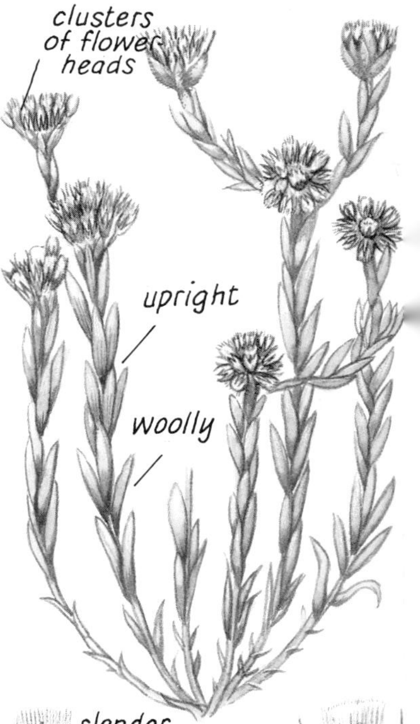

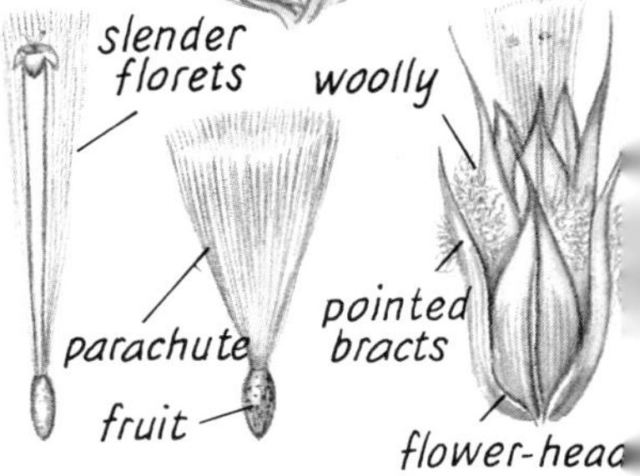

1 Small Cudweed *(F. minima)*; **2** Marsh Cudweed *(Gnaphalium uliginosum)*; **3** Heath Cudweed *(G. sylvaticum)*

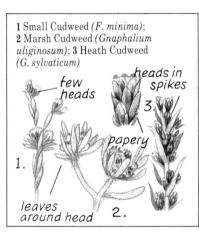

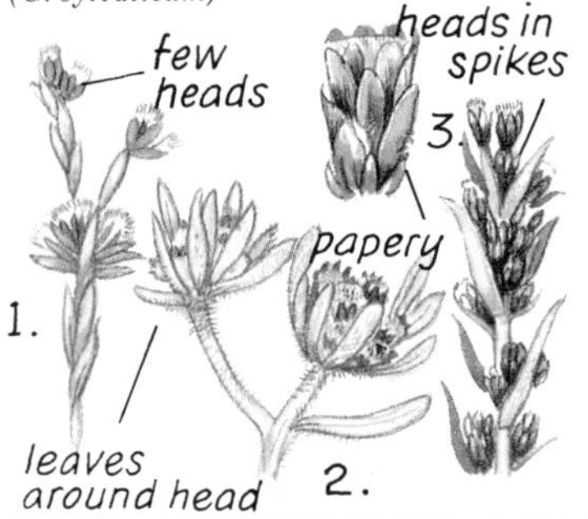

	COMMON CUDWEED
Type	annual
Height	5–39cm, rarely 45cm
Habitat	grassy places; dry soils
Flowering	July–August
	STEMS AND LEAVES
Stem	upright, some branched
Root	fibrous
Hairs	woolly, whitish
Stipules	absent
Leaves	spirally around stem, 10–30mm, spear-shaped, blunt, upright, edge often wavy
Leaf-stalk	absent
	FLOWERS
Position	heads of flowers (florets) enclosed by bracts, 20–35 in cluster at stem-tip
Bracts	4–4.5mm under head, outer woolly, inner yellowish, papery; none between florets
Type 1	inner florets ⚥, 1–4, 3–4mm, tubular
Type 2	outer florets ♀, 20–25, 4–4.5mm, tubular, very thin
Size	heads 4–5mm wide; clusters 10–12mm
Colour	yellow
Stalk	absent, heads stalkless
Sepals	a ring of hairs
Petals	5, joined, lobes equal
Stamens	5, joined into tube
Stigma	1, 2-lobed; style long
Ovary	1, below petals, 1-celled
	FRUIT
Type	nut-like, some with parachute
Size	0.6–0.7mm
Seeds	1, not released

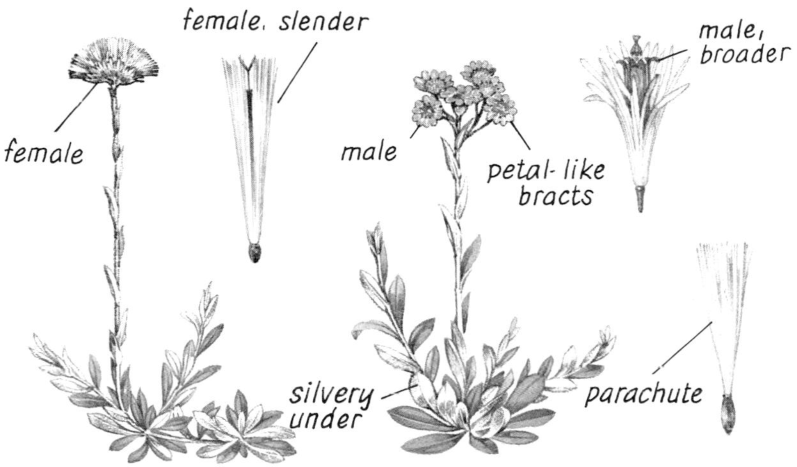

A small plant of mountains, or lower altitudes in the north. The flower-heads are enclosed by pink or white papery bracts which keep their form and colour after drying, hence the common name. Male and female flowers are on separate plants. *Status:* native; much of area, most common in north, mostly in mountains in south. *Similar species:* other species do not have male and female plants. Everlasting, of dry, sandy places in the south-east, has almost globular, yellow or orange flower-heads. Pearly Everlasting, an escaped garden plant, is more robust and has pearly-white bracts.

1 Everlasting *(Helichrysum arenarium)*; 2 Pearly Everlasting *(Anaphalis margaritacea)*

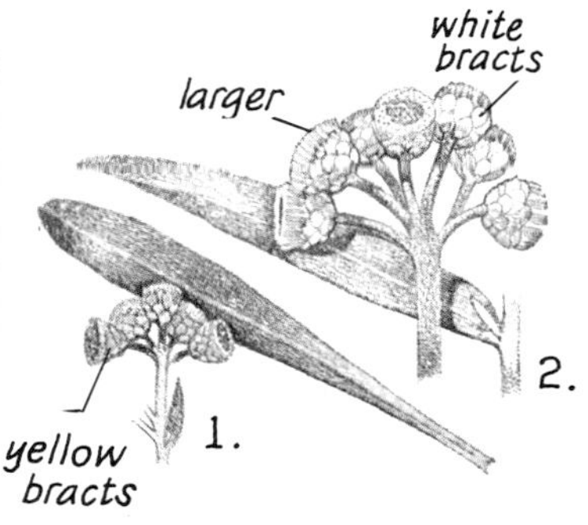

	MOUNTAIN EVERLASTING
Type	perennial
Height	5–20cm
Habitat	grassland, rocky slopes; dry, sandy or stony places
Flowering	June–July
	STEMS AND LEAVES
Stem	creeping, mat-forming; flowering stems upright
Root	woody stock, stems root
Hairs	woolly except above leaves
Stipules	absent
Leaves	basal or spiral on stem, 5–40mm, lower oval, broad-tipped, upper narrow, upright, edge unbroken
Leaf-stalk	short or absent
	FLOWERS
Position	♂ and ♀ on different plants; 2–8 daisy-like heads of florets
Bracts	many under head, woolly-based, papery, ♂ broad, petal-like; ♀ narrow; none between florets
Type 1	♂, 4–5mm, funnel-shaped
Type 2	♀, 6–7mm, very slender
Size	♂ heads 8–12mm; ♀ 5–7mm
Colour	white or pink
Stalk	absent; short under heads
Sepals	hair-like; ♂ thick-tipped
Petals	5, tubular, lobes equal
Stamens	5, joined into tube
Stigma	1, 2-lobed; style long
Ovary	1, below petals, 1-celled
	FRUIT
Type	nut-like, with parachute
Size	1–1.5mm
Seeds	1, not released

Common Fleabane *Pulicaria dysenterica*

A common, yellow, daisy-like plant of places where water stands for some of the year. Common Fleabane was used to repel fleas, and stems of the plant were strewn on floors for this purpose. Dried and burned, it acted as an insecticide against midges. The plant was also used to treat dysentery. *Status:* native; common, most of area. *Similar species:* Small Fleabane is annual, and has smaller flower-heads with very short outer florets. Elecampane has broad leaves and much larger flower-heads with broad bracts. Leopard's-bane has heart-shaped, long-stalked lower leaves and large flower-heads with fewer, long bracts.

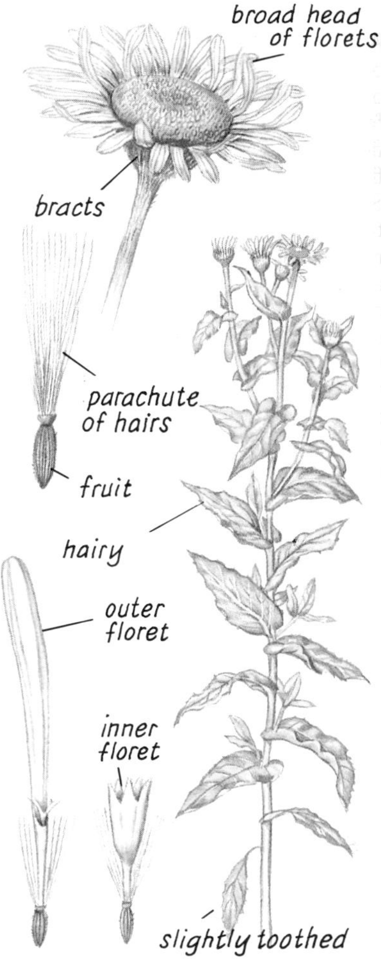

1 Small Fleabane *(P. vulgaris)*;
2 Elecampane *(Inula helenium)*;
3 Leopard's-bane *(Doronicum pardalianches)*

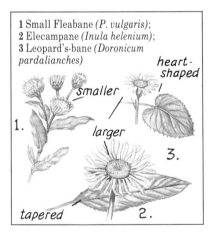

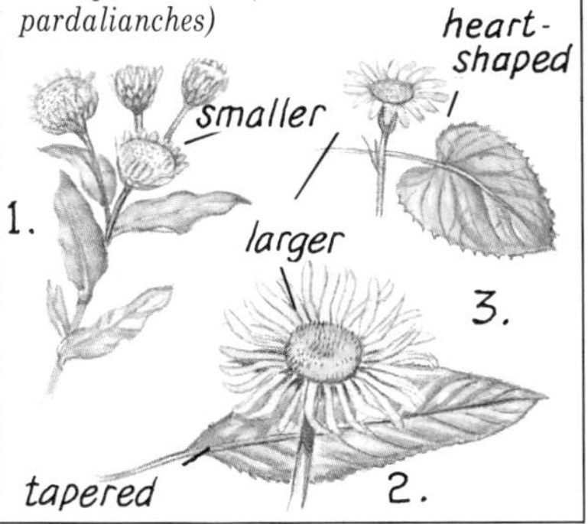

	COMMON FLEABANE
Type	perrenial
Height	20–60cm
Habitat	stream banks, meadows, marshes; damp places
Flowering	August–September
	STEMS AND LEAVES
Stem	upright, branched above
Root	fibrous; stems rooting
Hairs	sparse on stem, dense under leaves
Stipules	absent
Leaves	spirally around stem, 30–80mm, oblong, edge hardly toothed; upper spear-shaped, broad-based
Leaf-stalk	short below, absent above
	FLOWERS
Position	daisy-like heads of florets surrounded by bracts
Bracts	many around head, thin, hairy; none between florets
Type 1	inner ⚥, 5–6mm, tubular
Type 2	outer florets ♀, numerous, 8–11mm, very narrow, flat
Size	heads 15–30mm
Colour	yellow
Stalk	absent; to 25mm under heads
Sepals	a ring of hairs
Petals	5, joined, tubular, lobes equal or very unequal
Stamens	5, joined into tube
Stigma	1, 2-lobed; style long
Ovary	1, below petals, 1-celled
	FRUIT
Type	nut-like, oblong, ribbed, inner with parachute
Size	1.5–2mm
Seeds	1, not released

A waterside plant, often disregarded because the flower-heads lack the usual outer florets of daisy-relatives, and soon fade to brown. A variant with outer florets is much more attractive, and has flower-heads almost twice as large. Small, barbed bristles on the fruits stick to passing animals and are spread to new localities. *Status:* native; most of area, rarer in north. *Similar species:* two other species have divided leaves, upright flowers and fruits with two bristles. Trifid Bur-marigold has mostly three-lobed leaves and barbed angles on the fruits. Beggarticks has mostly five-lobed leaves and almost smooth-angled fruits.

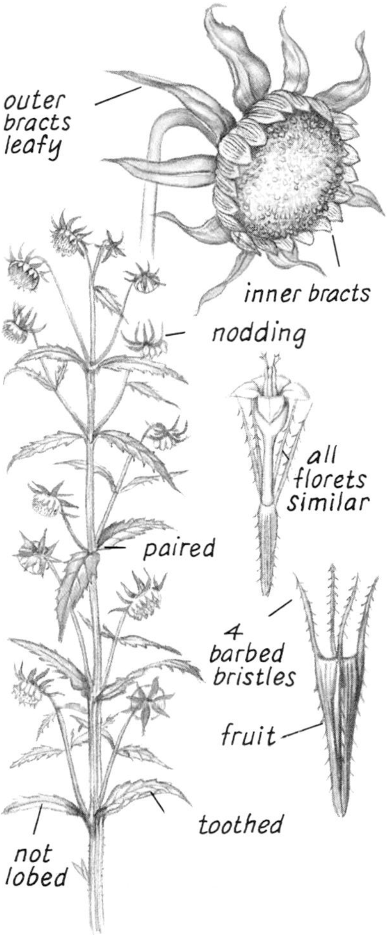

1 Trifid Bur-marigold *(B. tripartita)*;
2 Beggarticks *(B. frondosa)*

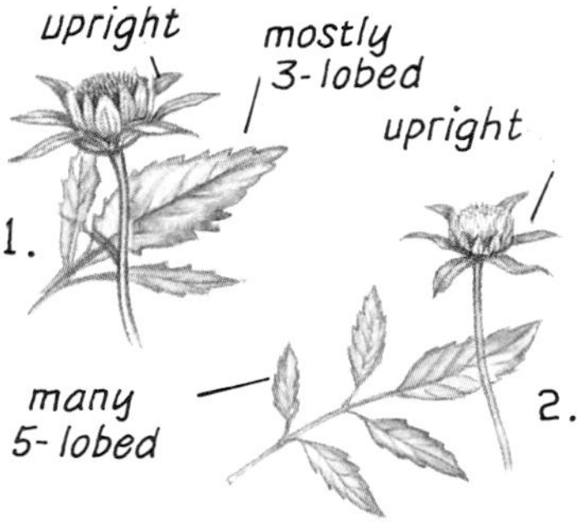

	NODDING BUR-MARIGOLD
Type	annual
Height	8–60cm
Habitat	ponds, streams; wet places
Flowering	July–September
	STEMS AND LEAVES
Stem	upright, branched above
Root	fibrous
Hairs	absent or sparse
Stipules	absent
Leaves	paired on stem, 40–150mm, spear-shaped, pointed, toothed
Leaf-stalk	absent
	FLOWERS
Position	daisy-like heads of florets enclosed by bracts, nodding
Bracts	2 rows around head, outer leaf-like, inner oval, papery, dark-streaked; scale-like between florets
Type 1	inner florets ⚥, many, 6–7mm, tubular
Type 2	outer rarely present, sterile, 10–12mm, flattened
Size	heads 15–25mm, rarely 45mm
Colour	yellow
Stalk	absent; long under heads
Sepals	4, bristle-like
Petals	5, joined, tubular, lobes equal, rarely very unequal
Stamens	5, joined into tube
Stigma	1, 2-lobed; style long
Ovary	1, below petals, 1-celled
	FRUIT
Type	nut-like, 4-angled, tip with 4 barbed bristles
Size	5–6mm
Seeds	1, not released

Yarrow *Achillea millefolium*

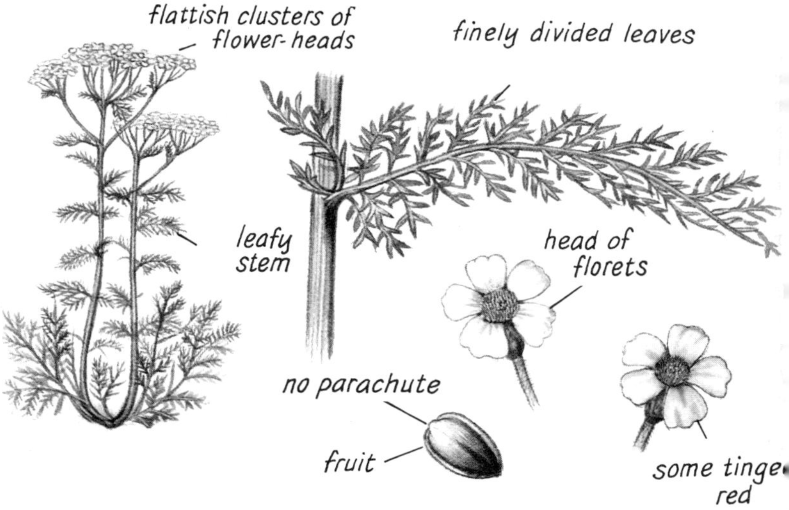

A common plant of road-verges, easily identified by the broad, flat clusters of small daisy-like flower-heads and feathery foliage. The cluster of heads functions as a single, large flower and attracts many insects, including beetles, butterflies and hover-flies. It has had many medicinal uses. Related species are grown in gardens for use as 'everlasting' flowers. *Status:* native; common, throughout area. *Similar species:* Sneezewort is readily distinguished by its undivided leaves and less numerous, much larger flower-heads. Acrid leaves were used as a form of snuff and to relieve toothache.

Sneezewort *(A. ptarmica)*

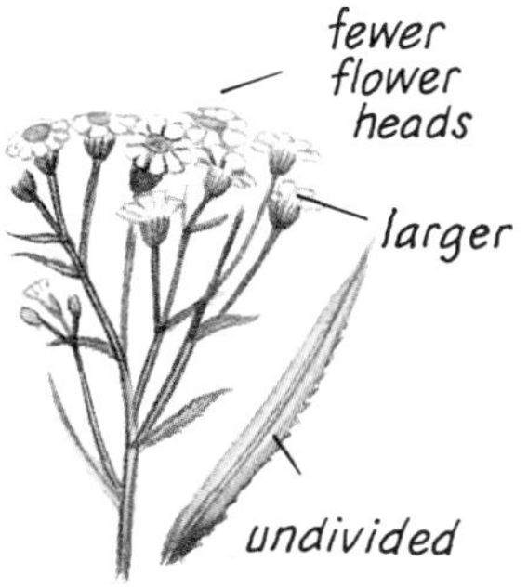

	YARROW
Type	perennial
Height	8–65cm
Habitat	grassy places; most soils
Flowering	June–August
	STEMS AND LEAVES
Stem	upright, grooved, branched above, strongly scented
Root	tap-root; stems root
Hairs	more or less woolly
Stipules	absent
Leaves	spirally arranged on stem, 50–160mm, oblong in outline, finely divided 2–3 times
Leaf-stalk	shorter than blade or absent above
	FLOWERS
Position	flat-topped clusters, many daisy-like heads of florets enclosed by bracts
Bracts	dark-edged around heads; scale-like between florets
Type 1	inner ⚥, 2–3mm, tubular
Type 2	outer florets ♀, 4–5mm, broad, 3-toothed
Size	heads 4–6mm wide
Colour	white or tinged red
Stalk	absent; short under heads
Sepals	absent
Petals	5, joined, tubular, lobes equal or very unequal
Stamens	5, joined into tube
Stigma	1, 2-lobed; style long
Ovary	1, below petals, 1-celled
	FRUIT
Type	nut-like, flattened, shiny, blunt, without parachute
Size	1.5–2mm
Seeds	1, not released

. tall plant with deeply divided dark-reen leaves, silvery beneath, and ranched clusters of insignificant eddish-brown flower-heads. Common long roadsides, it often has a dusty, eglected look. In ancient times it was elieved to have powerful magical roperties. Mugwort had many uses, as herbalist medicine, to repel insects, to avour ale, or as a herb for stuffing ucks and geese. *Status:* native; ommon, throughout area. *Similar pecies:* Wormwood has silky hairs on oth sides of the leaves and wider ower-heads. Sea Wormwood has trongly scented woolly leaves, cut into ery narrow segments.

1 Wormwood *(A. absinthium)*; **2** Sea Wormwood *(A. maritima)*

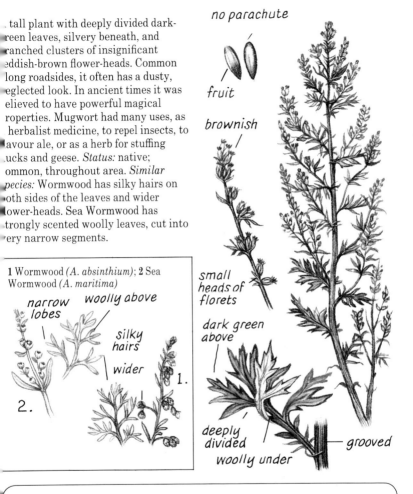

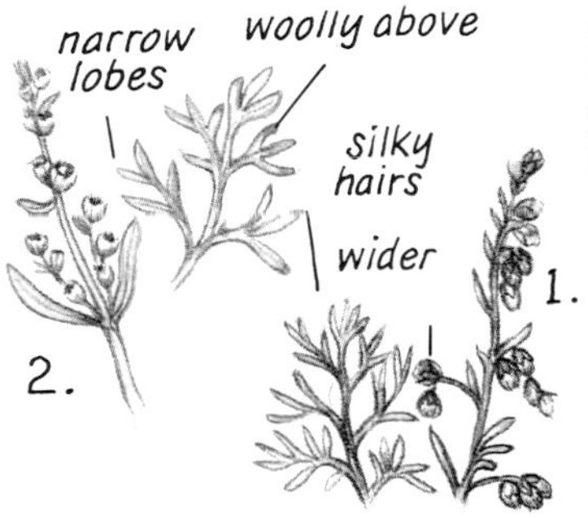

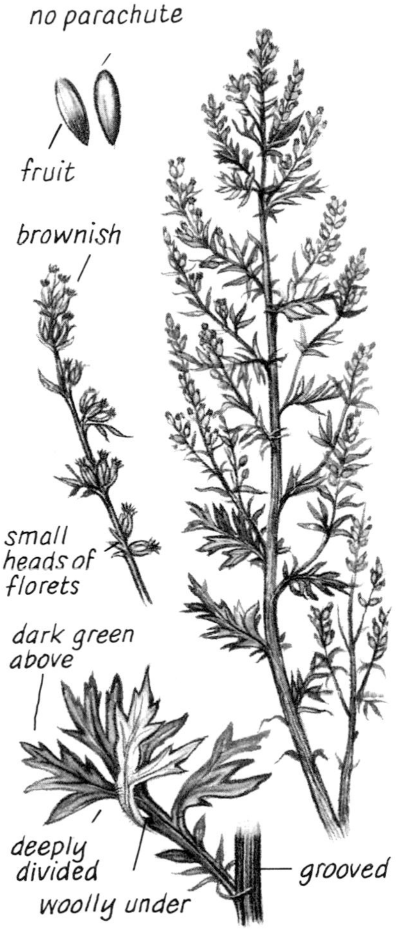

	MUGWORT
Type	perennial
Height	60–120cm, rarely 210cm
Habitat	waste ground, hedgerows
Flowering	July–September
	STEMS AND LEAVES
Stem	upright, grooved, reddish
Root	branched stock
Hairs	white; woolly under leaves
Stipules	absent
Leaves	spirally arranged on stem, 50–80mm, deeply lobed and toothed, lower broad, upper smaller, broad-based
Leaf-stalk	short or absent
	FLOWERS
Position	large, branched clusters of daisy-like heads with florets enclosed by bracts

Bracts	2.5–3mm around head, papery-edged; none between florets
Type 1	inner florets ⚥, 2–3mm, tubular, broader above
Type 2	outer florets ♀, 2–3mm, very narrowly tubular
Size	heads 3–4mm
Colour	reddish brown
Stalk	absent; short under heads
Sepals	absent
Petals	5, tubular, lobes equal
Stamens	5, joined into tube
Stigma	1, 2-lobed; style long
Ovary	1, below petals, 1-celled
	FRUIT
Type	nut-like, cylindrical, smooth, without parachute
Size	1–1.5mm
Seeds	1, not released

Scentless Mayweed *Tripleurospermum inodorum*

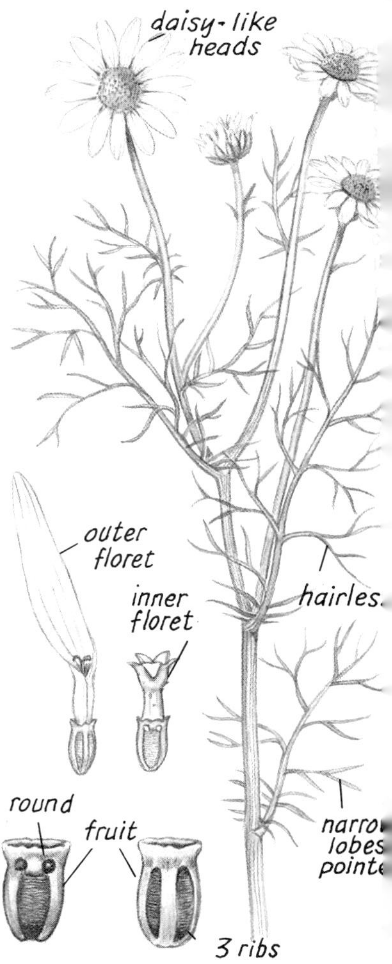

One of the Daisies of cornfields, that has large white and yellow flowers above finely divided leaves. Common on waste ground, it also colonizes new road-verges. *Status:* native; common, most of area. *Similar species:* Sea Mayweed is a low-growing coastal plant with shorter, fleshier leaf-segments. Both species have two brown oil-bearing glands on each fruit, but in this plant they are elongated, not round. Two species have flower-heads with a dome-shaped, hollow base and five-ribbed fruits. Scented Mayweed has pleasantly scented leaves. Pineappleweed has strong-smelling leaves and no outer florets.

1 Sea Mayweed *(T. maritimum)*; **2** Scented Mayweed *(Matricaria recutita)*; **3** Pineappleweed *(M. matricarioides)*

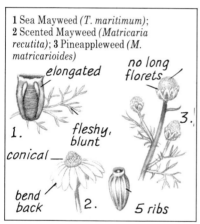

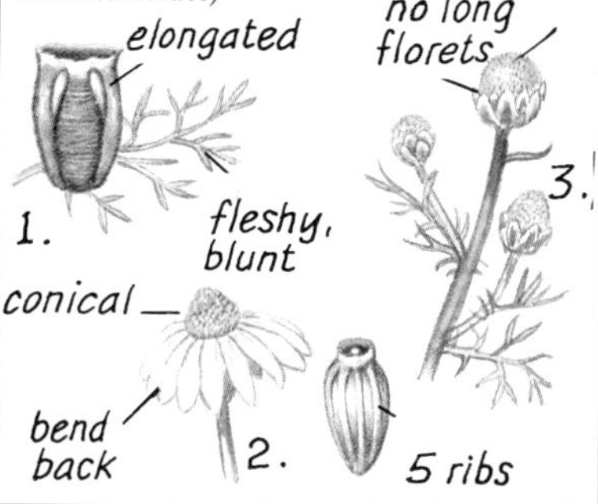

	SCENTLESS MAYWEED
Type	annual
Height	15–80cm
Habitat	cultivated and waste ground; most soils
Flowering	July–September
	STEMS AND LEAVES
Stem	upright, often branched
Root	fibrous
Hairs	absent
Stipules	absent
Leaves	spirally placed on stem, 20–100mm, finely divided 2–3 times into thin segments
Leaf-stalk	short or absent
	FLOWERS
Position	daisy-like heads of florets surrounded by bracts
Bracts	2 rows around head, oblong, papery-edged; none between florets
Type 1	inner florets ⚥, 3–4mm, tubular
Type 2	outer florets ♀, 12–22, 10–18mm, strap-shaped
Size	heads 15–45mm
Colour	yellow and white
Stalk	absent; long under heads
Sepals	an inconspicuous rim
Petals	5, joined, tubular, lobes equal or very unequal
Stamens	5, joined into tube
Stigma	1, 2-lobed; style long
Ovary	1, below petals, 1-celled
	FRUIT
Type	nut-like, oblong, 3-ribbed, without parachute
Size	2–3mm
Seeds	1, not released

ne of several white and yellow Daisies f the cornfield, distinguished from the layweeds by the scales betweeen the orets. Another distinction is in the hort, relatively broad leaf-segments, hich are almost woolly beneath when oung. *Status:* native; most of area, ometimes common. *Similar species:* tinking Chamomile is strong-smelling, nd has narrow scales between the lorets and rough fruits. It was a hated veed in the days of hand-scythes ecause it blistered the hands at arvest-time. Chamomile is a perennial vith sparsely-ribbed fruits rounded at he top. It is widely used to make Chamomile tea.

1 Stinking Chamomile *(A. cotula)*;
2 Chamomile *(Chamaemelum nobile)*

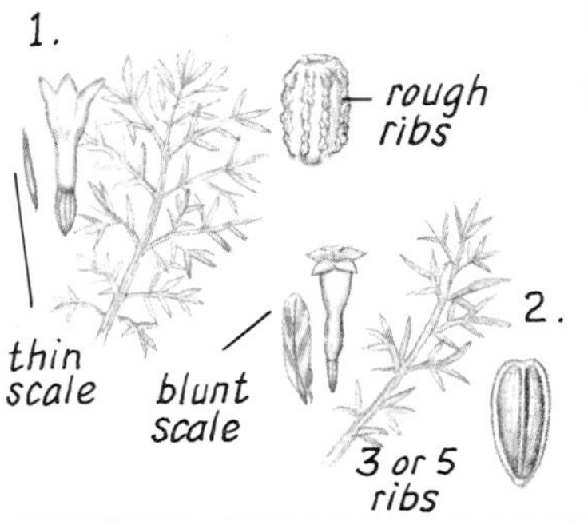

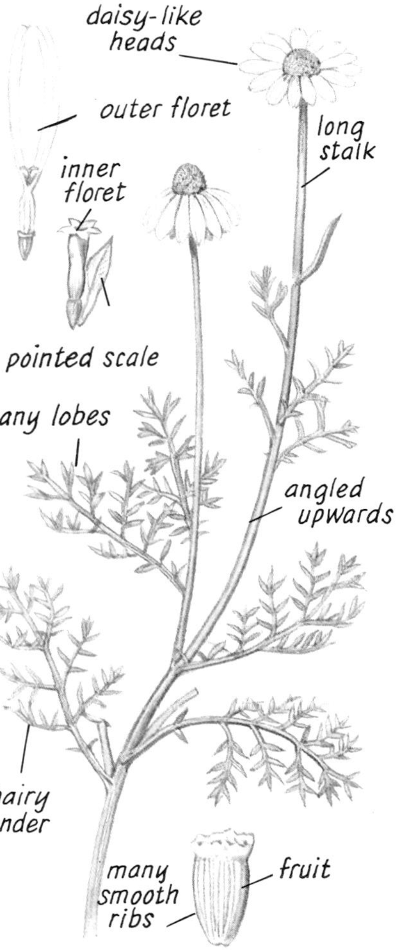

	CORN CHAMOMILE
Type	annual, slightly scented
Height	12–80cm
Habitat	cultivated and waste ground; lime-rich soils
Flowering	June–July
	STEMS AND LEAVES
Stem	angled upwards, many-branched
Root	fibrous
Hairs	fairly dense under leaves
Stipules	absent
Leaves	spirally arranged, 15–50mm, divided 1–3 times into short, narrow segments
Leaf-stalk	short or absent
	FLOWERS
Position	daisy-like heads of florets surrounded by bracts
Bracts	papery-edged around head; spear-shaped, long-pointed between florets
Type 1	inner ⚥, 3–4mm, tubular
Type 2	outer florets ♀, 5–14mm, strap-shaped
Size	heads 20–30mm
Colour	yellow and white
Stalk	absent; long under heads
Sepals	an inconspicuous rim
Petals	5, joined, tubular, lobes equal or very unequal
Stamens	5, joined into tube
Stigma	1, 2-lobed; style long
Ovary	1, below petals, 1-celled
	FRUIT
Type	nut-like, oblong, 10-ribbed, without parachute
Size	2–3mm
Seeds	1, not released

Tansy *Tanacetum vulgare*

A tall perennial, commonly seen by roadsides, with deeply-cut dark-green leaves and flattish clusters of button-like flower-heads. It was formerly used as an insecticide, rubbed over meat to keep flies away or strewn on floors. Medicinally, it was taken to destroy roundworms. It is still widely grown both for ornament and as a pot-herb. *Status:* native, naturalized in Ireland; most of area, most common in south. *Similar species:* Feverfew has broader lobes to the leaves and less dense clusters of flower-heads with white outer florets. It is sometimes taken for relief from migraines.

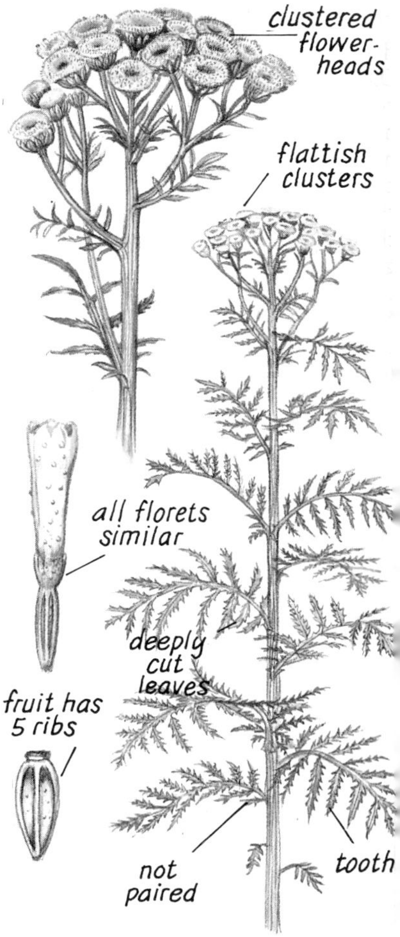

Feverfew *(T. parthenium)*

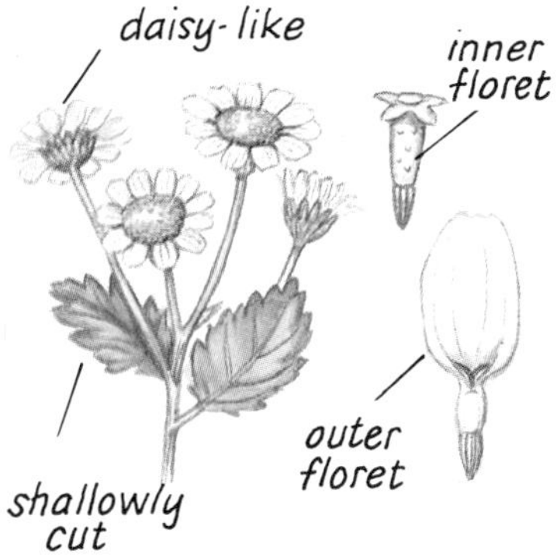

	TANSY
Type	perennial, strong-smelling
Height	30–150cm
Habitat	hedge-banks, waste ground
Flowering	July–September
	STEMS AND LEAVES
Stem	upright, often reddish
Root	creeping stock
Hairs	almost absent
Stipules	absent
Leaves	spirally on stem, 150–250mm, cut 1–2 times into paired, narrow, toothed lobes
Leaf-stalk	short or absent
	FLOWERS
Position	flattish clusters of daisy-like heads, the florets enclosed by bracts
Bracts	papery-edged around head; none between florets
Type 1	inner ⚥, 4–5mm, tubular
Type 2	outer florets ♀, 3.5–4mm, tubular or short flat part
Size	heads 7–12mm
Colour	deep yellow
Stalk	absent; short under heads
Sepals	inconspicuous rim
Petals	5, joined, tubular, lobes equal or slightly unequal
Stamens	5, joined into tube
Stigma	1, 2-lobed; style long
Ovary	1, below petals, 1-celled
	FRUIT
Type	nut-like, 5-ribbed, blunt-tipped, without parachute
Size	1.5–1.8mm
Seeds	1, not released

One of the most familiar of all Summer flowers, the large white and yellow Daisies adorning mile after mile of roadside, railway embankment and meadows. The long, unbranched stems make it a favourite ingredient in a bunch of wild flowers. It is related to the larger Shasta Daisy, originally from the Pyrenees and widely cultivated in gardens. *Status:* native; almost throughout area, very common in south. *Similar species:* Corn Marigold has branched stems and more deeply lobed leaves, but is most easily distinguished by the bright yellow outer florets. The fruits of the outer florets are flattened, with wing-like sides.

Corn Marigold *(Chrysanthemum segetum)*

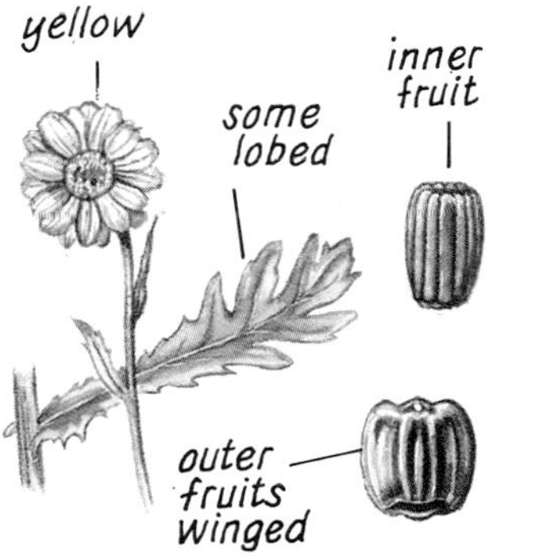

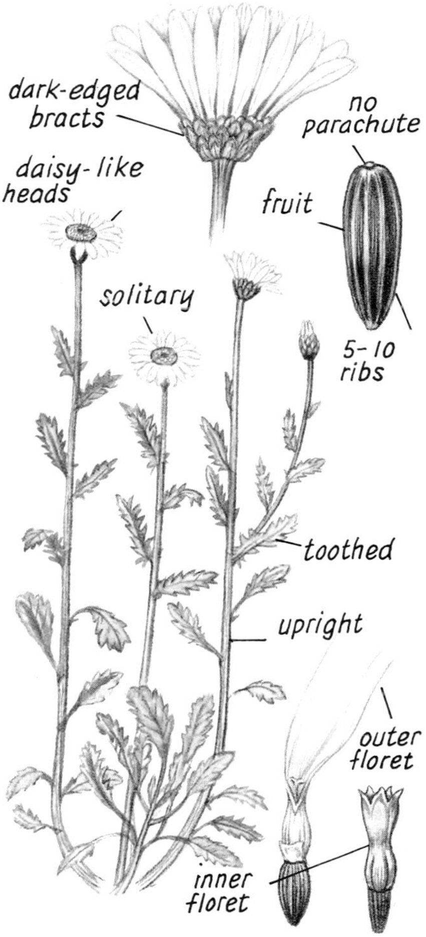

	OXEYE DAISY
Type	perennial
Height	20–100cm
Habitat	grassland; most soils
Flowering	June–August
	STEMS AND LEAVES
Stem	upright, rarely branched
Root	woody stock
Hairs	sparse or almost absent
Stipules	absent
Leaves	spirally arranged on stem, 15–120mm, lower rounded or oval, upper oblong, toothed or lobed, broad-based
Leaf-stalk	long on non-flowering stems, absent above
	FLOWERS
Position	solitary, daisy-like heads, florets enclosed by bracts
Bracts	dark, papery-edged around head; none between florets
Type 1	inner ⚥, 4–5mm, tubular
Type 2	outer florets ♀, 10–20mm, strap-shaped
Size	heads 25–50mm
Colour	white and yellow
Stalk	absent; long under heads
Sepals	absent or scale-like
Petals	5, joined, tubular, lobes equal or very unequal
Stamens	5, joined into tube
Stigma	1, 2-lobed; style long
Ovary	1, below petals, 1-celled
	FRUIT
Type	nut-like, cylindrical or slightly flattened, with 5–10 ribs, without parachute
Size	2–3mm
Seeds	1, not released

Colt's-foot *Tussilago farfara*

One of the earliest Spring flowers with clumps of scaly, purplish stems, each ending in a yellow flower-head. It rivals bulbous plants for early flowering because it has thick underground stems that store food. Large leaves arise direct from the ground after the flowers, each initially covered with thick, felt-like hairs and opening to make a dense, shady canopy beneath which few other plants survive. *Status:* native; very common, most of area. *Similar species:* Butterbur has thick flowering stems with many pink flower-heads and even larger, Rhubarb-like leaves. Winter Heliotrope has few, larger, vanilla-scented flower-heads.

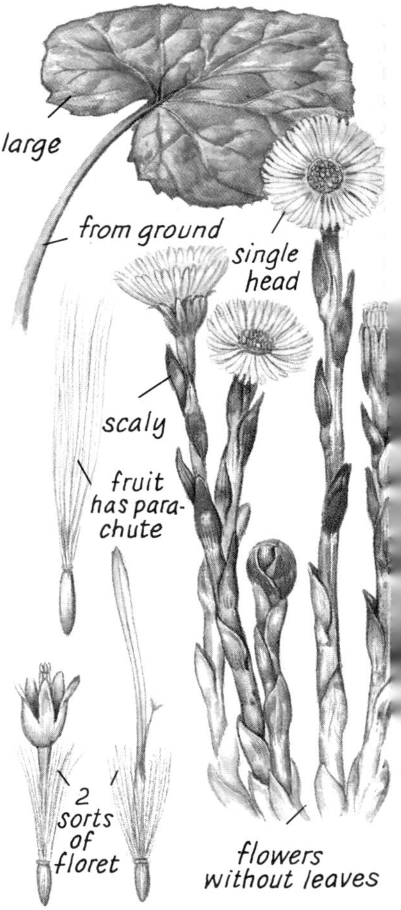

1 Butterbur *(Petasites hybridus)*;
2 Winter Heliotrope *(P. fragrans)*

	COLT'S-FOOT
Type	perennial
Height	5–15cm
Habitat	cultivated or waste ground, shingle; often clay soils
Flowering	March–April
	STEMS AND LEAVES
Stem	flowering stem upright, scaly, leafless, purplish
Root	creeping, underground stem
Hairs	stems woolly; felt-like hairs mainly under leaves
Stipules	absent
Leaves	from ground after flowers, 100–300mm, rounded or 5–12 angles, base heart-shaped
Leaf-stalk	about equals blade, grooved
	FLOWERS
Position	solitary daisy-like head of florets enclosed by bracts
Bracts	mostly 1 row around head, blunt; none between florets
Type 1	few inner ♂, 7–8mm, tubular
Type 2	outer florets ♀, up to 300, 6–15mm, flattened, narrow
Size	heads 15–35mm
Colour	bright yellow
Stalk	absent; short under head
Sepals	a ring of hairs
Petals	5, joined, tubular, lobes equal or very unequal
Stamens	5, joined into tube
Stigma	1, 2-lobed; style long
Ovary	1, below petals, 1-celled
	FRUIT
Type	nut-like, cylindrical, with parachute of long hairs
Size	5–10mm
Seeds	1, not released

A rather coarse-textured plant with dull, purplish flowers, although it is familiar to children for the flowering and fruiting heads. These cling with equal efficiency to woolly clothing or to the fur of animals, the latter being the plant's normal mode of dispersal. *Status:* native; common, throughout area. *Similar species:* two very similar plants have slightly larger flower-heads, the florets of which are not longer than the bracts. *A. pubens* has stalked heads with pale bracts, and *A. nemorosum* has more globular, darker, almost stalkless heads. Greater Burdock has larger, long-stalked heads but does not have hollow leaf-stalks.

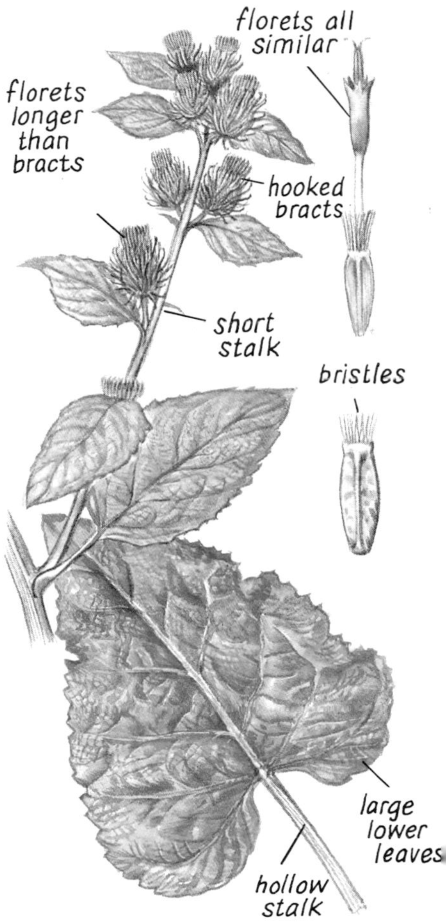

1 Greater Burdock *(A. lappa)*;
2 Lesser Burdock *(A. pubens)*;
3 Lesser Burdock *(A. nemorosum)*

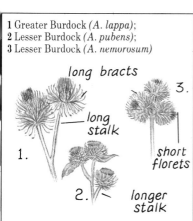

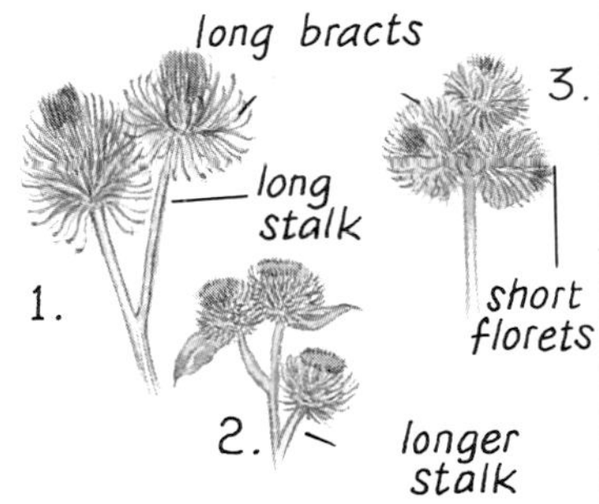

LESSER BURDOCK

Type biennial
Height 60–130cm
Habitat waste ground, hedges, woods
Flowering July–September

STEMS AND LEAVES

Stem upright, grooved, often reddish, many-branched
Root stout tap-root
Hairs on stems and under leaves
Stipules absent
Leaves spirally on stem, 30–400mm, most oval, pointed, often toothed, base heart-shaped
Leaf-stalk lower long, hollow, upper short

FLOWERS

Position clusters of almost globular, thistle-like heads of florets enclosed by bracts
Bracts hooked, many under head, 10–13mm, shorter than florets; thin scales between florets
Type florets ⚥, 12–15mm, tubular
Size heads 15–18mm
Colour reddish purple
Stalk absent; short or absent under heads
Sepals bristle-like
Petals 5, joined, lobes equal
Stamens 5, joined into tube
Stigma 1, 2-lobed; style long
Ovary 1, below petals, 1-celled

FRUIT

Type nut-like, oblong, mottled, short bristles at tip
Size 5–7mm
Seeds 1, not released

Common Ragwort *Senecio jacobaea*

This relative of the Daisy causes problems in pasture because it is toxic to livestock. One of the few creatures to tolerate the poison is the Cinnabar moth, whose black and yellow caterpillars take over the plant's chemical defence, making them distasteful to birds. *Status:* native; most of area, often very common. *Similar species:* Hoary Ragwort has hairier leaves with more pointed lobes. Two plants with wider-branched clusters of flowers are Oxford Ragwort, an introduced species on waste ground, which has black-tipped bracts, and Marsh Ragwort, in wet places and with green bracts.

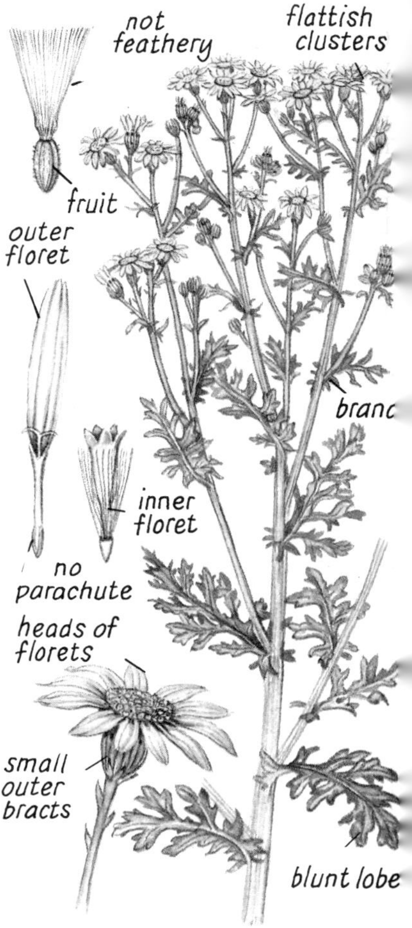

1 Oxford Ragwort *(S. squalidus)*;
2 Marsh Ragwort *(S. aquaticus)*;
3 Hoary Ragwort *(S. erucifolius)*

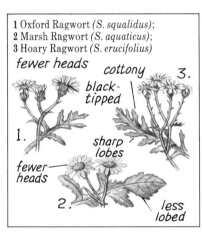

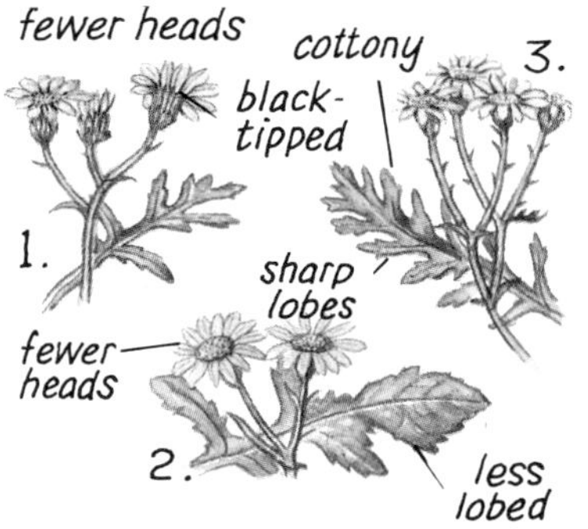

	COMMON RAGWORT
Type	biennial or perennial
Height	30–150cm
Habitat	grassy places, waste ground, dunes; most soils
Flowering	June–October
	STEMS AND LEAVES
Stem	upright, branched above
Root	short, upright stock
Hairs	none or sparse under leaves
Stipules	absent
Leaves	basal or spirally around stem, 25–200mm, cut into mostly blunt, toothed lobes, dark green
Leaf-stalk	short or absent
	FLOWERS
Position	dense, flat-topped clusters of daisy-like heads with florets enclosed by bracts
Bracts	oblong, pointed around head; none between florets
Type 1	inner ⚥, 5–6mm, tubular
Type 2	outer florets ♀, 12–15, 6–11mm, strap-shaped
Size	heads 15–25mm
Colour	deep yellow
Stalk	absent; short under heads
Sepals	a ring of hairs
Petals	5, joined, tubular, lobes equal or very unequal
Stamens	5, joined into tube
Stigma	1, 2-lobed; style long
Ovary	1, below petals, 1-celled
	FRUIT
Type	nut-like, 8-ribbed, inner with parachute of hairs
Size	1.5–2mm
Seeds	1, not released

One of the most familiar of garden weeds, multiplying rapidly by fruits which form even in the absence of pollinating insects and then survive many years in the soil. Silky parachutes carry tiny fruits aloft to colonize any piece of cleared ground. Some plants have a few strap-shaped florets at the edges of the flower-heads. *Status:* native; very common, throughout region, often a problematic weed. *Similar species:* Sticky Groundsel has sticky, strong-smelling foliage and fruit with hairless ribs. Heath Groundsel has outer bracts about half as long as the inner, and the fruit has stiffly hairy ribs.

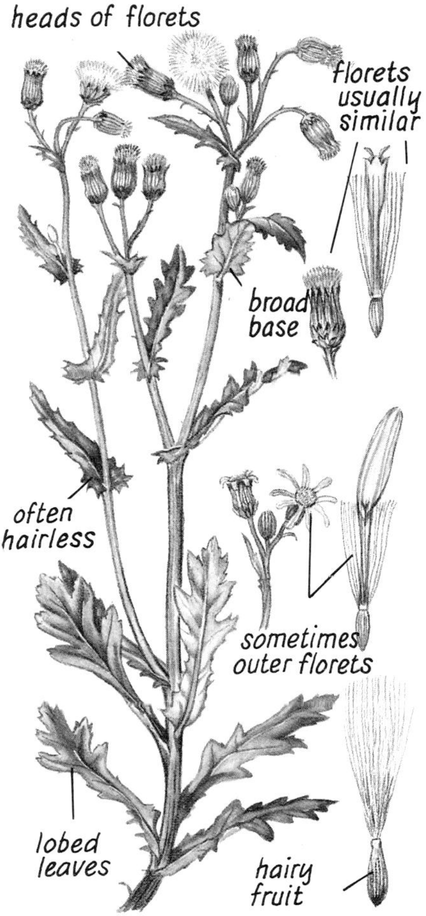

1 Sticky Groundsel *(S. viscosus)*;
2 Heath Groundsel *(S. sylvaticus)*

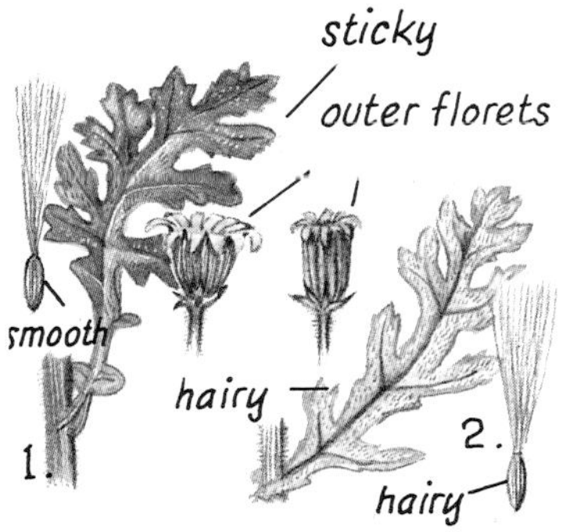

	GROUNDSEL
Type	annual
Height	8–45cm
Habitat	cultivated and waste ground
Flowering	January–December
	STEMS AND LEAVES
Stem	usually upright, rather succulent, few branches
Root	fibrous
Hairs	absent or slightly cottony
Stipules	absent
Leaves	spirally on stem, oblong, irregular, toothed lobes, blunt; upper broad-based
Leaf-stalk	absent or short
	FLOWERS
Position	cylindrical heads of florets, enclosed by bracts
Bracts	black-tipped around head; none between florets
Type 1	florets usually ⚥, 5–7mm, tubular
Type 2	outer florets sometimes present, ♀, up to 12, 8–10mm, strap-shaped
Size	heads 8–10mm, rarely 14mm
Colour	yellow
Stalk	absent; short under heads
Sepals	a ring of hairs
Petals	5, tubular, lobes usually equal
Stamens	5, joined, tube-like
Stigma	1, 2-lobed; style long
Ovary	1, below petals, 1-celled
	FRUIT
Type	dry, cylindrical, with hairy ribs, parachute of hairs
Size	1.5–2mm
Seeds	1, not released

Welted Thistle *Carduus acanthoides*

One of the small-flowered Thistles, this one is found most commonly in damp meadows, shady wood-margins and hedgerows. The flower-heads are popular with butterflies. *Status:* native; most common in south of area, absent from much of north. *Similar species:* Slender Thistle has long flower-heads with broader bracts, the whole head falling when the fruits ripen. Two other Thistles have fruits with feathery hairs to the parachute. Marsh Thistle has spiny-winged stems and rather narrow, sharply pointed leaves. Creeping Thistle is a problematic weed, with long, creeping, underground stems.

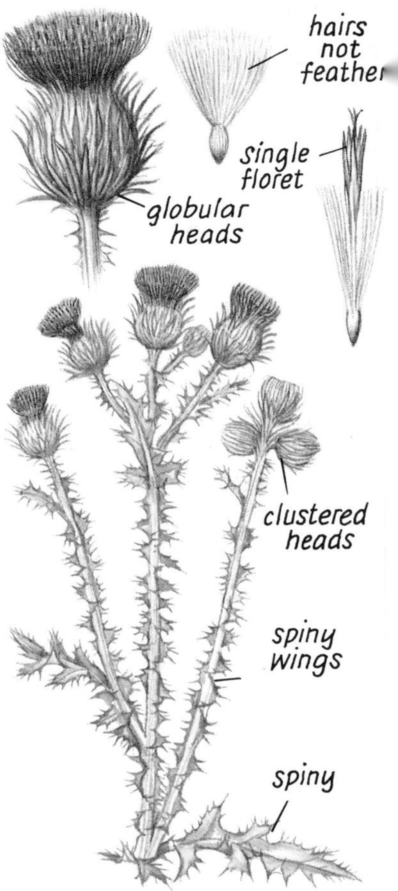

1 Slender Thistle *(C. tenuiflorus)*;
2 Marsh Thistle *(Cirsium palustre)*;
3 Creeping Thistle *(C. arvense)*

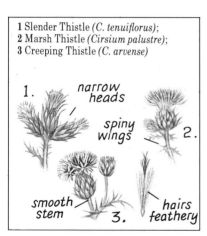

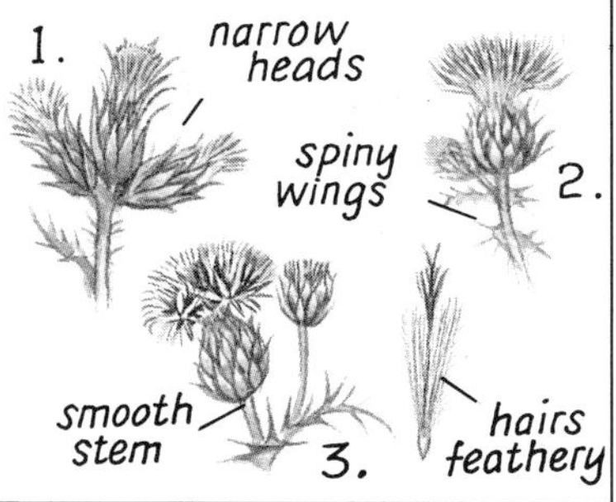

	WELTED THISTLE
Type	biennial
Height	30–150cm
Habitat	grassland, hedges, waste ground; damp soils
Flowering	June–August
	STEMS AND LEAVES
Stem	upright, branched, with wavy, spine-tipped wings
Root	slender tap-root
Hairs	sparse, on stems and bracts
Stipules	absent
Leaves	basal or spirally on stem, lobed, wavy, spiny; blade of upper joins stem-wings
Leaf-stalk	short below, upper absent
	FLOWERS
Position	almost globular heads of florets enclosed by bracts, mostly in small clusters
Bracts	many around head, narrow, spine-tipped; bristle-like between florets
Type	florets ⚥, 16–18mm, tubular
Size	heads 20–25mm
Colour	reddish purple or white
Stalk	absent; absent or short under heads
Sepals	a ring of hairs
Petals	5, joined, tubular, lobes slightly unequal
Stamens	5, joined into tube
Stigma	1, 2-lobed; style long
Ovary	1, below petals, 1-celled
	FRUIT
Type	nut-like, oblong, grooved, parachute of hairs 11–13mm
Size	3–4mm
Seeds	1, not released

A handsome plant with large, reddish-purple flower-heads above sharply spiny leaves. This is probably the plant adopted as a national emblem by Scottish kings. Thistle-down is light because the parachute usually detaches from the heavy nut-like base and floats away without effecting dispersal. *Status:* native; common, throughout area. *Similar species:* two other species have long, smooth stems below the flower-heads and softly prickly leaves with whitish hairs beneath. Melancholy Thistle has broad, rather blunt bracts; Meadow Thistle has smaller heads with spiny outer bracts. Musk Thistle has nodding flower-heads.

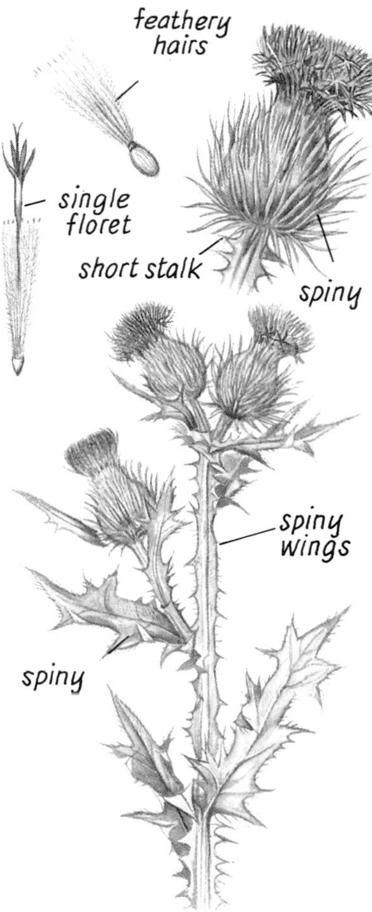

1 Melancholy Thistle *(C. helenioides)*; **2** Meadow Thistle *(C. dissectum)*; **3** Musk Thistle *(Carduus nutans)*

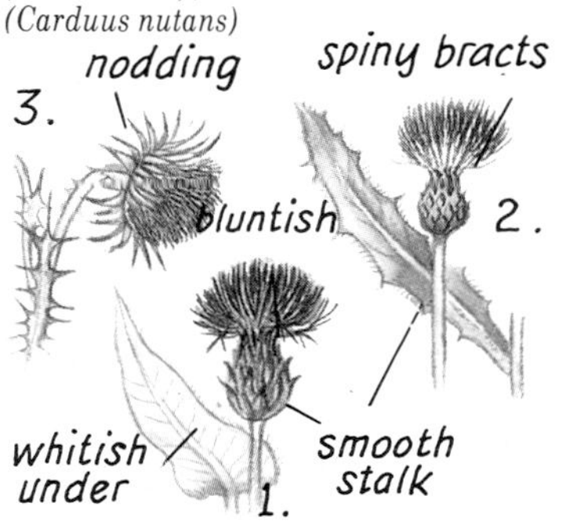

	SPEAR THISTLE
Type	biennial
Height	30–150cm, rarely 300cm
Habitat	grassland, hedges, waste ground
Flowering	July–October
	STEMS AND LEAVES
Stem	upright, with spiny wings
Root	long tap-root
Hairs	sparse under leaves, prickly hairs above
Stipules	absent
Leaves	basal or spirally on stem, 150–300mm, lobed, wavy, strongly spiny, end lobe spear-shaped; blade of upper joins stem-wings
Leaf-stalk	lower short, upper absent
	FLOWERS
Position	upright heads of florets surrounded by bracts
Bracts	many around head, spiny, slightly hairy; bristle-like between florets
Type	florets ⚥ or ♀, 26–36mm
Size	heads 30–50mm
Colour	reddish purple
Stalk	absent; short under heads
Sepals	a ring of hairs
Petals	5, joined, tubular, lobes slightly unequal
Stamens	5, joined into tube
Stigma	1, 2-lobed; style long
Ovary	1, below petals, 1-celled
	FRUIT
Type	nut-like, oblong, parachute of hairs 20–30mm, feathery
Size	3.5–5mm
Seeds	1, not released

Carline Thistle *Carlina vulgaris*

An unusual Thistle, the flower-heads have a ring of long, yellowish bracts, resembling the strap-shaped outer florets of Daisies. A more or less stemless species with larger flower-heads is grown for use in dried flower displays. *Status:* native; most of area, sometimes common. *Similar species:* another small Thistle is the native perennial Dwarf Thistle. This has a rosette of leaves and one to three reddish-purple flower-heads on short stems. The plant is familiar to people who take picnics in the country as the tufts of spiny leaves that abound in closely-grazed turf.

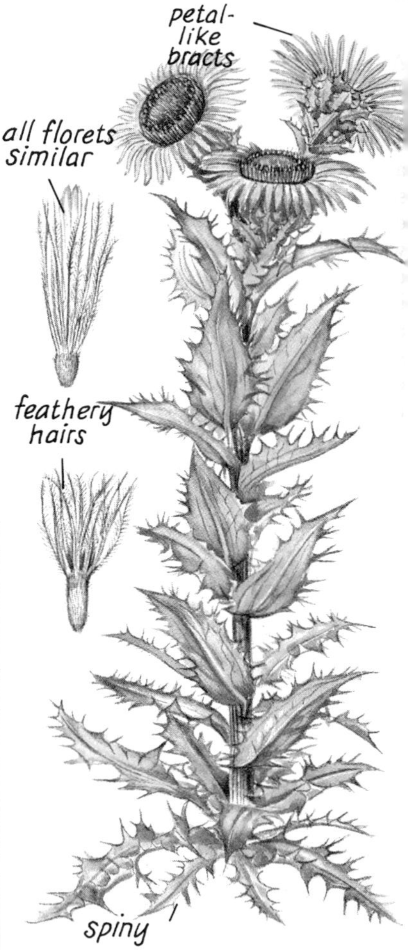

Dwarf Thistle *(Cirsium acaule)*

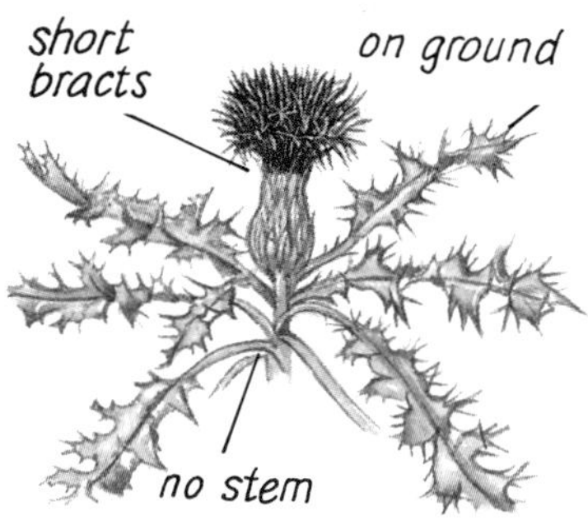

	CARLINE THISTLE
Type	biennial
Height	10–30cm, rarely 60cm
Habitat	grassland; lime-rich soils
Flowering	July–October
	STEMS AND LEAVES
Stem	upright, branched, purplish
Root	tap-root
Hairs	sparse, cotton-like
Stipules	absent
Leaves	basal or spirally arranged on stem, 70–130mm, oblong or spear-shaped, pointed, edge wavy, spiny, slightly lobed; upper broad-based
Leaf-stalk	absent
	FLOWERS
Position	2–5 heads of florets enclosed by bracts
Bracts	many around head, outer spiny, inner long, narrow, yellowish; bristle-like between florets
Type	florets ⚥, 10–12mm, tubular
Size	heads 20–40mm
Colour	reddish purple
Stalk	absent; short under heads
Sepals	ring of branched hairs
Petals	5, joined, tubular, lobes equal
Stamens	5, joined into tube
Stigma	1, 2-lobed; style long
Ovary	1, below petals, 1-celled
	FRUIT
Type	nut-like, cylindrical, with reddish hairs, parachute of feathery hairs 7–8mm
Size	2–4mm
Seeds	1, not released

A tall Thistle that has broadly winged stems and leaves covered with silvery-white hairs, it is biennial, spending the first Winter as a large rosette of leaves and producing purple flowers in the second year. The fruiting heads are eagerly sought by flocks of Goldfinches, which tear out the down to get at the nut-like seeds at the base. *Status:* native in south-east, naturalized elsewhere; absent from much of north. *Similar species:* the leaves of Woolly Thistle are only woolly beneath, the upper surface being dark green. The stem lacks wings and the parachute of the fruits has feathery hairs.

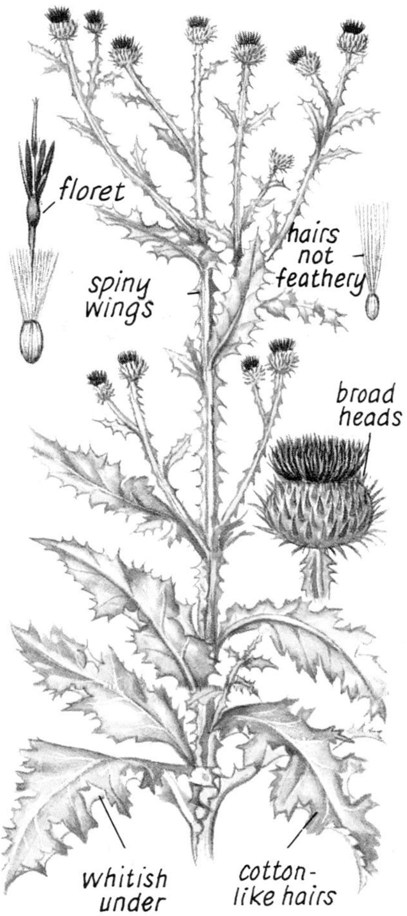

Woolly Thistle *(Cirsium eriophorum)*

COTTON THISTLE

Type biennial
Height 45–300cm
Habitat roadsides, hedges, waste ground
Flowering July–September

STEMS AND LEAVES

Stem upright, with spiny wings
Root stout tap-root
Hairs dense, white, cotton-like
Stipules absent
Leaves basal or spirally on stem, to 550mm, elliptical, with wavy lobes, spiny; blade of upper joins stem-wings
Leaf-stalk lower short, upper absent

FLOWERS

Position almost globular heads of florets surrounded by bracts
Bracts many around head, narrow, spiny; none between florets
Type florets ☿, 14–25mm, tubular
Size heads 30–50mm
Colour pale purple, rarely white
Stalk absent; sometimes long under heads
Sepals a ring of hairs
Petals 5, joined, tubular, lobes slightly unequal
Stamens 5, joined into tube
Stigma 1, 2-lobed; style long
Ovary 1, below petals, 1-celled

FRUIT

Type nut-like, oblong, 4-angled, wrinkled, parachute of toothed hairs, 7–9mm
Size 4–5mm
Seeds 1, not released

Saw-wort *Serratula tinctoria*

A wiry plant with small thistle-like flower-heads in loose, branched clusters above deep-lobed and sharp-toothed leaves. Saw-wort was used as a wound-herb and for treating ruptures. Its leaves were the source of a strong, greenish-yellow dye. The common name derives from the saw-like teeth on the edges of the leaves. *Status:* native; much of area except for north. *Similar species:* Alpine Saw-wort has toothed or unlobed leaves with woolly hairs beneath. Its small clusters of flower-heads are scented rather like Sweet Violet or vanilla. A mountain plant in the south, it is found at low altitudes in the north.

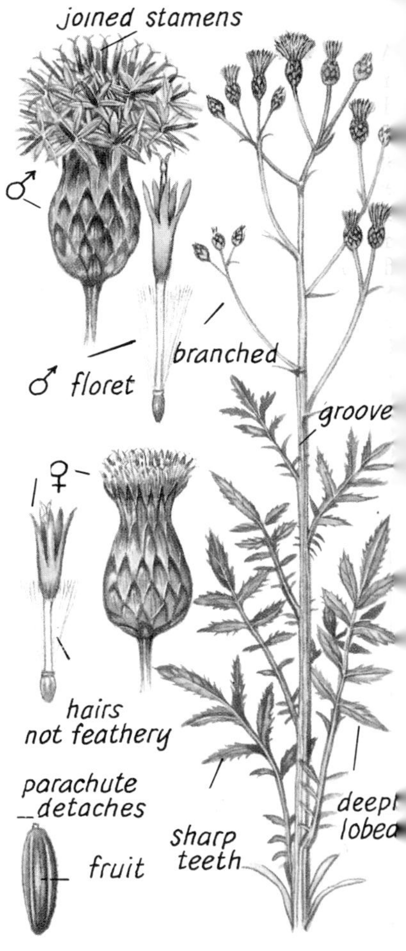

Alpine Saw-wort *(Saussurea alpina)*

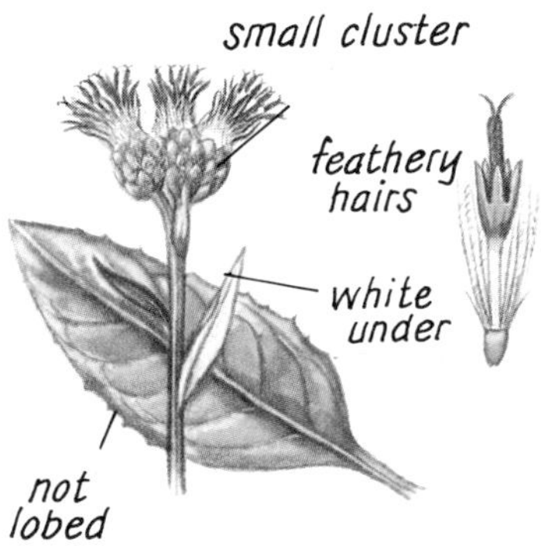

	SAW-WORT
Type	perennial
Height	30–90cm
Habitat	wood edges, grassland; damp, often lime-rich soil
Flowering	July–September
	STEMS AND LEAVES
Stem	upright, slender, grooved
Root	short, stout stock
Hairs	absent
Stipules	absent
Leaves	spirally arranged, 120–250mm, oval or spear-shaped, lobed, with sharp, bristle-tipped teeth
Leaf-stalk	lower short, upper absent
	FLOWERS
Position	thistle-like heads of florets enclosed by bracts; ♂ and ♀ on separate plants
Bracts	many around head, pointed, purple-tipped; scales between florets
Type 1	♂ florets, 10–12mm, tubular
Type 2	♀ florets, 7–10mm, tubular
Size	heads 15–20mm
Colour	purple, rarely white
Stalk	absent; often long under heads
Sepals	a ring of hairs
Petals	5, joined, lobes equal
Stamens	5, joined into tube
Stigma	1, 2-lobed; style long
Ovary	1, below petals, 1-celled
	FRUIT
Type	nut-like, oblong, smooth, parachute soon detached
Size	5–6mm
Seeds	1, not released

An attractive flower of Summer meadows, with large reddish-purple flowers that are thistle-like in construction but often confused with species of Scabious. Around the base of each flower-head are bracts which have a papery, blackish, horseshoe-shaped margin divided into feathery lobes. The flowers are much visited by butterflies. *Status:* native; most of area, more common in south. *Similar species:* Common Knapweed has a similar but smaller flower-head with narrower bracts tipped by a feathery, blackish lobe. The leaves are mostly undivided. Cornflower, a cornfield species that has become rare, has bright blue flowers and is grown in gardens.

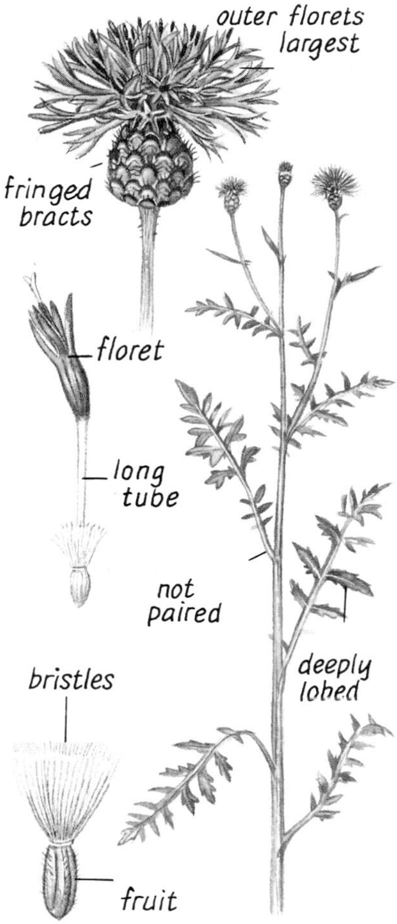

1 Common Knapweed *(C. nigra)*;
2 Cornflower *(C. cyanus)*

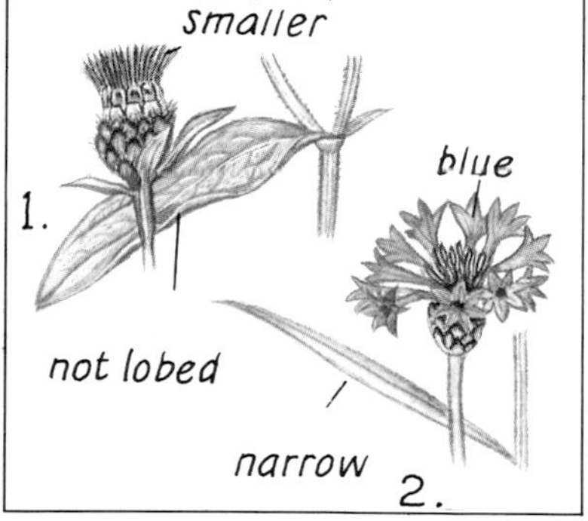

GREATER KNAPWEED

Type	perennial
Height	30–150cm, rarely 200cm
Habitat	grassland, hedges, cliffs; dry, often lime-rich soils
Flowering	July–September

STEMS AND LEAVES

Stem	upright, branched above
Root	stout, woody stock
Hairs	short, rough on leaves
Stipules	absent
Leaves	basal or spirally on stem, 50–250mm, mostly divided into paired lobes, toothed
Leaf-stalk	lower shorter than blade, upper absent

FLOWERS

Position	thistle-like heads of florets enclosed by bracts
Bracts	broad around head, each with feathery, blackish tip; bristle-like between florets
Type	florets ⚥, 12–23mm, tubular, outer often larger, sterile
Size	heads 30–50mm
Colour	reddish purple
Stalk	absent; long under heads
Sepals	a ring of hairs
Petals	5, joined, tubular, lobes slightly unequal
Stamens	5, joined into tube
Stigma	1, 2-lobed; style long
Ovary	1, below petals, 1-celled

FRUIT

Type	nut-like, oblong, slightly flattened, parachute 4–5mm
Size	4–5mm
Seeds	1, not released

Chicory *Cichorium intybus*

The bright blue flowers of Chicory are a beautiful sight along roadsides in late Summer. Opening early in the day, the flowers close soon after midday. Chicory has been cultivated for medicinal purposes, as a vegetable or as a coffee substitute, the roots being dried, roasted and ground. *Status:* native or often introduced; most of area, rare in extreme north and Ireland. *Similar species:* two Dandelion-relatives have stalked, deep-blue flower-heads. Alpine Blue-sow-thistle, an uncommon mountain plant, has reddish hairs above; Blue Lettuce, found only in the south-east of the area, is hairless.

1 Alpine Blue-sow-thistle *(Cicerbita alpina)*; **2** Blue Lettuce *(Lactuca perennis)*

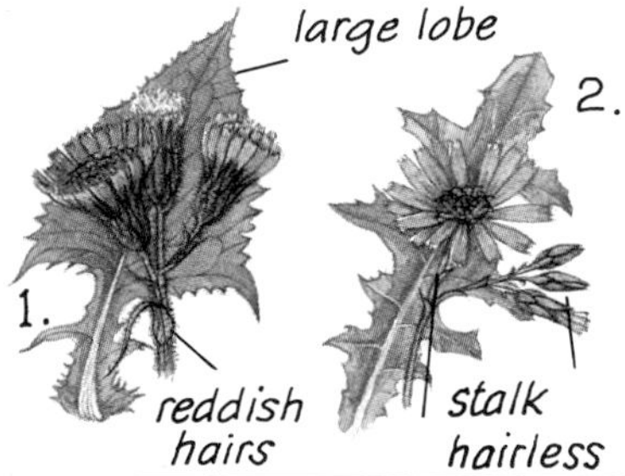

	CHICORY
Type	perennial
Height	30–120cm
Habitat	roadsides, grassland, waste ground; often lime-rich soil
Flowering	July–October
	STEMS AND LEAVES
Stem	upright, grooved, sap milky
Root	long, stout tap-root
Hairs	stiff on stems, gland-tipped among flowers
Stipules	absent
Leaves	basal or spirally on stem, 70–300mm, spear-shaped, most lobed or toothed, upper clasp stem
Leaf-stalk	lower short, upper absent

	FLOWERS
Position	dandelion-like heads of florets enclosed by bracts
Bracts	2 rows under head, inner long; none between florets
Type	florets ⚥, 12–18mm
Size	heads 25–40mm
Colour	bright blue
Stalk	absent; very short under heads
Sepals	a scaly rim
Petals	5, joined, flattened above, 5-toothed
Stamens	5, joined into tube
Stigma	1, 2-lobed; style long
Ovary	1, below petals, 1-celled
	FRUIT
Type	nut-like, almost egg-shaped, mottled, without parachute
Size	2–3mm
Seeds	1, not released

A familiar roadside plant, not for the pale yellow flowers, but for the fruiting heads which look like enormous dandelion-clocks. The greyish parachutes have feathery bristles, the fine hairs distinctly interwoven. The common name derives from these conspicuous fruits. Unlike the Dandelion, Goat's-beard has narrow, almost grass-like leaves, without lobes. Its long tap-roots were formerly used as a vegetable. *Status:* native; most of area, often common. *Similar species:* Viper's-grass has broader basal leaves and the oval bracts are much shorter than the florets.

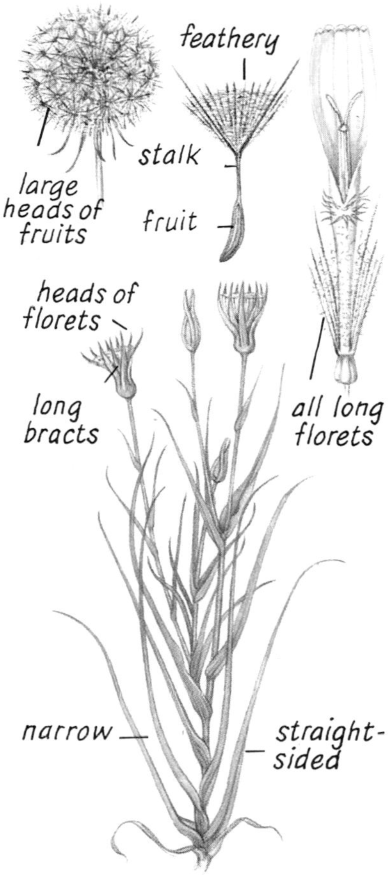

Viper's-grass *(Scorzonera humilis)*

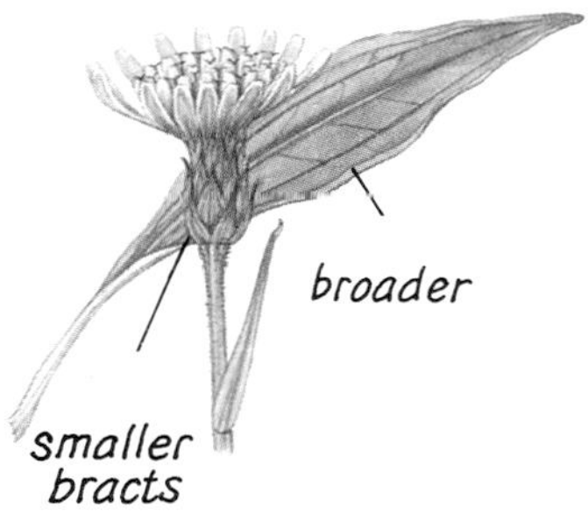

	GOAT'S-BEARD
Type	annual to perennial
Height	30–70cm
Habitat	grassland, roadsides, waste ground, dunes; dry soils
Flowering	June–July
	STEMS AND LEAVES
Stem	upright, scarcely branched; sap milky
Root	long tap-root
Hairs	more or less absent
Stipules	absent
Leaves	basal or spirally arranged on stem, narrow, veins whitish, long-pointed, edge unbroken, base sheaths stem
Leaf-stalk	absent
	FLOWERS
Position	solitary, dandelion-like head of florets surrounded by bracts
Bracts	1 row around head, 25–30mm, thin; none between florets
Type	florets ⚥, 20–25mm
Size	heads 15–22mm
Colour	yellow
Stalk	absent; long under heads
Sepals	a ring of hairs
Petals	5, joined, flattened above, 5-toothed
Stamens	5, joined into tube
Stigma	1, 2-lobed; style long
Ovary	1, below petals, 1-celled
	FRUIT
Type	nut-like, ribbed, long, thin tip, parachute 12–23mm, hairs feathery, interwoven
Size	10–22mm
Seeds	1, not released

Bristly Oxtongue *Picris echioides*

A relative of the Dandelion with prickly leaves and broad, heart-shaped outer bracts to the flower-heads. The prickly hairs have a swollen, whitish base and a tip with three microscopic hooks, like a miniature grappling-iron. *Status:* introduced; scattered through area, most common in south. *Similar species:* Hawkweed Oxtongue has narrow bracts and lacks the stalk-like part of the fruit beneath the parachute. Two further species have fruits with straight bristles in the parachute. Smooth Hawk's-beard is almost hairless and lacks the stalk-like part to the fruit, although it is present in the fine-haired Beaked Hawk's-beard.

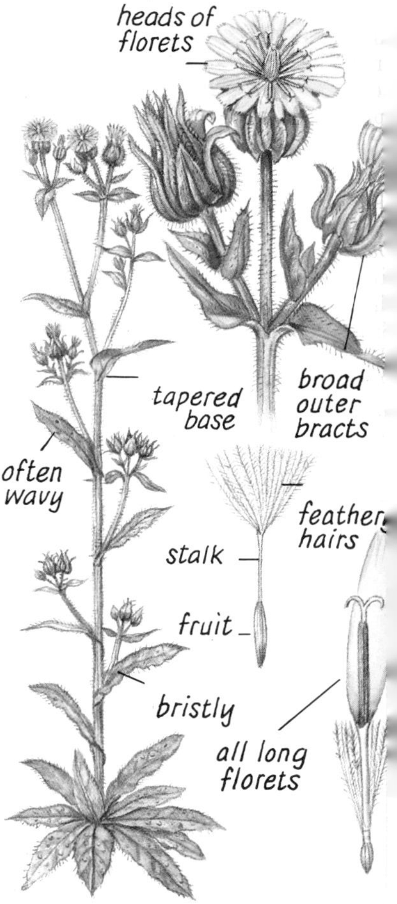

1 Hawkweed Oxtongue *(P. hieracioides)*; **2** Smooth Hawk's-beard *(Crepis capillaris)*; **3** Beaked Hawk's-beard *(C. vesicaria* subsp. *haenseleri)*

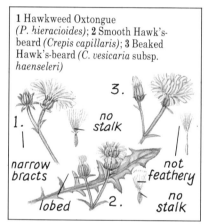

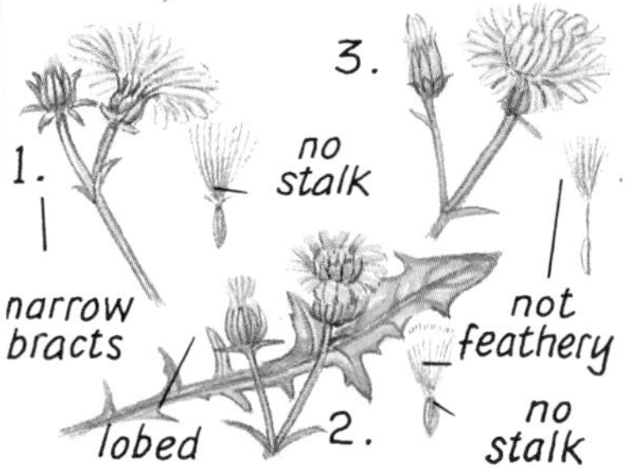

	BRISTLY OXTONGUE
Type	annual or biennial
Height	30–90cm
Habitat	roadsides, hedges, waste ground; often lime-rich soils
Flowering	June–October
	STEMS AND LEAVES
Stem	stout, upright; sap milky
Root	tap-root
Hairs	broad-based, stiff
Stipules	absent
Leaves	basal or spirally on stem, 35–250mm, spear-shaped or oblong, toothed or wavy
Leaf-stalk	lower short, upper absent
	FLOWERS
Position	loosely clustered dandelion-like heads of florets surrounded by bracts
Bracts	3–5 heart-shaped around head, inner longer; none between florets
Type	florets ⚥, 8–12mm, flattened
Size	heads 20–25mm
Colour	yellow or purple beneath
Stalk	absent; short under heads
Sepals	a ring of hairs
Petals	5, joined, flattened above, 5-toothed
Stamens	5, joined into tube
Stigma	1, 2-lobed; style long
Ovary	1, below petals, 1-celled
	FRUIT
Type	nut-like, ribbed, with stalk-like tip, parachute of hairs 4–6mm, feathery
Size	5–7mm
Seeds	1, not released

n abundant plant on waste land round towns or along roadsides, it has eshy, hollow stems bearing weakly piny leaves and dandelion-like flowers. t each leaf-base are two ear-like lobes, he shape being used to distinguish the pecies. Rather crisp leaves of Sow-histles are edible, like the related)andelion and Lettuce, or were fed to ivestock. *Status:* native; common, hroughout area. *Similar species:* ;mooth Sow-thistle has pointed lobes at he leaf-base and wrinkled fruits. 'erennial Sow-thistle has rounded lobes t the leaf-base and flower-heads about wice as large, the bracts usually overed with gland-tipped hairs.

1 Smooth Sow-thistle *(S. oleraceus)*;
2 Perennial Sow-thistle *(S. arvensis)*

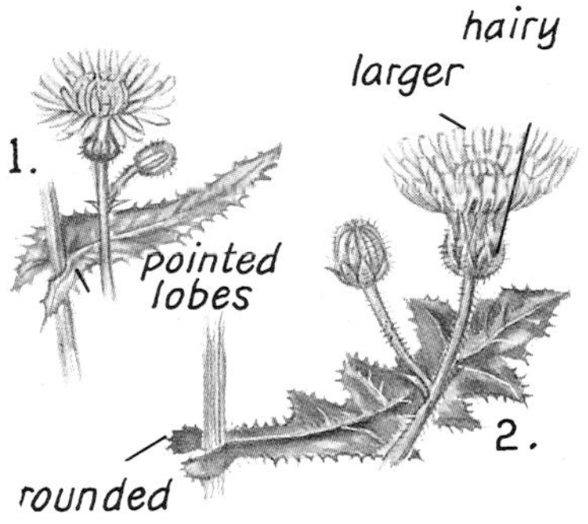

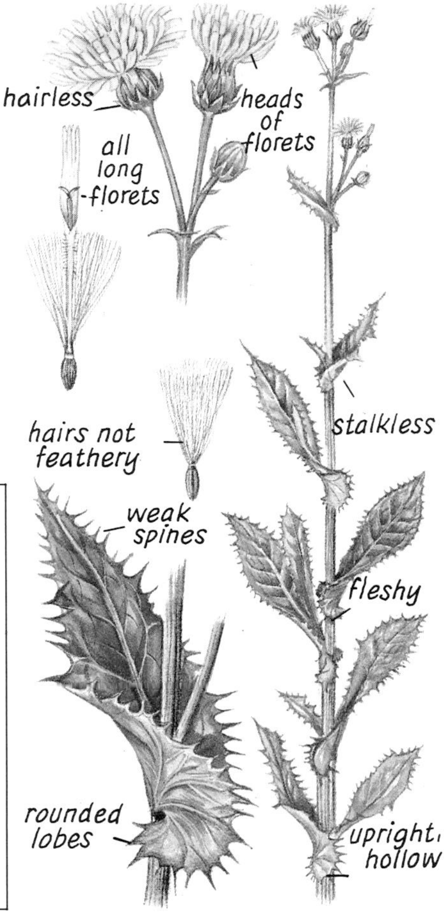

	PRICKLY SOW-THISTLE
Type	annual, some overwintering
Height	2–150cm, rarely 200cm
Habitat	cultivated and waste ground
Flowering	June–August
	STEMS AND LEAVES
Stem	stout, upright, 5-angled, hollow; sap milky
Root	slender tap-root
Hairs	absent
Stipules	absent
Leaves	basal or spirally around stem, often lobed, wavy, weakly spiny, base of upper leaves with ear-like lobes clasping stem
Leaf-stalk	mostly absent

	FLOWERS
Position	dandelion-like heads of florets enclosed by bracts
Bracts	long, smooth around head; none between florets
Type	florets ⚥, 10–15mm, flattened
Size	heads 20–25mm
Colour	yellow, some purple beneath
Stalk	absent; longish under heads
Sepals	a ring of hairs
Petals	5, joined, flattened above, 5-toothed
Stamens	5, joined into tube
Stigma	1, 2-lobed; style long
Ovary	1, below petals, 1-celled
	FRUIT
Type	nut-like, flattened, smooth ribs, parachute 6–9mm
Size	2–3mm
Seeds	1, not released

Cat's-ear *Hypochaeris radicata*

One of the most common of many yellow-flowered, dandelion-like plants, brightening the Summer meadow and roadside alike with its large, golden flower-heads. Often a problem on lawns, it is one of the best plants to try and establish if a lawn is being turned deliberately into an informal wild-flower meadow. The common name refers to small bracts on the stems, which in shape resemble cat's ears. *Status:* native; most of area except north-east. *Similar species:* Smooth Cat's-ear is an annual that has almost hairless leaves and flower-heads which only open in sunny weather. The florets are little longer than the bracts.

Smooth Cat's-ear *(H. glabra)*

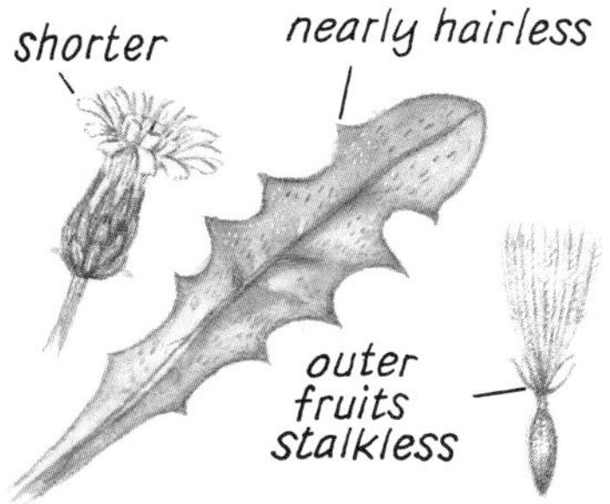

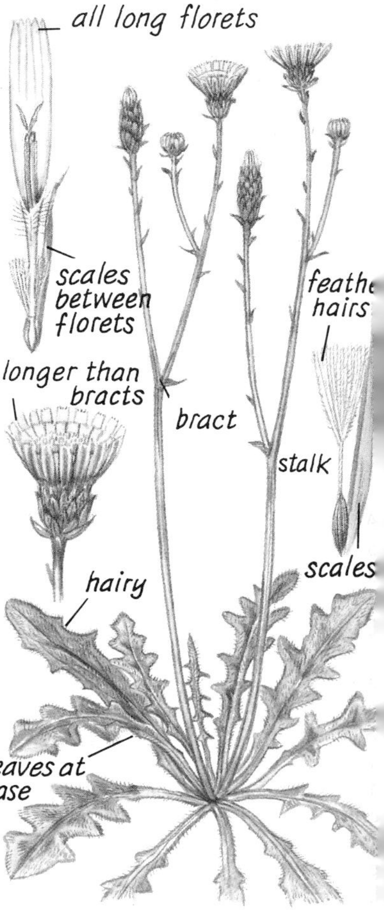

	CAT'S-EAR
Type	perennial
Height	20–60cm, rarely 100cm
Habitat	grassland, roadsides, dunes
Flowering	June–September
	STEMS AND LEAVES
Stem	upright, usually no leaves, few branches; sap milky
Root	tap-root
Hairs	rather stiff, on leaves
Stipules	absent
Leaves	basal rosette, 70–250mm, oblong or spear-shaped with wavy lobes or teeth
Leaf-stalk	shorter than blade
	FLOWERS
Position	few dandelion-like heads of florets enclosed by bracts
Bracts	many around head, spear-shaped, bristly; long scales between florets
Type	florets ☿, 12–18mm, flattened
Size	heads 25–40mm
Colour	bright yellow, outer florets greenish beneath
Stalk	absent; under heads
Sepals	a ring of hairs
Petals	5, joined, flattened above, 5-toothed
Stamens	5, joined into tube
Stigma	1, 2-lobed; style long
Ovary	1, below petals, 1-celled
	FRUIT
Type	nut-like, ribbed, rough, top stalk-like, parachute of feathery hairs 9–12mm
Size	4–8mm
Seeds	1, not released

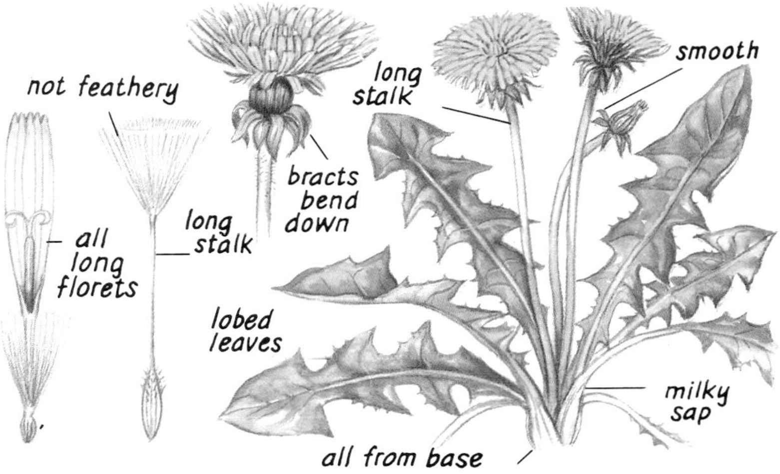

A weed, flavouring for a wine, food for pets or a salad vegetable; the lobed leaves and hollow-stalked flowers of Dandelions are familiar to most people. But their biology is complex and more than a thousand species have been described from Europe alone. *Status:* native; throughout area, very common. *Similar species:* Narrow-leaved Marsh-dandelion has upright pale-edged bracts and narrow sparsely-lobed leaves. Two related plants have small bracts on the stems and feathery hairs making up the parachute. Autumn Hawkbit is nearly hairless, often with branched stems, and Rough Hawkbit is hairy.

1 Narrow-leaved Marsh-dandelion *(T. palustre)*; **2** Autumn Hawkbit *(Leontodon autumnalis)*; **3** Rough Hawkbit *(L. hispidus)*

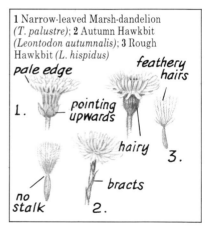

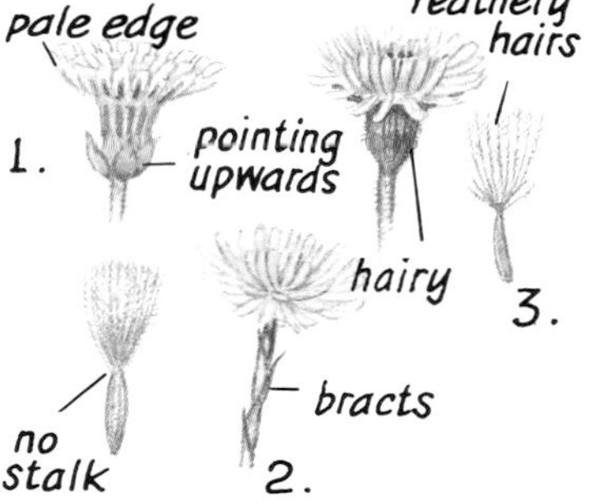

	COMMON DANDELION
Type	perennial
Height	5–40cm
Habitat	grassland, roadsides, lawns, waste ground
Flowering	March–October
	STEMS AND LEAVES
Stem	upright, unbranched, hollow, leafless; sap milky
Root	tap-root
Hairs	near top of flower-stalks
Stipules	absent
Leaves	basal, 50–400mm, oblong or spear-shaped, variably lobed and toothed
Leaf-stalk	short, edges often wing-like
	FLOWERS
Position	head of florets enclosed by bracts, solitary
Bracts	2 rows around head, inner upright, outer curved back; none between florets
Type	florets ⚥, 15–20mm, flattened
Size	heads 30–60mm
Colour	yellow, outer brownish under
Stalk	absent; long under heads
Sepals	a ring of hairs
Petals	5, joined, flattened above, 5-toothed
Stamens	5, joined into tube
Stigma	1, 2-lobed; style long
Ovary	1, below petals, 1-celled
	FRUIT
Type	dry, cylindrical, rough above, top stalk-like, parachute of hairs 5–6mm
Size	3.5–4mm
Seeds	1, not released

Nipplewort *Lapsana communis*

One of the dandelion relatives with small flowers, common by roadsides or as a garden weed. Lemon-yellow flowers open only in bright weather. Like the related Lettuce, the leaves are edible. The common name derives from a vague similarity in the shape of the buds and milky sap. *Status:* native; common, throughout area. *Similar species:* two other small-flowered species have fruits with a parachute. Great Lettuce has prickly stem-leaves with rounded ear-like lobes at the base, and fruits with a stalk beneath the parachute. Wall Lettuce has smaller flower-heads, usually with five florets, and fruits without a stalk beneath the parachute.

1 Great Lettuce *(Lactuca virosa)*;
2 Wall Lettuce *(Mycelis muralis)*

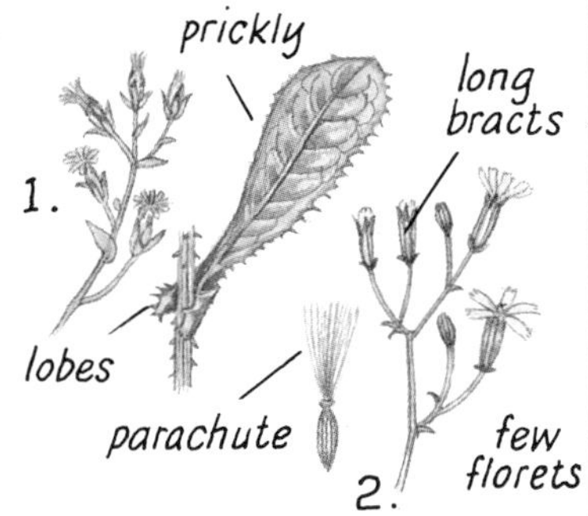

	NIPPLEWORT
Type	annual
Height	20–125cm
Habitat	woods, hedges, roadsides, waste ground
Flowering	July–September
	STEMS AND LEAVES
Stem	upright, leafy, widely branched above; sap milky
Root	tap-root
Hairs	absent except at base
Stipules	absent
Leaves	basal or spirally arranged on stem, 10–150mm, with wavy teeth, lower lobed
Leaf-stalk	lower shorter than blade, upper absent
	FLOWERS
Position	dandelion-like heads of florets enclosed by bracts
Bracts	8–10 around head, narrow, upright; none between florets
Type	florets ⚥, 8–15, 7–11mm, all strap-shaped
Size	heads 15–20mm
Colour	pale yellow
Stalk	absent; slender under heads
Sepals	a ring of hairs
Petals	5, joined, flattened above, 5-toothed
Stamens	5, joined into tube
Stigma	1, 2-lobed; style long
Ovary	1, below petals, 1-celled
	FRUIT
Type	1, nut-like, flattened, smoothly ribbed, without parachute, outer curved
Size	2.5–9mm
Seeds	1, not released

A tall plant with branched heads of dandelion-like flowers. Also like the Dandelion, its unusual reproductive biology has resulted in hundreds of very similar species. *Status:* native; most of area, most common in south. *Similar species:* probably the most common species in the northern half of the area, Common Hawkweed has nearly all of its broader leaves in a basal rosette and has hairy bracts. Fox-and-cubs is often grown in gardens for its orange or red flowers. Mouse-ear Hawkweed has creeping stems that produce rosettes of leaves, whitish with dense hairs beneath, and short stems ending with a single, lemon-yellow flower-head.

1 Common Hawkweed *(H. vulgatum)*;
2 Fox-and-cubs *(H. aurantiacum)*;
3 Mouse-ear Hawkweed *(H. pilosella)*

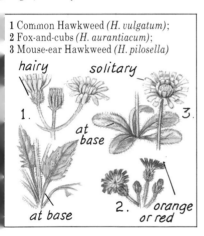

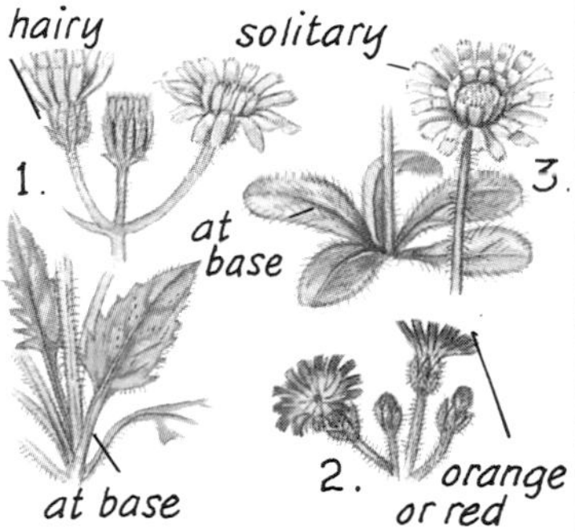

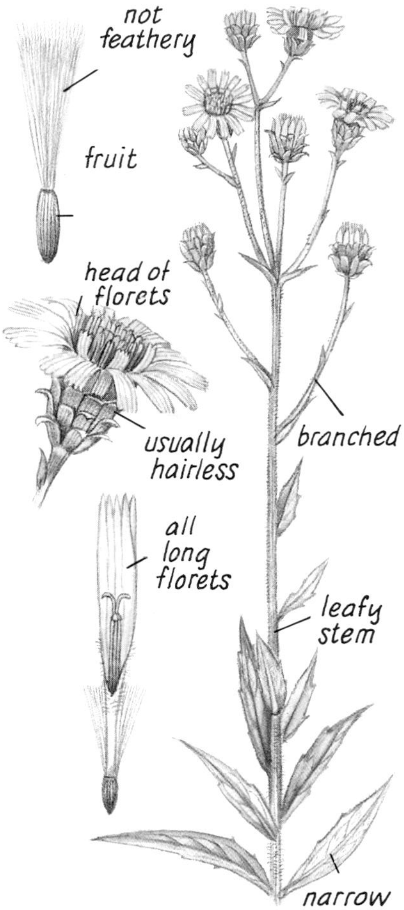

	HAWKWEED
Type	perennial
Height	30–100cm, rarely 150cm
Habitat	grassland, hedges, waste ground
Flowering	June–October
	STEMS AND LEAVES
Stem	upright, slender; sap milky
Root	fibrous with slender stock
Hairs	rather sparse
Stipules	absent
Leaves	many, spirally arranged on stem, 15–150mm, narrow, with few teeth, pointed
Leaf-stalk	lower short, upper absent
	FLOWERS
Position	dandelion-like heads of florets surrounded by bracts, in branched clusters
Bracts	many around head, 9–11mm, usually hairless, blackish-green; none between florets
Type	florets ⚥, 10–15mm
Size	heads 20–30mm
Colour	bright yellow
Stalk	absent; long under heads, with small bracts
Sepals	a ring of hairs
Petals	5, joined, flattened above, 5-toothed
Stamens	5, joined into tube
Stigma	1, 2-lobed; style long
Ovary	1, below petals, 1-celled
	FRUIT
Type	nut-like, smoothly ridged, parachute 5–6mm, hairs unequal
Size	3–4mm
Seeds	1, not released

Arrowhead *Sagittaria sagittifolia*

A water-plant with attractive white, blackish-centred flowers. Its leaves are remarkably variable. The plant lasts the Winter as a bright blue and yellow bud, sunken in the mud. Submerged leaves are at first ribbon-like, the tips expanded when later leaves reach the surface and float. Only leaves above water have arrow-shaped blades that give the plant its name. *Status:* native; most of area, rarer in north. *Similar species:* Water-plantain has small, pinkish flowers in branched heads, and the leaf-blades are broadly oval. Lesser Water-plantain has much narrower blades, and all flower-stalks usually arise at the same point.

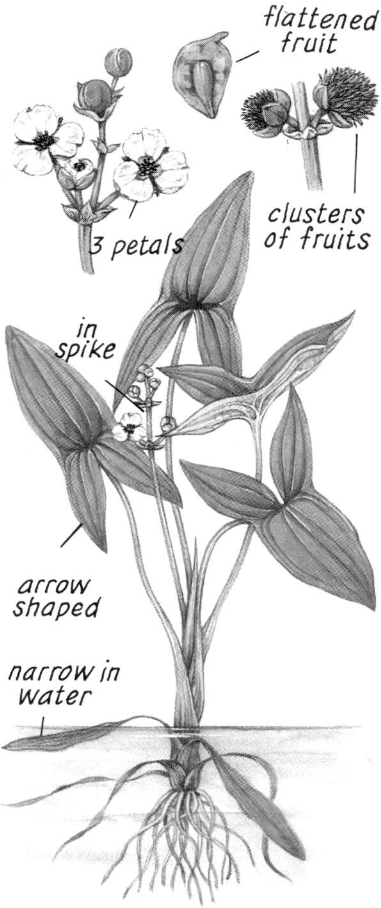

1 Water-plantain *(Alisma plantago-aquatica)*; **2** Lesser Water-plantain *(Baldellia ranunculoides)*

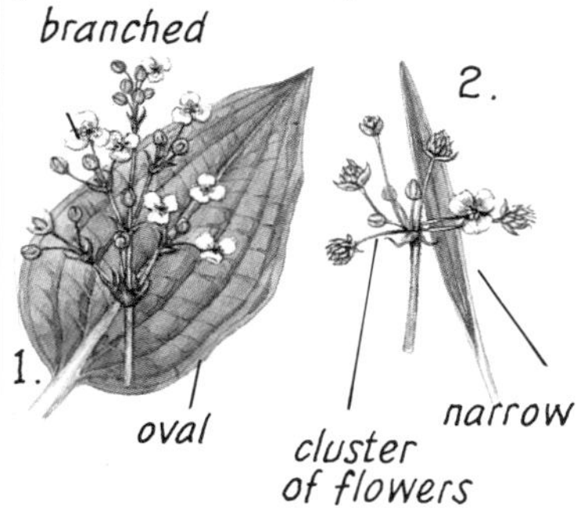

	ARROWHEAD
Type	perennial
Height	30–90cm
Habitat	ponds, slow rivers, canals; in shallow water on mud
Flowering	July–August
	STEMS AND LEAVES
Stem	flowering stems upright; creeping stems at base
Root	thick, white
Hairs	absent
Stipules	absent
Leaves	submerged ribbon-like, translucent; floating with broad tip; above water with blade 50–200mm, arrow-shaped
Leaf-stalk	much longer than blade

	FLOWERS
Position	rings of 3–5 around stem, ♂ and ♀ on same plant
Bracts	triangular, short
Type 1	♂, in upper part of head
Type 2	♀, at base of head, short-stalked
Size	18–25mm
Colour	white, centre dark violet
Stalk	about equalling flower
Sepals	3, 6–8mm, oval, edge whitish
Petals	3, 9–11mm, nearly circular
Stamens	many, shorter than petals
Stigmas	1 per ovary
Ovaries	numerous, 1-celled
	FRUIT
Type	many, in globular clusters, dry, flattened edges
Size	4–5mm
Seeds	1 per fruit, not released

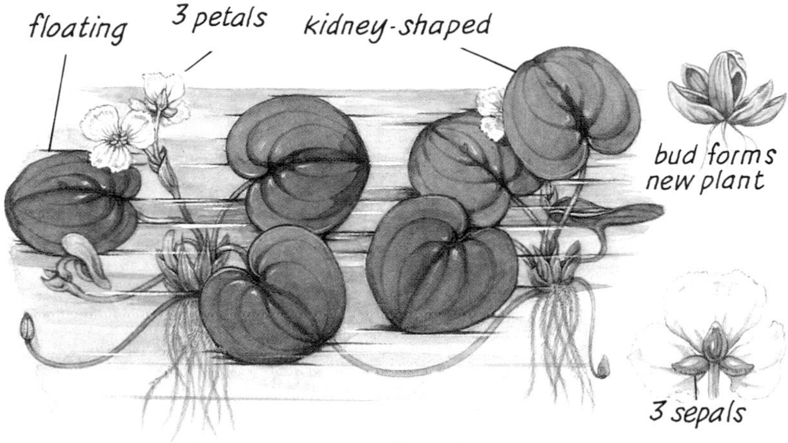

A water-plant with floating leaves like small Water-lilies, but white, three-petalled flowers carried above the water. It spends the Winter as a bud with scale-like leaves, protected from frost and ice in the mud at the bottom of the pond. Although rooted when growth commences, bubbles produced within the tissues soon cause it to float. *Status:* native; scattered through area, sometimes common, rarer in north. *Similar species:* Water-soldier is a floating aquatic plant that has similar flowers but very different foliage. Its tuft of long, pointed, spiny leaves floats in the Summer but sinks in the Winter.

Water-soldier *(Stratiotes aloides)*

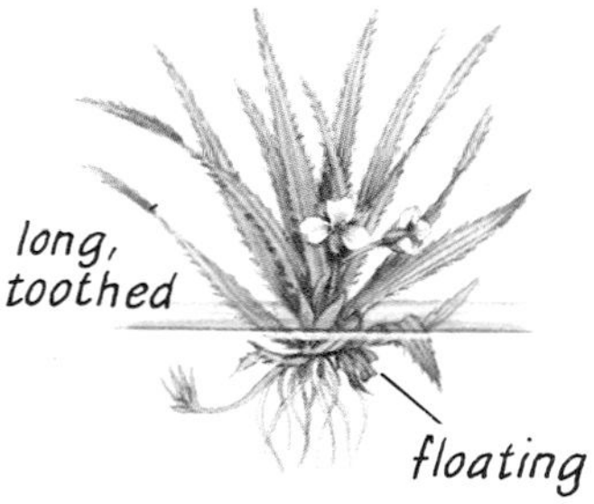

	FROGBIT
Type	perennial
Height	floating
Habitat	ponds, ditches; usually lime-rich water
Flowering	July–August
	STEMS AND LEAVES
Stem	long, rooting; over-wintering as bud
Root	fibrous
Hairs	absent
Stipules	large, translucent
Leaves	tufts along stem, blade 25–40mm, kidney-shaped to nearly circular, floating
Leaf-stalk	longer than blade
	FLOWERS
Position	♂ and ♀ flowers usually on different plants, above water
Bracts	broad, translucent
Type 1	2–3 ♂ from pairs of bracts
Type 2	♀ solitary from bract
Size	18–25mm
Colour	white, base yellow
Stalk	longer than flower
Sepals	3, 4–5mm, oval
Petals	3, 9–12mm, nearly circular, crumpled
Stamens	12, shorter than petals
Stigma	1, 2-lobed on each of 6 styles
Ovary	1, below petals, 6-celled
	FRUIT
Type	1, berry-like, not opening, almost globular, rarely produced
Size	*c*12mm
Seeds	many, *c*2mm, sticky-coated

Flowering-rush *Butomus umbellatus*

A beautiful plant, brightening banks of ponds and rivers with its heads of pink and purple. The attractive, three-petalled flowers seem quite out of context with the sedge-like (rather than rush-like) foliage that is usually associated with inconspicuous, blackish or brown flowers. Flowering-rush is often cultivated in ornamental ponds and is readily available commercially. The swollen stems at the base of the leaves are edible, but it would be a criminal act to take them from the scarce wild plants. However, if surplus garden plants are thinned out then culinary experiments could be attempted. Introduced as a garden plant to North America, Flowering-rush has escaped into the wild and has conquered the Great Lakes. *Status:* native; scattered through area, most common in south. (There are no similar species.)

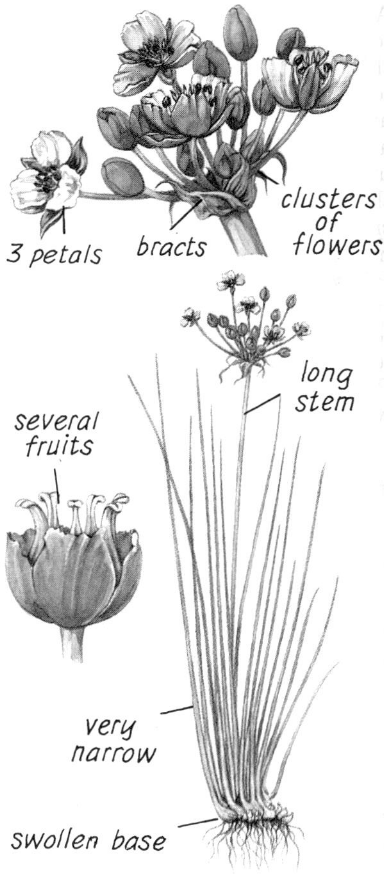

	FLOWERING-RUSH
Type	perennial
Height	50–150cm
Habitat	ditches, ponds, rivers, canals; edges of fresh-water
Flowering	July–September
	STEMS AND LEAVES
Stem	upright, leafless flowering stem
Root	thick, fleshy, underground stem
Hairs	absent
Stipules	absent
Leaves	all from base, 50–150mm, long and narrow, 3-angled, upright, pointed, edge unbroken, base sheaths stem
Leaf-stalk	absent

	FLOWERS
Position	many, in head at stem-tip
Bracts	narrowly triangular, papery
Type	⚥
Size	25–30mm
Colour	pink with darker veins
Stalk	longer than flower, unequal, to 100mm
Sepals	3, 8–10mm, oblong, purplish
Petals	3, 10–15mm, oval
Stamens	6–9
Stigmas	1 per ovary
Ovaries	6–9, 2-celled
	FRUIT
Type	6–9, capsule, almost egg-shaped, tip beak-like
Size	9–12mm
Seeds	many, 1.5–2mm, narrowly oblong

Broad-leaved Pondweed

An aquatic plant with broad, floating leaves and spikes of tiny flowers above the water. In slow rivers and canals the leaves align with the gentle current, and fish (especially young Pike) lie alongside, beautifully camouflaged until they move. *Status:* native; throughout area, common. *Similar species:* of many other species, most have only submerged leaves. Curled Pondweed has attractively curled and twisted, fine-toothed, translucent leaves. Fennel Pondweed has grass-like leaves and stipules joined into a sheath. Perfoliate Pondweed has broad leaves with the base clasping the stem.

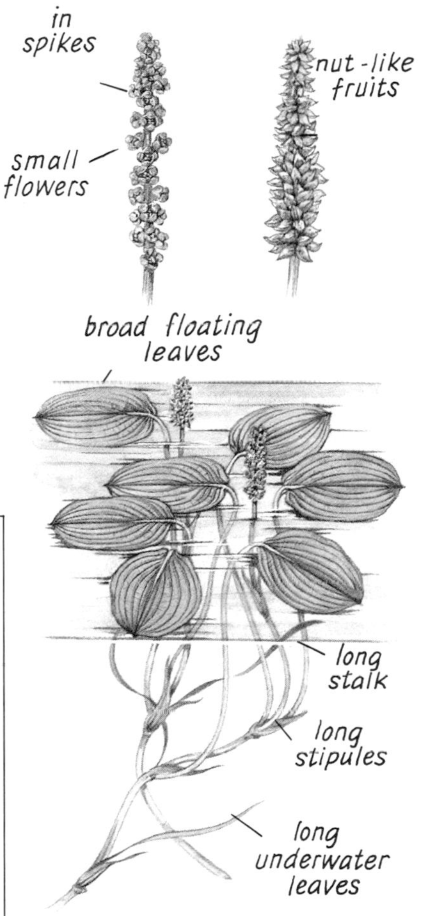

1 Curled Pondweed *(P. crispus)*;
2 Fennel Pondweed *(P. pectinatus)*;
3 Perfoliate Pondweed *(P. perfoliatus)*

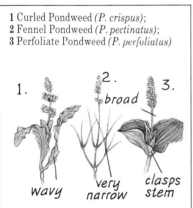

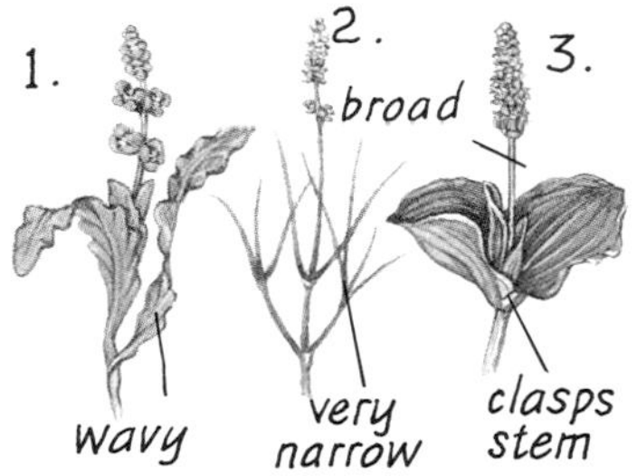

	BROAD-LEAVED PONDWEED
Type	perennial
Height	up to 100cm, rarely 500cm
Habitat	rivers, lakes, ponds; mostly on mud in fresh-water
Flowering	May–September
	STEMS AND LEAVES
Stem	long, submerged, rarely branched
Root	creeping, underground stem
Hairs	absent
Stipules	50–120mm, conspicuous
Leaves	on alternate sides of stem, blade 25–125mm, floating, elliptical to broadly spear-shaped; submerged leaves ribbon-like, grooved
Leaf-stalk	up to 500mm, jointed and wing-like near top

	FLOWERS
Position	many in crowded, stalked spike, from leaf-base or stem-tip, above water
Bracts	absent
Type	⚥
Size	3–4mm
Colour	green
Stalk	absent
Perianth	4 lobes, 1.5–2mm, rounded with stalk-like base
Stamens	4, very short
Stigmas	1 per ovary; style absent
Ovaries	4, 1-celled
	FRUIT
Type	in cylindrical spike, almost egg-shaped, pointed, olive-green, not opening
Size	4–5mm
Seeds	1, not released

Bog Asphodel *Narthecium ossifragum*

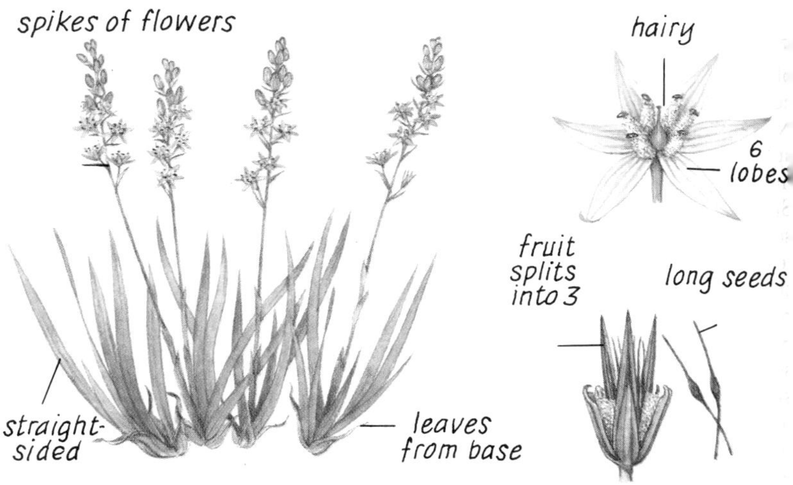

A pretty little plant of boggy places on moor and heath, flowering among the Sphagnum mosses and the Sundews. The leaves resemble a diminutive Iris and the yellow, six-petalled flowers deepen in hue to a reddish orange. The base of each of the six stamens has a fuzzy mass of hairs and the pollen-bearing anthers are usually a bright crimson. The flower-spikes were used to make a deep yellow dye. *Status:* native; throughout area, most common in north. *Similar species:* Scottish Asphodel differs in the small, white flowers and narrower leaves.

Scottish Asphodel *(Tofieldia pusilla)*

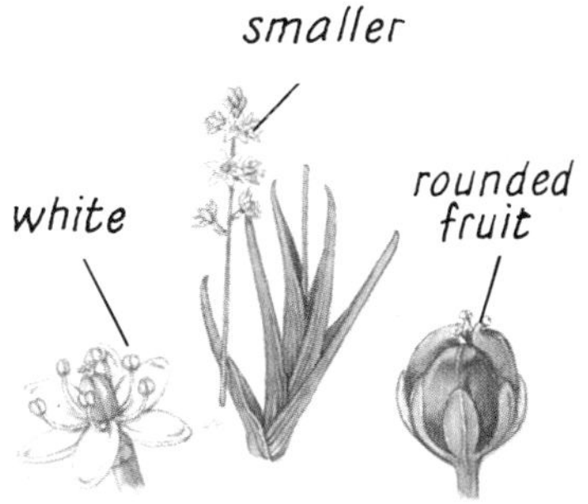

	BOG ASPHODEL
Type	perennial
Height	5–40cm
Habitat	bogs, heaths, moors; wet places, acid soil
Flowering	July–September
	STEMS AND LEAVES
Stem	flowering stems upright
Root	creeping, fleshy stem; roots thick, fibrous
Hairs	absent
Stipules	absent
Leaves	mostly basal, 50–300mm, slender, usually curved, with 5 parallel veins, pointed, edge unbroken
Leaf-stalk	absent
	FLOWERS
Position	many in stalked spike, 20–100mm long, at stem-tip, stalk with sheath-like leaves at base
Bracts	spear-shaped, equal to flower-stalk
Type	⚥
Size	12–16mm
Colour	yellow, turning orange
Stalk	about equal to flower
Perianth	6 lobes, 6–8mm, narrowly spear-shaped, spread apart
Stamens	6, anthers red, base woolly
Stigma	1, tip swollen; style short
Ovary	1, 3-celled
	FRUIT
Type	1, capsule, tapered, grooved, splits into 3
Size	10–14mm
Seeds	many, 8–10mm, middle swollen, ends thin, tail-like

Few botanical sights equal the beauty of the thick carpet of Bluebells that cover the floor of Spring woodland. Nowhere else in the world is this spectacle repeated, for Bluebells are native only to north-western Europe. Spikes of nodding bells are eagerly sought as cut flowers, although broken leaves may cause irreparable harm to the plant. *Status:* native; western part of region. *Similar species:* flowers of Squills are not nodding and have separate petals. Spring Squill has a single bract under each flower and is leafy when in flower. Autumn Squill lacks bracts and flowers before leaves appear. Grape Hyacinth has petals joined into a swollen tube.

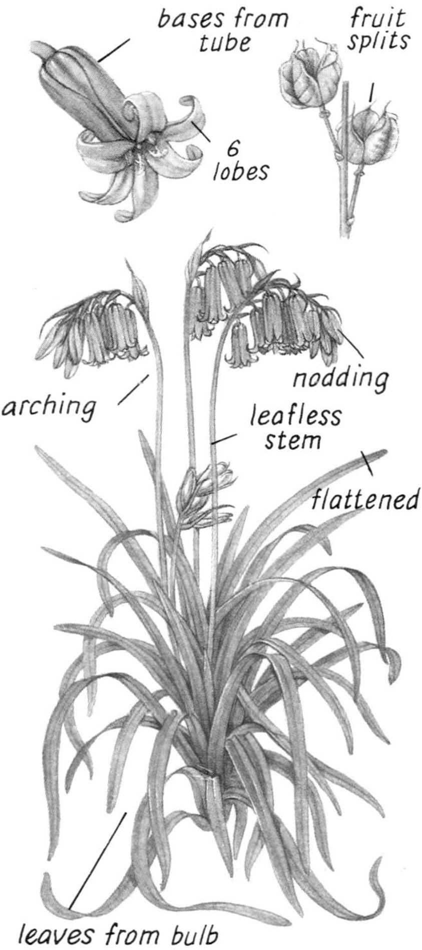

1 Spring Squill *(Scilla verna)*; **2** Autumn Squill *(S. autumnalis)*; **3** Grape Hyacinth *(Muscari neglectum)*

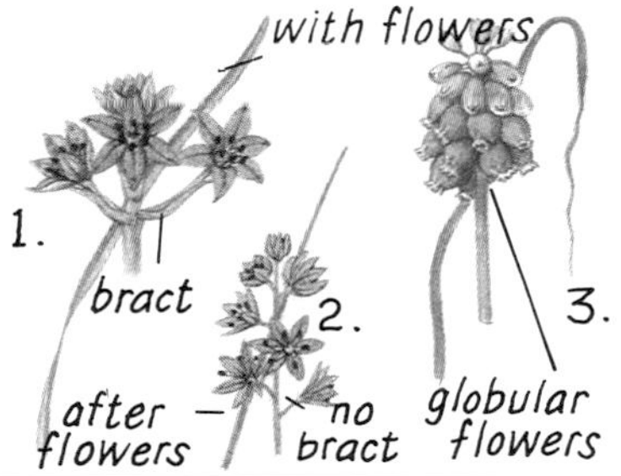

	BLUEBELL
Type	perennial
Height	20–50cm
Habitat	woods, hedges, sea-cliffs; light, usually acid soils
Flowering	April–June
	STEMS AND LEAVES
Stem	flowering stem upright, leafless, tip arching
Root	bulb 20–30mm, egg-shaped
Hairs	absent
Stipules	absent
Leaves	all basal, 20–450mm, narrow, straight-sided
Leaf-stalk	absent
	FLOWERS
Position	4–16, in stalked spike, 1-sided, drooping
Bracts	2 under each flower, bluish
Type	⚥, nodding
Size	15–20mm
Colour	violet-blue, rarely pink or white
Stalk	shorter than flower, lengthening and turning upright in fruit
Perianth	6 lobes, 15–20mm, bases joined, almost bell-shaped, lobes curved back
Stamens	6, unequal
Stigma	1; style fairly long
Ovary	1, 3-celled
	FRUIT
Type	1, capsule, almost globular, splits into 3
Size	10–15mm
Seeds	several, 3–4mm, blackish

Meadow Saffron *Colchicum autumnale*

Pinkish-purple crocus-like flowers of Meadow Saffron appear in Autumn, long before any foliage. Leaves and fruits follow in the Spring and are hard to reconcile with the flower of the previous year. Although potentially lethal, this plant yields a drug used to treat gout and arthritis. *Status:* native or sometimes introduced; scattered through area, mainly in south. *Similar species:* Spring Crocus has only three stamens and the grass-like leaves are present when the flowers open. Sand Crocus has a distinct stalk bearing the small flower, its petals joined only at the base and spreading widely apart.

1 Spring Crocus *(Crocus vernus)*;
2 Sand Crocus *(Romulea columnae)*

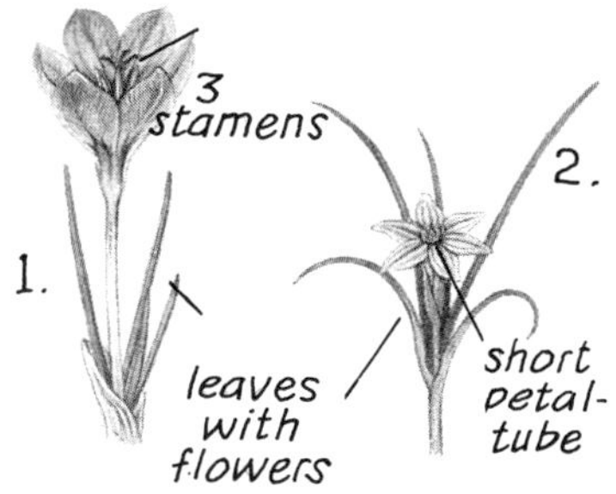

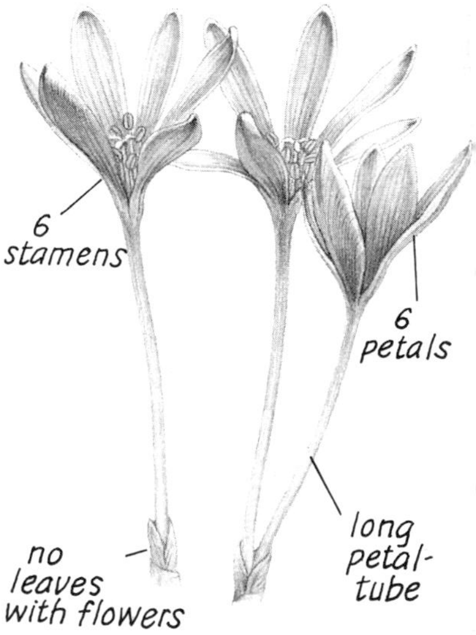

	MEADOW SAFFRON
Type	perennial
Height	80–300cm
Habitat	meadows, woods; damp, often lime-rich soils
Flowering	August–October
	STEMS AND LEAVES
Stem	absent in flower, short in fruit, sheathed by leaf-bases
Root	corm 30–50mm, with brown scales
Hairs	absent
Stipules	absent
Leaves	absent in flower, all basal, 120–300mm, oblong, straight-sided, glossy, blunt
Leaf-stalk	absent

	FLOWERS
Position	1–3, from corm
Bracts	absent
Type	⚥, crocus-like
Size	lobes 30–45mm
Colour	pale purple
Stalk	only stalk-like base of petals visible
Perianth	6 petal-like lobes, 30–45mm, bases joined forming apparent stalk, 50–200mm long
Stamens	6, anthers orange
Stigmas	3; styles long
Ovary	1, underground, 3-celled
	FRUIT
Type	1, capsule, oblong to egg-shaped, splits into 3
Size	30–50mm
Seeds	numerous, 3–4mm, almost globular

Attractive and unique in form, Fritillaries are found in wet meadows almost only where they are protected from flower-pickers and farmers seeking to 'improve' the land. The curious pattern of squarish markings is also visible within the translucent petals. *Status:* native or escaped from gardens; scattered through area, common in some southern localities. *Similar species:* two Lilies with nodding, spotted flowers are found in the south of the area. Martagon Lily has rings of leaves and purplish flowers; Pyrenean Lily has spirally-arranged leaves and yellow flowers. Also native in the south, Wild Tulip has yellow, upright flowers.

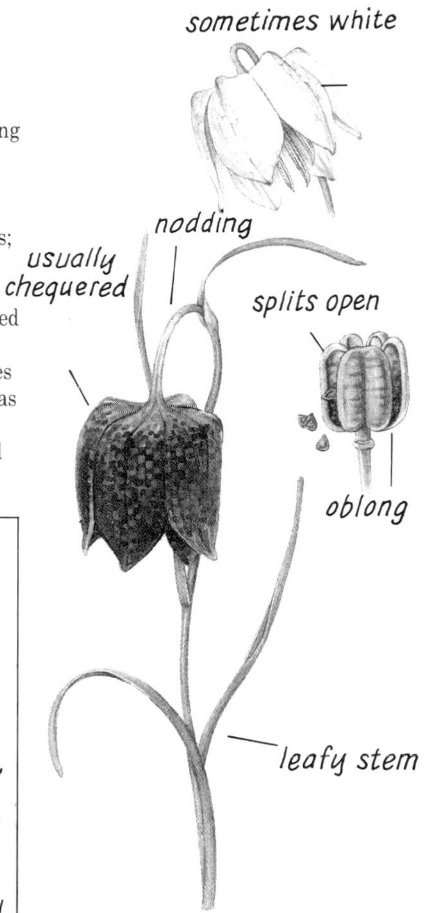

1 Martagon Lily *(Lilium martagon)*;
2 Pyrenean Lily *(L. pyrenaicum)*;
3 Wild Tulip *(Tulipa sylvestris)*

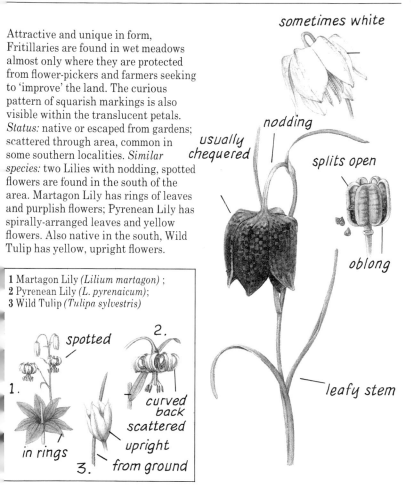

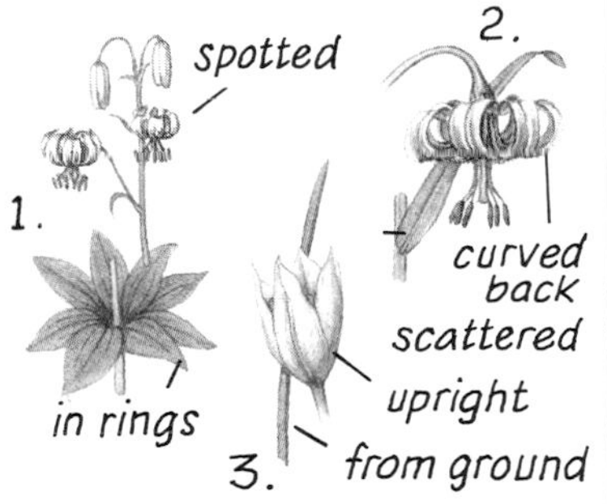

FRITILLARY

Type perennial
Height 20–50cm
Habitat grassy places; damp soil
Flowering April–May

STEMS AND LEAVES

Stem upright
Root small bulb with white scales
Hairs absent
Stipules absent
Leaves on alternate sides of stem, 3–6, 80–200mm, narrow, straight-sided, tip pointed
Leaf-stalk absent

FLOWERS

Position solitary, rarely paired, at stem-tip
Bracts absent
Type ⚥, nodding
Size 30–50mm
Colour purplish, usually chequered with light and dark markings, rarely white
Stalk almost equal to flower
Perianth 6 lobes, 30–50mm, all petal-like, equal, oblong, thickened at tip
Stamens 3, shorter than petals
Stigma 1, 3-lobed; style long
Ovary 1, 3-celled

FRUIT

Type 1, capsule, oblong, upright, splits into 3
Size 15–20mm
Seeds many, 5–7mm, almost circular, flattened, brown

Star-of-Bethlehem *Ornithogalum umbellatum*

A bulbous plant with starry, white flowers, each petal backed by a broad, green stripe. This makes the flowers hard to find when they close early in the day or in dull weather. Although the flowers arise at different heights on the stem, the lower stalks are much longer and turn upwards so that the flowers finish at nearly the same level. *Status:* native or escaped from gardens; scattered through most of region, most common in south-east. *Similar species:* Spiked Star-of-Bethlehem has long spikes, its numerous greenish flowers having almost equal stalks. Yellow Star-of-Bethlehem has few greenish-yellow flowers on leafy stems.

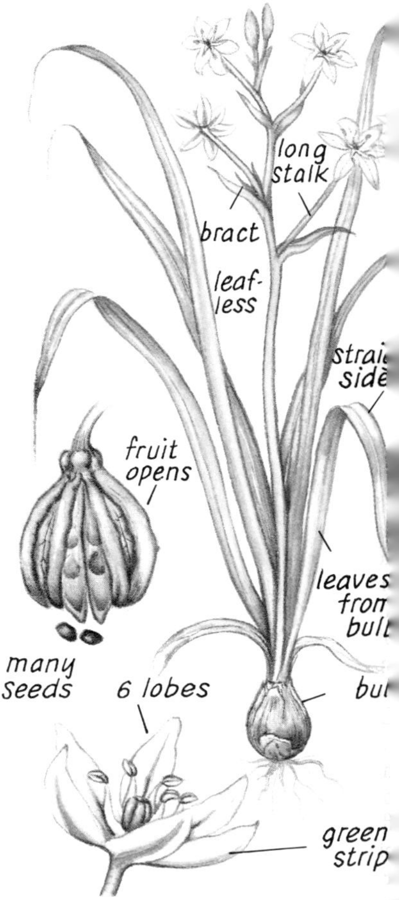

1 Spiked Star-of-Bethlehem *(O. pyrenaicum)*; **2** Yellow Star-of-Bethlehem *(Gagea lutea)*

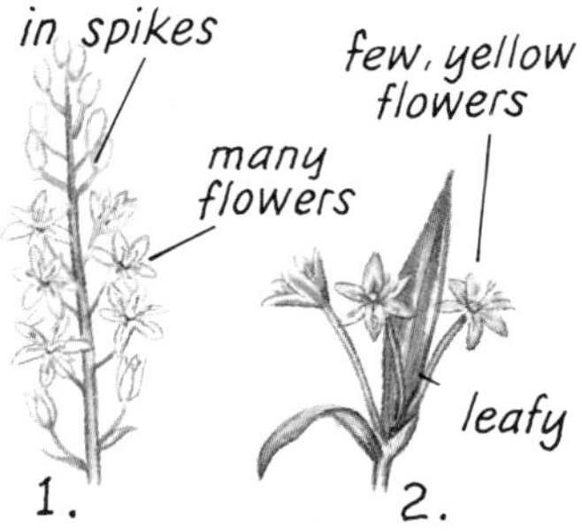

	STAR-OF-BETHLEHEM
Type	perennial
Height	10–30cm
Habitat	grassy places
Flowering	April–June
	STEMS AND LEAVES
Stem	flowering stem leafless, upright
Root	bulb, 15–30mm, usually many small bulbs at base
Hairs	absent
Stipules	absent
Leaves	all from base, 150–300mm, narrow, straight-sided, grooved with white stripe
Leaf-stalk	absent
	FLOWERS
Position	5–15, in short head
Bracts	narrow, whitish, equal to or less than flower-stalk
Type	⚥, mostly upright
Size	30–40mm
Colour	white, green striped beneath
Stalk	upper about equal to petals, lower longer, to 100mm
Perianth	6, 15–20mm, all petal-like, equal, spear-shaped or oblong
Stamens	6, about half length of petals
Stigma	1; style long
Ovary	1, 3-celled
	FRUIT
Type	1, capsule, roughly egg-shaped, 6-angled
Size	10–15mm
Seeds	many, 2.5–3mm, almost globular

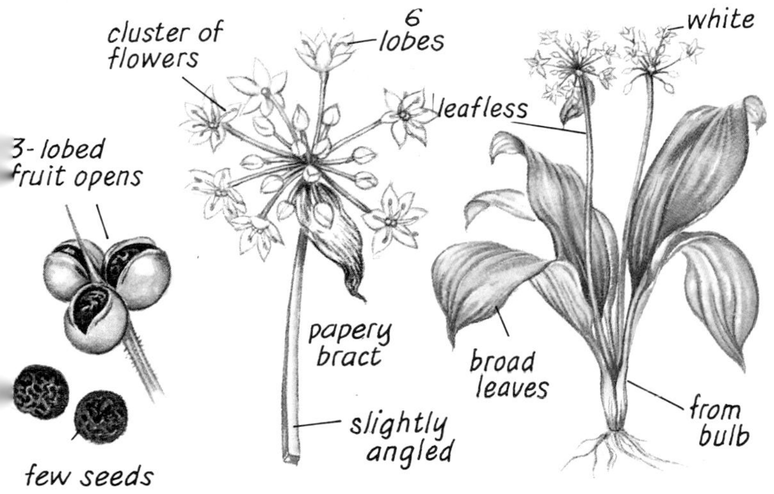

)ften in such quantity that it carpets he woodland floor with white, Ramsons ıdvertises itself by an overpowering mell of garlic. Cooking diminishes the ıroma. *Status:* native; most of area,)ften common. *Similar species:* other species have narrower leaves. Cut ıcross, the leaves of Three-cornered Leek are V-shaped and the flowers are .arger. Two species of grassy places have similar cylindrical leaves and tiny bulbs between the small, pinkish flowers. Wild Onion has one large sheath-like bract below the flower-head; Field Garlic has a two-lobed sheath, each half with a long, leaf-like tip.

1 Three-cornered Leek *(A. triquetrum)*; **2** Wild Onion *(A. vineale)*; **3** Field Garlic *(A. oleraceum)*

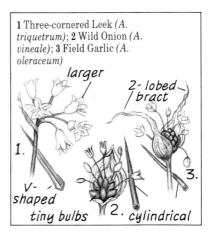

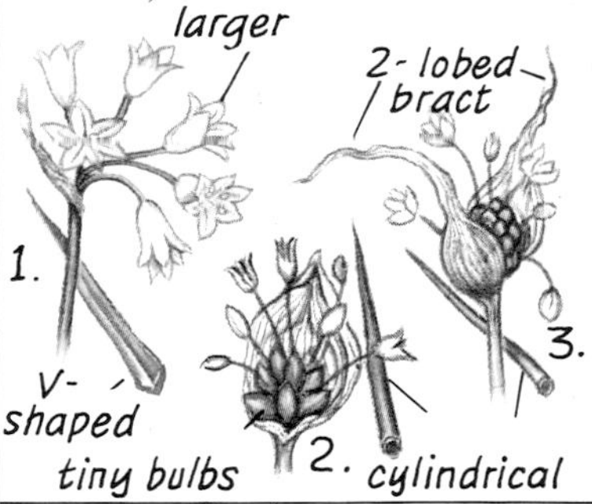

	RAMSONS
Type	perennial, smells of garlic
Height	10–45cm
Habitat	woods, hedges; damp soil
Flowering	April–June
	STEMS AND LEAVES
Stem	flowering stem upright, slightly 3-angled, leafless
Root	narrow bulb
Hairs	absent
Stipules	absent
Leaves	2–3 at base, 100–250mm, elliptical, pointed, edge unbroken
Leaf-stalk	shorter than blade, twisted
	FLOWERS
Position	6–20, in rounded cluster at stem-tip
Bracts	broad, oval, papery, below head, shorter than flower-stalks
Type	⚥
Size	16–20mm
Colour	white
Stalk	longer than flowers
Perianth	6 parts, 8–10mm, equal, all petal-like, spear-shaped, pointed
Stamens	6, shorter than petals
Stigma	1; style long
Ovary	1, 3-celled
	FRUIT
Type	1, capsule, deeply 3-lobed, each lobe splits open
Size	8–12mm
Seeds	few, 3–4mm, angular, black

Herb-Paris *Paris quadrifolia*

A curious plant with a collar of broad leaves beneath the solitary green flower. Four green sepals spread sideways making a cross, separating the very slender, insignificant petals. Although fairly uncommon in the region as a whole, the plants abound in some deciduous woodlands on chalk or limestone. Herb-Paris was believed to have powerful magical properties and was associated with witchcraft. Despite being used medicinally to treat a variety of ailments, the plant is toxic and should be treated with caution. *Status:* native; scattered through area, more common in east. Although no native species are similar, Herb-Paris is related to the Wake-Robin of North America, and several related species are grown in gardens. Most have larger, white or red flowers and some were used in folk-medicine by the North American Indians. (There are no similar species.)

HERB-PARIS

Type perennial
Height 15–40cm
Habitat woods; damp, lime-rich soils
Flowering May–August

STEMS AND LEAVES

Stem upright, unbranched, leafy
Root creeping underground stem
Hairs absent
Stipules absent
Leaves usually 4, in ring around stem, 60–120mm, oval, broadest towards tip, 3–5 main veins, pointed, edge unbroken, base wedge-shaped
Leaf-stalk almost absent

FLOWERS

Position solitary, at stem-tip
Bracts absent
Type ⚥, upright
Size 40–70mm
Colour green
Stalk 20–80mm, usually longer than flower
Sepals 4, rarely to 6, 25–35mm, spear-shaped, spread apart
Petals 4, rarely to 6, 20–30mm, very slender
Stamens 4–6, elongated
Stigmas 4–5 on separate styles
Ovary 1, 4–5-celled

FRUIT

Type 1, berry-like, globular, black, eventually opens
Size 14–18mm
Seeds many, 2.5–3mm, angular, flattened

Spiny, dark green 'leaves' of Butcher's-broom are in fact modified stems, as indicated by the flowers borne directly on the surface. The species is widely planted for ornament or as cover for game in woodland. *Status:* native, sometimes escaped from gardens; scattered through south of area. *Similar species:* no native plants look quite like Butcher's-broom, but Wild Asparagus is related and has similar true leaves and fruits. The needle-like foliage is similarly formed from specialized branches. Wild Asparagus has larger, stalked flowers with equal, petal-like lobes. Cultivated Asparagus belongs to the same species.

Wild Asparagus *(Asparagus officinalis* subsp. *prostratus)*

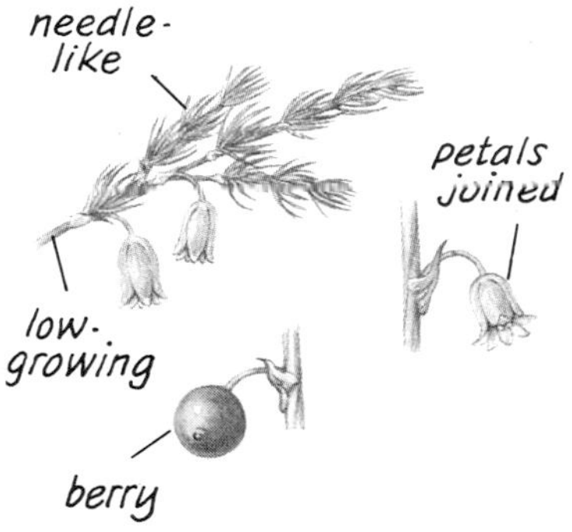

	BUTCHER'S-BROOM
Type	perennial, evergreen
Height	25–100cm
Habitat	woods, rocks; dry soils
Flowering	January–April
	STEMS AND LEAVES
Stem	upright; side branches leaf-like, 10–60mm, oval, thick, dark green, spine-tipped
Root	creeping, thick, underground stem
Hairs	absent
Stipules	absent
Leaves	on alternate sides of stem, to 5mm, narrowly triangular, papery, brownish; apparent leaves are special branches
Leaf-stalk	absent

	FLOWERS
Position	1–2, on upper surface of leaf-like branch; ♂ and ♀ flowers on different plants
Bracts	small, triangular, papery
Type 1	♂ with stamens
Type 2	♀ with ovary
Size	4–6mm
Colour	greenish, violet-spotted
Stalk	absent
Perianth	6 lobes, 2.5–3mm, inner smaller than outer
Stamens	3, bases joined, violet
Stigma	1; style short
Ovary	1, 1-celled
	FRUIT
Type	1, berry, globular, red
Size	9–15mm
Seeds	up to 4, 8–10mm, rounded, smooth

Solomon's-seal *Polygonatum multiflorum*

Graceful, arching stems of Solomon's-seal bear small clusters of nodding flowers at the base of broad, parallel-veined leaves. The plant propagates itself by thick, white stems, which run underground along the woodland floor. Round blackish berries contain several seeds. *Status:* native; scattered through most of area except Ireland. *Similar species:* Angular Solomon's-seal has angled stems and the scented, usually solitary flowers are broader at the middle. Lily-of-the-valley, a familiar garden plant, usually has two leaves at the base. The flowering stem bears short, nodding, sweetly-scented flowers. and the berries are red.

1 Angular Solomon's-seal *(P. odoratum)*; **2** Lily-of-the-valley *(Convallaria majalis)*

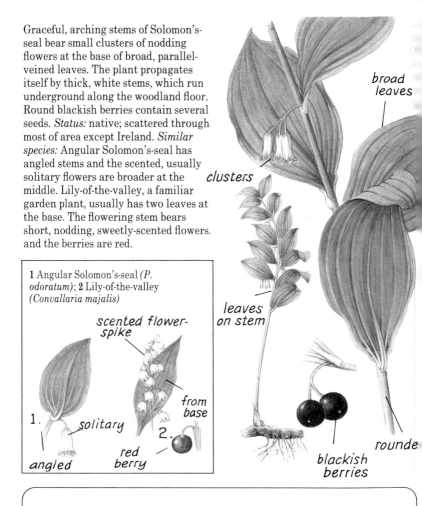

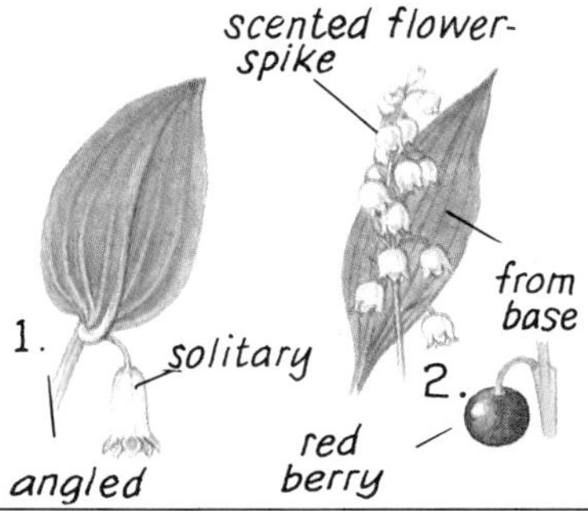

	SOLOMON'S-SEAL
Type	perennial
Height	30–80cm
Habitat	woods
Flowering	May–June
	STEMS AND LEAVES
Stem	upright, arching above, smoothly rounded sides
Root	thick, creeping, underground stem
Hairs	more or less absent
Stipules	absent
Leaves	on alternate side of stem, 50–150mm, oval or broadly elliptical, tip pointed, edge unbroken
Leaf-stalk	absent

	FLOWERS
Position	2–5, in branched cluster at leaf-base
Bracts	absent
Type	⚥, nodding
Size	9–15mm
Colour	greenish white
Stalk	shorter than flower
Perianth	6, equal, petal-like parts, bases form tube, narrowed in middle; lobes oval
Stamens	6, inside petal-tube
Stigma	1, 3-lobed; style long
Ovary	1, 3-celled
	FRUIT
Type	1, berry, globular, bluish black
Size	8–10mm
Seeds	up to 6, nearly globular

One of the first heralds of Spring, pushing its clean, white flowers up through the snow, Snowdrop can flower so early because it stores food in a bulb, enabling it to grow without the need to extract materials from the still-frozen ground. It is often grown in gardens, and has many named variants; most populations in the countryside originate from cultivated plants. *Status:* introduced or native in extreme south; most of area. *Similar species:* Summer Snowflake is a much larger plant of wet meadows and has broader, equal petals. Spring Snowflake differs in the shorter stems, usually bearing a solitary flower.

1 Summer Snowflake *(Leucojum aestivum)*; 2 Spring Snowflake *(L. vernum)*

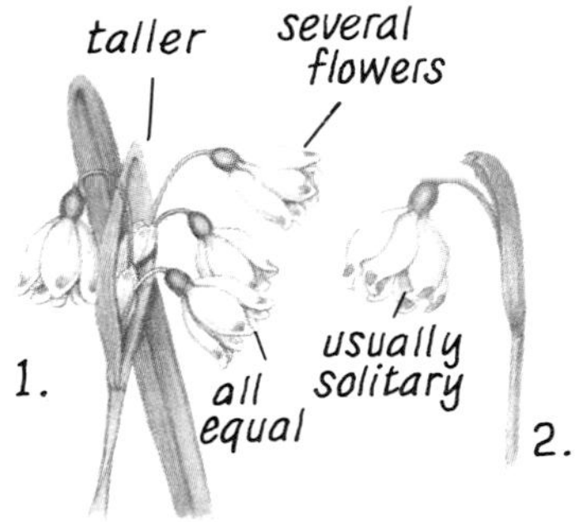

SNOWDROP

Type perennial
Height 15–25cm
Habitat woods, grassy places; damp soil, often by streams
Flowering January–March

STEMS AND LEAVES

Stem flowering stem upright, curved at tip, base with tubular, papery sheath
Root egg-shaped bulb, 10–20mm
Hairs absent
Stipules absent
Leaves all at base, 50–250mm, narrow, straight-sided, tip blunt
Leaf-stalk absent

FLOWERS

Position solitary, at stem-tip
Bracts leaf-like, papery-edged, tip forked
Type ⚥, nodding
Size 22–30mm
Colour pure white; inner lobes with green mark near tip
Stalk about equal to flower
Perianth 6 parts, petal-like, unequal; outer 3 14–17mm, elliptical, blunt; inner 3 6–11mm, oblong or oval, tip notched
Stamens 6, inside flower
Stigma 1; style long
Ovary 1, below petals, 3-celled

FRUIT

Type 1, capsule, egg-shaped
Size 12–15mm
Seeds many, 5–6mm, elongated, swollen in middle

Wild Daffodil *Narcissus pseudonarcissus*

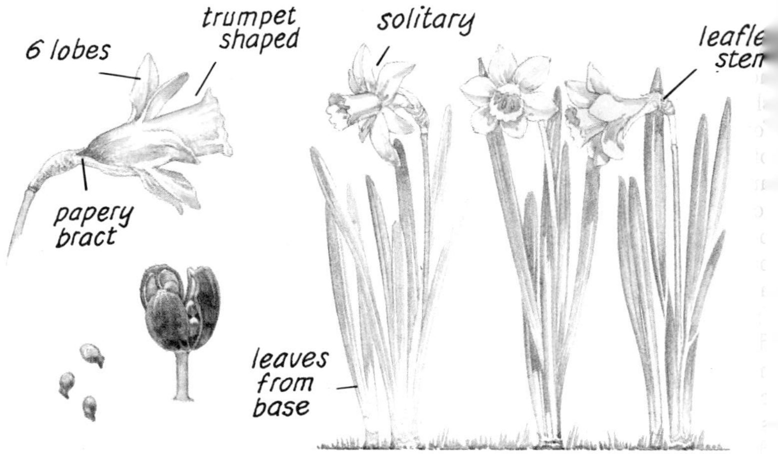

Familiar as a garden plant, the Daffodil was formerly much more common in the wild although its numbers were greatly depleted as people uprooted the bulbs. There are still a few places where great drifts of the nodding, yellow flowers flourish in deciduous woodland. *Status:* native or often introduced; southern half of area, fairly abundant in some localities. *Similar species:* Primrose-peerless is one of the long-established garden hybrids and is often naturalized. The central trumpet is much shorter than the whitish petal-lobes and the flowers are usually carried in pairs.

Primrose-peerless *(N. × medioluteus)*

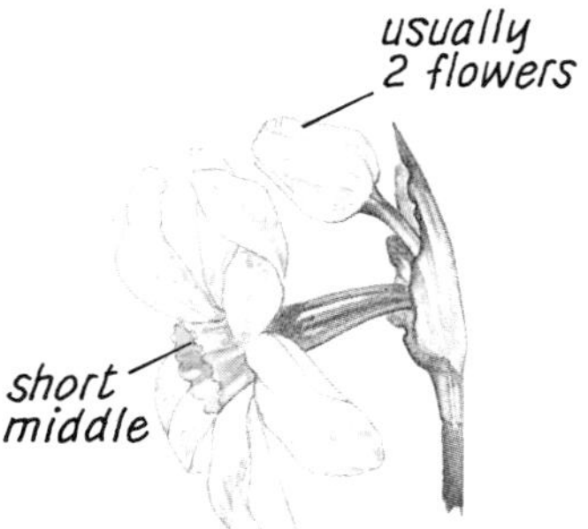

WILD DAFFODIL

Type perennial
Height 20–50cm
Habitat woods, grassland; damp soils
Flowering February–April

STEMS AND LEAVES

Stem flowering stem upright, slightly flattened, with 2 angles
Root bulb, 20–50mm
Hairs absent
Stipules absent
Leaves all at base, 120–500mm, narrow, straight-sided, bluish green, tip blunt
Leaf-stalk absent

FLOWERS

Position solitary, at stem-tip
Bracts 20–60mm, broad, papery
Type ⚥, often nodding
Size 35–60mm
Colour pale yellow, centre darker
Stalk short beneath flower; long stem bears bract and flower
Perianth 6, 35–60mm, equal, petal-like, bases form tube with trumpet-like extra tube on inner face; lobes oval, spread apart
Stamens 6, inside petal-tube
Stigma 1, tip swollen; style long
Ovary 1, below petals, 3-celled

FRUIT

Type capsule, oval or globular
Size 12–25mm
Seeds many, 4–5mm, egg-shaped, slightly roughened

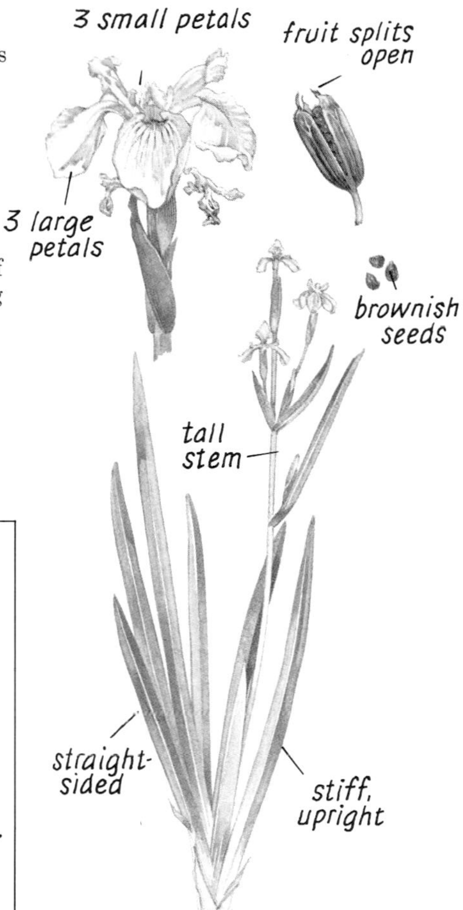

An imposing plant forming large clumps near water, with stiff, bluish, sword-shaped leaves. The yellow flowers are formed as in the various garden species of Iris, with three broad outer petals and three upright inner petals. Each lower petal is covered by a curious petal-like stigma, forming a tube between the two. *Status:* native; most of area, common. *Similar species:* Stinking Iris has thinner, evergreen leaves that flop over to one side. Its flowers are a mixture of yellow or dull violet and capsules split to reveal bright orange seeds. Blue Iris has violet or lilac flowers and the brown seeds have a loose, papery covering.

1 Stinking Iris *(I. foetidissima)*; **2** Blue Iris *(I. spuria)*

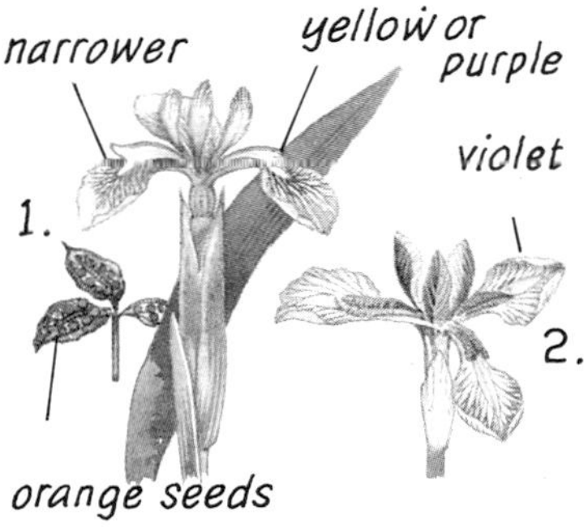

	YELLOW IRIS
Type	perennial
Height	40–150cm
Habitat	rivers, streams, ditches, marshes, woods; wet ground or shallow water
Flowering	May–July
	STEMS AND LEAVES
Stem	upright, often branched, leafy
Root	thick, creeping, underground stem; roots fleshy
Hairs	absent
Stipules	absent
Leaves	basal or on flowering stem, 120–900mm, narrow, straight-sided, bluish green, veins parallel, pointed, base sheaths stem
Leaf-stalk	absent

	FLOWERS
Position	2–3 clustered at stem-tip
Bracts	40–100mm, edges papery
Type	⚥, upright
Size	80–100mm
Colour	yellow, orange-blotched and purple-spotted at base
Stalk	shorter than flower
Perianth	6 petal-like parts, unequal, bases joined; outer 3 50–75mm, broad, turned downwards; inner 3 20–30mm, upright
Stamens	3, at base of outer petals
Stigmas	3, broad, petal-like
Ovary	1, below petals, 3-celled
	FRUIT
Type	oblong capsule, 3-angled
Size	40–80mm
Seeds	many, 7–9mm, brown, smooth

Lords-and-Ladies *Arum maculatum*

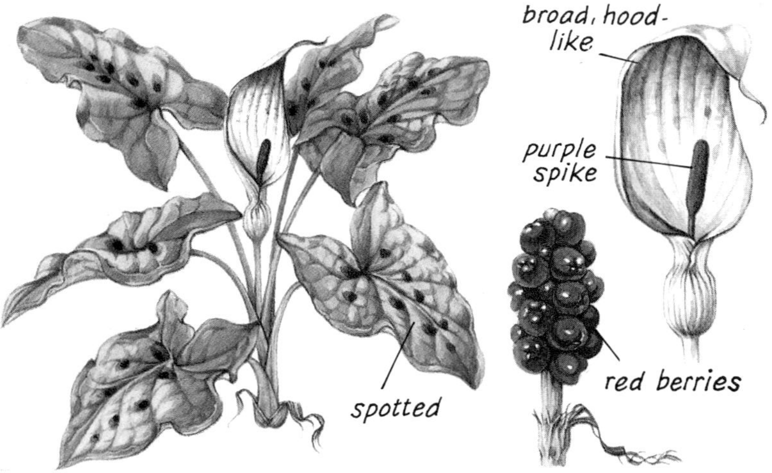

These peculiar flowers are actually complex flower-heads. A central spike-like part gives off a smell and heat which attracts small flies. The hood-like upper part funnels the flies into the base, to be trapped by backward-pointing hairs until they have pollinated the tiny flowers. *Status:* native; most of area except north, often common. *Similar species:* Italian Lords-and-Ladies produces its pale-veined leaves earlier and has a yellow spike-like part to the flower-head. Bog Arum has a smaller, white flower-head; Sweet-flag has iris-like foliage and a leaf-like upper part to the flower-head.

1 Italian Lords-and-Ladies *(A. italicum)*; **2** Bog Arum *(Calla palustris)*; **3** Sweet-flag *(Acorus calamus)*

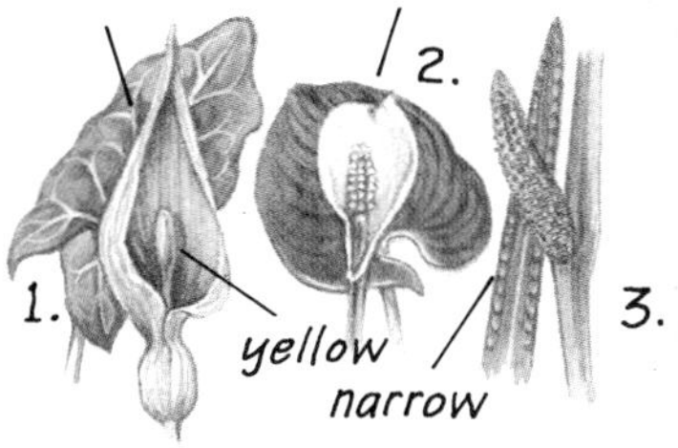

	LORDS-AND-LADIES
Type	perennial
Height	30–50cm
Habitat	woods, hedges; often lime-rich soils
Flowering	April–May
	STEMS AND LEAVES
Stem	upright
Root	fleshy underground stem
Hairs	absent
Stipules	absent
Leaves	basal, blade 70–200mm, with backward-pointing lobes, usually spotted
Leaf-stalk	15–25mm, base sheaths stem
	FLOWERS
Position	at stem-tip, petal-like bract encloses flower-head with purplish, spike-like upper part, ♂ and ♀ flowers on same plant
Bracts	150–250mm, upright, hooded
Type 1	♂ above ♀ flowers on spike
Type 2	♀ at base of spike
Size	1–2.5mm
Colour	yellowish green, sometimes marked with purple
Stalk	absent; head long-stalked
Sepals	absent
Petals	absent
Stamens	3–4
Stigma	1; style absent
Ovary	1, 1-celled
	FRUIT
Type	berries, in cluster 30–50mm long at stem-tip, scarlet
Size	4–6mm
Seeds	1–3, 3–5mm, globular, pitted

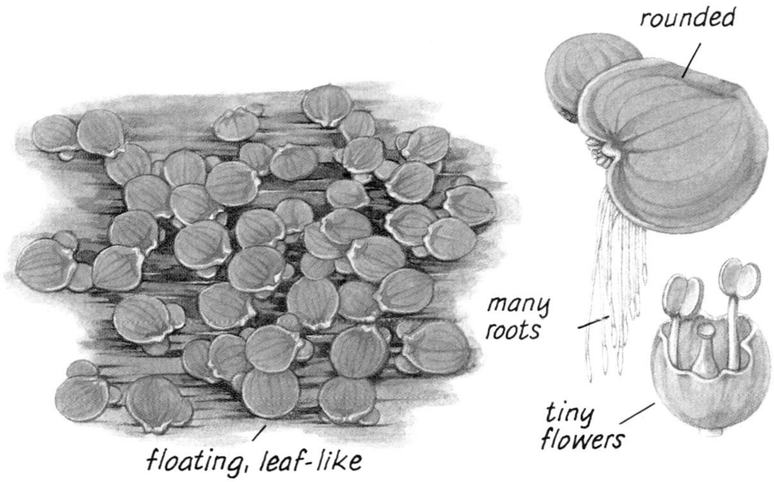

More like an alga than a flowering plant, the diminutive Duckweed forms a floating carpet of green on still water. Although tiny, Duckweeds are distantly related to Lords-and-Ladies. *Status:* native; most of area, fairly common. *Similar species:* two species have only a single root beneath. Fat Duckweed is swollen below, whereas Common Duckweed is smaller and flat below. Ivy-leaved Duckweed forms interconnected masses, usually floating just beneath the surface. The smallest native flowering plant, Rootless Duckweed makes a round blob up to one millimetre across.

1 Fat Duckweed *(Lemna gibba)*;
2 Common Duckweed *(L. minor)*;
3 Ivy leaved Duckweed *(L. trisulca)*;
4 Rootless Duckweed *(Wolffia arrhiza)*

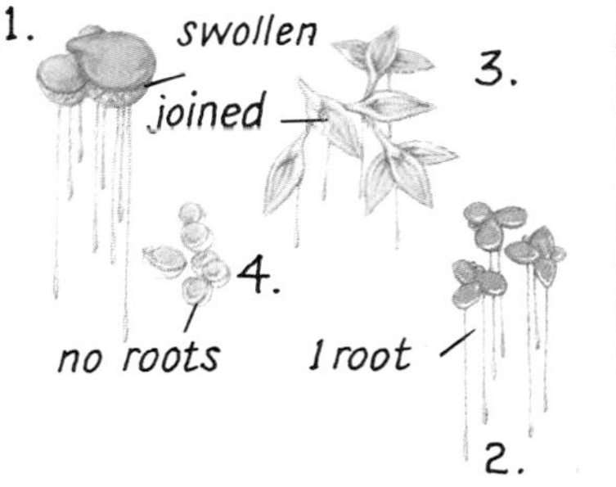

	GREATER DUCKWEED
Type	perennial, floating
Height	0.1–0.2cm, width 0.5–1cm
Habitat	ponds, ditches; fresh-water
Flowering	June–July
	STEMS AND LEAVES
Stem	solitary or 2–5 connected, flattened, oval or circular, leaf-like, often purple below, floating; smaller purplish buds sink and over-winter
Root	5–15 per plant, up to 30mm, straight
Hairs	absent
Stipules	absent
Leaves	absent; stems leaf-like

	FLOWERS
Position	♂ and ♀ flowers on same plant, few, rarely produced, 1 ♀ with 2 ♂ flowers in pocket
Bracts	tiny, cup-like, papery
Type 1	♂ with stamen
Type 2	♀ with ovary
Size	1–1.5mm
Colour	green
Stalk	absent
Sepals	absent
Petals	absent
Stamens	1 per flower
Stigma	1; style short
Ovary	1, 1-celled
	FRUIT
Type	1, more or less globular, not opening
Size	*c*1mm
Seeds	1–4, ridged or smooth

Broad-leaved Helleborine *Epipactis helleborine*

A tall, rather uncommon Orchid, usually found in the shade of deciduous trees or beneath hedges. Slightly nodding, green and purple flowers are borne towards the same side of the stem. *Status:* native; scattered through area. *Similar species:* Marsh Helleborine has short hairs on the base of the flowers and the frilled lower lip turns up at the edges. Two white-flowered species have the ovary and centre of the flower angled upwards, rather than horizontal or nodding. Narrow-leaved Helleborine has slender leaves, short bracts and pointed sepals. White Helleborine has oval leaves, bracts mostly longer than the flower, and blunt sepals.

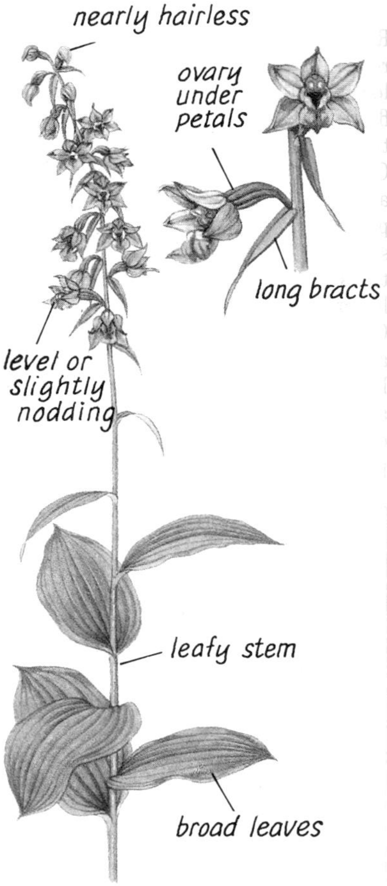

1 Marsh Helleborine *(E. palustris)*; **2** Narrow-leaved Helleborine *(Cephalanthera longifolia)*; **3** White Helleborine *(C. damasonium)*

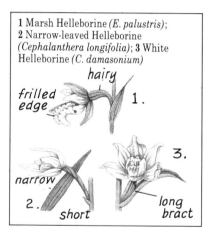

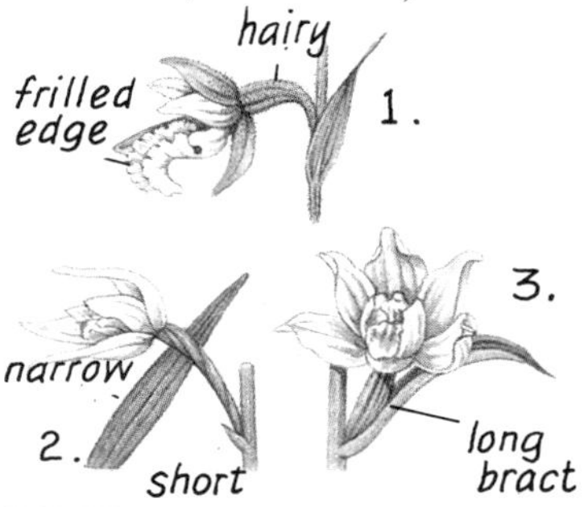

	BROAD-LEAVED HELLEBORINE
Type	perennial
Height	25–80cm
Habitat	woods, hedges
Flowering	July–October
	STEMS AND LEAVES
Stem	1–3, upright, often purple-tinged, leafy
Root	short underground stem, many roots
Hairs	few, short, near top of stem
Stipules	absent
Leaves	spirally arranged, to 170mm, lowest scale-like, middle broadly oval or elliptical
Leaf-stalk	absent
	FLOWERS
Position	15–50, in one-sided, spike-like head, 70–300mm long
Bracts	spear-shaped, lower equal flower, upper shorter
Type	⚥, nodding
Size	10–16mm wide
Colour	yellowish green and purple
Stalk	very short
Sepals	3, 9–11mm, petal-like, oval
Petals	3; 2 side petals oval; lower petal 6–8mm, hollow, end lobe bent back; spur absent
Stamen	1, stalkless
Stigmas	2; style absent
Ovary	1, below petals, 1-celled
	FRUIT
Type	1, capsule, oblong, angular, points downwards, splits lengthwise
Size	minute
Seeds	numerous, dust-like

Relatives of Bee Orchid have a remarkable method of pollination. The lower petal resembles an insect and the flower is pollinated as the male insect tries to mate with it. Plants of the Bee Orchid in northern Europe have largely abandoned the method and are self-pollinated. *Status:* native; scattered, southern half of area. *Similar species:* two species have greenish sepals, the lower petal marked with blue. Fly Orchid has a narrow, forked lower petal and thread-like side petals. The broad lower petal of Early Spider-orchid has an almost H-shaped mark. Late Spider-orchid has pink sepals, the broad lower petal with an upturned tip.

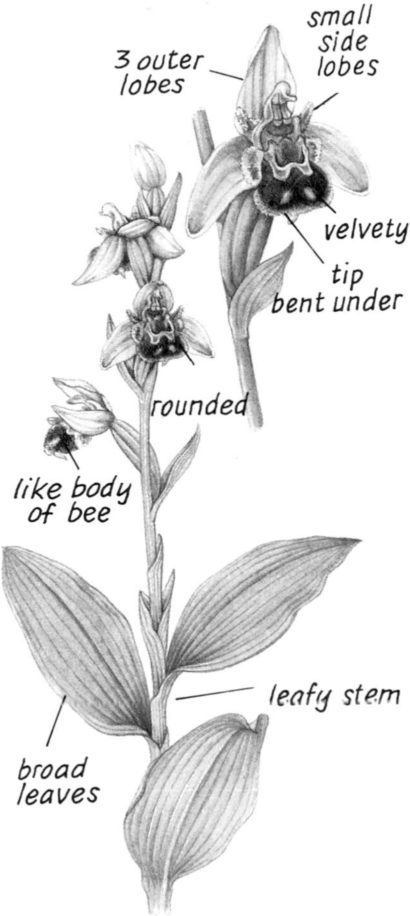

1 Fly Orchid *(O. insectifera)*; **2** Early Spider-orchid *(O. sphegodes)*; **3** Late Spider-orchid *(O. fuciflora)*

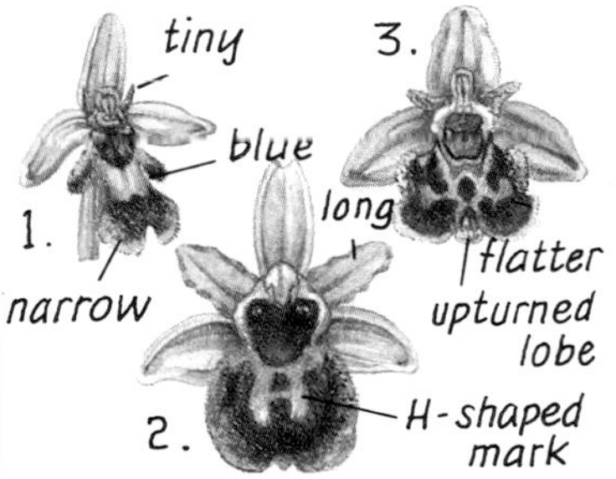

	BEE ORCHID
Type	perennial
Height	15–45cm, rarely 60cm
Habitat	grassy places, wood edges, hedges; lime-rich soil
Flowering	June–July
	STEMS AND LEAVES
Stem	upright, leafy
Root	egg-shaped or globular tubers; few, fleshy roots
Hairs	absent
Stipules	absent
Leaves	spirally arranged, 30–80mm, elliptical to oblong
Leaf-stalk	absent
	FLOWERS
Position	2–5, rarely 10, in spike-like head, 30–120mm long
Bracts	often longer than flower
Type	⚥
Size	23–30mm wide
Colour	pink, back green; brown lower petal with yellow mark
Stalk	very short
Sepals	3, 12–15mm, petal-like, elliptical or oblong
Petals	3; side petals spear-shaped; lower 12–15mm, almost globular, velvety, 3-lobed, the lowest bent under; spur absent
Stamen	1, stalkless
Stigmas	2; style absent
Ovary	1, below petals, 1-celled
	FRUIT
Type	oblong capsule, angular, splits lengthwise
Size	15–25mm
Seeds	many, minute, dust-like

Pyramidal Orchid *Anacamptis pyramidalis*

One of the most common Orchids on chalk grassland, often forming large colonies marked by their conical heads of magenta-pink flowers. The long, very slender, curved spur at the base of the flower is an adaptation to pollination by butterflies. *Status:* native; scattered through area, common in some localities. *Similar species:* Fragrant Orchid has more cylindrical heads of sweetly scented flowers. Another Orchid with a short, dense head of flowers, though short-spurred, is Burnt Orchid. The upper buds are purplish brown, as though burnt, and fade as the flowers age.

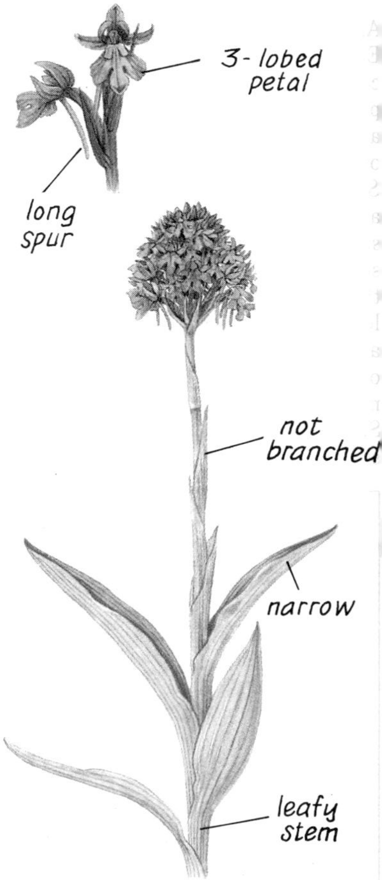

1 Fragrant Orchid *(Gymnadenia conopsea)*; 2 Burnt Orchid *(Orchis ustulata)*

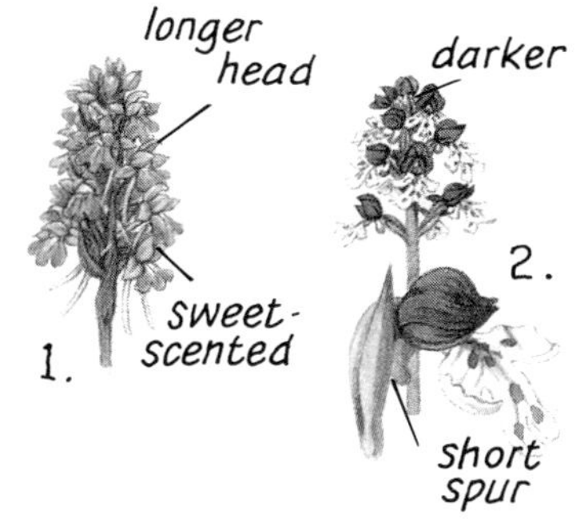

	PYRAMIDAL ORCHID
Type	perennial
Height	20–75cm
Habitat	grassy places, dunes; lime-rich soils
Flowering	June–August
	STEMS AND LEAVES
Stem	upright, slightly angled
Root	egg-shaped or globular tubers; few, fleshy roots
Hairs	absent
Stipules	absent
Leaves	spirally arranged, to 150mm, lower scale-like, upper narrowly spear-shaped, pointed, base sheaths stem
Leaf-stalk	absent
	FLOWERS
Position	many, in crowded, conical head, 20–50mm long
Bracts	narrowly spear-shaped, about equalling flower
Type	⚥, strong-smelling
Size	12–15mm
Colour	purplish pink
Stalk	very short
Sepals	3, 5–6mm, petal-like, spear-shaped
Petals	3; side petals form hood with upper sepal; lower 6–7mm, wedge-shaped, 3-lobed; spur 9–12mm, thin, curved
Stamen	1, stalkless
Stigmas	2; style absent
Ovary	1, below petals, 1-celled
	FRUIT
Type	1, capsule, oblong, angular, splits lengthwise
Size	10–15mm
Seeds	numerous, minute, dust-like

Although most native Orchids are rare, Early-purple Orchid can be more common than some of the meadow plants with which it grows. Its leaves are usually spotted and the thick spur of the purple flowers is tilted upwards. *Status:* native; scattered throughout area, sometimes common. *Similar species:* Green-winged Orchid lacks leaf-spots and has distinctive green veins on the hood-like sepals. Two Orchids have leafy stems, leaf-like bracts and the spur angled downwards. Common Spotted-orchid has broad leaves and a large middle lobe to the lower petal; Heath Spotted-orchid has narrow leaves and a small middle petal-lobe.

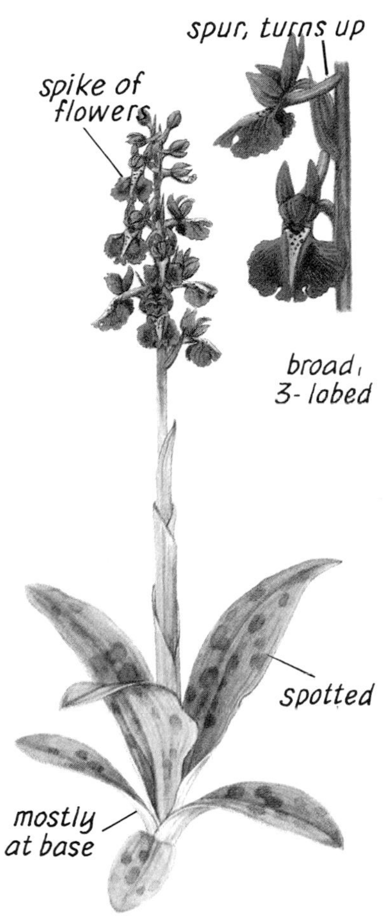

1 Green-winged Orchid *(O. morio)*; **2** Common Spotted-orchid *(Dactylorhiza fuchsii)*; **3** Heath Spotted-orchid *(D. maculata)*

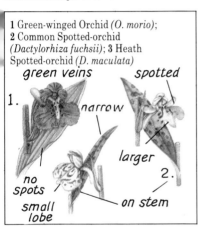

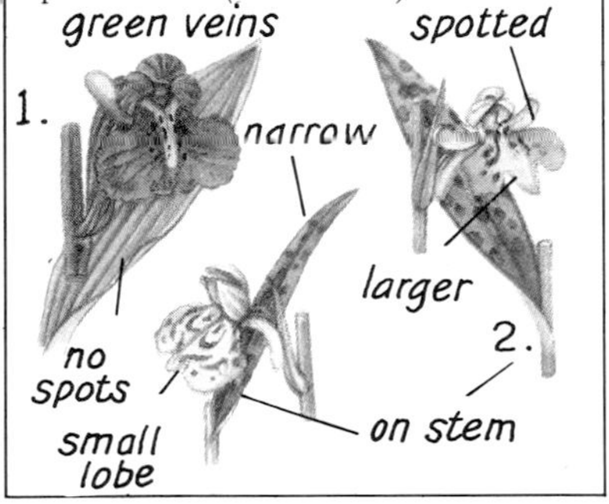

	EARLY-PURPLE ORCHID
Type	perennial
Height	15–60cm
Habitat	grassland, woods, hedges; mostly lime-rich soils
Flowering	April–June
	STEMS AND LEAVES
Stem	upright, rather stout
Root	egg-shaped or globular tubers; few, fleshy roots
Hairs	absent
Stipules	absent
Leaves	3–5, basal, oblong or spear-shaped, mostly with purple spots, blunt, base sheaths stem; upper scale-like
Leaf-stalk	absent
	FLOWERS
Position	many in spike-like head, 40–150mm long
Bracts	purple, shorter than flower
Type	⚥
Size	18–26mm
Colour	reddish purple, lower petal with darker spots
Stalk	very short
Sepals	3, 6–8mm, petal-like, oval
Petals	3; 2 side petals oval; lower 8–12mm, broad, 3-lobed; spur 8–11mm, blunt, level or angled upwards
Stamen	1, stalkless
Stigmas	2; style absent
Ovary	1, below petals, 1-celled
	FRUIT
Type	1, capsule, oblong, angular, splits lengthwise
Size	*c*20mm
Seeds	numerous, minute, dust-like

Greater Butterfly-orchid *Platanthera chlorantha*

A delicate woodland Orchid, with greenish-white flowers. At the base of each flower is a slender, curved spur which holds the nectar. Few insects other than butterflies and moths have tongues that are long enough to reach the nectar, the latter being drawn by a scent which is strongest at night. The long lower petal acts as a landing platform where the insect can alight. *Status:* native; scattered throughout area, most common in south. *Similar species:* Lesser Butterfly-orchid is smaller in all its parts and is more common in the north. Also more common in the north, Small-white Orchid has tiny flowers lacking a spur.

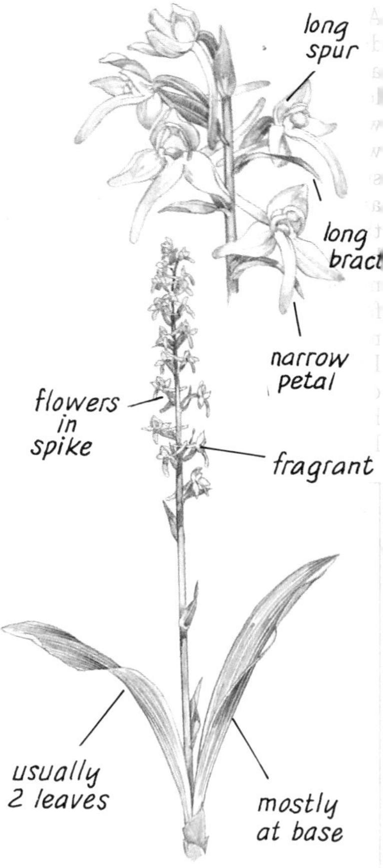

1 Lesser Butterfly-orchid *(P. bifolia)*;
2 Small-white Orchid *(Pseudorchis albida)*

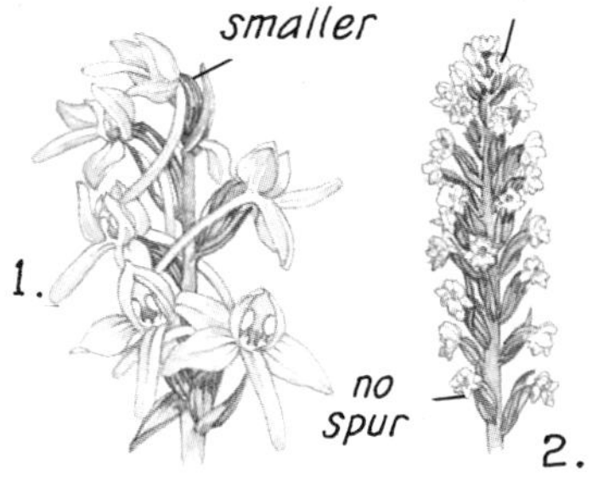

	GREATER BUTTERFLY-ORCHID
Type	perennial
Height	20–40cm, rarely 60cm
Habitat	woods, grassy places; mostly lime-rich soils
Flowering	May–July
	STEMS AND LEAVES
Stem	upright, leafy
Root	swollen, tapering tubers; few, fleshy roots
Hairs	absent
Stipules	absent
Leaves	spirally arranged, to 200mm, usually 2, elliptical, blunt, 1–5 small leaves above
Leaf-stalk	absent
	FLOWERS
Position	many, in spike-like head, 50–200mm long
Bracts	nearly equal to flower
Type	⚥, strongly scented
Size	23–35mm
Colour	greenish white
Stalk	very short
Sepals	3, 10–11mm, petal-like, oval to nearly triangular
Petals	3; side petals spear-shaped; lower 10–16mm, narrow, tapered, blunt; spur 19–28mm, slender, usually curved
Stamen	1, stalkless
Stigmas	2; style absent
Ovary	1, below petals, 1-celled
	FRUIT
Type	cylindrical capsule, angular, splits lengthwise
Size	*c*25mm
Seeds	numerous, minute, dust-like

A small-flowered Orchid with distinctively twisted flower-spikes. The almost tubular flowers have a frilled lower petal. When a bee seeks nectar which collects at the base of the flower, waxy masses of pollen grains from the stamen become cemented to its tongue and are carried to other flowers. Once the pollen is removed, the stigma becomes exposed for pollination. *Status:* native; scattered through area except for much of north. *Similar species:* mainly a plant of pine-woods, Creeping Lady's-tresses spreads by means of creeping stems. The smaller flowers have a concave lower petal with a tip like the lip of a jug.

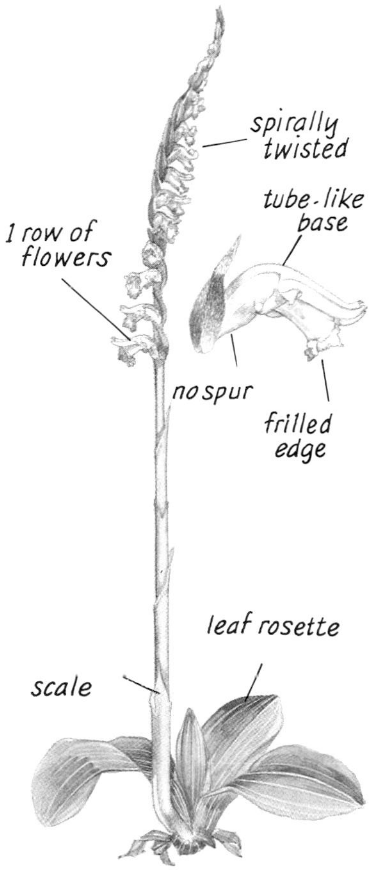

Creeping Lady's-tresses *(Goodyera repens)*

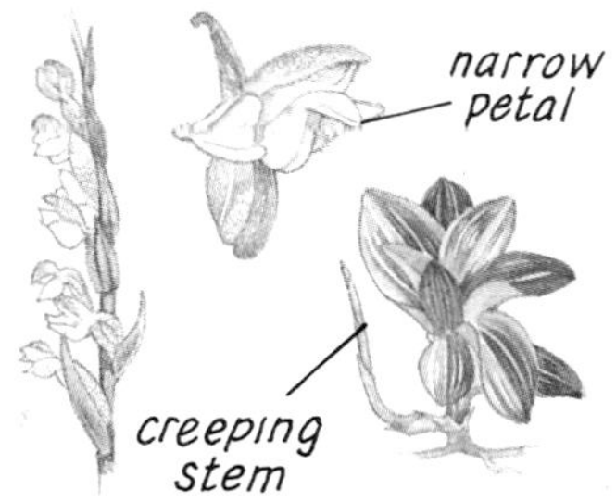

	AUTUMN LADY'S-TRESSES
Type	perennial
Height	7–20cm
Habitat	grassy places, dunes; usually lime-rich soils
Flowering	August–September
	STEMS AND LEAVES
Stem	upright, slender, not leafy
Root	swollen, tapered tubers; few, fleshy roots
Hairs	gland-tipped, on upper part of plant
Stipules	absent
Leaves	4–5 in rosette at base, 20–35mm, oval, bluish green; 3–7 scale-like above
Leaf-stalk	absent
	FLOWERS
Position	7–20 in spirally twisted row, 30–120mm long
Bracts	shorter than flower
Type	⚥, scented
Size	4–5mm
Colour	white
Stalk	very short
Sepals	3, 6–7mm, petal-like, oblong, blunt
Petals	3; side petals oblong; lower 6–7mm, oblong, tip rounded, frilled; spur absent
Stamen	1, stalkless
Stigmas	2; style absent
Ovary	1, below petals, 1-celled
	FRUIT
Type	1, capsule, egg-shaped, angular, splits lengthwise
Size	5–6mm
Seeds	numerous, minute, dust-like

Common Twayblade *Listera ovata*

Contrary to the popular image, many Orchids have greenish, insignificant flowers. Common Twayblade's most obvious feature, giving rise to its common name, is a pair of broad stem-leaves. Nectar secreted on to the lower petal attracts beetles and flies. As the insect's head touches the centre of the flower, a drop of cement squirts out and sets rapidly, anchoring the masses of pollen. *Status:* native; throughout area, sometimes common. *Similar species:* Lesser Twayblade is smaller, the lower petal with pointed lobes. Two species have basal leaves. The large petal of Musk Orchid is three-lobed; that of Fen Orchid is frilled and points upwards.

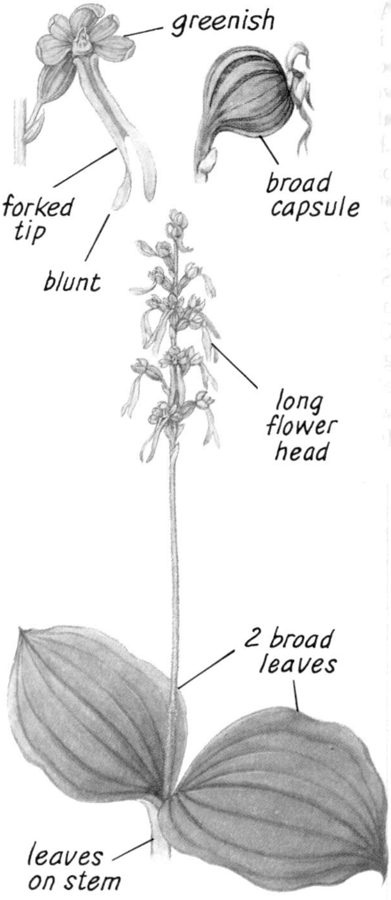

1 Lesser Twayblade *(L. cordata)*; **2** Musk Orchid *(Herminium monorchis)*; **3** Fen Orchid *(Liparis loeselii)*

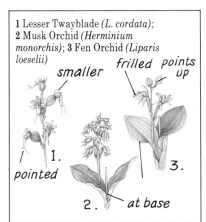

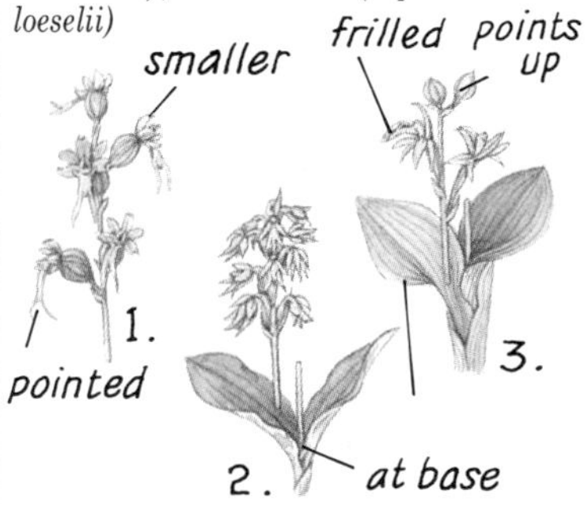

	COMMON TWAYBLADE
Type	perennial
Height	20–60cm
Habitat	woods, hedges, pastures; damp, usually lime-rich soil
Flowering	June–July
	STEMS AND LEAVES
Stem	upright, leafy, scale-like below
Root	horizontal underground stem; many roots
Hairs	gland-tipped on upper part of stem
Stipules	absent
Leaves	2 almost paired on stem, 50–200mm, broadly elliptical, 3–5 main veins, blunt
Leaf-stalk	absent
	FLOWERS
Position	many, in spike-like head, 70–250mm long
Bracts	much shorter than flowers
Type	⚥, scented
Size	14–20mm
Colour	yellowish green, with reddish edges
Stalk	much shorter than flower
Sepals	3, 4–5mm, oval
Petals	3; side petals oblong; lower 10–15mm, oblong, bent down, tip forked; spur absent
Stamen	1, stalkless
Stigmas	2; style absent
Ovary	1, below petals, 1-celled
	FRUIT
Type	1, capsule, globular, splits lengthwise
Size	*c*10mm
Seeds	numerous, minute, dust-like

An unusual Orchid, its long, twisted, ribbon-like lower petal has two slender lobes near the base. Although generally very rare in the region, it is fairly abundant on stabilized sand-dunes in the extreme south-west. Here, its tall, pale flower-heads rise above surrounding plants and are easily visible at a distance. *Status:* native; south of area, scattered, mostly rare. *Similar species:* although no other native species is quite like the Lizard Orchid, several others have slender, greenish flowers. Frog Orchid has an elongated, much shorter, lower petal with a pair of narrow lobes near the tip. It is fairly common on chalk grassland.

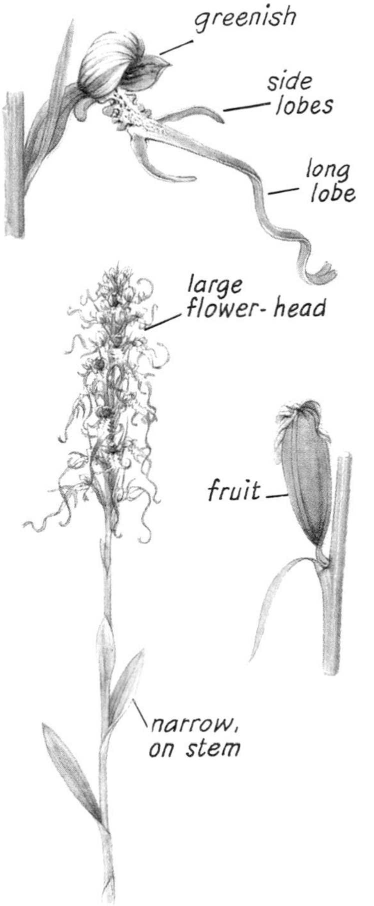

Frog Orchid *(Coeloglossum viride)*

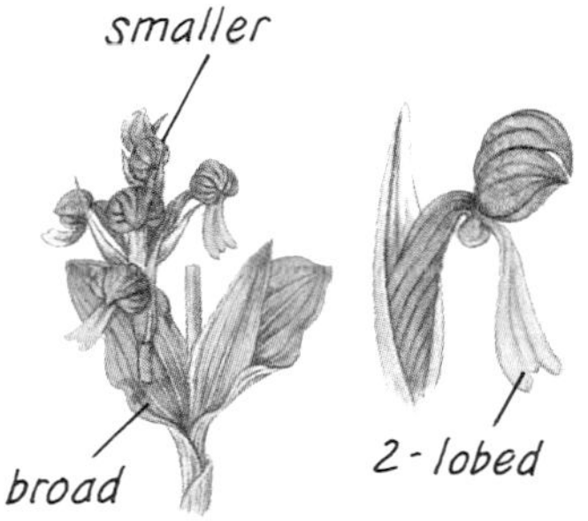

	LIZARD ORCHID
Type	perennial
Height	20–40cm, rarely 90cm
Habitat	woods, grassy places, dunes; lime-rich soils
Flowering	May–July
	STEMS AND LEAVES
Stem	upright, stout, leafy
Root	egg-shaped or globular tubers; few, fleshy roots
Hairs	absent
Stipules	absent
Leaves	4–6 spirally arranged, to 150mm, narrowly elliptical or oblong, base sheaths stem; lowest scale-like
Leaf-stalk	absent
	FLOWERS
Position	many in spike-like head, 100–250mm, rarely 500mm long
Bracts	narrow, shorter than flower
Type	⚥, strong-smelling
Size	35–55mm
Colour	greenish, purple markings
Stalk	very short
Sepals	3, 7–10mm, oval, blunt
Petals	3; side petals narrow; lower 30–50mm, ribbon-like, twisted, furry at base, 2 long side lobes, tip forked; spur 3–4mm, conical
Stamen	1, stalkless
Stigmas	2; style absent
Ovary	1, below petals, 1-celled
	FRUIT
Type	cylindrical capsule, angular, splits lengthwise
Size	*c*30mm
Seeds	numerous, minute, dust-like

Bird's-nest Orchid *Neottia nidus-avis*

This curious, pallid Orchid with parchment-coloured flowers is usually found growing in the thick layers of leaf-litter of deciduous woodland, especially beneath Beech trees. Lacking green pigment, it looks like a parasite but is a saprophyte, for the plant obtains its nourishment from dead and decaying plant material. The short, fleshy roots form a thick, tangled mass, which give rise to the common name. *Status:* native; scattered through area. *Similar species:* Coralroot Orchid has few smaller, greenish-yellow and white flowers. The very rare Ghost Orchid has the large petal and blunt spur pointing upwards.

1 Coralroot Orchid *(Corallorhiza trifida)*; 2 Ghost Orchid *(Epipogium aphyllum)*

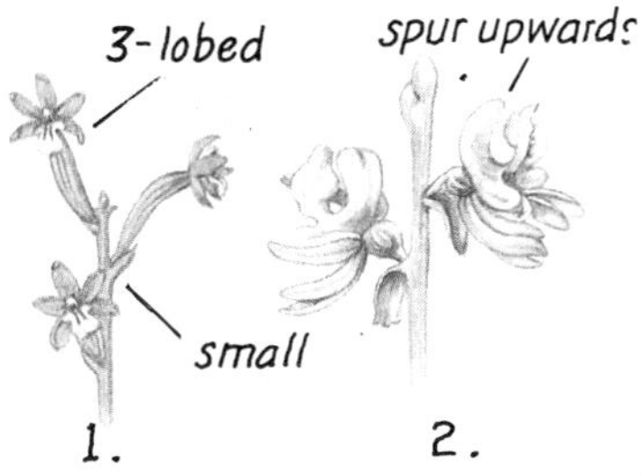

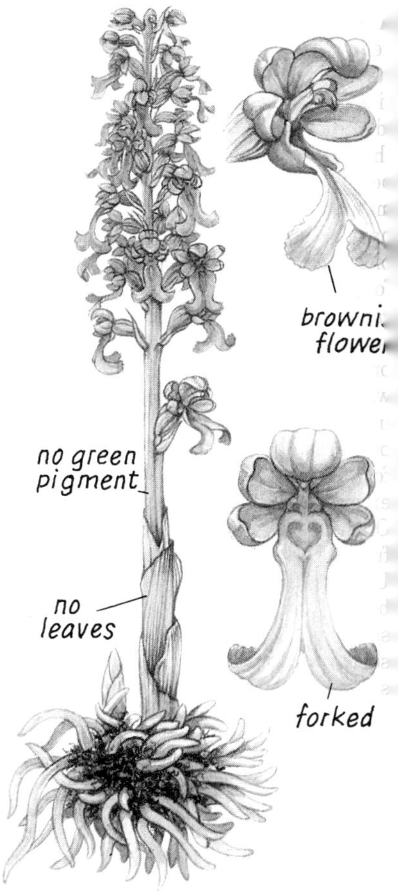

	BIRD'S-NEST ORCHID
Type	perennial, saprophyte
Height	20–45cm
Habitat	shady woods; lime-rich soils, often on leaf mould
Flowering	June–July
	STEMS AND LEAVES
Stem	upright, with dense scales
Root	short underground stem, hidden by many short, fleshy roots
Hairs	gland-tipped, in flower-head
Stipules	absent
Leaves	spirally arranged, scale-like, papery, brownish
Leaf-stalk	absent
	FLOWERS
Position	many, in spike-like head, 50–200mm long
Bracts	shorter than flower
Type	⚥, scented
Size	12–16mm
Colour	pale brown, darker on lower petal
Stalk	much shorter than flower
Sepals	3, 4–6mm, petal-like, oval
Petals	3; side petals oval; lower 9–12mm, 2-lobed, angled downwards; spur absent
Stamen	1, stalkless
Stigmas	2; style absent
Ovary	1, below petals, 1-celled
	FRUIT
Type	swollen, angular capsule, splits lengthwise
Size	10–12mm
Seeds	numerous, minute, dust-like

A large, pouch-like petal, of lemon-yellow spotted with crimson, surrounded by slender, chocolate-brown side petals and sepals, could not be identified as any native flower other than the Lady's-slipper Orchid. The beauty of this exotic-looking flower is matched by its scarcity. Its numbers have been greatly reduced by people picking flowers and uprooting plants for cultivation. In most of its former range, it is extremely rare or extinct. It survives today only through strict laws preventing removal of material from the wild, and international controls on import and export. Although it is possible to obtain legitimate material for your garden, cultivation is extremely difficult for, like other Orchids, the Lady's-slipper needs a fungus present in its roots to survive. Unless conditions are exactly right for both Orchid and fungus, the Orchid soon perishes. *Status:* native; very rare, scattered through area. (There are no similar native species.)

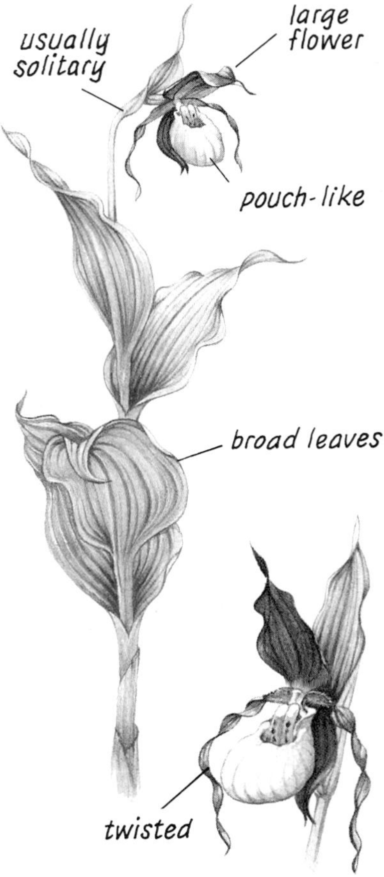

	LADY'S-SLIPPER
Type	perennial
Height	15–45cm
Habitat	woods; lime-rich soils
Flowering	May–June
	STEMS AND LEAVES
Stem	upright, leafy
Root	creeping underground stem
Hairs	short, denser above
Stipules	absent
Leaves	3–4, spirally arranged, 70–170mm, lower scale-like, upper broadly elliptical to oval, base sheaths stem
Leaf-stalk	absent
	FLOWERS
Position	1–2, at stem-tip
Bracts	large, leaf-like
Type	⚥
Size	60–90mm
Colour	reddish brown, lower petal yellow, red-spotted within
Stalk	very short
Sepals	3, 35–50mm, petal-like, spear-shaped, lower 2 often joined except at tips, pointing downwards
Petals	3; side petals 40–60mm, slender, twisted; lower 25–35mm, rounded, hollow, pouch-like; spur absent
Stamens	2, stalkless
Stigmas	3; style absent
Ovary	1, below petals, 1-celled
	FRUIT
Type	oblong capsule, angular, splits lengthwise
Size	*c*40mm
Seeds	numerous, minute, dust-like

INDEX

INDEX

INDEX

INDEX

Societies and Useful Addresses

Botanical Society of the British Isles
c/o British Museum (Natural History),
Cromwell Road, London, SW7 5BD

Fauna and Flora Preservation Society
79/83 North Street,
Brighton, BN1 12A

English Nature
Northminster House,
Peterborough, PE1 1UA

Scottish Natural Heritage
12 Hope Terrace, Edinburgh,
EH9 2AS

Countryside Council for Wales
Plas Penrhos, Penrhos Road,
Bangor, Gwynedd, LL57 2LQ

Royal Society for Nature Conservation
The Green, Nettleham,
Lincolnshire, LN2 2NR

Wild Flower Society
Rams Hill House,
Horsmonden, Tonbridge,
Kent, TN12 8DD